STRANGE STORIES
AMAZING FACTS

THE READER'S DIGEST
BOOK OF

Strange stories

amazing facts

Stories that are bizarre,
unusual,
odd,
astonishing,
incredible . . . but true

PUBLISHED BY
THE READER'S DIGEST ASSOCIATION LIMITED
London New York Montreal Sydney Cape Town

Contents of Strange

stories, amazing facts

STRANGE STORIES, AMAZING FACTS

was edited and designed by The Reader's Digest Association Limited.

Copyright © 1975 The Reader's Digest Association Limited,
25 Berkeley Square, London W1X 6AB.

First revise, 1976

CONTRIBUTORS

Carol Alway BA   Russell Ash BA (DUNELM), FRAI
Isaac Asimov   Carolyn Barber BSc   Raymond Baxter
Eric Beardsley   John Beattie
Richard Beckett
David Bellamy PhD, FLS
Patrick Brown MA (CANTAB)   Alan J Charig MA, PhD
Erika Cheetham MA (OXON)
John O E Clark BSc, ARIC
Leonard Cottrell   Nona Coxhead   Dr John Douglas
Ernest Dudley, *BBC 'Armchair Detective'*
Rex Dutta   Jane Ford
Rupert Furneaux   Fernando Gay
J C G George   Tony Geraghty   Sergius Golowin
Ian Grant BA   Nigel Hawkes BA
Roberto Cabral del Hoyo   Robert Jackson
Marcus Jacobson FI Mech E, MSAE (USA), MI Prod E
Ken Johnson   Dr Stephan Kaiser
Hamish Keith   George Hall Kirby MA
Sushma Kumar MA (BOMBAY)   Onni Kyster
Joan Levy BA   Harry Ludlam   Magnus Magnusson
Eric Maple   Ian Moffitt   Patrick Moore
Nancy Elizabeth Murray BA
Venetia Newall MA, FRGS, FRSA
George Ordish   David Owen   Cyril Pearl
Henry F Pulitzer DSc   Ian Ramsay
Maurice Richardson   Charles J M Rondle MA, PhD
Peter Schirmer
Dr Tony Smith, *The Times* Medical Correspondent
J P C Sumption BA
John Taylor, Editor of *Style International*
Professor John Taylor
Sunil Wadhwani B Tech (Indian Institute of Technology, Madras)
Royston Wells   Hugh Ross Williamson FRSL

ARTISTS AND PHOTOGRAPHERS

John Bavosi   Norman H Burkett
A C Cooper Ltd   Henry Cooper and Son
Jackson Day Design   Mike Freeman
David A Hardy FRAS   Alex Von Koettlitz
Julian Lusby   Tom McArthur MSIA
Gordon Moore
Peter Morter MSIA   Pat Oxenham
John Tebbutt   Reece Toothill   George Tuckwell
Mike Wells   Michael Woods   A J Wyatt

part

1

Contents

The universe . . . eternally fixed or forever exploding?

The enigma of
space

—◦—

A DROP IN THE OCEAN OF SPACE *When viewing his home against the backdrop of the universe mankind must needs be humble. The earth (top left) is third closest to the sun and*

PORTRAIT OF THE UNIVERSE

How stars are born—from here to eternity

Looking at the sun and the stars is like gazing backwards down a time tunnel. What is seen from the earth is not the stars as they are, but as they were when the light rays reaching earth left the various heavenly bodies.

Light travels at 186,000 miles a second (nearly 700 million mph), and at this speed takes eight minutes to reach earth from the sun. By the same token the closest star to earth's solar system, Proxima Centauri, is seen not as it is, but as it was 4·25 years ago.

With powerful telescopes, it is possible to look back millions of years into the past of the universe and, by linking telescopes with sensitive photographic plates,

even further back—to a staggering thousands of millions of years ago.

But despite man's ever-increasing knowledge and use of more and more sophisticated equipment such as deep space probes, the earth is still an insignificant dot against the overwhelming backcloth of space.

The earth occupies third place from the sun in a system of nine planets—some with moons, others without—in orbit around the sun. This, the solar system, is a tiny speck in a breathtakingly huge spiral, 100,000 light years across, known as a galaxy.

This galaxy, in turn, is one of countless others in yet another system of galaxies

one of the smaller planets of the solar system. But the sun's vast empire is unimpressive when seen in its galaxy, the Milky Way (left), which contains innumerable suns, or stars, many with larger solar systems. The Milky Way itself is insignificant when pictured against its neighbouring galaxies (above), while in the infinity of the universe it is but a pinprick.

11

that is so incredibly vast it defies our imagination.

Distances between earth and the nearest objects in space were first measured by a method of trigonometry known as parallax. This involves taking triangulated sightings on a star at six-monthly intervals or, in effect, using the diameter of the earth's annual orbit around the sun as the baseline of a triangle. If the baseline of a triangle and the angles at each end of it are known, the remaining dimensions of the triangle can be worked out.

Threefold success in 1838

Astronomers in the 17th and 18th centuries tried to calculate star distances by the parallax method, but it was not until 1838 that three astronomers, within a few months of each other, successfully and independently made parallax calculations of star distances.

Friedrich Bessel, director of the Konigsberg Observatory in Germany, measured a star called 61 Cygni as being just less than 11 light years away; James Henderson, Astronomer Royal for Scotland, announced that Alpha Centauri was 4·3 light years from earth; and F. G. W.

DISTANCE LENDS ENCHANTMENT *The most distant known galaxy is 3C-295, in Boötes. It was photographed in 1960 with the 200 in. Palomar reflector.*

COLOUR CLUE *According to the 'red shift' in the galaxy's spectrum, it is 5000 million light years away. It is probable that some quasars are even more remote.*

Struve, working at Dorpat in Russia, gave a value of the distance for Vega, now acknowledged to be 27 light years away.

Later, the parallaxes of other stars were calculated, but beyond a distance of 100–150 light years, the trigonometric method leaves an increasing margin of error—because of the very tiny angle at the apex of the triangles involved.

Star distances can, however, be measured by other methods, many based on how luminous a star is. To the naked eye, all stars may seem white, or nearly so, but this is not the case.

In the constellation of Auriga, for example, the star Capella is yellow. Betelgeux, in Orion, is reddish and Rigel is slightly blue.

An analysis of the spectrum of any distant object in space reveals its chemical elements and the temperature at which they are reacting, as well as the speed at which the body is travelling. From these clues, astronomers can get an idea of the true brightness of a star, and by correlating this to its apparent brightness, as seen on earth, make an accurate estimate of its distance.

An estimation of the speed of a distant object stems largely from a scientific principle laid down in 1842 by the Austrian physicist Christian Doppler. This principle—known as the Doppler effect—is best demonstrated by relating it to the whistle of an approaching train. As a train draws near, the pitch of the whistle climbs higher, until the train passes. Then, as it recedes in the distance, the tone falls.

The 'red shift'

Two later 19th-century astronomers—Sir William Huggins in London, and a German, Hermann Vogel—independently made use of Doppler's principle.

When applied to light waves, the Doppler effect shows up in colour. At the red end of the spectrum, light waves are longer: at the violet end, shorter.

So, redness in light coming from a celestial body is taken to mean that it must be moving away from earth.

This phenomenon is known as the 'red shift'. Conversely, light waves from a source that is *approaching* the observer tend to move up the spectrum towards the violet end, where they become stronger and more frequent.

The so-called radial velocities of many

stars have been measured in this way. Thus, Sirius is approaching our solar system at 5 miles a second and Altair at 16. Aldebaran, on the other hand, is receding at 34 miles a second and Capella at 18.

Some other explanation for violet and red shifts in stars and galaxies may, of course, be possible. But most modern astronomers accept the principles of the Doppler effect.

In 1924 Dr Edwin Hubble, of Mount Wilson Observatory in California, using the superior instruments then available, learnt more about the 'red shift'. He found that whole galaxies must be travelling away from earth at tremendous speeds. Hubble concluded that the whole universe is expanding, with everything in it moving further apart from everything else. And as the galaxies move further and further away from our own, the radiation of light we get from them gets weaker and weaker. This, said Hubble, is why starlight is too feeble to illuminate our night skies.

The 'Big Bang'

Why should the universe be expanding? The idea ties in with one of the main theories about the birth of the universe, expounded in 1930 by the Belgian astronomer Georges Lemaître. His was the 'Big Bang' theory, which suggested that about 10,000 million years ago all the matter of the universe was contained in a primal atom—which he described as a super dense 'cosmic egg'.

This, he said, exploded, and its many fragments became galaxies—one of which contains our solar system—all moving apart at incredible speed.

Another popular belief—'The Steady State' theory—was advanced in 1948 by British cosmologists Hermann Bondi, Thomas Gold and Fred Hoyle, who suggested that the universe is eternal and that it has always existed.

They said that matter is continuously created, apparently from nothing, at the rate of 62 atoms of hydrogen per cubic inch of space every 1000 million years.

This is sufficient to form new galaxies to fill in the gaps caused by the expansion of the universe.

The 'Pulsating Universe'

In 1965 the American astronomer Professor Allan Sandage adapted the 'Big Bang' theory, and developed it into his 'Pulsating Universe' theory.

He suggested that the universe is created, destroyed and then re-created in 80,000 million-year cycles. At the moment, he said, the universe is only 10,000 million years along the expansion stage, and it will continue to expand for another 30,000 million years before the galaxies overcome the force of the 'Big Bang' and begin to contract.

Eventually, he maintained, moving at millions of miles an hour, they will converge and fuse again into their primal atoms which will then explode once more to re-start the whole cycle.

A universe, in other words, not without end but with an infinite number of endings . . . and beginnings.

FACTS ABOUT OUR NEIGHBOURS

OUTSIDE the earth's planetary system, the nearest star to the sun is Proxima Centauri, at a distance of 4·25 light years.

But it is by no means the brightest star in earth's heavens. The four brightest are Sirius, the dog-star (8·7 light years away), far-distant Canopus (900 light years), Alpha Centauri (4·3 light years) and Arcturus (36 light years).

The most distant body that can be seen with the naked eye from earth is the Great Spiral Galaxy in the star cluster or constellation known as Andromeda—more than 2 million light years away. It appears only as a faint blotch of light.

The largest star visible to the naked eye is probably Alpha Herculis, a red giant— the name given to stars that are cooling.

The smallest-known stars are about the size of planets—less than 10,000 miles in diameter. The smallest yet detected is Wolf 457 which, at 3/1000ths the size of the sun, is smaller than the earth. Some may be less than 1100 miles across.

By the standards of earth's solar system, the largest stars are enormous. The variable star VV Cephei, at 1000 million miles in diameter, for example, is 1220 times the size of the sun. (A variable star is a pulsating star, growing bright, then dim, in a regular pattern or rhythm.)

The most densely populated area of the heavens is considered to be that part of the Milky Way, or earth's galaxy, in the constellation, or star cluster, known as Cygnus, the swan.

THE SUN ECLIPSED BY THE EARTH *This photograph was taken from the US Apollo-12 command ship during its expedition to the moon in November 1969.*

THE SAVAGE SUN

It is a normal star, like millions of others

In the order of the universe, the sun is an ordinary, typical, medium-sized star. Yet its energy and violence almost defy imagination.

It is a dense mass of glowing matter, a million times the volume of the earth and in a permanent state of nuclear activity. Every second, 4 million tons of hydrogen are destroyed in explosions which start somewhere near the core, where the temperature is 13 million degrees Centigrade.

More energy than man has used since the dawn of civilisation is radiated by this normal star in a second.

The earth's entire oil, coal and wood reserves would fuel the sun's energy output to the earth alone for only a few days.

Tongues of hydrogen flame leap from the sun's surface with the force of 1000 million hydrogen bombs. They are forced up by the enormous thermonuclear explosion at the core of the sun where 564 million tons of hydrogen fuse each second to form helium. Matter at the core of the sun is so hot that a pinhead of it would give off enough heat to kill a man 100 million miles away.

Slow-burning bomb

The sun, therefore, is like a vast hydrogen bomb burning slowly. It is only its vast size that makes its energy output so phenomenal. In fact, its output is about one-fifth that of the human body —in relation to volume.

Sometimes the sun's surface is gashed by dark patches known as 'sun-spots', thousands of miles across, probably caused by magnetic disturbances, but not fully understood. From the sun's surface tens of thousands of fountains of blazing gas, called spicules, spurt out every second. They reach out 6000 miles, then fall back within minutes.

Sun-spot activity increases about every 11 years. Over the same cycle, earthly phenomena of aurora variation, magnetic storms and radio blackouts occur.

Solar flares

Loops of bright gas, or prominences, arch 100,000 miles into the sun's outer atmosphere, or corona. But these are small compared with solar flares.

These eject electromagnetic waves, which travel at the speed of light and reach earth in about eight minutes. They are followed by other particles which take half an hour to reach earth. A day later, slower particles arrive.

One of the largest recorded flares occurred on November 12, 1960. Astronomers detected a gigantic explosion on the sun. A cloud of hydrogen, 10 million miles wide, stretching back 46 million miles, collided with the earth, and started a violent chain of disturbances.

Aurorae, normally seen within 1500 miles of the poles, displayed much more spectacular, shimmering coloured ribbons than usual. This was caused by particles from the solar flare streaming into the upper atmosphere.

Two days later, teleprinters produced nonsensical messages and radio communications were blacked out. Electric lights flickered as if a thunderstorm raged, yet the skies were clear. Some of these effects lasted over a week.

A suggested explanation of this is that solar flares in some way send out nuclei of hydrogen atoms and electrons. These, travelling at 400 to 600 miles per second, begin to reach the earth's atmosphere about 50 hours after the flare and produce the disturbances.

THE SAD TALE OF HSI AND HO

ONE DAY in the year 2136 BC, a hungry dragon tried to eat the sun. The Emperor of China and his people were terrified.

At first, a tiny bite was taken out of one side of the orb. Then a quarter, a half, and suddenly the whole sun had gone, and there was nothing but a strange circle of white light around the black space where the blazing disc had been.

The frightened, but resourceful, Chinese knew what to do. They ran around in the strange twilight, shouting and screaming defiance at the dragon, beating drums, banging gongs and whacking hollow wooden ducks until the startled dragon moved reluctantly away from its unswallowed meal.

The sun was saved, but the emperor, now more angry than scared, ordered that the Imperial Astronomers, Hsi and Ho, depicted here attending their emperor in happier times, should be beheaded for failing to warn him in time of the dragon's approach.

Astronomers have long been amused by the anonymous rhyme which has come down to us as their epitaph:

Here lie the bodies of Hsi and Ho,
Whose fate, though sad, was visible:
Being killed because they did not spy
Th' eclipse which was invisible.

A total eclipse of the sun was seen at that time in China, but Hsi and Ho, as experienced astronomers, should have predicted it.

What happens is that as the moon moves around the earth and the earth around the sun, there are times when the three are lined up in such a way that the moon blots out the sun's light for anything up to seven and a half minutes.

MYSTERIES OF THE MOON

Where a stone can lie untouched for 3000 million years

Even the rocks returned to earth by the Apollo missions have failed to answer the many puzzles of the moon. Still, today, it remains the controversial satellite, which has been the source of myth and legend since prehistoric man looked at it—and wondered.

The moon is earth's closest companion in its endless journey round the sun. The distance between the earth and moon is 239,000 miles. It takes 27·3 days for the moon to complete a full revolution around the earth, and it takes exactly the same time for the moon to spin once on its own axis. This means that the moon remains at a standstill in relation to the earth's movement so that it always presents the same face to earth. Only the astronauts have so far seen its far side.

It was once thought that the moon was part of the earth, and that it broke away to leave a huge hole now filled by the Pacific Ocean. This theory has long since been discounted by mathematical calculations which show that the size of the moon and the volume of the Pacific do not correspond.

Probably, the moon and earth were born about the same time—about 4700 million years ago. And they evolved from the same accumulation of dust and gases carried in the solar winds of the sun.

Russian probe

In October 1959 a Russian moon probe —Luna III—circled behind the moon and took photographs which were later transmitted back to earth. As expected the photographs showed mountains, valleys and craters. But there was no sign of life. It is now known that the moon is entirely sterile—as it has undoubtedly been throughout its entire violent history.

Since then, more probes, including the manned US Apollo missions, have circled behind the moon and scientists now have detailed maps of the entire surface.

In July 1969 the most valuable cargo in history was delivered in lead-sealed containers to the Lunar Receiving Laboratory in Houston, Texas. It consisted of 50 lb. of rock and dust brought back to earth by the crew of Apollo 11 from the moon's Sea of Tranquillity.

There were 46 rocks brought back by Apollo 11—all from the top layer of the lunar surface. They were small, ranging between the size of a pea and 5 in. long. At first glance, they looked very much like ordinary earth rocks, but when they were examined under microscopes, startling differences appeared.

The lunar rocks were pitted with small, glass-lined pock marks. Some were covered with spatters of glass which formed whitish patches on the surface. And the soil samples showed they were made up of 50 per cent glass—most of it sharp and angular without colour. A further 10 per cent of the glass particles were spherical and coloured red, brown, green, yellow and violet. On earth, very little glass is found in the soil.

Different proportions

All rocks, whether from earth, the moon or elsewhere, are basically composed of the same elements which existed in space before the solar system was formed. So what lunar scientists found in the moon rocks was not a difference in elements but a difference in proportions.

The ratio of uranium to potassium, for example, was four times higher in the moon rocks than in those found on earth, and 15 times greater than the ratio in meteorite samples found on earth. In all, 68 of the more than 100 known elements have been found in moon rocks.

The puzzle of the moon has been heightened by researchers who tested the effects of moon dust on bacteria and plants. Certain bacteria were exposed to four lunar surface samples. On three of them there was no effect. But when they were exposed to sub-surface samples brought back to earth by Apollo 12—they died. No explanation for the results of the tests has yet been found.

In other tests, corn was exposed to the samples as representative of a complex plant, with no apparent effect. But simple algae exposed to moon dirt appeared to thrive on the 'food' from space, and grew greener for no explicable reason.

Gases from the sun

Scientists have already managed to uncover some information, however, which may lead to untold breakthroughs in knowledge of the universe. The moon rocks are now known to contain particles from the sun, imbedded in them in the form of gases. And these gases may provide the vital key to how the sun works and how long it will sustain life on earth.

One thing is certain. The moon is much more complicated than scientists had expected. It is not a kind of billiard ball frozen in space and time as had been thought. It was an active volcanic mass 4600 million years ago, that later stilled to an endless silence.

The first rocks found by the astronauts were more than 3000 million years old— and these turned out to be young by the standards of the moon. At least one rock was 4600 million years old. On earth, it is only by searching out remote crannies in Greenland that rocks 4000 million years old can be found.

The other striking thing about the lunar rocks is that they have not been subjected to erosion by winds, water and the other disturbances on earth. The rocks picked up by astronauts had been lying where they were for 3000 million years without moving a fraction of an inch.

PACK UP YOUR TROUBLES *Heavily laden astronaut Edwin E. Aldrin climbs down the ladder to set foot on the moon for the first time. The photograph was taken by fellow-astronaut Neil Armstrong.*

ROCK OF AGES *This 5 lb. rock, brought back by astronauts from the Apollo 12 mission to the moon, is 3000 million years old.*

PLANET	DISTANCE FROM SUN IN MILLIONS OF MILES	DIAMETER (Miles)	LENGTH OF DAY	LENGTH OF YEAR
MERCURY	36	3100	59 days	88 days
VENUS	67	7700	243 days	224.7 days
EARTH	93	7926	23 hrs 56 min.	365¼ days
MARS	141.5	4200	24 hrs 37 min.	687 days
JUPITER	483	88,700	9¾ hrs	11¾ yrs
SATURN	886	75,100	10¼ hrs	29 yrs
URANUS	1783	29,600	10¾ hrs	84 yrs
NEPTUNE	2793	31,200	15¾ hrs	164¾ yrs
PLUTO	3666	3600 (?)	6 days 9 hrs	247¾ yrs

OUR NEAREST NEIGHBOURS

The solar system in which we live

There is no general agreement about how the planets were formed. The most widely accepted theory is that about 5000 million years ago swirling clouds of matter began to condense. Through the action of centrifugal force, the heavier molecules were concentrated near the centre of the eddies, and the lighter, gaseous material was thrown out towards the periphery. Such is the theory. What is *known* is that nine satellites began orbiting round the sun. These are the planets.

The earth we live on

The planet on which man lives is the third closest to the sun, with the third shortest orbit. It has the fifth fastest rota-tion, the fifth strongest gravity, the third hottest surface temperature and the fifth greatest mass.

It also has something none of the others has—an atmosphere that can support life in all the manifold forms that exist on our planet. There may be satellites circling other stars in other parts of the universe that have the right ingredients for some sort of life to evolve, but the earth is the only one in the Solar System.

Earth's distance from the sun (93 million miles) gives it a temperature of 60°C (140°F) maximum. Harmful radio-active rays are prevented from reaching it by a magnetic field, known as the Van Allen belt, which traps these rays and holds them captive far out in space.

MASS RELATIVE TO EARTH	ATMOSPHERE	SURFACE TEMPERATURE (Max)
.05	None	400° C (752° F)
.81	Carbon dioxide, water, nitrogen	500° C (932° F)
1.00	Nitrogen, oxygen, water, carbon dioxide, Argon	60° C (140° F)
.11	Carbon dioxide, water, nitrogen (?)	21° C (70° F)
317.8	Hydrogen, helium, methane, water (?)	−130° C (−200° F)
95.2	As Jupiter	−160° C (−256° F)
14.5	As Jupiter	−210° C (−346° F)
17.2	As Jupiter	−230° C (−382° F)
.8 (?)	Not known	Not known

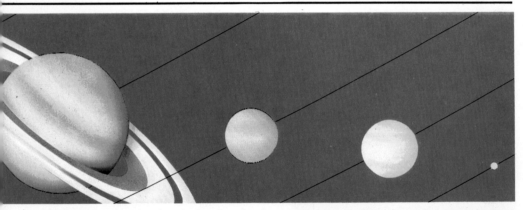

THE NINE PLANETS *A scale drawing showing the size of the satellites in relation to the sun, part of which is seen curving in the background. The sun is vastly bigger than any of its planets.*

The tilt of the earth's axis produces the seasons; and the composition of the atmosphere—oxygen, nitrogen, water vapour, carbon dioxide and argon— provides the ingredients vital for the sustenance of organic life.

Mercury, the smallest planet

This is the smallest and least hospitable of the inner planets. Until recently it was thought that Mercury's day was the same length as its year—88 earth days. Astronomers said that one side of the planet was always hidden from the sun, in permanent intense cold, while the other side, always under the sun's rays, would be so hot that soft metals such as lead or tin would be boiled away.

ASTRONAUTS' VIEW *The earth seen from Apollo 11, 100,000 miles away, on its journey to the moon. Africa can be clearly recognised.*

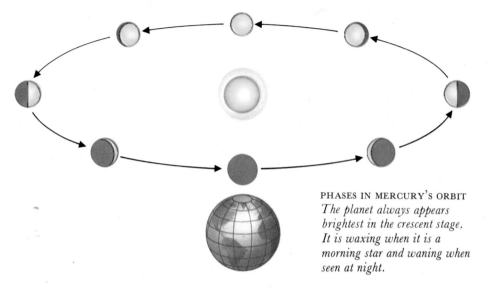

PHASES IN MERCURY'S ORBIT
*The planet always appears
brightest in the crescent stage.
It is waxing when it is a
morning star and waning when
seen at night.*

But this belief has now been proved false: it arose through the coincidence that Mercury always presents the same face to the earth at the same point in its orbit round the sun. So the 'cold' side of Mercury is not so cold after all. If ever an astronaut is able to take a trip to the planet—the distance ranges from 50 to 136 million miles, and the journey would take well over six months—he will find the temperature at night much the same as on a comfortable summer day back on earth, 22°C (72°F).

Because Mercury's orbit round the sun is only half as much again as its rotation, the astronaut would have to wait up to 176 earth days for the scorching dawn. If he were in some way able to stay until 'noon', the temperature would reach 400°C (752°F) and the mercury in his instruments would boil.

Assuming that the astronaut could somehow survive, the great weight of his insulating equipment would probably not hamper his movements too much. Because of Mercury's small gravity pull, a 150 lb. man would weigh only 50 lb.

A drive round Mercury

The planet's surface would be scorched hard, and there would be no seas or rivers to impede a vehicle throughout the 10,000 miles it would cover in a trip right round the circumference.

Mercury's orbit is more elliptical than that of any other planet except Pluto, so the temperature varies from one Mercurian day to another. On one of the hottest days a visitor would see a cratered, rocky landscape under the blinding light of a huge sun. At night, since Mercury has no moon, only the stars and the distant luminosity of Venus and the earth would be visible.

The truth about Venus

Although it is much closer to the sun than is the earth—67 million miles compared with 93 million—the surface of Venus is protected from the burning heat by permanent dense cloud. Only 50 years ago astronomers visualised a planet teeming with life beneath this cloud; a kind of tropical, steamy jungle through which some of the more imaginative saw dinosaur-type monsters roaming. Others even interpreted the halo sometimes seen around the dark edge of Venus as the glow of cities at night.

Now the Venusian clouds have been pierced by American and Russian space probes, and the fantasies have melted away. The reality is far different. Poisonous carbon dioxide envelops the planet, sealing in a temperature of 500°C (932°F) at the surface. Dust and ice crystals fuse together into a yellowish 'smog' through which only occasionally a pale sunlight filters, making the rocks glow red.

All around is sand, littered with boulders scoured into weird shapes by constant dust storms. In the stifling heat, nothing can grow. The ice particles in the cloud melt and turn to vapour long before they could reach the surface as rain.

Venus is almost as big as the earth, with a diameter of 7700 miles compared with 7900, and its gravity slightly less. It rotates on its axis in the opposite way from the earth. So if it were possible for a man to land on Venus, the sun, if he were ever able to catch a glimpse of it through the 'smog' shroud, would rise in the west and set in the east. There are no seasons, and as the planet takes 243 days to spin on its axis and only 224·7 days to orbit the sun, a Venusian day is longer than a year.

One of the biggest problems the scientists would have to solve before the three-month flight to Venus could even be thought of is the planet's enormous atmospheric pressure of 1500 lb. per square inch, 100 times that of the earth's atmosphere. So even if an astronaut could survive all the other perils, unless he were protected in some way, he would be crushed to death.

Despite the harsh facts revealed by modern astronomers, Venus has always aroused the fanciful imagination. If only its permanent envelope of cloud were to disperse so that water could reach the surface, releasing free oxygen into the atmosphere, then indeed this gloomy, lifeless inferno might be transformed into something approaching the science-fiction writer's dream.

Mars and its 'canals'

The first visitor to Mars may well bring back a specimen of the only organic life that exists in the Solar System outside our world. But if he does, it will be no little green man. His sample is likely to be nothing more romantic than a primitive kind of moss.

The notion that Mars was so similar to the earth that it could be peopled by a race of men persisted until the end of the 19th century. It was given a powerful impetus when, in 1877, Giovanni Schiaparelli of Milan reported the discovery of narrow, regular lines crossing the Martian deserts. He marked them on his map of the planet and called them *canali*, Italian for channels.

Schiaparelli himself made no firm claim that these channels were artificially made, but the word 'canals' stuck and, fuelled by music-hall jokes and science fiction, popular imagination easily drew the inference that where there are canals there must be canal builders.

The American astronomer Percival Lowell also saw the *canali*, and supported the theory that they were evidence of life. Intelligent Martians, he reasoned, had dug this vast system of canals to irrigate the deserts from the reservoirs of moisture held in the Martian ice-cap.

Lowell, who established an observatory at Flagstaff, in Arizona, specially to study Mars, reasoned that the planet was undeniably short of water. Proceeding from the conviction that the canals were artificial, he came to this conclusion: 'Mars is inhabited by beings of some kind or other: this is as certain as it is uncertain what those beings may be.'

No Martians

Lowell's views fostered the fascinating picture of a world in which lived a highly cultured race, living in peace and toiling to conserve every drop of precious water.

But his theories were not accepted without opposition. It was pointed out that the polar ice-caps must be very thin —not more than a few inches deep—and so could hardly be the source of a vast planet-wide irrigation and pumping system. Moreover, other observers using telescopes as large and as powerful as Lowell's either failed to see the canals at all or surmised that they were simply natural formations.

Research carried out over the last 50 years has finally exploded the Martian Man theory. The 'canals' are just geological cracks which imaginative astronomers have joined up into long straight lines. Mars in fact is less hospitable to organic life than the Sahara or Antarctica.

Even so, the first man to visit Mars will see a fascinating new world, more closely resembling the earth than any other of the sun's planets. Mars does have an atmosphere, though not one that an earth man could breathe. The 'air' is thinner than that at the summit of Mount Everest, and is mostly carbon dioxide with hardly a trace of oxygen. Seen through this atmosphere the sky would appear dark blue. Mars is further from the sun ($141\frac{1}{2}$ million miles) than is the earth (93 million). So the sun would appear smaller.

The Martian day is half an hour longer than the earth's, but the Martian year is nearly twice as long as ours—23 earth months. The phenomenon of gravity would reduce an astronaut's weight to a little over a third of normal. A complete circuit of the planet at its equator would cover more than 13,000 miles.

The explorer of Mars would land on an apparently lifeless surface carpeted with brownish dust and pitted with craters.

Mountains rise to perhaps three times the height of Everest.

If the spaceman had landed near the equator he would find the noon temperature comfortable, about 22°C. At the poles he would find not a thick polar ice-cap, but a thin layer of carbon dioxide which in the melting season turns to vapour. As the seasons change, strong winds rush in from the cooler polar atmosphere to replace the rising currents in the equatorial zone.

It would be in the Martian spring that the first man from the earth would search for life. At this time, as the ice-cap retreats, observers on earth have seen expanding dark areas which appear to move towards Mars' equator.

It is possible that the explorer would radio back disappointing news. Once, it was thought that these dark areas were belts of vegetation, changing with the seasons. But a more likely explanation is that they are merely highland rocks, swept clean of dust by the strong winds.

Nevertheless, the spaceman on Mars could well find the hardy lichens that some scientists are confident grow there. These would be able to extract the water necessary for their existence from the rising vapour, or even reach down to reserves of water below the parched surface. It is just possible that the 'rocks' lying among the lichen may be in fact rounded, limbless animals that can extract water from the iron oxide in the planet's red dust.

Jupiter – a mass of gas

It is safe to say that man will probably *never* land on Jupiter. For all the known

THE 'CANALS' OF MARS *Mars, the planet that has intrigued scientists and laymen alike since the dawn of astronomy. The white polar cap is a thin layer of carbon dioxide.*

facts indicate that there is nothing to land on. If Jupiter has a surface—and this is by no means certain—it is likely to be nothing more than a plastic slush of compressed hydrogen.

Jupiter, the biggest planet, is the most like the sun. It produces its own energy and comprises mostly hydrogen and helium, the basic building materials of the universe. Because of its great size and therefore its immense gravity—it is bigger than all the other planets put together—Jupiter has retained its original hydrogen, which encircles it completely, making life impossible. Other planets lost their atmospheric hydrogen when, heated by the sun's rays, it broke away from the gravitational pull.

But although hydrogen is the lightest substance known, Jupiter's gravity is so powerful, and the planet so remote (483 million miles) from the sun, that no

JUPITER'S RED SPOT *Studio model showing the Red Spot (top) and relative size of the earth.*

external force has been able to tear away this shroud of gas.

When the sun, following the fixed pattern of the stars, expands and burns up the inner planets, the character of Jupiter may undergo a spectacular change. According to the latest predictions, the enlarged sun, with a greater gravitational pull, will then suck away Jupiter's hydrogen, and the planet could then shrink to a dense globe of heavy elements. Life based on the element carbon could then be possible on the surface and Jupiter could become another earth.

But this is very much a glimpse into the distant future—about 7000 million years

hence. In the meantime, the giant planet will have to be explored from one of its moons. There are 12 of these and the biggest, Callisto, is bigger than Mercury. From it, Jupiter would appear as a massive disc covered with bands of swirling coloured clouds.

In the unlikely event that a man could be equipped to penetrate Jupiter's atmosphere, he would first have to pass through the clouds that surround the planet. These are likely to be of ammonia and methane, and as the explorer sank through them he would see them condense into ammonia rain and snow. Before this rain could reach anywhere near the mysterious core of the planet, the ammonia would evaporate back into the clouds, giving off enormous discharges of electricity that by comparison would make earthly lightning seem like sparks from a cigarette-lighter.

Five thousand miles up, the pressure would be intense and on the surface the astronaut would be two and a half times his normal weight. There would be no free oxygen to breathe at any stage of the journey. The clouds would have a temperature of $-140°C$ ($-220°F$), colder than anything known on earth except artificially produced liquid gases. The faint sun, so distant as to be just a flickering star, would rise and set every nine and three-quarter hours.

For such a massive planet this rotation is astonishingly fast. The centrifugal force generated causes matter to be heaped up at the equator, so that the giant Jupiter is more noticeably flattened at the poles than is the earth.

Jupiter's journey round the sun takes $11\frac{3}{4}$ years. But this would have little meaning to a visitor since, owing to its distance from the sun, there are no recognisable seasons.

The first astronaut to visit Jupiter would certainly be briefed to make a special study of the so-called Red Spot, which first appeared on astronomers' drawings as long ago as 1631. The Red Spot is so called because of its ruddy glow, varying in intensity at different times, sometimes disappearing altogether. What exactly it is has long baffled observers. One guess is that it is a vast cloud of gas rising from Jupiter's 'surface'. Another is that it could be some form of solid matter floating in the planet's atmosphere. What is known beyond much doubt—because it has been carefully studied and measured through telescopes—is that the Red Spot is a very big spot indeed: it is estimated to be 30,000 miles by 7000 miles.

The rings of Saturn

The most easily identifiable planet is Saturn. And, though faint, it can be seen without a telescope. What makes it so distinctive is its unique system of glowing rings girdling its equator. The rings are concentric, like those seen in a cross-section of a felled tree.

It is a huge planet, 740 times the size of the earth and only a little smaller than Jupiter. Like Jupiter, it is probably composed mainly of hydrogen and helium, with a core of liquid or metallic hydrogen.

Saturn has three rings and ten moons, one of them—Titan—almost as big as Mercury. From Titan the rings would

THE RINGS OF SATURN *Partly covering the planet's northern hemisphere, the rings appear as a thin belt of light, casting shadow on the disc. This photograph was taken at Mount Wilson observatory.*

THE SUPERSTAR THAT CAME IN WITH A BANG

The Crab Nebula in Taurus, named by the amateur astronomer Lord Rosse. Its light takes 6000 years to reach the earth.

This is how Lord Rosse actually saw the Crab through his telescope.

be seen to be made of particles of ice-covered rock caught in the planet's gravitational pull. The rings have a total diameter of 170,000 miles, but are only about 10 miles thick. It is possible that the rock particles are the remains of an eleventh moon that was shattered by some cataclysm.

Landing on Saturn would present the same problems as a journey to Jupiter. And it would be even colder: −160°C (−256°F). Day on the planet would be a matter of just 10¼ hours, but a year on Saturn lasts a generation in man's terms —29 earth years.

Uranus, no holiday planet

Everything about Uranus gives it the quality of somewhere to be avoided by a migratory race of spacemen in search of a new planet to populate.

The sun, because of its immense distance—1783 million miles—would appear only as a bright star, and its rays, struggling through an atmosphere of ammonia and methane, would make no impact on the slushy surface of frozen hydrogen. The temperature is −190°C (−310°F). In these unpleasant conditions the astronaut would live, at most, only a single year of Uranian time; for the year on this planet is 84 times longer than that on earth.

Despite its vast distance from the sun, the fact that Uranus orbits in a plane at right angles to its axis gives it a variation of seasons, though the difference between them is rather more blurred than is the case on earth.

One of the most fascinating facts about Uranus is the manner of its discovery. A young amateur astronomer named William Herschel was busy at his home-made telescope one evening in 1781, carrying out what he called his 'review of the heavens', when an unfamiliar luminous disc in the sky aroused his interest. When other astronomers worked out the orbit of the disc it was realised that Herschel, without knowing it, had discovered a new planet—Uranus. He was rewarded by George III with a pension, gave up his job as a musician to devote his life to the study of the heavens, and became the first man to show how the stars are arranged to make up the Milky Way.

The eternal cold of Neptune

If a year on Uranus is an earthly lifetime, the journey round the sun that creates this yardstick of time takes the remote Neptune almost twice as long—more than 164 years. The planet spins on its axis once in 15¾ hours, but the sun is 2793 million miles away. So it is not surprising that the temperature is as low as −230°C (−382°F).

Mysteries of far-away Pluto

Very little is known about Pluto, the remotest of the sun's planets, 3666 million miles from the centre of the Solar System. Clyde Tombaugh confirmed its long-conjectured existence at the Lowell Observatory in 1930.

Its atmosphere, if any, cannot be analysed with any accuracy; nor can any guesses yet be made about its surface temperature. But Pluto is almost certainly a cold—unbelievably cold—dead planet.

YANG WEI-TE, chief astronomer and the court official in charge of the calendar, prostrated himself before the Sung emperor of K'hai Feng, the ancient capital of China, and said with modest pride: 'I have observed the appearance of a guest star.' But it was the end of that star, not the birth.

It was 1054, and the people of China were amazed as their heavenly 'guest' grew as bright as Venus, its reddish-white colour becoming visible even in daylight. Within a month it faded and was soon forgotten.

But what the Chinese observers had seen was the explosion of a massive star—called a supernova—in the constellation of Taurus. Today, the remains of that explosion are known as the Crab Nebula, a luminous shell of gas that is still expanding in all directions at 700 miles a second; a gigantic, white-glowing cloud, whose violent borders are laced with red, feathery filaments.

It was rediscovered by astronomers after the invention of telescopes and, in 1758, the French astronomer Charles Messier, who drew up a catalogue of star clusters and nebulae, called the faint patch of gas, shining dimly in the heavens, Messier 1.

Later, in the 19th century, the amateur astronomer Lord Rosse looked at the patch through his huge, home-made telescope at Birr Castle, near Athlone, in Ireland, and named it the Crab Nebula.

Radio astronomy has since identified the Crab as a source of X-rays in space.

THE DREADED OMEN IN THE SKY

Comets meant fireworks in the heavens and disaster on earth

When they saw a comet in the sky, the ancients were stricken with dread. A ball of fire half the size of the moon, with a tail stretching across the sky, obviously boded no good for somebody. The skies were the home of capricious gods and such a disturbance in the heavens meant danger on earth.

Well into Christian times, comets were regarded as bad omens. In 1066 a comet was seen as William the Conqueror was preparing to invade England. Soon after, Harold, the Saxon king, was defeated by William and old heads nodded. It was only to be expected after such a portent.

Though their roles as harbingers of doom are now discounted by most people, scientists are still intrigued by comets. Like the planets and the earth, they are in orbit round the sun. However, many of them fly so far away into space that they are visible from earth only once or twice in a century, or even longer.

Although their composition is still a matter of conjecture, it is known that they are not solid like meteorites, but are composed of small, icy particles, and gases millions of times less dense than air.

Some scientists say that the head of a comet is like a 'dirty snowball'. Others retort that, if so, it is the sort of snowball thrown by a very nasty boy, since the particles are made of rock coated by ice.

However, it seems to be agreed that comets are flimsy affairs that would not do much more than local damage in a collision with the earth.

The comet's long tail is believed to be composed of gas and dust forced out of the head by radiation from the sun.

A comet does not give out light, but reflects the light of the sun. It thus grows brighter as it approaches and fades as it hurtles away into space.

Regular visitor

While there are some small comets that orbit the sun every two or three years, the only really bright one to be seen regularly is Halley's Comet. Watching it in 1682, Edmond Halley, Britain's Astronomer Royal, thought that this might be the same brilliant comet that had been recorded several times in the past. Checking with his records, he decided it was in fact appearing once every 76 years and was the same phenomenon that had preceded the Battle of Hastings.

Halley's discovery has proved a boon for historians, who can now often pinpoint the date of events described by the ancients as preceded by an ominous comet.

In 1973 high hopes were raised by the appearance of a hitherto unknown comet —named Kohoutek, after its discoverer, Czechoslovakian astronomer Lubos Kohoutek. It was expected to leave a fiery trail, and American astronauts orbiting the earth in the Skylab space laboratory stood by to take spectacular photographs.

But everyone was disappointed. According to Russian scientists a coating of cosmic dust prevented Kohoutek's tail from forming for all the world to see.

HALLEY'S COMET IN 1910 *This is the most spectacular comet to orbit the sun regularly. Its next visit is due in 1986.*

HALLEY'S COMET IN 1066 *King Harold of England sees the comet as an omen of doom.*

HEAVEN'S ARTILLERY

Meteorites and their constant threat to earth

As recently as October 30, 1937, the earth missed a major disaster by less than three seconds. It happened when a minor planet, Hermes, weighing about 500,000 tons, passed within half a million miles—travelling at the speed of light, 186,000 miles per second. A slight change in the angle of its course and it would have pierced the atmosphere and smashed into the earth with an explosion that would have obliterated an entire city.

The threat that the earth may be hit by a giant meteorite is with us constantly. Scientists estimate that about seven small meteorites bury themselves in the ground each year. Others hurtle into the sea.

Every day the earth is bombarded by rocks from space called meteoroids. Usually they are small and disintegrate with the friction caused by their entry into the atmosphere. The result is the bright glow of their flight path, frequently seen streaking across the night sky.

When this happens, the meteoroid splits into meteors. If one of these meteors manages to penetrate all the way to the earth's surface, it is known as a meteorite.

Iron from the skies

Meteorites are usually circular because the friction burns off the jagged surfaces. They are composed either of stone or an alloy of nickel and iron. Scientists believe meteorites probably come from somewhere within our solar system and are the remains of comets and asteroids. (Asteroids are minor planets which have their orbits in the void between Jupiter and Mars.)

Twenty thousand years ago, an iron-nickel meteorite, weighing an estimated 2 million tons, blasted a hole nearly a mile wide and 570 ft deep in America's Arizona desert. Its destructive force was bigger than a 30 megaton H-bomb or 30 million tons of TNT.

On the morning of June 30, 1908, an enormous area of the Tunguska region of Siberia was totally devastated by what may have been a gigantic meteorite.

Shock waves from the impact were so violent that an engine driver, 350 miles away on the Trans-Siberian railway, thought his engine had exploded.

Because of the site's remoteness, and the harsh terrain, it was not until 1927 that a scientific expedition was able to investigate the meteorite. The blast had flattened trees over several miles and effects were felt over 1500 square miles, but no craters were seen. It is believed that the Siberian meteorite could have weighed 1 million tons. It broke up before it hit the earth at more than 90,000 mph.

The biggest meteorite strike so far witnessed by man also occurred in Siberia, in 1947. Hundreds of people saw a brilliant ball of light as it sped southwards across the sky, shedding a trail of sparks. Within four or five seconds it vanished and a giant pillar of brownish smoke rose 20 miles into the atmosphere.

On the slopes of the Sikhote Alin

MILE-WIDE CRATER *A huge meteorite left this scar in the Arizona desert 20,000 years ago.*

mountains, investigators found more than 100 holes, up to 75 ft across and 40 ft deep.

The meteorite apparently broke up just before impact and strewed meteoric iron for miles. Scientists believe the meteorite weighed about 1000 tons.

In parts of Carolina, 3000 shallow pits surrounded by circular walls of earth are the result of meteorite strikes during the last 50,000 years. Everything in an area of 500 square miles was obliterated by the blasts and the heat they generated.

Fortunately, no populated area has yet been hit by a meteorite. If it were, the destruction and loss of life could be so great as to leave no one alive to record them for posterity.

UNRAVELLING THE TRUTH ABOUT THE STARS

The long fight to put the earth in its place

The first man to suggest that our world was not the centre of the universe, but travelled round the sun in company with the other planets, was a Greek, Aristarchus of Samos. He lived from 310 to 230 BC, and his theory was so revolutionary that it was dismissed as absurd by most of the leading philosophers of his day.

Men had, of course, been gazing at the heavens since the beginning of time, and the accurate sitings of ancient monuments, such as the Pyramids and Stonehenge, indicate that precise astronomical observations were being made by engineers and priests 5000 years ago at least.

But the ancients put forward no theory to explain the behaviour of those celestial bodies whose movements they had plotted with such accuracy.

They simply assumed that the earth was the focal point of the universe and that the other bodies in space danced to the earth's tune. What the tune was and who composed it they regarded as an eternal mystery.

Aristarchus's ways of estimating the relative distances of the sun and the moon from the earth were essentially accurate—but his inability to make precise observations caused him to calculate the sun's distance from the earth at 1/19th of the true figure.

Rotating sphere

His calculations were based on those of the Greek mathematician, Pythagoras, who 100 years before had claimed that the earth was a sphere rotating on its own axis. This idea had been greeted with derision by learned contemporaries who believed the world was flat. So it is not surprising that Aristarchus, who was unable to prove his theory, was completely disregarded.

No other theory of the universe was propounded until 400 years after Aristarchus's death, when Claudius Ptolemaeus, known as Ptolemy, came up with a much more acceptable explanation.

He deduced that the earth was the supreme body, lying stationary at the centre of the universe. The sun and moon moved round it in circular orbits along with the five visible planets—Mercury, Venus, Mars, Jupiter and Saturn. This comforting notion instantly captured the approval of the authorities.

To explain the fact that the planets did not move in perfect circles, Ptolemy plotted a cumbersome system of smaller individual circles or epicycles, which he believed they must follow while they were, at the same time, travelling round the central earth.

Although the Ptolemaic theory relied on many clumsy explanations, it formed the unquestioned basis of astronomy for 1700 years—until Copernicus came to the fore in the 16th century.

A mere planet

Nicolaus Copernicus, born in Poland in 1473, was a devout churchman fascinated by astronomy. By the time he was 40, and after a lifetime's study of the heavens, he was convinced that Ptolemy's theory was utterly wrong.

He devised a completely new theory in which the earth was a mere planet moving round the sun. But even though Copernicus had broken away from the central-earth dogma, one basic truth eluded him: planets move in ellipses, not circles.

And he had another major problem. As a church canon he knew that his superiors would resist the idea of the earth losing its central role. Even a rumour of the new theory prompted the religious reformer Martin Luther to denounce Copernicus as a fool who wanted to turn the science of astronomy upside-down.

Like the hapless Aristarchus, Copernicus had no telescope or any other mechanical means of proving his theories to sceptics. He was therefore reluctant to publish his great book of astronomical theories, *Concerning the Revolutions of the Celestial Bodies*.

When friends finally persuaded him to have the book printed in 1542, his misgivings proved justified. Without his knowledge the publisher added a preface to the 400 pages of text, charts and diagrams. This unauthorised introduction stressed that the book's theories were merely aids to calculations and need not be taken literally.

Happily, it is unlikely that Copernicus ever saw the book in print, for by the

MASTER ASTRONOMER *Tycho sits alongside his mural quadrant, in effect a huge brass protractor, while behind him his student Kepler observes the stars. Assistants keep time and record findings.*

time a copy reached him in May 1543 he was dying.

Strangely, the Catholic Church did not realise the implications of Copernicus's work until 73 years after his death, when the heretical astronomer Galileo unwittingly drew attention to it. The scandalised Vatican then placed *The Revolutions* on its index of prohibited books—and there it remained until 1822.

The genius who was wrong

The Church had influential backing for its views from the remarkable Danish nobleman Tycho Brahe, who was born in 1546. He could never accept the idea that the earth moved round the sun and intended his work specifically to prove the Ptolemaic theory correct. Despite this, he became the greatest observational astronomer since Aristarchus.

When Tycho was 30, the King of Denmark made him landlord of the island of Hven, in the Baltic, and provided him with enough money to build a house and observatory there.

From this lonely base, and using only a giant quadrant, Tycho made a 20 year study of the heavens, and produced a magnificent and comprehensive star catalogue, including tables which gave thousands of accurate 'fixes' on the changing positions of the planets against their background of stars.

Tycho allowed nothing to interfere with his studies—particularly shortage of cash. To ensure that islanders paid their rents, he had a prison built into the

29

observatory, and anyone threatening his supply of funds by defaulting on payment was promptly locked up.

Hven became a famous scientific centre, and eminent visitors included James VI of Scotland, later James I of England. But the clamour of protest from irate islanders, constantly threatened with prison, eventually prompted the Danish king to withdraw his support.

An inexorable fate

Tycho went to live in Prague, where .he engaged as his assistant the astronomical genius Johannes Kepler. In later years, Kepler was to announce: 'Tycho and I were joined by inexorable fate.'

When Kepler studied the volumes of tables drawn up by Tycho he found that the island astronomer had paid particular and painstaking attention to the movements of Mars. Kepler quickly realised that the observations demolished the long-cherished notion that Mars travelled in a circular orbit.

It was perhaps providential that Tycho died in 1601 while Kepler was still toiling with his figures regarding Mars—checking each complicated calculation as many as 40 times to ensure absolute accuracy. He spent five years at the task before he

was confident that his earlier suspicions were correct: Mars, earth and all the other known planets had elliptical paths —and, in defiance of Tycho, they travelled round the sun.

Kepler, described by Einstein as 'an incomparable man', was then able to draw up his *Laws of Planetary Motion*, upon which calculations are based to this day.

Towards the end of his life, Kepler was put under surveillance as a suspected heretic, and people even spat at him in the streets. But when he died in 1630, the tide of science was running his way, despite a Church rearguard action.

Among Kepler's admirers was one of the most colourful characters in the history of astronomy—Galileo Galilei—the first serious astronomer to use a telescope and the last to be persecuted for claiming that the earth moved round the sun.

Galileo made his own telescope while he was teaching mathematics at Padua University in Italy. He used it to good effect, discovering among other things the moon's craters, some of Jupiter's satellites, sunspots and the stars of the Milky Way.

Everything he saw convinced him that Aristarchus, Copernicus and Kepler were right in suggesting that the earth moved round the sun. But in 1616, Galileo was

THE STARGAZERS' TOOLS

From the Pyramids to radio astronomy

About 5000 years ago, the Egyptians built what is still the world's biggest clock. It was designed to register time not only in hours, but in days, seasons and even centuries.

It is the Great Pyramid of Cheops, which was built in the 26th century BC, and is the largest in the group of pyramids at Gizah on the banks of the Nile. The only surviving example of the Seven Wonders of the Ancient World, the Great Pyramid is probably the world's oldest astronomical observatory, and still attracts much scientific and occult speculation.

In 1853 the French physicist Jean Baptiste Biot visited Gizah and decided that the pyramid was a huge sundial. But it recorded more than just the time of the day, for the Egyptians had built it on such a scale, at such a latitude, and at such a

precise angle that it could also indicate the precise day of the year.

On the ground adjoining the northern and southern faces wide, level pavements, or 'shadow-floors', had been constructed. In the winter the pyramid would cast its shadow on the pavement to the north, and in the summer the highly polished southern face would reflect a triangle of sunlight on to the southern pavement.

Accurate forecasts

The paving blocks had been cut in widths similar to the gradations by which each noonday shadow or reflection succeeded its predecessor. Thus the days could be measured and such seasonal pointers as the equinoxes and solstices accurately forecast.

The equinoxes are the two days each year when the sun crosses the equator,

MODEL UNIVERSE *Johannes Kepler worked out in miniature the spacing of the planets.*

TOMBS THAT TELL THE TIME *As well as being burial chambers for the pharaohs, the Pyramids at Gizah were also designed as observatories—and giant calendars.*

31

THE FIRST RADIO TELESCOPE *American Karl Jansky built his telescope on a farm in New Jersey in 1931. He called the strange array of aerials and old car wheels his 'merry-go-round'.*

while the solstices are the two days when it is furthest from the equator.

The 19th-century British astronomer Richard A. Proctor put forward the theory that the Great Pyramid would have made an almost perfect observatory.

The descending passage which leads down to a pit in the heart of the pyramid was set at an angle of 26° 17′, the exact alignment to aim it at the Pole Star.

The Egyptian's Pole Star was not the present one. Over the centuries the gravitational pull of the sun and moon on the imperfect sphere of the earth, moves the earth's axis very slightly. This means that the Pole Star changes every few thousand years. When the pyramid was built the Pole Star was Thuban in the constellation, or star-cluster, of the Dragon. Today it is Polaris in the constellation of Ursa Minor.

But as the earth has moved, so the Great Pyramid has moved with it and aligned itself on the new Pole Star.

Proctor also pointed out that the pyramid's central grand gallery would have provided an ideal platform from which the priests of ancient Egypt could have observed and recorded the movements of stars and planets. By stationing observers at different levels in the gallery, an astronomer could track the changing movements of the stars using the entrance as a guideline.

The enigma of Stonehenge

It is now thought that the building of Stonehenge—the great circle of giant stone slabs on Salisbury Plain in the English county of Wiltshire—was begun around 1900 BC, about 700 years after the construction of the Great Pyramid.

Until recently it was popularly believed to have been built by the Druids as a sun-worshipping temple and a site for human sacrifice. But modern archaeology has deduced that the mysterious structure predates the Druids by more than 1000 years, and was in fact built in three stages over a period of 500 years.

The ditch and inner embankment which circle the complex are thought to ordered by the Church in Rome to stop supporting what had become known as the 'Copernican system'.

Galileo publicly recanted, and at once began work on a book called *Dialogue of the Two Chief World Systems*, in which the whole question was fairly discussed from the two opposing points of view. Before having the book published, however, he took the sensible precaution of getting clearance from Rome.

Yet, when the book appeared, the Church summoned him to answer a charge of heresy, even though their own censors had approved the book. At his trial he was ordered to make a further public recantation. Kneeling, he read a statement pledging that he was ready to 'curse, abjure and detest' the theory that the earth moved round the sun. The alternative was undoubtedly the stake.

As a further precaution, Galileo was ordered to be cut off from the world in his villa at Arcetri. Visitors were forbidden, and the only people he was allowed to meet were those who looked after his personal needs. To add to his troubles the rebellious astronomer became totally blind in the later years of his life.

When Galileo died in 1642, the pope forbade the erection of a monument over his tomb. And yet within 50 years the central-earth theory had completely crumbled.

The picture widens

The Royal Observatory at Greenwich was founded in 1675 on the orders of Charles II, who was keen to have a new catalogue of stars compiled for ships' navigators. The building, designed by Sir Christopher Wren, was an immense success, but unfortunately the man chosen as official astronomer, the Rev. John Flamsteed, though a skilled observer and an almost obsessive perfectionist, was painfully slow at calculation.

He had only one assistant, who was thoroughly unreliable, and after 29 years of work the two of them had still not finished the catalogue. Nevertheless, 400 copies were published in the incomplete form against Flamsteed's wishes. He got hold of 300 of them and publicly burnt them in protest.

When he died in 1719, the catalogue was still not ready—but by then the whole scheme was obsolete, for better navigational techniques had been perfected.

In 1781 an amateur astronomer, the young German-born William Herschel, made a most remarkable discovery while

have been built about 1800 BC—by Neolithic, or New Stone Age, people who first arrived in Britain about 3000 BC.

The Beaker people, a highly developed late Stone Age-early Bronze Age race, are accredited with hauling and erecting the bluestones, 60 monoliths each weighing 4 tons, which they probably brought by roller and barge from the Presely Mountains in South Wales. The inner trilithons—two uprights with a cross bar—in sarsen sandstone, were erected about 1500 BC, probably by the Bronze Age Wessex people.

Then followed construction of the outer circle uprights and lintels, with work ending about 1400 BC.

In 1963 the American astronomer Professor Gerald Hawkins claimed he had finally decoded the mysteries of Stonehenge, and that it could be described as a sort of prehistoric computer, its function being to make intricate calculations of sunrises and sunsets, the movements of the moon and the eclipses of both sun and moon.

SHADOWS AT STONEHENGE *Did the ancients build it as an observatory to plot the movements of the sun and moon?*

He suggested that by moving marker stones around an outer circle of holes, priests or astrologers could calculate suitable times for crop-planting, predicting weather-cycles, or for divination.

In 1845 the world's largest telescope was built in Ireland by an amateur astrousing his telescope at his English home. He spotted a small red disc in the sky and sent a report to the Royal Society entitled *An Account of a Comet*.

Experts worked out the object's orbit and decided that Herschel had indeed found something unusual, but it was more unusual than a comet. He had discovered the first new planet since Grecian times— a monster taking 84 years to circle the sun. It was named Uranus and earned Herschel a knighthood.

The sidereal day

When in 1931 a young radio engineer named Karl Jansky pieced together what he called his 'merry-go-round'—a strange array of aerials attached to old car wheels —he had built the first radio telescope. Jansky realised that no matter how powerful an optical telescope is, the star images that reach the lenses are distorted by the atmospheric blanket round the earth.

He built his telescope to investigate static—the hissing and crackling which plagues long-distance radio communications. He picked up plenty of static, but there was also a steady hiss which reached its peak exactly four minutes earlier each day. This matched the period of the earth's rotation in respect to the stars, as opposed to the sun—23 hours 56 minutes. Astronomers call this the sidereal day.

Jansky rightly concluded that he was picking up signals from the Milky Way.

An amateur astronomer, the American Grote Reber, built a steerable dish-shaped aerial 30 ft in diameter in the garden of his Illinois home. He amplified and recorded the stellar signals to produce the first crude 'radio map' of the sky.

Reber focused radio signals by altering the angle of his dish. The shape and size of a radio source were accurately assessed by interpreting its transmissions from various angles. Reber's studies revealed that the shape of some stars was quite different from the way they appeared when viewed through optical telescopes.

The 3000-ton saucer

Among the scientists impressed by Reber's studies was an Englishman named Bernard Lovell. He set up two trailers full of radar equipment in a field near Lower Withington, Cheshire, to track meteors. Lovell's apparatus gradually developed into the great radio-astronomy observatory of Jodrell Bank, containing a giant saucer-shaped steerable radio telescope weighing 3000 tons that pirouettes on a circular railway track.

SEARCHING FOR GALAXIES *The Earl of Rosse's telescope enabled him to observe other galaxies for the first time in 1845.*

nomer, the third Earl of Rosse. It had a 72 in. metal mirror and was suspended between two stone walls. It was this telescope which made man realise that there are other galaxies beyond his own.

There are still no telescopes powerful enough to show these galaxies in detail. Even the 200 in. Hale complex at the Mount Palomar Observatory in America is not up to the job. An extra-large reflecting telescope is sited on Mount Semirodriki, in Russia's northern Caucasus. The telescope's power comes from a unique 232·6 in. diameter mirror and collects $1\frac{1}{2}$ times more light than the one at Mount Palomar. It weighs 800 tons and is accurate to within several millionths of a metre.

The world's largest steerable radio telescope is at the Max Planck Institute for Radio Astronomy in Bonn in West Germany. Its dish has a massive 328 ft diameter. But even more impressive is the largest telescope of all—at Arecibo, Puerto Rico. Unmovable because it is formed in a natural 1000 ft wide hollow between hills, the bowl can pick up signals as weak as 1/100th of a millionth of a millionth of a watt. The signals it sends out to space, trying to contact other civilisations, would seem to the receivers to be as bright as a million suns.

WHEN A STAR DIES

Fifty tons in a matchbox

Near the brilliant Dog-Star Sirius lies a faint dot of light, a much smaller star known as the Pup. Although it is smaller, the material at its centre is so dense that one matchboxful would weigh 50 tons.

The Pup, or Sirius B, was first spotted through a telescope by American Alvan Clark in 1862, although 30 years earlier the Prussian astronomer Friedrich Wilhelm Bessel had noticed deviations in the orbit of Sirius which led him to believe they were caused by another nearby star.

In fact the Pup is not at all faint, except in relative terms. It is so outshone by its brilliant neighbour Sirius that a powerful telescope is needed to see it.

The two stars revolve once in 50 years around a common centre of gravity. While the Pup has as much mass as the sun—enough to make Sirius wobble in its orbit—its diameter is only 24,000 miles, compared with 865,370 miles for the sun, so that the same mass is crammed into 1/27,000th of the sun's volume.

Abnormally small

In other words, the Pup is 27,000 times more dense than the sun. Its surface temperature is 2000°C hotter than the sun, and each square inch of the surface radiates $3\frac{3}{4}$ times more heat and energy than the sun, yet the Pup's luminosity is only 1/360th of that of the sun. It was these facts that first led astronomers to realise that the Pup is abnormally small.

The Pup was the first recorded of a class of stars now known as White Dwarfs, though many more stars of this type have since been identified. Among the most dense listed in the Astrographic Catalogue is a star known as +70 8247. It is about half the size of earth, but every cubic inch of it weighs 620 tons.

Astronomers believe that these exceptionally dense stars are in the final stages of evolution and nearing extinction.

Stars are thought to begin life by condensing from clouds of gas and dust, shrinking under the force of their own gravity as their cores heat up. Nuclear reactions begin and the hydrogen of which they are largely composed is converted into helium, releasing energy and causing the stars to shine brilliantly in the heavens, like the sun.

The red giant stage

When the hydrogen supply runs low, further nuclear reactions begin and the star swells, getting hotter and more dense at the core and cooler at the surface. At this stage it is known as a red giant.

When all the nuclear reserves are exhausted, if a star is big enough, it may explode as a supernova. A smaller star may collapse in on itself under the force of gravity, becoming a White Dwarf.

A White Dwarf, therefore, is a dying star, with no means of re-heating and no future but extinction. The next stage is for it to collapse in on itself still further and condense into a neutron star, shrinking so much that it forms a dense mass that would weigh 20,000 million tons per cubic inch.

OUR OWN SUN—A YELLOW DWARF

THE SUN is classified as a Yellow Dwarf star midway between the largest and the smallest stars, and between the hottest blue-whites and the coolest red stars. Rigel, for example, is between 25,000 and 50,000 times more luminous. The cool Antares, a red super giant, is 27 million times bigger.

The nuclear reaction which keeps the sun shining involves a mass-loss of about 4 million tons a second, but the sun is so huge that it is not expected to expand into a red giant for at least 8000 million years.

When this happens, immense heat will be released and if earth is not actually swallowed up, life as it is now will not be able to survive. However, even if the earth's inhabitants of that time manage to protect themselves from the heat in some way, their descendants will have to cope with the extreme cold which will ensue when the sun reaches the White Dwarf stage.

SIGNALS FROM OUTER SPACE

Stars that 'broadcast' to the universe

The radio signal from outer space was weak, but it was being broadcast at precise intervals of 1·33730113 seconds. Professor Anthony Hewish, heading the group of Cambridge University astronomers who first heard it in 1967, said the signals were 'as regularly spaced as a broadcast time signal'.

Graduate student Jocelyn Bell had discovered the signals by accident while working with radio telescope equipment designed to record weak signals.

Despite their training and professional caution, the astronomers could hardly restrain their excitement. Could it be that some unknown civilisation, far out in space, was trying to contact earth? Again and again, they pinpointed the signals coming from the same spot in the sky, showing they came from outside the solar system.

But as the signals continued without variation for months on end, it was apparent that they had found a new kind of star—one that emitted regular but natural bursts of radio energy.

Visible pulsar

Since then, many more of these stars, now called pulsars, have been detected by radio telescopes, but so far only one has been tracked down as a visible star. Astronomers at the Steward Observatory in Arizona discovered it in 1969. Faintly flashing in time with its radio signals, it lies in the Crab Nebula, somewhere between 5000 and 6000 light years away.

An early theory was that a pulsar might be a rapidly vibrating White Dwarf star, a sun that has used up most of its energy and collapsed. But though they are small, even White Dwarfs are not thought small enough to vibrate at sufficient speed to emit the signals.

Enormous density

Radio astronomers estimate that if a pulsar were as big as our sun—865,370 miles in diameter—the radio signal from its furthest point would take longer to reach us than one from its nearest point.

The result would be a continuous radio rumble, not a regular intermittent signal. Because the pulses are clear and precise—sometimes coming over at a rate of 30 a second—the experts believe that pulsars must be quite small heavenly bodies in which the atomic components have compressed to make their density enormous.

Pulsars are now believed to be the remnants of massive stars which have collapsed under the weight of their own gravity and imploded—collapsed violently inwards on themselves. They are so dense that on earth a single cubic inch of pulsar material would weigh 10,000 million tons.

The rate at which a pulsar sends its signals may depend on its rotation in space. A pulsar has a powerful magnetic field, and the magnetic pole may not coincide with the pole of rotation. As the star spins round, earth comes regularly into the 'emission beam', rather as a ship out at sea comes regularly into the rotating beam of a lighthouse.

But most pulsar signals appear to be slowing almost imperceptibly, and scientists expect that eventually they will go 'off the air' and become untrackable.

BRIGHTER THAN A MYRIAD SUNS

Racing to the edge of the universe—and beyond?

Of all the objects in the sky, probably the most puzzling are the quasars. They were identified as recently as 1963, and as yet we have no real idea of their true nature. They are believed to be the brightest and the most remote objects known to man. But we cannot yet be sure that there is not some major mistake in interpreting the evidence.

Astronomers are accustomed to surprises. But the discovery of quasars aroused total astonishment. The Milky Way numbers 100,000 million stars, many of them brighter than the sun. Yet one quasar is 200 times as bright as the entire Milky Way galaxy. And all this light comes from an object one thousandth of the diameter of our galaxy.

The first quasar was spotted on a radio telescope at Mount Palomar in California by the Dutch astronomer, Maarten Schmidt.

He was trying to find a Milky Way star, thought to be the source of unusual radio signals. At the charted spot in the sky he found the radio signals, but they did not come from a star. The object emitting them was much brighter than any star and was so far away that its distance was estimated at 1000 million light years. (A light year, the distance travelled by light in a single year, is 5,865,696 million miles.)

Moreover, the object showed what scientists call a 'red shift' on the colour spectrum. This was particularly significant, because it meant that it was rushing away from earth through space.

When a train approaches a station, its noise rises in pitch, but as it recedes into the distance the note falls. This is called the Doppler effect after the Austrian scientist who investigated it. A similar effect can be observed in stars, although in this case it is produced from light and not from sound.

Receding into space

If the light from a heavenly body is directed through a prism and broken up into a colour spectrum, much information can be discovered about the star. And it is an established belief among astronomers that if the red part of the spectrum is displaced—a 'red shift'—this means that the star being observed is receding into space, just as a falling note tells the listener that the train has passed.

The spectrum of Maarten Schmidt's quasar had a most pronounced 'red shift'. The logical conclusion, therefore, was that this object was not only incomparably brighter than anything observed hitherto and the most distant body in the sky, but was also hurtling even further outwards into space at enormous speed.

The newly found object was named a quasi-stellar radio source, now shortened to quasar. Since 1963 about 200 quasars have been found—the last one by an international team of scientists working in Arizona in 1974.

This may be the most distant object known to man. It was estimated to be travelling away into outer space at more than 177,000 miles a second—faster than any previously observed quasar. Some

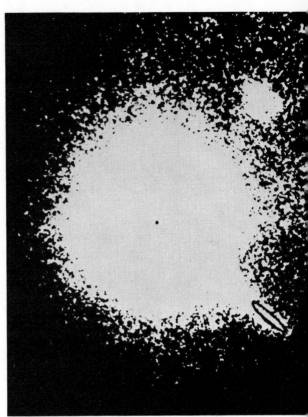

QUASAR 3C273 *The first quasar was found in 1963 by Maarten Schmidt, who was investigating radio signals from what he at first believed to be a star.*

scientists think that quasars are formed by large numbers of stars exploding in quick succession.

Chain of exploding stars

To astronomers, exploding stars are nothing new, for about once a century this type of explosion takes place in the Milky Way, creating a supernova, an exploding star which is suddenly much brighter than an ordinary one.

The theory is that quasars may be a chain-reaction of supernovae, one exploding star causing another to go off like artillery shells in a blazing warehouse.

But this is by no means the only theory. It has even been suggested that the universe is composed not just of matter, but also of a negative substance called 'anti-matter'. Could the colossal release of energy by the quasars be caused by the collision of matter and anti-matter in outer space?

Assuming that the 'red shifts' are true Doppler effects, caused by the hurtling of quasars into the outer fringes of space, this raises the question of whether space is infinite or not. Either concept is difficult for the human mind to grasp. We can imagine neither a boundary to our universe nor space going on forever.

The further away a quasar is, the faster it seems to be travelling. If this acceleration continues, there should eventually come a point where the quasar would be travelling faster than light.

In this case, its light and radio waves would never reach us and it would pass beyond the boundary of the observable universe. The distance involved would be more than 10,000 million light years.

It may be that all the material in the universe was created at one particular moment (the Big Bang theory), and that the expansion which this initiated, and which we are witnessing in the quasars, will continue indefinitely. In this case the universe has a limited future before every galaxy and star dies away.

An alternative is the concept of the cyclic universe. According to this theory the outward rush of the quasars will reach a limit and will then be reversed. In the far distant future (perhaps 60,000 million years from now) the stars will coalesce again into a single point.

In which case the universe will be reborn and a new expansion will begin.

MYSTERY OF THE BLACK HOLES

Could they be universes running in reverse?

Imagine a star made of matter so dense that enough to go into a matchbox would weigh 10,000 million tons. If a rocket is to escape from earth's gravity, it needs to reach a speed of about 25,000 mph. But the gravity of this star would be so enormous that there would be no escaping from it even at 670,000,000 mph —about the speed of light.

Indeed, light itself would not be able to escape, making the star forever invisible.

Such stars are believed to exist in the universe. As light cannot leave them, no one has ever seen one, but astronomers have good reasons to suppose they are there. They are called black holes.

One of the first clues to their existence came from the odd behaviour of a star called Epsilon Aurigae, a giant 60,000 times as bright as the sun. Once every 27 years this star fades to less than half its usual brilliance.

An invisible partner

Scientists know that Epsilon Aurigae has a partner, which swings with it round a common centre of gravity. The fading was presumably caused by the partner getting in the way of the view from earth. But why, in that case, does the partner emit neither light rays nor radio waves like other stars?

The answer seems to be that the partner is a black hole—invisible, small but enormously heavy.

Scientists are able to explain how a black hole could be created. The heat of stars like the sun comes from continuous nuclear fusion—the process that goes on in the hydrogen bomb. After thousands of millions of years, the store of nuclear fuel in the star begins to be exhausted. Then the star cools down and eventually implodes—that is, collapses inwards in a matter of seconds, with terrible violence.

A White Dwarf

The sun will do this in about 8000 million years. It will end up as a small cool object called a White Dwarf. But the forces of gravity in stars $1\frac{1}{2}$ times the size of the sun are much stronger. When they implode they squeeze smaller than White Dwarfs, until the centre becomes so hot that it explodes outwards. The exceptionally bright mass which results is known as a supernova.

When this happens a tiny part of the star remains at the centre, fantastically compressed by gravity. This is known as a neutron star.

But there are much larger stars, some as much as 50 times the size of the sun. When one of these collapses it will contract even smaller than the neutron star. If it is only two-thirds the size of a neutron star the gravitational pull would be so strong that nothing could withstand it.

Not even light could escape and even if the star was white hot nothing could be seen. For this reason the phenomenon is called a black hole.

Compared with the vastness of other objects in the universe, black holes are tiny. For example, a collapsed star ten times bigger than the sun would be compressed into a black hole less than 40 miles across.

Because they emit neither light nor radio waves, astronomers can only speculate about their presence by the behaviour of neighbours under their influence.

Having so enormous a force of gravity, black holes suck into themselves any matter that comes into their part of the heavens. One theory even has it that they will eventually suck up everything in the entire universe.

Meanwhile, they are busy absorbing part of their neighbours. One supergiant star in the Cygnus constellation, called HDE 226868, which is believed to be paired with a black hole, seems to be losing clouds of swirling gas into its invisible neighbour.

Once it gets closer to the black hole, the gas becomes invisible, entering what is called the 'event horizon'. There is a limit to the pull even of black hole gravity and there must come a point where light can neither escape nor be pulled back. On this 'event horizon', light would stand still or move very slowly.

An immortal spaceman

This raises the fascinating possibility that light images on the 'event horizon' would go on being seen more or less forever. For instance, if an astronaut headed for a black hole, he might still be seen going through the 'event horizon' for millions of years afterwards.

However, the prospects of any man landing on a black hole are small indeed. Closing in on the 'event horizon', those parts of his spacecraft or his body nearer to the black hole would receive more pull from the gravity. The results would be to stretch him out into a streak miles long, while the compression reduced his volume.

If the spaceman was able to observe a clock far away from the black hole, the hands would appear to move faster as he approached the 'event horizon' until he was unable to see them. As he went through the 'event horizon' the hands would reverse, start slowing down and he would appear to be going backwards in time, though the time as measured by a watch on his wrist would not change.

Once through the 'event horizon' the spaceman would be unable to escape. In fact the harder he tried to avoid his fate, the faster he would meet it, since the energy expended in the attempt would produce increased mass and hence increased gravitational attraction.

As the spaceman approached closer to the black hole, he and his spacecraft would be torn to shreds by the tremendous force of gravity long before touchdown. In a small black hole, say one of twice the sun's mass, it would take only 20 millionths of a second for him to fall to the centre. In fact for the experience to have any noticeable duration the black hole would have to be very large. Even in one a million times the size of the sun the falling process would take a maximum of only ten seconds.

Backwards through another universe

One mind-boggling theory is that if a man ever did enter a black hole and avoid destruction, he might find himself in another universe travelling backwards in time. This idea is based on the way in which a black hole appears to behave like the rest of the universe, only in reverse. For while the universe is continually exploding outwards, a black hole is forever imploding, or turning in on itself.

And while science can explain matter compressed into an astonishingly dense pinprick, it cannot account for matter disappearing absolutely. Thus, as the universe represents a process of seemingly endless outward expansion, so the black hole represents inward expansion without a foreseeable limit.

It has been suggested that a black hole may exist in our own galaxy of stars; and some scientists even think there may be a little one in the middle of the sun, and that this is affecting the sun's production of certain kinds of radiation.

According to some theories, man could use a black hole to produce energy for his own purposes by directing matter towards it and storing the gravitational energy sent out by the black hole as it sucks the matter in. It would thus be used as a sort of cosmic garbage can, giving out energy for any unwanted rubbish thrown in.

Still other scientists dispute the very existence of black holes.

Only one thing is certain. Black holes are one of the most intriguing concepts to come to man's attention this century. And they are going to occupy the thoughts of astronomers for years to come.

The miraculous mechanism that is ourselves

The astonishing human body

THE MOST AMAZING MACHINE

All in a waterproof case

Engineers have never devised a machine to equal nature's supreme achievement: the human body. Athletes can sprint at 25 mph, throw a ball at nearly 100 mph, jump over 7 ft. But even our everyday activities are powered by a system which, in its complexity and efficiency, would make the most sophisticated robot seem inadequate.

Take the circulatory system. Every minute of our lives the heart pumps 10 pints of blood—30 pints during brisk exercise—round 60,000 miles of arteries, veins and capillaries. An adult body contains between 6 and 10 pints of blood: the average for a man is 10 pints, containing $2\frac{1}{2}$ million million red cells (to carry oxygen) and 2500 million white cells (to fight disease). Some white cells have a life cycle of only 12 hours: red cells have a life of about 120 days.

The capillaries—tiny tubes servicing the bloodstream—have a total surface area that would cover a $1\frac{1}{2}$ acre field. Not all are opened at once; otherwise all the blood in the body would drain into them within seconds, like floodwater into a swamp.

One part of the body that needs blood all the time is the lungs. Their capillaries filter and purify the bloodstream by breathing—and during an average lifetime we breathe 500 million times.

Blood and water

Blood, it is said, is thicker than water. But in fact 60 per cent of the body *is* water, 10 gallons of it, or 60 per cent of the

Up to
5 million
hairs

20 sq. ft.
skin

650
muscles

About
206
bones

Over
100
joints

60,000 miles
arteries,
veins and
capillaries

13,000 million
nerve cells

average person's weight. Blood, on the other hand, is about a mere 10 per cent.

Fat people often like to think that a lot of their weight is due to water retention, but in fact fatty tissue contains only 20 per cent of water, so that the body of an obese person contains proportionately less water than that of a lean person.

A human being also contains an odd assortment of other substances: enough fat for seven cakes of soap, enough lime to whitewash a small shed, the carbon equivalent of a 28 lb. bag of coke, enough phosphorus to make 2200 matches, as much iron as there is in a 1 in. nail. For good measure there is a spoonful or so of sulphur and an ounce of various metals—apart from iron.

Chemicals from food

A strange and motley collection. Yet the body cannot function efficiently unless it is all there. If, for instance, a person's diet is deficient in iodine his thyroid gland enlarges, causing the dramatic swelling of the neck called goitre. In fact, all but one of the factors necessary to health—the oxygen we breathe—have to come from our food. This is why doctors say that we should have a wide and varied diet throughout life.

A baby is born with 305 bones, but some of these fuse together later until there are about 206 (though the number can vary slightly) operated by 650 muscles and over 100 joints. The tendons anchoring muscle to bone are strong enough to stand a stress of 8 tons per square inch, and the thigh bones take a strain of half a ton per square inch while walking.

All this wonderful complex of nature's machinery is encased in a flexible, waterproof suit—the skin. The average man has 20 sq. ft of it, which wears away and is replaced every few weeks. Set in the skin are up to 5 million hairs (unless the man is going bald), each one of which lasts about three years.

Nine thousand taste buds come to our aid in choosing what we like, aided by 13,000 million nerve cells; 4 million 'receptors' in the skin enable us to feel, distinguish hot from cold, experience pain or comfort.

To achieve all this and to move itself about, the human body, like any machine, needs fuel. In the course of a lifetime the average person consumes 50 tons of food and 11,000 gallons of liquid. If he is a town dweller, he walks about 7000 miles; if he lives in the country, he walks almost 28,000 miles.

A QUESTION OF SIZE

| Old Stone Age man 5 ft 9 in. | New Stone Age man 5 ft 6 in. | Bronze Age man 5 ft 8 in. | Anglo-Saxons 5 ft 7 in. | Medieval Europeans 5 ft 6 in. | Modern man 5 ft 8 in. |

CONTRARY to popular belief, modern man is shorter than his earliest ancestors. Skeletal studies show that, with slight variations, over the ages we have lost an inch compared with the average 5 ft 9 in. of Old Stone Age man (400,000–8000 BC). The 'midget ancestors' myth probably stems from the way in which suits of armour are displayed. On the wearer's body, the plates were more widely separated and so were 'taller'.

CONTROL ROOM

The brain and its workings

The world's most complex computer is composed of just three pounds of grey-white matter shaped rather like an oversized shelled walnut. This is the human brain, whose thousands of millions of working components control everything we do every moment of our lives; in a split second it has the ability to make literally thousands of inter-connections.

Each working part is a nerve cell known as a neuron, the primary unit of the brain's still unplumbed abilities. So minute that hundreds of them could fit on the head of a pin, neurons both conduct electrical impulses and generate the power to send directions racing along the nervous system. These impulses move from one nerve fibre to another, dispatching messages through the brain.

The body's central nervous system, the control room for thought and action, includes not only the brain but also the spinal cord, which is the link between instructions from the brain and every sense we have.

Soft hemispheres

The brain's most obvious external features are two soft hemispheres which make up the cerebrum. These hemispheres are 'mirror images' of each other, with the right hemisphere controlling movement and sensations on the left side of the body, and vice versa.

The cross-over is caused by the twisting of the nerve pathways to and from the hemisphere controls.

White matter beneath the cortex, the grey covering of the brain, makes up the hemispheres which are bridged by tissue called the *corpus callosum*.

Most information is stored subconsciously, so it is true to say that people are not aware of all that they know. However, this varies from one individual to another.

Left-handed child

In most people the left hemisphere is dominant, with the result that the majority of us are right-handed. In those who are left-handed, the right hemisphere of the brain is dominant. For this reason it is unwise to force a left-handed child to be right-handed. Even in ambidextrous people, one hand is usually dominant.

Recent research in Britain and the United States demonstrates clearly that each hemisphere is associated with different functions. The left controls speech, reading, writing and calculations. The right, the 'cultural' side, is concerned more with visual appreciation, the arts and abstract thought. We also know that one hemisphere turns itself off when the other is in use, making it impossible to think of two things at once.

Western education, with its emphasis on the three Rs, has tended in the past to concentrate on development of the left

Movement — Speech — Hearing — Sensation — Vision — Cerebellum — Brain stem

hemisphere, but more attention is now being paid to the right side.

Beneath the cerebral hemisphere lies the cerebellum, the vital link between the brain and the spinal cord, which co-ordinates the actions of muscles and determines how fast they will work. The cerebellum also has two hemispheres of its own. It is associated with balance and muscular co-ordination.

Buried under these is the brain stem which controls the heart, the lungs and the digestive system.

The male brain is on average slightly heavier than that of a female. That is due only to the fact that men usually have heavier bodies than women, and need rather bigger brains to have comparable intelligence.

The massive memory section in the cerebral cortex is believed to contain enough potential connections to receive ten new items of information every second of life. And the brain each day makes 100 times more connections than the world's telephone systems.

THE CURE OF MIND OVER MATTER

Ancient yoga principles in the service of medical science

The system of self control practised for centuries by the yogis of India may well be the answer to medical complaints that doctors have been unable to cure.

Doctors call it 'Biofeedback' and its key is 'patient, heal thyself'. Researchers have found that with the initial aid of sensitive machines, patients can control certain automatic or involuntary body functions previously thought to be uncontrollable. The principle is mind over matter.

Doctors and scientists working in Britain, America and Europe say that some illnesses connected with the heart, brain, muscle groups and circulatory systems can be overcome, if not cured completely, by Biofeedback.

Although research is incomplete, it is believed that Biofeedback stems from our ability to control alpha brain-waves and the electrical impulses from the lymphatic system located just below the cortex.

Alpha waves, discovered in 1935, normally occur only when our eyes are closed, or sometimes when we stare into the distance. The brain normally produces only beta waves, but alpha waves have a much slower frequency than beta and generally cause the body and nervous system to slow down and relax.

Heartbeat stopped

Many years ago, British doctors in India sent back reports that yoga followers could perform amazing feats, including stopping their heartbeat and walking on burning embers with no apparent injury.

The reason was that yogis had obtained extraordinary control of their bodies and minds by exercise and mental discipline. In so doing they had apparently learned to control alpha and beta waves—although they would not have known them under such names.

Like yoga techniques, therefore, Biofeedback is concerned with control of the autonomic system—that part of our nervous system which operates without conscious control, like the systems controlling breathing, heartbeat and blood pressure.

'My hands are warm'

In 1910 the German hypnotist Johann Schultz found that when he taught patients self-hypnosis by talking themselves into a relaxed state, he had surprising results. For instance, when they repeated the phrase 'My hands are warm', their hands did in fact grow warmer.

In 1964 American doctors confirmed Schultz's early experiments, wiring up volunteer housewives to instruments which monitored skin temperature. The wives were then asked to relax and feel their hands getting warmer. Clearly and indisputably the instruments registered an increase in heat from their hands.

This was a highly important experiment because it had now been scientifically proved that the autonomic system could be controlled. if only in one small way.

Since 1964, however, doctors have made spectacular advances. The technique has been extended to the treatment of insomnia, anxiety, blood pressure and asthma; and experiments are already being conducted on the relief of epilepsy, stroke paralysis, pains in the back, migraine and tension headaches.

43

The essential part of such treatment is the 'backfeed'. This means that patients must be able to 'tune in' to the particular body function over which they are trying to win control. Once the patient can see his heartbeats or brain-waves recorded on an electric meter, or can hear them as a fluctuating tone, he is on his way to controlling them.

Asthmatics, for example, are sensitive to such irritants as dust, pollen and fumes —but a lot of their trouble stems from their own nervous tension. An asthmatic patient is treated in a soundproof room and wired to an instrument called an electromyograph. If he is relaxed, he hears only a slow clicking.

But he is then told to visualise dust, flowers or whatever causes his attacks. Usually he grows tense at the very thought of these things, and the machine clicks faster and faster until the patient knows he is on the verge of a full-scale attack. All caused by tension.

When he learns that this tension is his enemy, he can learn to control it by listening to the clicks and trying to slow them down. Later he can dispense with the machine altogether and by his own efforts lead a fuller, happier life.

THE EYE OF ENLIGHTENMENT

Mystery inheritance from our remote ancestors

For thousands of years oriental mystics have credited man with a third eye, called the Eye of Enlightenment. A Sanskrit manuscript of AD 1526 said it was 'the granter of divine knowledge, as lustrous as the light of all suns shining at one and the same time'.

Now Western scientists seem to be taking their first hesitant steps towards agreeing with this extraordinary claim.

The organ the Eastern sages were talking about may be the pineal gland, a pea-sized knob of grey and white tissue, shaped like a pine-cone and buried at the back of the skull almost exactly on the mid-line of the brain.

This is one of the most primitive parts of the brain, and a study of creatures which have not greatly changed their forms since ancient times reveals that, like an eye, the pineal gland can be sensitive to changes of light. The tuatara of New Zealand, for instance, has a central cleft in its skull, covered with a transparent membrane, which lets light through to the pineal. The gland responds to changes in light, and probably controls camouflage colour changes in the skin.

These findings are strengthened by experiments conducted by the German scientist Eberhardt Dodt. He showed that the pineal of a frog is a wavelength discriminator, which converts the light energy of certain wavelengths into nervous impulses within the frog's body.

It is now thought that these nervous impulses stimulate the output of hormones, the chemical messengers which control the processes of life in the bodies of all animals. In the frog the pineal may control skin colouring, and there is evidence to suggest that its influence may also extend to other parts of the body such as the sexual organs.

Survival of a species often depends on reproduction being restricted to one certain season of the year. It may be that the pineal, which was able to judge the season from the length or intensity of the sunlight, had the job of telling the sexual organs when to grow and function.

For thousands of years argument raged over what the pineal did in man. Was it merely a leftover from our distant past, with no modern function to perform? Or was it a real gland—a piece of tissue producing hormones?

The seat of reason

In the 4th century BC the Greek anatomist Herophilus said it was 'the valve which regulates the flow of thought'. Over 2000 years later the French philosopher René Descartes called it the seat of 'the rational soul'.

The mystery is still unsolved although in 1958 an American scientist, Aaron Lerner, discovered a hormone produced by the pineal gland. The hormone, which he named melatonin, controls the spread of melanin, the pigment that gives colour to the skin and hair.

Melatonin is manufactured from another chemical, serotonin, which scientists have found to be present in large quantities in the pineal gland. In fact the gland seems to be the serotonin reservoir for the whole brain.

Serotonin was soon found to be a far from rare chemical in nature. It was first discovered in the salivary glands of the octopus, while bananas and plums are also rich in serotonin. The species of fig tree called Bo, under which Buddha sat and obtained enlightenment, also abounds in the chemical.

Scientists made a staggering discovery about the chemical in 1954: it seems to be the key to rational thought. The fig tree in Buddha's garden may have been a tree of enlightenment in the most literal sense.

When serotonin is present in the brain, man can 'think straight'. But when it is absent, then strange hallucinations occur, resembling the symptoms of the mental disease schizophrenia.

This seemed to point the way to an instant cure. Would it be possible to cure schizoids by dosing them with serotonin? Unfortunately, attempts to do so have so far proved to be failures.

It seems that serotonin is greatly affected by the drug known as LSD (lysergic acid diethylamide). A few millionths of a gram of LSD can produce powerful hallucinations, and it appeared highly unlikely that such a tiny quantity could wreak such changes by itself.

By 'tagging' LSD molecules with radio-activity, it was found that they go directly to particular parts of the brain, where they block out serotonin. Thus it seems that an LSD 'trip' is the result of serotonin deficiency.

For all these discoveries, the pineal gland is still a mystery. But it does seem clear that from its ancient role as a monitor of sunlight, it has developed other functions.

In 1898 the German physician Otto Heubner reported a case in which a boy suffering from a damaged pineal gland possessed sexual organs greatly over-developed for his age. In experiments on female rats it was shown that the larger the pineal gland, the smaller the ovary. Both cases suggest that the secretion of the pineal affects sexual development.

An intriguing possibility is that, although buried deep inside the human brain, the gland might still be affected by light seeping through, however faintly. In this case, bodily processes and emotions could still be as affected by sunlight—and moonlight—as the songwriters have always insisted.

BUDDHA UNDER THE BO TREE *It was here that the Buddha saw man's problems in a clear light and so developed his philosophy.*

WINDOW TO THE WORLD

Helen Keller (1880–1968) lived in a world of blackness and silence. Blinded and made deaf by a fever when she was 19 months old, she overcame her handicaps to become one of America's most famous authors and lecturers. When she was 6½-years-old, her teacher, Anne Sullivan, began to spell words into Helen's palm while the child felt the objects with the other hand. The breakthrough came when the teacher spelled the word "water" while holding Helen's other hand under a pump. Her sense of touch rapidly became her window to the world.

THEY FEEL NO PAIN

But they're not so lucky as you think

When Elizabeth Andrews' leg swelled up, her parents and doctor put it down to childhood rheumatism. But the swelling stayed and got worse. Months later, doctors X-rayed her and found she had broken several bones in her ankle. In all that time, Elizabeth had never felt a thing.

Elizabeth, born in England, is one of only 11 people in the world during the last 50 years known to have seldom, or in some cases never, felt pain. When others would be screaming with agony, Elizabeth would simply carry on as though nothing had happened.

One of the other ten, who also lived in England, was known as the 'human pincushion'. At the age of 50 he confessed he had felt pain only three times in his life. As a seven-year-old, he was hit in the head with an axe, and he reported a headache. At 14 he admitted feeling a twinge as a surgeon probed for buckshot embedded in his finger. And at 16 he said it hurt a little when another doctor set his broken leg without anaesthetic.

Normal mortals might at first enjoy being one of these painless beings, but pain can be a life saver. Without a sense of pain, we would never know, for instance, of an imminent appendicitis attack until it burst into deadly peritonitis. Pain is the body's early-warning system of danger.

Two sorts of pain

Most people experience two distinct feelings of pain. Touch a boiling kettle, for instance, and you will experience immediately a short, sharp pain which tells you to snatch your hand away. Then comes the second kind of pain, a dull ache which goes on until the burn is medically treated and begins to heal.

Both types of pain are carried to the brain through the spinal cord, but each has its own separate nerve system. The first is flashed to the brain through a network of small tissue-sheathed nerves called A-Delta fibres, to notify the brain of the problem so that the body can quickly react to overcome it.

The throb is transmitted more slowly through larger, unprotected nerves called C fibres. It tells the brain that the hand has been injured and, unless treated, will continue to hurt until healing takes place.

But the brain is where pain becomes a mystery. Some people can stand more pain than others: they have a higher 'threshold' of pain. And pain thresholds can vary not only from person to person, but also according to circumstances.

Thrill of competition

Vladimir Kutz, the Russian runner, rose to the top in the athletic world because of his ability to change pace many times during a long race. This feat usually causes great discomfort, but he was able to shrug it off when possessed by the thrill of competition.

Similarly, in the heat of battle a soldier can be badly wounded, but go on fighting with little apparent distress. Yet the same man would complain bitterly if a booted comrade trod on his toe while he was taking a shower.

But, generally, the amount of pain felt is determined by the amount of attention it gets. The reason is that when we worry we tend to become tense and stiffen our muscles. This in turn squeezes the pain nerves and we feel pain—either in the area of greatest tension, or as a general ache, or as discomfort in the area where the nerves finally meet. The result, quite often, is a headache.

The pain tends to increase the worry even more, so the vicious circle of anxiety-tension-pain gets worse. It is for this reason that when the nerves in a particular part of the body are damaged permanently, as can happen in amputation, the patient can continue feeling 'phantom' pain from a limb he no longer has.

In one study carried out at Harvard University Medical School during the 1950s, doctors gave 162 people injections after operations, telling them that the injection was the pain-killing drug morphine. The result was that half of them reported pain relief before being told what the injection really contained. It was a sterile mixture of salt and water.

Research shows that people who work in hard physical jobs have a higher pain threshold than office workers. And women, perhaps because their bodies are geared to the pains of childbirth, have a higher pain threshold than men.

THE PRICK OF A NEEDLE

The ancient art of acupuncture still yields results

Western doctors have found hundreds of new ways to find and fight disease. But they are only just beginning to discover the oldest medical weapon in the world: the Eastern needle technique of acupuncture.

Experts can use acupuncture to diagnose killer heart disease—months before the most delicate Western instruments would notice anything wrong at all.

They can end the blinding pain of migraine headaches, ease the agony of arthritis and stomach ulcers and carry out major operations. All with no more equipment than a set of needles, and the rules laid down in the world's oldest medical textbook: the Chinese *Yellow Emperor's Classic of Internal Medicine*, written more than 4500 years ago.

The philosophy of acupuncture goes back to the Emperor Fu Shi, who lived about 3000 BC. According to tradition, he was the compiler of one of the world's oldest known scripts, the *I Ching*, or Book of Changes.

Yin and Yang

In the book he put forward the theory that the universe was the battleground of two opposing forces, Yin and Yang.

Between them, Yin and Yang composed the world and everything in it. Yin was the negative aspect of things, the feminine, the passive, cold and odd numbers. Yang was positive, masculine, the active, heat and even numbers.

According to the theory man, like everything else, is made up of Yin and Yang; normally the two forces are more or less in balance. But when the body is hit by illness, they get out of hand, so that some parts of the body have either too much or too little of one or the other. The needles of acupuncture are designed to restore the balance by blocking off or stimulating the flow.

The Chinese believe that Yin and Yang flow round the body through special channels called 'meridians', each of which is associated with one particular organ.

It is on these meridians—12 in all—that the 900 acupuncture points are placed. This is why the needles often seem to be so far from the organs they are trying to treat. The liver 'meridian', for example, runs from near the liver down to the inside of the leg to the big toe; the pancreas meridian, from the waist to the left armpit; the one for the intestines, from the point of the chin through the navel to the groin. Only the heart meridian makes any immediate sense to Westerners. It runs from over the heart down the inside of the arm to the little finger of the left hand—exactly the path of the pain felt by some angina sufferers.

The Chinese also believe that each of the meridians is linked with a pulse—six

PINPOINTED *An ancient Chinese acupuncture chart shows the positions of some of the 900 needle points on the network of 'meridians'.*

on each wrist. And expert acupuncture diagnosticians are said to be able to feel all the pulses with such sensitivity that they can not only define a present illness, but describe past ones and predict future ones, too.

In the West, researchers have found that the meridians closely follow the paths of electrical resistance on the body. Dr Pierre Conne in Switzerland, who is not an acupuncturist himself, has shown that it is possible to detect some disorders by testing the pattern of these resistances. And one French study reported that the electrical patterns along the meridians could reveal a developing coronary thrombosis months before it would show up on a modern, western electrocardiogram.

Scientists have put forward other theories to account for acupuncture's effects, ranging from the idea that the small pain of the needles distracts the patient from his illness, to the simple notion that it works because the patient believes it will.

Modern acupuncture uses steel needles instead of the traditional needles of stone or wood. And instead of twirling them about by hand to keep on stimulating the desired point, the job is normally done by running a weak electric impulse through them.

Otherwise the treatment has not changed. It is medicine's most ancient and mysterious weapon.

THE FLEXIBLE BARRIER

Skin is tough and elastic—the perfect wrapper

An all-over, skin-tight garment for a man or woman would require 6 yds of material 13 in. wide—and an extremely good tailor.

And yet every few weeks the natural processes of cell reproduction give each human being 20 sq. ft of new and perfectly fitting skin. This completely replaces the old one, which is continually being worn away by friction in such activities as washing and moving.

Skin keeps moisture out and, at the same time, prevents the body—which is 60 per cent water—from drying out. It acts as a barrier against dirt and germs. Together with underlying fatty layers, it rounds out the body's contours and provides a cushion against bumps and knocks. It is also very elastic, the perfect wrapper for our bodies.

There are three layers of skin, the outer epidermis, the middle dermis and the subcutaneous layer.

All the skin's vital structures are located in the dermis, the relatively thick underlayer. This is covered by the paper-thin epidermis, which has an outer part consisting of flat, dead cells. As the outer cells get worn away, new ones move up from the dermis, where they have been formed, to take their place in a never-ending succession throughout life.

There are millions of nerve endings below a layer of outer cells in the skin. These are receptors for the sense of touch. Between them, they detect five different sensations—pain, heat, cold, pressure and contact. Every touch sensation is a combination of some or all of these.

In the sensitive areas, such as the fingertips or lips, there are as many as 1300 touch receptors to every square inch of surface. Less sensitive regions, such as the shoulders, have only about a fiftieth of that number.

A cooling system

In each square inch of skin there are 700 sweat glands releasing salty water, which evaporates and keeps the body cool.

Normally the daily loss of sweat is about half a pint. However, in very hot climates this can increase 12 times. That is why white people in the tropics are advised to take salt tablets to make up for the loss of perspiration. Otherwise there is a risk of collapse through heat-stroke.

Apart from sweating, body heat can be lost through the skin by radiation. The heat is lost from blood pumped through yards of capillary blood vessels just under the skin's surface, giving a flushed appearance. Contractions of the same blood vessels prevent heat loss in the cold and make the skin turn white.

Goose pimples are caused by tiny muscles in the hair follicles which contract when a person is cold, so producing bumps on the skin. Originally the purpose was to make the hair stand up, either to give a more fearsome appearance when fighting or for greater protection against the cold. This reaction now occurs to only a slight extent in man, although many animals, such as dogs and cats, still display the characteristic more dramatically.

The skin also has bulb-like hair follicles and oil-producing sebaceous glands—100 of them to every square inch. The oil lubricates the skin and hair, helping to make them waterproof.

Another major factor is melanin, a dark pigment which gives colour to the skin and hair. But it also acts as a filter, keeping out the potentially dangerous ultra-violet light in the sun's rays. This is why a white man's skin tans when exposed to sunlight. Clumping of the melanin—an hereditary trait in many fair-skinned people—causes freckles.

Like old clothes, skin goes 'baggy' with age. It wrinkles because of lack of firmness and support from the fatty, subcutaneous tissue which gradually disappears in most people as they grow older. Just as the skeleton shrinks and other organs function less efficiently, the loss of the fatty layer is the failure of the body to rejuvenate itself—part of the process of ageing.

In effect, the skin becomes too big—and the wrinkled form is maintained and regenerated. Unfortunately, the skin does not shrink to fit the smaller model. Even in younger people, wrinkled skin, caused by prolonged stretching and sudden release, takes many weeks to return to normal, and even then some wrinkling may remain. This is particularly the case after childbirth with some women, on whom stretch marks may be permanent.

That the skin copes as it does with un-ending assaults on the body by abrasives, sharp objects, sunrays, heat and cold, yet allows us to remain healthy and efficient within, is one of man's most remarkable adaptations to his environment.

Gland secretes sweat through a pore to the surface of the skin

Follicle from which a hair grows

Capillary vessels circulate blood through the skin

Outermost layer consists of dead cells

Dermis, the deeper layer of the skin

Epidermis, the outer layer of the skin

CROSS-SECTION OF SKIN *The two main layers are the dermis and the epidermis. Passing through the dermis are hair follicles, ducts from sweat glands and capillary vessels.*

SUPERFLUOUS PARTS

UNTIL recently the thymus was thought to be a useless vestigial organ, but now doctors have found that it in fact masterminds the body's whole defence system, dispatching cells to fight invading germs. It is further thought that diseases like multiple sclerosis, where the victim produces unruly antibodies which attack healthy cells, may be caused by a thymus disorder. Tonsils and adenoids were also considered superfluous, but in fact protect the throat and nose against germs. The well-known useless organ, the appendix, may after all be part of the infection-fighting lymphatic system. And bodily hair, hitherto thought to have been made redundant by our wearing of clothes, actually adds to the skin's sensitivity. That no definite role has yet been discovered for the brain's pineal gland or for the muscles of the outer ear does not necessarily mean that they have no part to play.

THE BATTLING BODY
How it fights the invisible enemy

The body is a battleground in which a never-ending war is waged against disease-producing germs. The air we breathe teems with potential killers—bacteria, invisible to the unaided eye—which, fortunately, are normally quickly vanquished by the natural defences of a healthy body.

Bacteria, or the even smaller viruses, can invade through any opening, such as the mouth, nose and ears, or a cut or scratch in the skin. Illness or infection is caused only when they penetrate into the tissue or bloodstream.

The first defences of the body are the outer skin and the membranes around interior organs. Areas prone to invasion, like the mouth and eyes, are protected by saliva and tears, both mildly antiseptic liquids. The stomach acids, besides digesting food, also kill off the many dangerous invaders that are often swallowed with it.

White cells in action

Once a germ has penetrated any vulnerable area, the body's 'infantry', the white cells of the blood, spring to its defence. The average human body contains 3000 million of these. When germs invade, they rally and multiply at the site of the infection and kill the enemy by absorbing and digesting it. Hence the name phagocytes ('eating vessels') given to these invaluable fighters.

Many of these phagocytes themselves die in the battle which rages in an infected area, such as a boil. All the time, the germs are releasing poisonous substances. These toxins act as antigens which stimulate a different sort of white cell producing defence chemicals—antibodies.

Each antibody evolves to deal with a particular infection. In a lifetime the body may encounter as many as 100,000 different antigens, each one bringing into operation the force of antibodies

No demobilisation

Even when the battle is won, the victorious body does not disband its antibodies. They persist in the bloodstream for a time, being reinforced occasionally by fresh ones manufactured in the liver and the lymphatic system. So, if the same germs should return, the correct antibodies are ready and waiting to repel the attack. This is the natural defence system that gives the body immunity to a second onslaught of certain diseases, such as measles and smallpox.

Immunity to the common cold is short-lived, because there are so many different viruses causing it that the body can never build up a resistance to them all. Artificial immunisation, vaccination, has been developed as a defence against some diseases. The most familiar example is, of course, smallpox. The vaccine which the doctors inject contains the germs of cowpox, a closely related but less dangerous disease. These germs stimulate a reaction which produces a resistance to the much more dangerous disease.

Immunity acquired either through having had a disease itself, or through vaccination, is called *active* immunity.

There is another kind of protection, called *passive* immunity, in which the body does not have to manufacture the defence antibodies for itself. This kind of immunity can be obtained by an unborn baby from its mother's bloodstream, or from breast-feeding in the first few days of a baby's life.

A WHITE BLOOD CELL *approaches a cluster of bacteria.* | *Contact is made with the enemy, and the deadly battle begins.* | *The white cell surrounds the invading germs and 'eats' them.*

LARKS AND OWLS

The inner clock that rules our lives

Guess what time it is—without looking at your watch! The chances are you will be right to within half an hour. Or try waking up at a particular time—without an alarm clock. The chances are you can do that, too.

Just about everyone can, with a little practice, because the human body has its own built-in clock.

There is a complex series of interacting rhythms in nearly everything the human body does. It sleeps to a rhythm, eats to one, blinks to one, even breathes through first one nostril then the other—all in a rhythm.

Three main rhythmic cycles affect body time: the daily rhythm of the revolving earth; the monthly orbit of the moon round the earth; and the yearly journey of the earth round the sun.

Not only man

Not only mankind is affected by these great natural tides. Every animal and plant feels them too. Sometimes a body clock can keep accurate time to the precise minute, as in the case of the bean aphid which can either lay eggs or produce young according to the season of the year and the length of the day. So perfect is this insect's adaptation to natural time that when the daylight lasts longer than 14 hours 55 minutes, live offspring are born to take full advantage of the extra warmth. If the day is shorter, the aphid lays eggs to wait for the next sunrise.

Man's time sense is both mental and physiological—the world over. He feels hungry every three to four hours. His brain cells show two to three hour cycles of activity. Even dreams run in cycles. Man dreams in a 90 minute rhythm, cats in cycles of 30 minutes, rats 12 minutes, and the elephant 120 minutes.

Circadian rhythm

Man's natural rhythm of life lies between the length of the 24 hour solar day, and the lunar day, which is 50 minutes longer. For this reason it is called the circadian rhythm, meaning literally 'about a day'. Under normal conditions, the circadian rhythm is constantly influenced by the rising and setting of the sun. But people isolated from outside stimuli—such as prisoners kept constantly in cells without natural light—revert automatically to a longer natural cycle.

The circadian pattern may be controlled partly by the hypothalamus—tissue about the size of a sugar lump at the base of the brain. The substance it uses is a chemical messenger called cortisol. The hypothalamus is highly adaptable. Once the prisoner in a darkened cell has adapted to the longer rhythm, he will follow it for months on end despite being alone and in darkness.

However, since the rhythm makes him adopt a longer day, after some weeks he will tend to underestimate how long he has been in the cell.

Most humans do have contact with natural stimuli, and their slightly shorter version of the circadian rhythm is vitally important to them. Temperature, blood pressure, pulse, breathing and hormone activity all rise and fall in time with the world's slow spin.

A cycle for illness

Similarly, ability, temper and even resistance to infection are controlled by the circadian clock. This may be why some epileptics have seizures only at certain times of the day. Or why pregnant women get morning sickness.

Experiments have shown that mice injected with pneumonia germs at 4 a.m. survive better than those injected at any other time of day. This could be important to humans. If vulnerability to disease is rhythmic, then response to vaccination is likely to be rhythmic too.

Circadian rhythms account for the differences between 'owls', people who are wide awake at night and stay up late, and 'larks', who rise early, do their best work in the morning, and go to bed early.

Larks tend to be inward-looking, pensive people. Owls are normally more outgoing. Manual workers tend to be larks, while brain workers are usually owls. Surprisingly, although owls go to bed later than larks, both groups tend to get up at about the same time. In larks, body temperature and efficiency rise more quickly, but by evening they have 'peaked out'; whereas owls at that time are still building to their peak.

Regular air travellers experience 'jet lag'—a feeling of bewilderment and lethargy when they make rapid journeys from one time zone to another.

The phenomenon is caused by the individual's circadian rhythm being out of step with clock time in his new part of the world. Gradually he will adapt to new rhythms, but the process will take as much as a week.

The best known cycle is that of menstruation in women. This monthly tide of physiological change can alter a woman's moods dramatically, and affect her susceptibility to illness. Men also follow a monthly cycle of hormonal activity, but its effects are less obvious.

Oysters sense the moon

A remarkable experiment with oysters shows that the rhythm is extremely persistent. The oysters were taken, from Long Island Sound, 1000 miles inland in a sealed and darkened tank. At first, they continued to follow their normal rhythm, opening and closing according to the cycle of the tides on their home beach. After 15 days their rhythm had changed—to what it would have been if the sea's tides had washed over their new home.

They opened when the moon, which controls the tides, reached its highest point over their new location—perhaps because of subtle changes in atmospheric pressure caused by the moon's gravitational pull.

In humans, birth and death follow the cycles. Most babies are born—and most heart attacks occur—between midnight and 6 a.m. More babies are conceived in August and September than in February and March. And science has even confirmed some age-old beliefs.

For example, people born in May and June—at least in the Northern Hemisphere—tend to be more intelligent than those born in January and February. It could be that the longer hours of sunlight in summer cause this. Sunlight seems to spur the hypothalamus into greater activity, and this in turn stimulates the body's hormone system.

The cosmic rhythm

The sun's own cycle—the 11 year rise and fall of sunspots, which are dark smudges that can be seen on the sun at the same time as it hurls vast fountains of energy into space—also has its effects upon life. The Russian historian A. L. Tchijevsky claimed in the 1940s to have found a link between this cosmic rhythm and wars and epidemics on earth.

The Japanese professor Maki Takata found a relationship between human blood and the sun. He had developed a method by which gynaecologists could check the menstrual cycles of women. This involved comparative tests of the blood of both sexes. In January 1938 hospitals throughout the world, which used the 'Takata reaction', reported that the results were changing for men as well as women. Takata cross-checked and analysed the results for 20 years, and discovered that they changed mainly when a group of sunspots passed across the centre of the sun: that is, when the sun was pumping a concentrated stream of radiation towards earth. The burst of hospital reports corresponded exactly to a sudden surge in the sunspot cycle after several years of quiet.

Takata also noticed that his test results showed a sudden change a few minutes before sunrise each day—as if the blood itself 'foresaw' the break of day. 'Man,' Takata declared, 'is a living sundial.'

He could just as well have been talking about animals or plants. Whatever and wherever it is, life seems completely in step with a cosmic clock.

HOW THE COCKTAIL-PARTY EFFECT WORKS

THERE is always a confused clatter of sounds at a noisy party, but we can still hear our name if it is mentioned on the other side of the room. This ability is known as the cocktail party effect. But it is not really our name we hear—only the sound. The ear transmits whatever sounds it hears to the brain which then interprets them. Because of the familiarity of our name, we are instructed by the selective mechanism of the brain that we have heard it spoken above the other noises. The brain also interprets information from the other sense organs and tells us what we see, taste and feel.

MALADIES OF FATE

Diseases that influenced the world's history

Abraham Lincoln was heartbroken when an unknown illness killed his mother. He was only nine, an urchin on a farm so poor that it had no pasture and the Lincolns' cow had to forage in the woods.

Lincoln never knew what malady had brought him such grief and so affected his life. But doctors know today. The science of medical detection has begun to catch up with the past.

In 1818 the uncle and aunt of Nancy Hanks Lincoln took to their beds with fatigue, stiffness of the legs and red tongues. In a few days they were dead and Nancy followed them to the grave soon after.

Their neighbours in Pigeon Creek, Indiana, spoke of the 'milk sickness' and pointed to their cows, suffering from an ailment called 'the trembles'. How right they were was shown in 1927, when the malady was identified.

Mrs Lincoln died from drinking the milk of a cow which had eaten poisonous white snakeroot. If there is grass to eat, cattle shun snakeroot, so she was in fact the victim of poverty.

Only by sheer luck can the most famous of American presidents have avoided sharing his mother's fate.

The cancer of war

In 1887 the intelligent and likeable Crown Prince Frederick of Prussia developed a growth on his left vocal cord. When early treatment failed, his German doctors diagnosed cancer and advised him to have his larynx removed. However, an eminent British throat specialist, Morell Mackenzie, said there was no sign of cancer, and the operation was, therefore, not performed.

On June 15, 1888, only 99 days after ascending the throne, Frederick died of cancer of the throat. His son, Kaiser Wilhelm, a far less intelligent man and a warmonger, thus began his fateful reign.

Many medical men believe that Frederick's life could have been saved if the German doctors had had their way, and the world might have been spared the horrors of the First World War.

Death in the bath

The infamous Jean Paul Marat, one of the most ruthless leaders of the French Revolution, was stabbed to death in his bath in 1793.

There is no mystery about how he died. His assassin was an idealistic girl named Charlotte Corday, whose sharpened table knife severed the aorta near his heart. But his habit of spending most of the day isolated in his bath made the killer's task considerably easier.

By studying contemporary accounts, doctors know that he suffered from pruritis and *pityriasis simplex*, itching skin diseases contracted during the years he spent hiding in cellars and sewers. To obtain relief he would sit in his bath, and write his rabble-rousing editorials there.

The unbearable itching probably helped to inspire the venomous outpourings from his pen that led to the worst excesses of the revolutionary terror. It was ironic that it should also have contributed to his own death.

IN TIME OF PLAGUE

The disease that changed the course of history

The greed of fur trappers was responsible for the last major outbreak of bubonic plague, in which 60,000 people died in just seven months.

It happened in Eastern Siberia in 1910 after worldwide demand had pushed up the price of marmot skins by 400 per cent. The animal, a rodent whose skin is sold as a substitute for sable, had traditionally been hunted by Mongols who knew its ways—and the strange illness that sometimes afflicted it.

No Mongol would hunt a sick animal, and, although the flesh and fat of a marmot were considered a delicacy, there was a local taboo that the lump of fatty tissue under the arm—an auxiliary lymphatic gland—should never be eaten. There was a legend that the gland contained the soul of a dead hunter, and the Mongols also

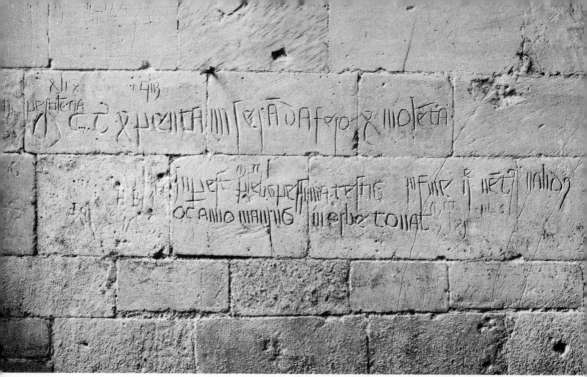

A TESTIMONY TO PLAGUE *When translated from Latin these rough inscriptions on the wall of a church tower at Ashwell, Hertfordshire, tell of plague in 1350 and a storm in 1361.*

knew that this gland tended to become diseased. This disease sometimes infected humans, and if a hunter fell ill, the Mongols left him to his fate.

In 1910 thousands of Chinese moved into Northern Manchuria to take advantage of the boom in furs. The Chinese thought it a stroke of luck when they came across a sick, easily caught creature. If a hunter fell ill they nursed him tenderly, not knowing that the sickness he had contracted from the animals was bubonic plague.

The plague spread from the hunting grounds to the town of Manchouli, the terminus of the Chinese Eastern Railway. Finally it spread 1700 miles along the rail route, killing tens of thousands.

Spread by fleas

Plague is not normally a human disease, but one of rats. It is caused by bacteria—micro-organisms not much larger than 1/1000th of a millimetre—and it is carried from one rodent to another by fleas.

There are two main forms of the disease, bubonic and pneumonic. If fleas from an infected rodent bite a man, swelling occurs at the bite mark, under the arm or in the groin. These swellings, or buboes, give bubonic plague its name. Pneumonic plague is contracted by breathing in the bacteria, as when handling an infected rodent, then transmitted from person to person on the breath.

During an epidemic, or pandemic as the greater epidemics are called, as much as 90 per cent of the population may be in-

fected. Of those who contract bubonic plague, between 60 and 80 per cent will die. In pneumonic plague the mortality rate is even higher and reaches more than 99 per cent.

Man seems to have suffered from outbreaks of plague since the beginning of recorded time. In Babylon in 3000 BC there was a plague called Namtar (Namtar was the demon of plague).

Plague has wiped out so many hundreds of millions of people that it can definitely be said to have changed the course of history.

In AD 54 the most devastating plague the world has known began to spread from Egypt along the great trade routes. It travelled through Asia Minor to Constantinople, Greece, Italy and even as far as the Rhine.

The disease raged for 52 years. In that time, 100 million people are estimated to have died—a large proportion of the then-known world's population.

With the decline of the Roman Empire came the break-up of the trade routes, and there were few reports of plague for about eight centuries. One, however, is mentioned by the Venerable Bede in his *Anglo-Saxon Chronicle*. He writes of a 'great pestilence' in England and Ireland in AD 664, and specifically describes what could only be a bubo.

Graveyard for victims

Early in the 13th century, missionaries of the Nestorian sect—a group who believed, among other things, that Christ had two natures—were travelling the new routes between Europe and Asia. Graves of missionaries dating from the years 1338 and 1339 have been discovered alongside the routes. Some of these wanderers were known to have caught plague in Outer Mongolia, and this, together with the presence of the common rat in Europe (first recorded in the 12th century), is believed to be the main cause of the Black Death that ravaged the European continent for the next 60 years, and which continued to terrorise the world for nearly four centuries.

Terrible death

The term Black Death, coined in the 14th century, comes from the medieval Latin use of the word 'black' as meaning 'terrible'.

In 1348 about 1 million people were wiped out in Florence. In that same year Pope Clement VI, who was then living in Avignon, proposed a pilgrimage to Rome. Just over a million people went on the journey of about 500 miles. Only 100,000 returned.

At the height of the epidemic, the Rhône river was consecrated to provide a graveyard for victims who could not be disposed of in any other way.

By the end of the 14th century, 25 million deaths had occurred—a quarter of Europe's population.

According to one estimate, there were 45 outbreaks of plague between 1500 and 1720. The most notorious reached London in June 1665.

One of the prevention methods used in London against the spread of the plague was to burn cats, dogs, mice and rats. But this precaution was a case of too little too late. By 1666, more than 68,000 Londoners had died and Europe feared another pandemic.

But then, on September 2, 1666, fire broke out in Pudding Lane, in the heart of London's most populous area. The fire raged for four days, leaving four-fifths of the city devastated. But the great blaze wiped out the unsanitary conditions that had helped the contagion to spread.

Last major outbreak

The last major outbreak of plague in Europe occurred in Marseilles in the south of France in 1720. There are pictures and descriptions of plague doctors clad in thick clothes with leather gloves, and a mask with a beak containing herbs to ward off smells which they believed carried the disease.

No one knows why the plague declined so dramatically in the 18th century. But perhaps an adage of the time had something to do with it. The advice was that, if the plague occurred in your area . . . 'go quickly, go far and return late'.

ALL FALL DEAD

IN ALL innocence, children have for centuries sung a nursery rhyme with the most sinister undertones:

> Ring a ring o' roses,
> A pocket full of posies,
> Atishoo! Atishoo!
> We all fall down.

The song arose in the London streets in 1665 during an epidemic of plague. *Ring o' Roses* refers to small, red rash-like areas on people infected with plague, or the Black Death. *Pocket full of posies* was a reference to the fact that from ancient times people believed that evil smells were the poisonous breath of demons who afflicted them with disease. Sweet-smelling herbs and flowers were thought to ward them off.

To this day, judges in England carry nosegays on many ceremonial occasions—a memory of the distant days when their predecessors carried flowers as a protection against gaol fever (typhus).

Atishoo! Atishoo! During the plague, sneezing was a symptom of plague victims. *We all fall down.* As, indeed, thousands of people did—dead.

An estimated 25 million people died during the infamous epidemic of the Black Death, which swept into and across Europe from distant Asia in the middle of the 14th century.

In playing ring o' roses, children sing while acting out a sinister parody of the dread plague.

Secrets of the planet on which we live

Wonders of the natural world

━━━━━━•❯━━━━━━

EARTH'S INNER CRUCIBLE

Hidden deep in the earth's crust: a giant foundry

Beneath the thin crust of the earth is a dynamic smelting pot, in which are created all the basic metals used by man. The earth's interior is fiery hot. Only 30 miles down, where volcanic lava is formed, the temperature is around 1204°C (2200°F). At the centre of the earth, known as the core, the temperature could be as high as 4000°C (7500°F)— about the same as at the surface of the sun.

The core is probably made of a dense material, possibly iron with nickel and silicon. It is also believed to consist of two parts: a solid inner core, about 820 miles in diameter, and a molten outer core, about 1440 miles thick.

Expelled upwards and outwards from this natural crucible through fissures in the earth's crust, the minerals and metals cool, crystallise and form veins of ore.

The outer core is surrounded by the mantle, a 1800 mile thick layer of heavy, dense silicate rock, rich in iron and magnesium. Above this is the world we see around us.

It is made of two types of crust—the Oceanic and the Continental. The Oceanic crust is the sea-bed, less than 200 million years old, made of sediment, shale and limestone and less than 5 miles thick.

The Continental crust is about 30 miles thick and very much older— approximately 3500 million years—and has a varied composition, although most of it is granite. This is the crust which forms the earth's land masses.

The layers of rock which make up the Continental crust contain the record of the earth's history, for trapped in them are fossils. There are traces of palm trees in Britain, glaciers in Brazil and marine life on the plains of Kansas. Whale relics lie on hilltops, for most parts of the world have been under the sea at least once in the distant past.

So far, man's exploration of the mysteries beneath his feet extends only as far as the deepest borehole ever drilled. This well, known as Baden No. 1, in Beckham, Oklahoma, reached a depth of 30,050 ft (5·69 miles) in February 1972.

Knowledge of the earth's deeper layers is based on intelligent guesswork and the study of pressure waves caused by earthquakes. These studies suggest that there are sudden changes in density in some parts of the earth.

This change is called the Mohorovicic Discontinuity or, more popularly, the Moho. Attempts to drill to the Moho have so far been prevented by the massive cost, but the chances are this may be possible soon by drilling the Oceanic crust, which is shallower.

Why should man want to drill into the earth? The main reason is that one day it may be possible to harness the vast energies of the earth's internal furnace.

Grand Canyon, a gash 1 mile deep, 4–18 miles across and 280 miles long, provides a good visual example of the upper layers of the earth.

It was formed entirely by erosion caused by the Colorado River, a slow, inexorable

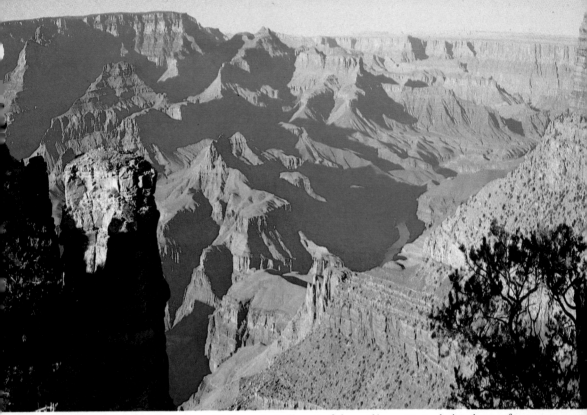

PATTERNS OF THE EARTH'S PAST *Cutting a deep slice out of the earth's crust to probe into layers of years gone by is a daunting operation. But nature has already done the job at Arizona's Grand Canyon, where it is possible to see rock formations dating back some 2000 million years.*

natural process that commenced about 10 million years ago.

Twelve major layers of rock are visible from the rim of the canyon. The bottom layer is quite different from any of the others. It is made of Brahma and Vishnu schist—an almost black, heavy rock that is more than 2000 million years old.

Going down the chasm walls, the bands measuring the passing eras show distinct changes in colour—the whites and browns of sandstone, the pinkish hue of granite and the almost black schists. Perhaps the most striking is a grey-blue limestone belt about halfway down, which was formed about 335 million years ago.

Above this are alternating layers of sandstone and shale, each 1000 ft thick.

They contain the fossils of insects, fern fronds and the stubby-toed ancestors of today's frogs.

The next layer, pale-hued, seems to have been formed by windblown sands, indicating a long period of desert conditions. Near the top are yellowish limestone layers that must have been laid down in warm seas, judging by the number of marine snails, sponges and corals.

Above these come the first traces of man —prehistoric tribes who arrived on the scene about 10,000 years ago.

And there are many more layers to be built up in the future, for the earth is still young. Astronomers believe it will survive up to 10,000 million years, before it is destroyed when the sun finally dies.

FROM THE CREATION TO NOW, IN 100 YEARS

MAN's existence has occupied only a tiny fraction of the earth's history. It is almost impossible to imagine the vast sweep of time since the earth was born out of gas and cosmic dust 5000 million years ago.

Imagine the planet's history condensed into a single century. On the time scale produced by this leap of imagination, the oldest-known rocks began to form at the dawn of year 15, and life in its most primitive form of bacteria and algae appeared in the year 26. Until the year 80 life evolved

slowly as the continents drifted about, and it was not until eight years ago that the first amphibians struggled ashore.

Dinosaurs were dominant three years ago, but by the following year they had become extinct.

Three weeks ago, the first man emerged in Africa, using tools and walking upright. The last Ice Age ended two hours ago, the Industrial Revolution started two minutes ago . . . and three seconds ago man set foot on the moon.

WALL OF FIRE *In 1973 a new volcano on the Icelandic island of Heimaey erupted, and the lava overwhelmed this fishing village.*

LEFTOVER *White Island, in the Bay of Plenty, New Zealand, is part of an eroded volcano invaded by the sea.*

MOUNTAINS OF FIRE

How volcanoes build and destroy

At eight o'clock on the morning of May 8, 1902, the volcano of Mount Pelée in the French Caribbean island of Martinique erupted. Within three minutes the town of St Pierre was totally destroyed. Every street and building was a ruin. Ships in the harbour were wrecked, the cathedral was flattened and nearly 30,000 people died. Only two men survived—one of them a prisoner condemned to death. His cell was very strong, but the roof collapsed and he was buried for three days before being rescued.

It was the worst volcanic disaster this century. But there have been even more destructive eruptions. On August 27, 1883, Krakatoa, in the Sundra Straits between Java and Sumatra, blew up, killing 36,000 people. The eruption was heard 3000 miles away, and the ensuing wall of water raised by the explosion sank dozens of ships.

The skies above Krakatoa turned murky yellow, then darkness fell. A rain of thick, black mud drenched Batavia, 100 miles from the island. Areas 40 miles away were smothered by a rain of ash that fell remorselessly at the rate of 3 ft an hour.

BIRTH OF AN ISLAND *The island of Surtsey was born on November 14, 1963. Eight days later the island was still growing.*

CRASH VICTIM *The steam and gas that pour from Stromboli are caused by the collision of the African and European continental plates.*

In one mighty explosion the volcano shattered its cone, and 5 cubic miles of dust was scattered over 300,000 sq. miles. With the lava expelled, the volcano collapsed, and was invaded by the sea.

Eighty years later, Icelandic fishermen watched a reverse process take place, and had a glimpse of how volcanoes helped to form the surface of the earth.

Captain Gudmar Tomassón's boat was trawling off Iceland on November 14, 1963, when suddenly the sea started to 'boil'. Through a vast cloud of steam the black column of a volcanic island rose above the surface. Within weeks the new island was 567 ft high and 1·3 miles long. It was named Surtsey, after a legendary Norse giant.

Following its violent birth, Surtsey evolved gently. Birds were the first to arrive bringing seeds with them. In June 1967 the first flower—a white sea rocket —bloomed. Sea currents brought more seeds, and within three years four kinds of plants and 18 mosses were established. Fulmars and guillemots made the island their home. But it will not be a permanent home. Already Surtsey is shrinking as the sea wears away its brittle lava.

It will not be the first volcanic island

THREE-MILE INFERNO *Iceland's Helka (background picture) is a 3 mile ridge that has erupted since 1104. In 1947, lava was thrown 20 miles up, and the dust covered 25 square miles.*

to vanish. In 1900 a 150 ft long island appeared in Walvis Bay, South-west Africa. Three months later, as cartographers were preparing to enter it on charts, the crew of a survey ship found that it had disappeared.

The lava that pours from volcanoes does not come from the earth's core. The source is at least 40 miles below the surface, where hot gases melt rock and create the pressure that forces the lava through the crust. Once the pressure has been released, the eruption stops.

There are more than 500 active volcanoes in the world, and most of them are on the Ring of Fire which circles the Pacific Ocean. Outside this ring there is a chain of volcanoes running across the Atlantic from Tristan da Cunha through the Azores to Iceland. Another group in the Mediterranean includes Vesuvius, Etna, Stromboli and Vulcano.

ATLANTIS—LEGEND OR FACT?

The island that exploded an empire

Once, a beautiful island, prosperous and powerful, dominated an empire that stretched to Africa and Europe. Its inhabitants were cultured and well versed in the arts of war, but they offended morality and as a punishment were overwhelmed by the waters of the sea, which swallowed them up.

So wrote the Greek philosopher Plato, and for centuries this story has provided material for romantics and poets, whilst defying the logic of history and geology.

Plato's name for this lost paradise was Atlantis, and he located it beyond the 'Pillars of Hercules', which today we know as the Straits of Gibraltar. It was a land larger than Libya and Asia, and could therefore have existed only in that vast ocean to the west of Greece—the Atlantic.

It is probably because of Plato's reputation as a great scholar that his story has been given serious consideration—for all the known facts have indicated that no such island could have existed in the Atlantic. Plato's account was based on stories told by his ancestor, Solon, who in turn had heard them from Egyptian priests. According to them, the disaster

WAS THIS ATLANTIS? The island of Santorini is all that remains of Thera, which was destroyed by volcanic eruption in the 15th century BC. Evidence points to its being Plato's fabled land.

The Lost World. The map shows Thera's location before it was destroyed by a cataclysm.

had occurred 9000 years before Solon's birth. But geological evidence shows that the Atlantic Ocean has existed in its present state for several million years, and contains no signs of a once-inhabited island sunk beneath its surface.

The civilisation that Plato described closely resembled that of the Minoan Empire, which was centred on the island of Crete. It was a highly advanced society, with written laws, a knowledge of metal-working and engineering techniques that included canals, tunnels, harbour works, air-conditioning in the houses, and even flush lavatories.

Late in the 15th century BC, this civilisation disappeared, as abruptly and mysteriously as Plato's Atlantis. For centuries its disappearance puzzled scholars, who were unable to see how such a sophisticated society could be eclipsed in such a short time. But recent archaeological findings suggest that the Minoan Empire was destroyed by one single, enormous volcanic explosion.

It is known that the volcanic island of Thera, in the Aegean Sea, exploded in about 1470 BC. The 4900 ft mountain erupted with such violence that the central portion of the island dropped into a hole 1200 ft below the sea. The surrounding area, now known as the island of Santorini, was covered in a 100 ft thick layer of volcanic ash, and it is beneath this layer that relics of the Minoan Empire have been found.

But how can this cataclysm be related to Atlantis? The simple answer may be that—as so often happens when history is translated or rewritten—Plato misinterpreted the writings of Solon. If the eciipse of Atlantis had occurred 900 years before the birth of Solon, not 9000 years, then this would put the event close to the eruption of Thera. And Plato may well have incorrectly translated the size of Atlantis as 800,000 square miles instead of 80,000 square miles. An island of this size would fit neatly into the Aegean Sea.

Word confusion

Two other possibilities strengthen the belief that Plato made a mistake. The Greek word for 'greater than' is very similar to the word for 'midway'. Was Atlantis, therefore, midway between Libya and Asia, not 'greater than'? And were the Pillars of Hercules really the Straits of Gibraltar? Two promontories on the coast of Greece, near Crete, are also called 'Pillars of Hercules'.

On the evidence available it seems the mystery of Atlantis has been solved.

Archaeologists have uncovered a complete town in the ash of Santorini, and its similarities to the fabulous Atlantis leave little doubt that Plato's paradise is a legend no longer.

WHEN THE GEYSER BLOWS OFF STEAM

AMERICAN scientist John Rinehart has discovered that the timetable of geysers, which usually erupt at regular intervals of between a few seconds and several hours, is changed at full moon and new moon.

A geyser is caused by heat deep in the earth warming up ground water in a complex underground fault system. Deep down at the bottom of the system the water is heated well beyond its normal boiling point, but does not boil because of the immense pressure of the water. Finally, some steam is produced, lifting the column of water and the pressure is lessened. The water boils and the geyser erupts.

Geologists believe that at times of full and new moons the earth's crust changes so much, because of the moon's gravitational pull, that the fault systems through which the steam travels are warped. As a result, the steam takes longer to reach the surface. This has altered the timetable of one geyser's eruptions by more than an hour.

Blast off! One of Yellowstone Park's 10,000 geysers erupts in a jet of superheated steam.

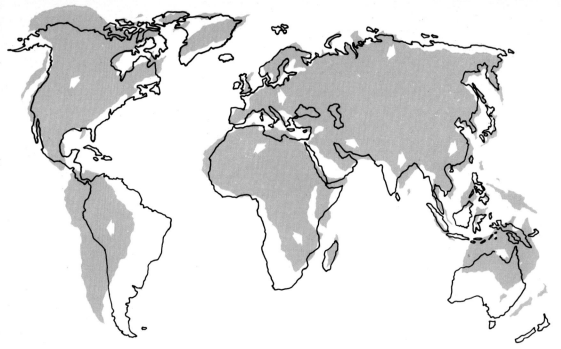

CHANGING WORLD *The continents are still drifting today. Eventually—within 50 million years— Africa will split in two. North and South America will separate, and a great slice of the Californian coast will tear off on its own. The Indian sub-continent will slide eastwards, and Australia will sideswipe Borneo. The Atlantic will widen, while the Pacific shrinks. The coloured areas above show how geologists estimate these movements will develop.*

OUR JIGSAW WORLD

Continents that once were one

Look at a map of the world and it becomes clear that, if the continents could be moved around, as in some vast jigsaw puzzle, the bulge of Africa would fit snugly into the shape of the Americas.

As long ago as 1912, the close match between the outlines of the two continents helped to put a German meteorologist, Alfred Wegener, on the trail of a startling theory. He reasoned that earth's seven continents had once been joined together in a single land mass—a supercontinent to which he gave the name Pangaea, meaning 'all lands'. Floating on a sea of molten rock, they had drifted apart over hundreds of millions of years, like runaway islands.

Wegener's theory made sense of the distribution patterns of many animals and plants, both living and extinct. For instance, many freshwater fish in South America have close relatives in Africa, and it is unthinkable that they could have crossed thousands of miles of open sea to get from one continent to the other. Monkeys, too, are found in the wild only in South America and Africa, and they are hardly likely to have evolved separately in both places.

Despite clues like these, it took half a century before Wegener's theory was widely accepted. The evidence came from a study of magnetic patterns on the ocean floor. When the rock that forms the sea-bed is first laid down it is molten, and iron particles in it, like minute compasses, swing to point towards the magnetic Pole. Once the rock has solidified, these compasses are trapped in position, and can swing away from the Pole only if the rocks that hold them also move. It was discovered in the 1960s that the compasses of the ocean floor have pointed in different directions at different times.

Final confirmation came in 1968, when the US research ship *Glomar Challenger* set off on one of the most fruitful voyages of scientific exploration the world has ever known. By drilling a series of cores up to $3\frac{1}{2}$ miles deep in the ocean floors, the geologists on board *Glomar Challenger* were able to build up a picture, not only of what happened in our planet's past, but also of what is likely to happen to the earth in the future.

Our present system of seven continents, it is now believed, formed some 150 million years ago, when two super-continents, which geologists have named Laurasia and Gondwanaland, began to break up and move gradually apart.

Both the land and the ocean floor rest on a number of separate plates, each made of rock 40 to 60 miles thick. It is these plates that are afloat, borne on a sea of molten rock.

The plates move across the globe at a rate between ½ in. and 6 in. a year, and although this may not seem much of a speed, they move vast distances over the ages. Africa, for instance, was once over the South Pole; and parts of the United States were over the North Pole. The coal of Northern Europe and the deposits of oil in Alaska and beneath the North Sea could have been laid down only in the tropics, and have since drifted to their present northern latitudes.

When plates collide, mountains can be formed, like folds pushed up in some enormous blanket. It was in this way that the Himalayas were created, when India, moving north at what in geological terms was the breakneck speed of 15 miles in a million years, crashed into Asia.

Where plates grind against one another, earthquakes are common. New material for the earth's crust is formed by molten rock bubbling up from cracks in or between the plates. In some places, this produces volcanoes. In mid-Atlantic, the molten rock that wells up from a rift thousands of feet deep has created a mountain range as high as the Rockies, and is very slowly forcing the European and American continents apart.

THE TILTING ISLAND

How Britain is recovering from the Ice Age

Britain's geography is changing. The island is tilting along a line running from Devon, through South Wales and across the middle of England to north Yorkshire. Land to the north and west of the line is rising, while the land to the south and east is sinking.

During the Ice Age, Britain was covered in ice from Scotland to the north bank of the Thames. The enormous weight of ice pushed the land down, and even now, 25,000 years after the ice melted, northern Britain is slowly springing back into position—with the result that the other parts are sinking slightly, like a gigantic see-saw.

All the countries bordering the North Sea are affected. For example, the west coasts of Denmark, northern Germany, Holland and south-east England are sinking, while Scandinavia is rising.

Geologists estimate that the rise or fall is about 5 in. every 100 years, although the rate varies considerably. London has slid 15 ft downwards since Roman times, which partly accounts for the tide's advance up the Thames. During Roman times the river was tidal to London Bridge; now it reaches 19 miles upstream.

Harlech Castle, on the mid-Wales coast, shows the opposite process. When the castle was built by Edward I in 1286, the watergate led directly from the castle wall into the sea, but today the sea is at least half a mile from the walls.

PROUD AND ISOLATED *Harlech Castle, built in 1286 with its watergate directly accessible from the open sea, is now about half a mile inland— because the area is lifting slowly.*

CONTINENTS IN COLLISION

Earthquakes can be more destructive than H-bombs

There are about 1 million earthquakes a year. Some are so small that they can be detected only with the most sensitive instruments. Others release enormous amounts of energy—the equivalent of two and a half times the size of the world's biggest thermonuclear device—a Russian test bomb of 58 megatons, detonated in 1961.

Earthquakes are caused by the movement of the 40 mile thick plates of rock under the earth's crust. There are about 12 of these plates which float on the molten rock in the earth's interior. Where two plates meet there are faults in the earth's surface. The friction as one plate grinds along the edge of another leads to earthquakes, and also causes the fissures through which molten rock bubbles up, forming volcanoes.

The most serious earthquakes happen along two belts—where plates are grinding against each other.

One of the belts is known as the Ring of Fire, and almost completely circles the Pacific. It runs up the coast of South America, Mexico and California to Alaska. Then it swings westwards through the Aleutian Islands before turning southwards through Japan and the East Indies.

The second earthquake line is the Alpine belt, running eastwards from Spain through the Mediterranean to Turkey, the Himalayas and the East Indies. Here the African and Indian plates are moving north, both of them

DEATH OF A TOWN

The town of Yungay, Peru, was built below a mountain, Nevados Huascaran. It straddled the line where the American and Pacific continental plates meet.

On May 31, 1970, friction between the plates caused an earthquake, and millions of tons of ice, rock and mud buried the town.

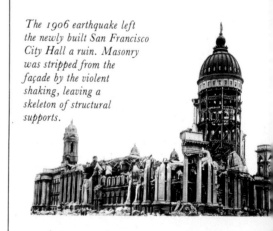

The 1906 earthquake left the newly built San Francisco City Hall a ruin. Masonry was stripped from the façade by the violent shaking, leaving a skeleton of structural supports.

grinding slowly against the Eurasian plate.

Stresses may also build up in faults for other reasons. One is that the gravitational pull of the moon, besides causing the tides, also acts on the surface of the land, drawing it up by as much as 1 ft as the moon passes overhead. Then, when the moon is on the other side of the earth, the land sinks back.

When the stresses below the surface build up, the crust splits along fault lines and vibrations spread out from the fault. The primary waves move at 5 miles a second along the line of the fault. Then come the secondary waves which vibrate at right angles to the fault, causing the earth to buckle. These secondary waves are responsible for the greatest damage to buildings. Seismologists cannot explain why there are these two kinds of vibration.

The waves sometimes cause the ground to open and close. In 1692 the geologist Sir Charles Lyell saw the ground in Jamaica 'rolling like the sea'. Fissures opened and people were swallowed in the cracks. Then the gaps closed over them.

By measuring the stresses building up along the faults, and by studying the time-cycle of past earthquakes, scientists can make reasonably accurate forecasts of when and where earthquakes will strike.

At present it is not possible to prevent earthquakes. But there is hope. American researchers believe that the dangerous friction that builds up between two continental plates could be eased.

They suggest that boreholes, $2\frac{1}{2}$ miles deep, could be drilled along the line of a fault and, one by one, filled with water, which would lubricate the plates as they pass each other.

Only buildings standing right on the fault would then be in danger, and sensible town planning could prevent even that.

CALIFORNIA'S TERRIBLE WOUND

This image of the San Francisco peninsula with the city and bay on the right was built up by radar. It clearly shows the San Andreas fault as a dark, straight streak. The fault runs for 650 miles through California, parallel with the Pacific coast.

JUST before dawn on April 18, 1906, San Francisco was shaken by an earthquake. Buildings collapsed and then, because the earthquake had ruptured water mains, fires roared through the city unchecked, devastating 4 square miles. Nearly 700 people died.

The city was rebuilt, but some time in the future it could be destroyed again unless a way is found of preventing earthquakes.

San Francisco straddles the San Andreas fault, the meeting place of the Pacific and American plates. The fault runs south-east to north-west, a few miles inland. The Pacific plate is edging past the American plate at a rate of about 1 in. a year, tearing a great area of California away from the mainland and into the Pacific. In 20 million years the site of Los Angeles, at present 400 miles south of San Francisco, will have moved almost as far to the north of it.

But the movement of the plates is not smooth. Every so often the great blocks bind on each other, although the pressures pushing them continue. Eventually something gives. There is a great convulsion which results in an earthquake. This happened in 1906. Since then all has been quiet. But at the base of the fault 40 miles down, tension is building up.

MAN AGAINST THE DESERT

Sahara's burning sands on the move

The desert is on the move. Right across Africa the Sahara is creeping south at an average rate of half a mile a month—in some parts four times as fast.

A 4000 mile belt below the desert is affected by drought. Animals die, crops wither, people starve. Survivors crowd into a dwindling area of savannah grassland, where overgrazing speeds the process. When rain does fall, it comes in sudden downpours which do more harm than good by washing away what little topsoil there is.

Whole countries in the Sahel, the semi-arid zone below the Sahara, are threatened with extinction. Weather experts predict that the earth is in for decades of low rainfall, which may turn richly cultivated areas into dustbowls.

What is causing this disastrous switch in the weather pattern? The reasons are not fully understood, but certain factors are accepted by many climatologists.

Basically, there has been a marked decrease in the supply of energy that generates the world's weather and moves it in great swirls round the globe. Both the North and South Poles have become colder, and this has had its effect on a ring of high-altitude winds, known as the 'Circumpolar Vortex', which circles the North Pole. The vortex has widened, and

so shifted south, pushing in front of it belts of descending dry air which are believed to be the cause of the intensely dry Sahara region.

Because of the southward movement of the high-pressure belts, the rains are diverted to fall in the ocean or further south in equatorial Africa.

Ocean currents, set in motion by the turning of the earth, also play a part in forming deserts. Icy currents from the polar regions come up against the edges of continents. Winds blowing landwards over these waters become cold and can carry little moisture, though they may bring fog and mist. What little moisture they have, rarely condenses into rain.

Mountain barriers often trap rain and leave the country beyond them desiccated. Winds reaching Asia's Gobi Desert and the centre of the Sahara have crossed enormous tracts of territory and deposited all their water on the way.

Major changes in the world's patterns of weather are neither new nor permanent, although they may seem so when measured against a human time scale. It seems that, from 4000 BC to 2000 BC, the Sahara was rich grassland. The earliest paintings found in the desert, executed on rock walls at Tassili in southern Algeria in about 8000 BC, showed humans hunting buffalo, elephant, lion and antelope.

Around 4000 BC, later tribes painted their cattle grazing. Still later paintings showed war chariots, Nile boats, camels and bearded warriors with shields and spears, indicating that the inhabitants of Tassili knew of the Egyptians far to the east. The last tribes left about 2000 years ago, and the area is now desolate.

Man has done much to spread the desert by his misuse of the soil. Cutting down trees, uncontrolled grazing and over-cultivation have created dustbowls where there was once rich land. Is man equally able to put the damage right? Given time, money and skill, he can. The key is water —in the right place, in the right quantity, at the right time.

But it is not as simple as it seems. Lavish irrigation without drainage can draw salts to the surface and render the land incapable of growing anything—an expensive lesson which some Middle Eastern governments have learnt in recent years. Dams can clog up with silt, and the tapping of rivers and deep wells can lower the water table seriously.

Ironically, there is enough water in the world to satisfy man's needs for ever more. The oceans hold 360 million tons for every person on earth. The problem is to make it drinkable by removing the salt. There are many ways of doing this —chemicals, distillation or freezing.

The most successful, so far, is multi-stage flash evaporation, developed in Britain. Sea water is heated under pressure to prevent it boiling. It passes through chambers where the pressure is lowered, causing the brine to boil and release salt-free vapour. The steam condenses on coils filled with sea water, which is warmed to start the process all over again.

The inhabitants of Kuwait once collected the meagre rainfall (less than 6 in. a year) in rooftop storage tanks or court-yard reservoirs, and supplemented it with water brought by sailing vessels from Iraq and peddled in the streets from goatskin bags.

Now this enormously wealthy oil state can afford to distil tens of millions of gallons a day from the Persian Gulf, and deliver it in a fleet of modern road tankers. As the distilled water has no taste, 5 per cent of brackish water is added to provide taste and minerals.

In the Gulf states, where temperatures over $38°C$ ($100°F$) are not uncommon, men grow vegetables in plastic-screened houses. The houses are kept cool by drawing air through a curtain of waste water, after it has been processed through the desalination plant. Plants are fed with a water-nutrient mixture through plastic tubes. Tomatoes are ready for picking in three months, cucumbers in six weeks.

SANDS OF TIME *Man is losing his battle against the desert. The Sahara is moving south, threatening the 4000 mile Sahel belt with drought and starvation. Yet once, it seems, the Sahara had plentiful water; prehistoric drawings found on rocks indicate that game once abounded.*

EARTH'S FROZEN WATER SUPPLY

Masses of ice that form the world's glaciers

Nearly three-quarters of the world's total stock of fresh water is locked up in the form of glaciers—great rivers and ribbed sheets of ice, covering the poles and slowly chiselling pathways down the world's highest mountains.

In places, the ice sheets are more than 2 miles thick. They are estimated to contain enough water to fill the Mediterranean basin six times over, or to raise sea levels all round the world by 200 ft. If they melted, London, New York, Paris and many other of the world's principal cities would be submerged.

A controlled man-made melting of the glaciers, however, could be beneficial. The Russians, with 10,000 mountain glaciers in their country, are studying ways of melting them to relieve droughts in central Asia. Then they hope to induce snow artificially in winter.

Glaciers are formed when more snow falls in winter than is melted in summer. As the amount of excess snow increases, year by year, the snowflakes at the bottom are pressed by the weight of those above them into a denser granular mass. As the pressure mounts further, these in turn are recrystallised into granules of ice, roughly in the shape of a sphere. Eventually, these are compressed yet further into a rock-like mass.

If that were the end of the story, the glaciers would remain fixed to the spot. But, with gravity tugging at it, the rock-like mass 'melts' into a plastic substance, which is almost liquid but still frozen, and the glacier starts to slide under the force of gravity.

Glaciers normally move a few inches a day, but some notable exceptions have been recorded. In 1966, at Mount Steele in the Yukon, a glacier was observed from the air to be travelling at 2 ft an hour.

About 25,000 years ago, the glaciers advanced over the land, in the last great Ice Age. Most of Canada and northern Europe lay under a crushing weight of ice, and in the Southern Hemisphere even parts of Australia were in the grip of ice.

Glaciers, moving relentlessly down valleys, plane off the rocks in their path,

GOUGING VALLEYS OUT OF THE EARTH *The vast glaciers of Alaska, some of them at heights above 10,000 ft, move inexorably across the landscape, creating deep valleys along their route. Glaciers account for 3 per cent of Alaska.*

carving the valleys into U-shapes. When the glaciers began their retreat, about 18,000 years ago, the melting waters were sometimes trapped in valleys. Britain's Lake District, and the Great Lakes of North America were formed in this way.

The Ice Ages brought extinction to many species of animals, but allowed others to expand their range, for it gave them a route over the frozen sea between continents. The ancestors of the modern horse, for instance, crossed from America to the plains of Eurasia, more than $1\frac{1}{2}$ million years ago, using the bridge over what is now the Bering Strait.

The same bridge was used, in the opposite direction, by the ancestors of the American Indians, who crossed from Siberia to Alaska to begin the colonisation of America more than 25,000 years ago.

WILL THE ICE AGE RETURN?

The world is cooling—helped by man

Some scientists are convinced that the world's climate is getting colder every year, threatening a return to the conditions of the last Ice Age which ended 25,000 years ago, when hairy mammoths wandered across northern Europe and polar bears swam in the Thames.

Records going back to the 14th century show that the Northern Hemisphere has been cooling gradually, producing more severe winters. Since 1940, Britain has experienced five winters with a whole month averaging below freezing point, while there were none between 1896 and 1939. The winter of 1962–3 was the worst since 1740.

Even a small drop in average temperatures, as little as a degree in some places, could put an end to cereal growing in northern areas, although it would boost the fishing industry of south-west England.

Marine biologists stationed at Plymouth say that increasing numbers of cold-water fish, such as cod, ling and lemon sole, are already invading the sea around Devon and Cornwall. If the trend continues, local trawlermen can look forward to bumper harvests.

Some experts say that the oceans act as a thermostat to keep the world in a recurring cycle of Ice Ages, followed by warm, interglacial periods. The Arctic is almost completely landlocked, except for the insignificant Bering Strait and the gap between Norway and Greenland, where there is an underwater ledge only 300 ft or so deep. As the warm Atlantic sweeps over this ledge into the chillier Arctic, the ice cap melts and its moisture falls on the surrounding lands as snow, which builds up into glaciers.

Icy winds, now relieved of their moisture, blow from the advancing glaciers and wither fertile land into desert. More and more moisture from the oceans is locked up in the mountains of ice, until the sea level falls and exposes the Norway-Greenland ledge which acts like a gigantic thermostat. The Arctic, now cut off from the warm Atlantic, freezes over, and the glaciers, no longer fed by snow, begin to melt under the summer sun. The ocean level rises, and the cycle begins again.

Effect of pollution

Mankind's own activities may even be hastening the return of the ice. The millions of tons of dust that pour into the atmosphere from factory chimneys all over the world prevent sunlight getting through, and so make the planet colder.

The dust layer not only reflects much of the sun's light, but also lets much of the infra-red radiation from the earth's surface escape, resulting in a net loss of heat.

If the spread of pollutants is not checked, the earth may cool by $3\frac{1}{2}°$C (6°F) within 50 years. This could set off a steady growth in the polar ice caps, which could themselves worsen the situation by reflecting even more of the sun's radiation. Scientists point out, however, that in the past, volcanoes have thrown out far more dust than man without, apparently, any serious long-term effects.

Can anything be done to stave off a new Ice Age? One possible method would be to spread vast areas of black plastic over the creeping glaciers, or scatter millions of tons of coal dust on them.

The black material would absorb more of the sun's heat and melt the ice. But this process, if taken too far, would bring its own problems, causing a dangerous rise in sea levels that would drown major cities like London, Paris and New York.

PATTERNS FROM THE SKY

The jewel-like structure of snow, and how it 'speaks'

Countless billions of snow crystals have fallen on the earth, each a faultless piece of design; and, so far as is known, no two have ever been found to be identical.

Formed by the crystallisation of water vapour in the air into geometrical forms, the shape of the crystals depends on the temperature of the air.

Simple needle and rod shapes are formed at the cold, high altitudes where water vapour is scarce. More complex and beautiful hexagonal shapes come from lower, warmer altitudes, abundant in vapour.

Snowflakes form when crystals fall into a warm, lower atmosphere, melting slightly and bunching together.

On the ground, incidentally, snow speaks, or rather squeaks, its own comment on the temperature. The approximate temperature of snow can be measured by the sound it makes underfoot.

A deep crunch means that the temperature is only slightly below 0°C (32°F). At −5°C (23°F) the pitch rises and the snow creaks higher up the scale.

At −15°C (5°F) the sound is unpleasantly high, like the highest notes on a violin being badly played.

A frost that is even more severe sounds like the scraping of a knife over a plate.

Hail is formed differently from snow. Liquid water is frozen around an ice crystal, which acts as the nucleus on which a hailstone is built. Small hailstones can be carried repeatedly through the freezing zone in the atmosphere by updraughts, building up successive layers like an onion.

When these become too heavy to be supported by the updraughts, they fall.

Freak accident

In 1930, five German glider pilots, carried into a thundercloud above the Rhön Mountains, bailed out of their aircraft. Carried by the strong upcurrents into the regions of supercooled vapour, the men became the nuclei of enormous hailstones. They were covered by layers of ice until finally they fell, frozen. Only one of the pilots, Guy Murchie, survived. The ice packed around him cushioned his fall, yet killed his companions.

Hailstorms can damage crops so badly that farmers in Italy regularly fire 50,000 firework rockets into potential hailstorm clouds, to try to disperse them by shattering the hailstones before they fall.

Perhaps one of the world's strangest monuments, at Barton, Lincolnshire, commemorates a fierce hailstorm which occurred on July 3, 1883.

The inscription reads:

'In memory of the great hailstorm at Barton, July 3, 1883, 10.30 to 11 p.m. Ice 5 in. long, 3 in. wide — 15 tons of glass broken — ice weighed 2½ oz.'

The 'ice' referred to the size of some of the largest hailstones.

The monument is built of bricks which were newly made and still hardening at the time of the storm. They bear the deep indentations made by the hailstones.

The United States suffered its worst snowstorm in 1921 when, at Silver Lake, Colorado, 87 in. fell in 27½ hours.

Britain's highest known snowfall, at Tredegar, Gwent, was 65 in. in February 1953. There are, however, many areas where snow is not measured.

ANATOMY OF A SNOWFLAKE *The shapes of snow crystals change with temperature. Thin needles and rods form at colder, high altitudes, and complex, beautiful hexagonal shapes at warmer, lower levels.*

WATER—ANCIENT, BUT INEXHAUSTIBLE

The unending cycle of use and purification

Earth retains all the water ever created—an estimated 326 million cubic miles of it. Water responds to a variety of powerful forces—the heat of the sun, the pull of earth's gravity and the tidal forces of the sun and moon. The result is a natural cycle in which water has been used, purified and re-used for 3000 million years.

The accepted theory of how water was formed is that a chemical reaction between hydrogen and oxygen took place as the earth cooled. This produced H_2O, two parts hydrogen to one of oxygen. As gases that formed the earth cooled and became liquid particles, a dense cloud blanketed the earth.

A 60,000-year downpour

When the temperature dropped, the clouds shed their water, a downpour that lasted for 60,000 years, filling the oceans and the lower land basins that were formed when the molten crust hardened.

Although water is still produced by man-made and natural processes, the levels of the oceans and the amount of water on the earth remain relatively constant. The amount of man-made water is relatively small, and water produced during the formation of volcanic rock is balanced by water lost in the weathering of minerals and when it is trapped by sediments.

About 97·2 per cent of the earth's water lies in oceans and 2·15 per cent is held in ice caps and in the ancient glaciers of the high mountain zones.

The remainder is spread over an area ranging from 3 miles below the earth's surface to 7 miles up in the atmosphere.

Rivers and streams account for only 0·0001 per cent, or 300 cubic miles. Other surface water totals some 55,000 cubic miles, and is divided between inland seas and fresh and saltwater lakes.

In addition, the earth has a reserve supply of some 200,000 cubic miles of water below the surface. That in the upper layer, called the aeration zone, clings to soil and rocks, is absorbed by plants, or returns to the air through evaporation.

Deep-lying water, in what is called the saturation zone, feeds swamps, rivers, lakes and wells. The Sahara Desert has an underground reservoir of some 150,000 cubic miles.

The atmosphere holds about 3100 cubic miles of water—enough to cover the earth with 1 in. of rain if it fell at one time. This atmospheric water falls as rain and is replaced by evaporation every 12 days or so. Most rain falls in the sea or runs into rivers. About one-sixth soaks into the earth to nourish growth.

Wonders of water

Water has many unique properties. A skin forms, for example, where water meets other materials. Water molecules are more attracted to each other than to other substances, and consequently they squeeze together forming a dense layer. This phenomenon is called surface tension.

The same attraction of molecules also gives water its ability to climb uphill. Capillary action, as it is called, causes water to move upwards through the ground, to the roots of plants and through stems and leaves.

Water absorbs more heat than almost any other common substance, without a considerable rise in temperature.

When a kettle of water is put on to boil it is subjected to a temperature that would cause many substances to melt or burst into flames. But the water soaks up the heat until a temperature of $100°C$ ($212°F$) is reached; then the water boils and steam bubbles burst through the surface tension.

Another of water's unique qualities is that it floats when frozen and, although it expands at freezing point, it becomes less dense. The force of water expanding as ice in the earth cracks rocks, helping to produce soil.

In Arctic regions huge icefloes form, and cover the surface of lakes and oceans with a protective insulating blanket, preventing further freezing. This helps life to go on under the blanket of ice.

There is no life, for instance, on the 16 ft thick pack ice of the North Pole, but it teems in the ocean beneath.

If ice did not float it would build up gradually from all the ocean beds, and eventually cover our planet in a solid glacier-like mass. Life as we know it would then be unable to survive.

71

OCEANS WILD AND WIDE

The importance of the earth's great seas

Water covers 70 per cent of the earth's surface—and in the ocean deeps is a dark, sunless world of spectacular canyons, great plains and mountain ranges.

Much of the ocean floors are plains that stretch for hundreds of miles at an average depth of 13,000 ft. Rising from these flat areas, called abyssal plains, are mid-ocean ridges which girdle the globe, only occasionally breaking the surface to form islands. The Mid-Atlantic Ridge, reaching 10,000 miles from Iceland to the Antarctic, is by far the world's longest mountain range. Its highest peaks are the Ascension Islands, the Azores and Iceland.

From the ocean floor in the mid-Pacific rises the world's highest mountain —the Hawaiian volcano, Mauna Kea. It is 31,000 ft from base to peak—overtopping Everest by nearly 2000 ft—but only the top 13,823 ft show above the surface.

Sunlight can penetrate to a depth of only about 800 ft, and many of the creatures that live in the perpetual midnight of the depths have evolved their own luminous lighting system. Their survival depends ultimately on a constant drizzle of food reaching the ocean floor—waste matter from the levels above.

Trenches split the floor of some oceans. The deepest known is the Challenger Deep, in the Marianas Trench, discovered by the British survey ship *Challenger* in 1873, off the island of Guam in the Pacific. It is 7 miles deep, and if Everest (29,028 ft) were placed in it, there would be a mile of water above the summit.

Just as mountains are barriers to movement on land, so the ranges of the sea act as barriers to ocean dwellers. For undersea creatures have to keep to the levels for which they are adapted. At 13,000 ft there is pressure of nearly 3 tons to the square foot.

Most of the great land masses are skirted by continental shelves, which slope gradually for up to 200 miles before plunging steeply into the deep. Some parts of a shelf are split by vast canyons. The Hudson Canyon, off New York, is 150 miles long and 16,500 ft deep. These canyons may be caused by avalanches of mud and water—called turbidity currents—that roll down the shelves to the ocean floor.

The oceans absorb heat from the sun and spread it across the world in the form of vast currents. These are driven by the winds, which are themselves created by the effect of the sun's heat. All major currents move in a circular path, called a gyre, caused by the earth's rotation.

One of the most powerful currents is the Gulf Stream which, when it leaves the Caribbean, is 50 miles wide and up to 1500 ft deep. This warm current broadens and flows across the Atlantic at a speed of about 4 knots. In the North Atlantic, the flow divides—part flowing north past Scotland, while the other sweeps south.

The daily rise and fall of tides is caused by the gravitational pull of the moon and sun. The effect of each pull causes, in effect, a bulge in the ocean. When the sun and moon are pulling on the same side of the earth, large tides—the spring tides—occur. Neap tides, the smallest, happen when the sun and moon pull at right angles. The largest tides occur where

A WALL OF WATER *Monster waves like this can hit with a force of 3½ tons per square foot. Waves are ripples from a storm centre, and the giants are created when ripple patterns are in phase.*

the sea runs into bottlenecks, as in the Bay of Fundy on America's east coast.

Waves are whipped up far out to sea by wind. They move across the water, which merely rises and falls as the swell passes. In shallower water the energy is concentrated, and the wave rears up and breaks.

Waves in mid-ocean often reach a height of 40 ft. In 1933 the American ship USS *Ramapo* survived a 112 ft wave—the highest recorded.

The level from which altitudes are measured is called 'sea level'. This is an average of the ocean levels, for in reality the sea is not level at all. If, for example, the Pacific Ocean were suddenly frozen in a calm, without a ripple on its surface, there would be 'plateaux' and 'depressions' in the water, with a difference of as much as 60 ft. This is caused by differences of atmospheric pressure, and by the 'slurping' effect of the tides.

WHEN THE SEA TREMBLES
The killer waves that follow an earthquake

On April 1, 1946, an earthquake shook the abyssal plain deep beneath the Pacific Ocean. The wave it generated travelled the 2250 miles to Hawaii in 4 hours and 34 minutes, an average speed of 490 mph. When it struck the town of Hilo the wave was more than 45 ft high. It killed 173 people, injured hundreds more and caused £50 million worth of damage.

The 'tidal wave' was a tsunami, caused by the movement of the sea-bed in the earthquake. Tsunamis are the most terrifying waves of all, hurtling silently across the ocean to crash on to the nearest shore. Ancient monuments along the coast of Japan carry the inscription 'When you feel an earthquake, expect a tsunami', a piece of advice which reflects Japan's long history of tsunami disasters.

The word tsunami is Japanese, and was adopted by scientists of other countries to replace the misleading term 'tidal wave', since tsunamis are not tidal at all. The wave spreads from the centre of the disturbance, like the ripples from a pebble tossed into a pond. But the waves generated

are so long and in deep water the swell is so slight that ships do not notice them. The energy stored in the tsunami is only about one hundredth of the total energy of the earthquake, but it can equal the power of a multi-megaton nuclear weapon.

As the tsunami approaches the shore and gets into shallower water, its energy becomes more concentrated and the wave height increases. Usually the wave is preceded by a trough which sucks out water along the shore, beaching ships like an abnormally low tide.

The effects of a tsunami are nearly always terrifying—and sometimes extraordinary. An oceanographer caught in a Hawaii tsunami of 1946 reported that one house was plucked from its foundations, carried hundreds of yards and set down again—so gently that the breakfast the occupants were cooking was not spilt.

After the 1946 disaster, a tsunami warning system was set up in the Pacific—the ocean most affected. Seismographic stations distributed across the Pacific notify tidal stations whenever an earthquake is detected.

CREST OF THE GREAT WAVE OF KANAGAWA *Tsunami near the coast of Japan, as depicted by Housai, the great 19th-century print-maker. In the background is the cone of Fujiyama.*

THE MEDITERRANEAN WAS A DESERT

How the sea-bed revealed its secret

Six million years ago, the Mediterranean sea dried up, leaving a barren desert lying 10,000 ft below the level of the Atlantic. Then the ocean burst through the Straits of Gibraltar, and its water cascaded into the Mediterranean basin in the most spectacular waterfall the earth has ever seen.

It was like turning on a gigantic tap to fill a bath 10,000 ft deep and about 2000 miles long. Ten thousand cubic miles of water poured through the gap in a torrent 1000 times greater than Niagara. Even so, it took more than 100 years to fill the basin up to the level we know today, flooding vast areas and leaving only mountain peaks above the water to form islands such as Malta and Sardinia.

The evidence for this story has come from geological drilling into the bottom of the Mediterranean, carried out from the US research ship *Glomar Challenger*. In 1970 the ship, which was amassing scientific data about the theory of how the continents have drifted apart, sailed through the Straits of Gibraltar and began to drill into the soft sediments lying in the sea-bed, 6000 ft below.

Six hundred feet through the sediments, its crew of scientists found a layer of gravel—unusual for ocean beds.

More holes were drilled, and they revealed even more extraordinary findings. The types of rock that lay below the sediments were what geologists call evaporites; they are found only in places where seas have dried up.

The scientists were at first unable to believe that the Mediterranean had once been a desert. Yet was it so impossible? The climate of the region is dry and,

even today, the sun sucks up water from the surface of the Mediterranean faster than rain and rivers can fill it. Evaporation is at the rate of 1000 cubic miles of water every year, and only the flow from the Atlantic keeps the basin full.

Suppose that at some time in the past the Straits had closed, isolating the Mediterranean from the Atlantic. It would have taken only 1000 years to dry up the Mediterranean completely, turning it into a deep parched canyon, something like Death Valley in California.

There was one final piece of evidence which clinched the argument. Seventy years ago a deep gorge was discovered in southern France, cut into granite and lying hidden beneath millions of years of deposits. It looked like the gorge of an ancient river, but it lay hundreds of feet below the level of the Mediterranean.

Although the scientists on board *Glomar Challenger* did not know it at the time, an exactly similar gorge lay at the other end of the Mediterranean, under the River Nile. Russian scientists had been mystified by it while building the Aswan Dam.

Only one explanation is possible: the gorges must have been cut by rivers flowing into the Mediterranean basin when the level of the sea was much lower than it is today. The rivers, flowing across what is now the bottom of the ocean, cut canyons which have also been found in the ocean bed.

So the Mediterranean was once a sea, then a deep, hot canyon, dotted with isolated salt lakes. Then, after a million and a half years, it became a sea again, as the dam burst at the Straits, and water came crashing in from the Atlantic.

POWER BEYOND BELIEF

The devastating winds produced by earth's rotation

An average hurricane releases as much energy as several atomic explosions. Its power output in a single minute could keep the United States in electricity for 50 years.

But hurricanes cannot be harnessed. They pour their energy unfettered into the atmosphere, often spreading death

and disaster across vast coastal areas.

The hurricane that struck Bangladesh in 1970 produced a tidal wave which killed at least 500,000 people. In 1900 at Galveston, Texas, a hurricane created storm tides that swept 6000 people to their deaths. Another 1000 people were drowned in 1954, when a large ferryboat

HURRICANE FROM ABOVE *The 90 mph hurricane Gladys photographed in 1968 by the crew of Apollo 7 from a height of 113 miles above the surface of the earth. The hurricane was about 150 miles south-west of Florida at the time; in the background is the island of Cuba.*

was sunk by a hurricane in Hakodate Bay, in Japan's northernmost island.

A hurricane is created at sea. The water temperature must be at least 27°C (80·6°F), which means that Northern latitudes are normally spared. The warm sea creates a funnel of air which rises to perhaps 40,000 ft, producing vast cumulus clouds. High air currents are distributed, and more air from below is drawn into the funnel. Earth's rotation gives it a twist, and the hurricane is born—a mass of storm winds up to 400 miles in diameter, swirling round at up to 200 mph.

At the centre of every hurricane is the eye, an area of warm, calm breezes about 20 miles in diameter, which appears to be created by centrifugal force thrusting the winds outward. Places hit by a hurricane have a brief period of peace while the eye passes, then turmoil resumes as the other half of the hurricane arrives.

Hurricanes are constantly recharged at sea, as the water's heat makes air rise faster and faster in the central funnel. But on land, this power source is instantly cut off. Forests and mountains slow it by friction, and it can no longer draw up water vapour to power its condensation heat engine. So hurricanes rarely last more than a day on land.

The terrible tornado

The hurricane is the giant of nature's violent storms, but its cousin the tornado, operating on a much smaller scale, is even more destructive. A tornado springs up without warning and usually lasts less than an hour.

One of the most devastating in history ripped through Missouri, Illinois and Indiana in 1925, leaving 800 people dead and nearly 3000 injured, yet it was only 300 yds wide. The winds were so fierce that buildings collapsed, oak trees were uprooted, trains were overturned and smashed. Winds on the outside edges of a tornado can reach speeds of 500 mph.

Tornadoes occur on hot, humid days in central areas of the United States, the West Indies, the South Pacific and Australia. They are funnel clouds which start to rotate gently, and within minutes start twisting violently. The funnel travels forward at between 25 and 40 mph. In its centre, air surges upwards at 100–200 mph, which creates enough suction power to drag objects as big as cars and wooden houses into the whirling spout, where they spin to the top and fly out again.

SMALL, BUT DESTRUCTIVE *The tornado, although smaller than a hurricane, can wreak death and terrible destruction during its short existence.*

AWESOME SPECTACLE IN THE SKY

The power that may have created life

From the very earliest times, man has speculated about the great power and destructiveness of lightning, one of nature's most awesome spectacles.

Lightning is, in scientific terms, a visible discharge of atmospheric electricity. When a giant spark leaps from one part of a thundercloud to another it appears as sheet lightning. A spark travelling from a cloud to the ground produces forked lightning.

Collision of droplets

No one is quite sure how the electricity builds up—but many scientists believe it is caused by collisions between water droplets in a thundercloud. The theory is that when falling drops of water strike smaller drops, some of the energy in each one is transformed into a charge of positive electricity on the new, larger drop. The air around it gains an opposite, negative charge.

As it falls, each drop grows bigger as moisture in the air condenses on it. When the drop reaches a size of about $\frac{1}{5}$ in. across, it splits into two, each half still carrying its positive charge. If the drops fell straight to earth the charge would have no effect, but inside a thundercloud there are powerful draughts of air which carry the drops up, so that the whole process is repeated time and again. As the charge on each drop increases, the thundercloud becomes a gigantic accumulator, storing electricity.

Within about 15 minutes, the electrical charge stored in the raindrops becomes so great that it breaks down the insulating effect of the air. It is then that the lightning flash occurs.

Flash heat

Thunder is caused when the flash heats the air around it to temperatures up to $16,666°C$ $(30,000°F)$—three times the temperature of the sun's surface—so that it expands and explodes.

The sound of the explosion travels more slowly than the lightning flash, so by counting the gap between the flash and the thunder it is possible to estimate the distance of the lightning. A five-second delay equals 1 mile.

It is estimated that in any one year throughout the world there are 16 million thunderstorms, 1800 taking place at any given moment. One of the worst tragedies caused by lightning was at Brescia in Italy, in 1769. A flash hit the state arsenal,

FORKED LIGHTNING *One branch usually strikes the earth and acts as the main discharge channel, splitting to reach the ground by several paths. The other branches stop in mid-air.*

exploding more than 100 tons of gunpowder and killing 3000 people.

Perhaps the most disastrous fire created by lightning was at San Luis Obispo in California, on April 7, 1926. It raged for four days, spread over 900 acres, burnt nearly 3 million barrels of oil and destroyed $15 million worth of property. Amazingly, only two people died.

But despite lightning's deadly power, the number of people killed each year is small. In Britain, the average is 11.

Life-giving force

Lightning also has beneficial effects. It causes nitrogen and oxygen in the air to combine and dissolve in raindrops. When the rain falls to earth and soaks into the soil, it provides plant life with nitrates—a valuable fertiliser.

And lightning may have been one of the original causes of life on this planet. In a fascinating experiment at the University of Chicago, a mixture of gases—hydrogen, methane, ammonia and water vapour—all of which are thought to be similar to the earth's early atmosphere, was prepared. Artificial lightning, which is an electrical charge, was then sent through the mixture. As a result of this, complex chemicals known as amino acids were formed. Such acids are known to be the basic building blocks of all forms of life on earth.

RIBBON LIGHTNING *An unusual type of electrical discharge to the earth, the strokes are displaced as the wind blows the channel sideways. Here, the discharge has multiple strokes.*

BALL LIGHTNING *Gas combustion could be the cause of this rare form of lightning, which appears as a ball about 8 in. in diameter, and lasts a few seconds before exploding or disappearing.*

ILLUSIONS OF GRANDEUR

Cities, lakes and mountains that vanish into thin air

In 1913 an American expedition, led by Donald MacMillan, set out to discover a mysterious Arctic mountain range that had been sighted by the explorer Robert Peary. The party sailed as far as possible through the ice floes, then set out on foot over the ice until the vast mountain range, which Peary had called Crocker Land, came into view. But as the men moved towards it, the mountains receded, and when the men stood still, the mountains stood still as well. Finally, as the sun disappeared below the horizon, the mountains dissolved to nothing, leaving only a vast, desolate expanse of ice as far as the eye could see. The men realised that they, and Robert Peary too, had been fooled by one of nature's strangest tricks—a mirage.

Mirages are usually associated with deserts, but they can appear anywhere. They occur when layers of air of different temperatures, and different density, are superimposed. The light waves are bent and refracted irregularly as they pass from an object through the unequal layers. The result is that it is possible to see objects that are far beyond the horizon.

The Arctic explorers wasted much time and a great deal of money on their fruitless journey, but they at least survived. In the desert, thirsty men have been driven mad by the sight of shimmering 'lakes' that can never be reached. The Arabs call them 'Lakes of Satan'.

Mirages in battle

Mirages have been recorded in battle. In 1798 Napoleon's army in Egypt saw a muddled landscape with lakes that vanished, and blades of grass that turned into palm trees. So confused were they that the men are said to have fallen to their knees, praying for deliverance from the impending end of the world.

Gunners of the British artillery had to stop firing at one point during the desert campaign of the First World War, when a false landscape completely blotted out the enemy's position. On another occasion, a German submarine captain saw the city of New York hovering above him as he peered through his periscope. He is said to have beaten a hasty retreat.

FIRE IN THE SKY

The dazzling spectacle of the auroras

The Northern Lights, according to Scandinavian folklore, are reflections from the golden shields of the warrior-maiden Valkyries as they escort the souls of dead heroes through the heavens to Valhalla.

Scientists have a less romantic explanation for the phenomenon. They believe that auroras are created in much the same way as pictures on a television screen. Television pictures are produced by a beam of electrons, which is focused on to a fluorescent screen by electro-magnets. The earth's magnetic field has the same effect on charged particles coming from the sun, and focuses them on to the 'screen' of the sky above the poles.

At the poles the magnetic fields are funnel-shaped, and as the particles spiral down they excite atoms in the upper air. It is these atoms that cause the lights of the aurora. Oxygen atoms produce the red, yellow and green lights; nitrogen produces violet, blue or green.

Auroras appearing in the Northern Hemisphere are called Aurora Borealis, and in the Southern Hemisphere, Aurora Australis. They are usually visible after the eruption of a solar flare, when a small part of the sun's surface suddenly brightens causing a violent solar storm. During the storm, the nuclei of atoms and electrons escape from the sun's atmosphere and shoot towards the earth, travelling at 400–600 miles per second.

The aurora's magnificent spectacle is seldom seen outside the polar regions, but it has been observed in the Mediterranean. Long ago, the Greek philosopher Aristotle wrote: 'Sometimes on a fine night we see a variety of appearances in the sky: chasms ... trenches ... blood-red colours.' He then went on to theorise that the air was turning into liquid fire.

THE SEASONING OF LIFE

The humble compound that flavoured history

Common salt, the humble seasoning taken for granted at mealtimes, is the stuff of history. It is so vital to human survival that wars have been fought over it, empires have been founded on it and have collapsed without it, and civilisations have grown up around it.

The word 'salary' is a constant reminder of salt's importance. Roman legionaries were given a salarium—a salt allowance. Later, the word came to mean a cash allowance to buy salt. From this it was a short step to its present meaning.

Man realised from his earliest days that he had to have salt or perish, for without it the delicate salt and water balance in the body is upset and death occurs through dehydration.

It began with Stone Age tribesmen following their cattle to salt licks—outcrops of salt rock the animals had located for their own survival. The humans carried salt from the life-giving rocks back to their caves, but eventually they discovered a more reliable supply—brine salt springs.

Primitive cultures developed around these springs at places such as Droitwich in England, the Moselle region of France, and Saale in Germany. Over thousands of years entire forests were destroyed by man to provide wood fires for evaporating water from the precious salt.

The demand for salt even altered landscapes. Ancient peoples created coastal lakes when they dug up sea-soaked peat, burnt it, and retrieved salt by boiling the ashes in sea water.

While early Europeans were turning salt production into one of the first industries, similar operations were going on in other parts of the world. The earliest settlements in China were near salt pans on the Yellow River. In the Jordan Valley, villages grew up in about 8000 BC by the salt-laden Dead Sea, and on Mount Sodom, which is also rich in salt.

Over thousands of years the development of transport enabled people to move away from the salt sources. Early Egyptian farmers, for instance, were supplied by boat with salt from swamps at the mouth of the Nile.

The sea has always been the world's main source of supply, and significant

SALT PANNING *In some parts of the world, shallow salt-water pools are created by man to evaporate in the sun and provide salt that is panned for commercial use.*

SALT OF THE EARTH *The areas of great salt concentrations in today's world are a clue to where yesterday's seas may have been.*

phases in history have been directly influenced by its level. When oceans shrink they leave behind coastal salt ponds and salt-impregnated marshes. When the seas rise they engulf these salt-rich areas.

In 500 BC the sea was at its lowest recorded level—3 ft below its present line. It was then that the Greek and Phoenician civilisations reached their peaks. They had vast amounts of home-produced salt available for trade, and the Phoenicians increased their salt treasure by gathering stocks from as far as Spain.

Around 400 BC the Via Salaria, or Salt Road, came into being in Italy—and it still exists today as the oldest road in the country. Salt was carried along it from Rome to the Sabine people in Italy's central regions.

The salt trade flourished for 1000 years around the North Sea, the Mediterranean and the Atlantic... but the sea was rising. By AD 500 it had reached 3 ft above today's level. In Europe, trade declined as salt works vanished under the encroaching waves.

Meanwhile, Arab lands, with access to the Dead Sea, enjoyed a new prosperity, trading precious salt for gold, marble and other luxuries.

The Arabs' powerful role continued until the 9th century. Then the sea receded, and the English, French and Dutch were able to start salt production again. The sea intervened in the 16th century by again flooding the salt works along the coasts of Europe. Huge excava-tions on England's east coast became lakes.

Hundreds of ships plied the oceans to carry salt from nations with plentiful supplies to those hit by the flood. The traders quickly realised that in parts of Africa their commodity was held more precious than human freedom, and salt developed into a powerful factor in the slave trade. Families in the salt-starved interior would sell children into slavery for a handful of salt.

Today the world consumes 169 million tons of salt a year—some from underground brine deposits, some from salt lakes or rock. But 30 per cent of the output is still from coastal pans, which are just as vulnerable to a rise in sea level as the pans which were submerged centuries ago. Our descendants hundreds of years from now will presumably be obtaining their salt from land now beneath the sea.

THE TREASURED METAL

The measure of wealth for men and nations

The world's currencies have revolved around gold for nearly 3000 years—since King Croesus of Lydia struck the first 2500 pure gold coins. It is still the ultimate standard of wealth, yet nearly every country has gold in the ground, and there are at least 10,000 million tons of it in the water of the oceans, waiting to be harvested.

One of the obstacles to recovering this vast natural treasure is its sheer elusiveness. In most places on land where gold appears, it is a mere fleck in the earth's crust; in the sea, one of the heaviest concentrations is 10 milligrams of gold to 1 ton of salt water, so 2835 tons of water would have to be filtered to produce 1 oz.

Even in a profitable mine, the rate of extraction can be as low as 1 part gold to 300,000 parts of waste rock.

Geologists are certain that every major goldfield in the world has now been discovered in the relentless hunt for what has been dubbed the 'noble metal', but still demand increases.

It began when Stone Age men were attracted by shining specks in river gravels. They picked the specks out and found that they had acquired a heavy, pliable substance which could be hammered into pleasing shapes—the world's first gold ornaments.

What these early men did not realise was that their crude workmanship bore the stamp of eternity. Gold is impervious to the ravages of time. It is not tarnished by air, water or most corrosives; and it can be melted down time and again without shedding any of its quality. A single ounce can be drawn out to make an unbroken wire 35 miles long—or hammered into a sheet 1/250,000th of an inch thick.

Gold is normally found in rock veins, or just lying loose as nuggets—the prospector's dream. The veins are fissures deep in the earth, which were penetrated by gold-rich quartz between 2 million and 10 million years ago. The loose gold was also trapped in rock at one time, but escaped through erosion and was pounded into pellets as it was washed along streams and rivers towards the sea.

The biggest pure gold nugget ever found was 2 ft long and 1 ft across, and weighed over 150 lb. It was discovered in 1869 by two Cornishmen, John Deason and Richard Oates, prospecting near Moliagul in Victoria, Australia. The huge nugget—dubbed the Welcome Stranger—was 98·66 per cent pure gold. Deason and Oates sold it for £9532.

The largest gold-bearing nugget in history was the 630 lb. Holtermann nugget, turned up in 1872 at a mine in Hill End, New South Wales. It yielded more than 187 lb. of gold.

The famous California gold rush of 1848 was triggered off by a man named James Marshall, who fished a hatful of gold grains from the American River at Coloma, near Sacramento.

The Yukon stampede began in 1896, when gold was found among gravel at the River Klondike at a place called Bonanza—a word that has now come to mean sudden, unexpected wealth. But the greatest goldfield in the world had already been discovered thousands of miles away—and sold for exactly £10.

George Harrison, a prospector in South Africa, found traces of gold in the Witwatersrand basin. In 1886 Harrison was so poor that he sold his claim for £10. What he had given up for a pittance was the opportunity of becoming a multimillionaire, for the Rand was to become the world's major source of gold.

Forty-six years after Harrison's discovery, Emmanuel Jacobson and Allan Roberts began drilling on a farm called Aadenk, in the Orange Free State. They reached 4064 ft before their money ran out and they had to give up. In 1950 other prospectors continued the operation, and after going down only 400 ft more the gold-bearing Basal Reef of the Rand was opened up. Allan Roberts was so poor when he died that his friends had to pay for his funeral, yet the Rand, in which he and his partner had such faith, now produces more than 70 per cent of the world's gold.

Tutankhamun's coffin

Probably the biggest solid gold object in existence is the coffin of the Egyptian King Tutankhamun, which weighs 2450 lb. Other huge golden works from ancient times have long since disappeared, presumably melted down. One was a gold garment weighing over a ton, which adorned the statue of Athena on the Acropolis in Athens.

Many smaller treasures have passed down through history. Gold goblets dating from 2500 BC have been found at Ur, on the Persian Gulf. The Etruscans, who lived in central Italy from 900 BC, were perhaps the greatest goldsmiths of all time, and they have bequeathed us a little bowl encrusted with 137,000 microscopic golden globules forming a peach-

like bloom. It was not until 1933 that modern craftsmen learnt this skill.

Today's goldsmiths cannot hope to tackle such impressive assignments as their predecessors, partly because the raw material is so expensive, but mainly because so much of it is now hoarded away as ingots in vaults.

At one time, alchemists firmly believed that they could solve the supply problem by turning common metals into gold. Physicists now have the knowledge to create gold from lead or platinum by means of nuclear fission—but it would cost millions of pounds to produce just a golden pinhead.

So man must go on digging his precious metal from the ground, unless some practical technique is discovered enabling him to extract gold from the sea. So far, it has eluded him.

Dr Fritz Haber, a German chemist, announced at the end of the First World War that he would repay Germany's war debt from the gold in the North Sea. He tried and failed . . . but perhaps his ideas will be revived one day.

LUCKY STRIKE *The largest ever gold-bearing nugget was found in 1872 at a mine in New South Wales. It yielded 187 lb. of gold.*

THE BIG SPLIT

THE HUGE diamond in Jacob Asscher's hand was an awe-inspiring sight even for one of the world's most experienced gem cutters. It was 2.45 p.m. on February 10, 1908, and Asscher was preparing to break up the biggest diamond in history—about 5 in. across, nearly 1½ lb. in weight.

Watched by a group of assistants at his company's headquarters in Amsterdam, Asscher laid a diamond-cleaver along a meticulously plotted groove in the stone. The slightest miscalculation,

and he would have nothing but a worthless heap of diamond fragments. He rapped down a heavy steel rod . . . and the tool blade snapped. Asscher wiped his brow and called for another blade.

On his next blow, the blade did its work. The stone fell apart—and Jacob Asscher fainted.

When he recovered, the master jeweller had two pieces of priceless stone—one 14½ oz., the other 7½ oz. He continued cutting carefully until he had 105 separate diamonds.

THE ORIGINAL STONE

The Cullinan diamond, named after its original owner, was the largest ever found. Discovered in 1905 at Pretoria, South Africa, it was bought by the Transvaal Government in 1907 for £150,000 and presented to Edward VII on his 66th birthday. The life-size picture shows how the stone was split and then cut, to become part of the most famous collection of jewels in the world.

THE SEVEN LARGEST PIECES

THE PRINCIPAL FINISHED GEMS

Set in
brooch worn by
the Queen Mother

Set in
pendant owned
by the Queen

Set in
Imperial State Crown

Star of Africa
in Queen's Sceptre

Set in
necklace worn by
Queen Elizabeth

Set in
Queen Mary's
Crown

Set in
Queen Mary's
Crown

JEWEL OF FIRE

The brilliant stone that lasts for ever

The word diamond comes from the Greek *adamas*, meaning invincible —an apt description for the hardest substance on earth. The mineral is composed of pure carbon, and is formed deep within the earth under enormous pressures and temperatures.

A diamond's weight is measured in carats, equal to one-fifth of a gramme, and there are about 142 carats to the ounce. The word carat is believed to be derived from an Arabic word *qirat*, meaning the weight of four grains.

It is the extraordinary 'fire' of diamonds that makes them so attractive. A diamond splits up light like no other gem, gloriously reflecting the colours of the spectrum.

To obtain this brilliance, the stone must be precisely cut and polished. First the stone is marked for cutting by a planner, who is an expert on correct cutting for its particular shape and atomic structure. He marks the stone with indian ink to show where it should be cut.

Diamond cuts diamond

If the stone is to be cleaved, the cleaver cuts a groove, using another diamond as a cutting tool. He mounts the diamond in a holder and inserts a steel wedge into the groove. With a sharp blow from a mallet the diamond is split.

Sawing is done by means of a paper-thin disc of phosphor-bronze coated with diamond dust. The disc spins at about 4000 rpm, and will cut through a 1 carat rough stone in four to eight hours. The diamond is then faceted and polished, using diamond dust as the polishing medium.

South Africa's first find

The first major diamond discovery in South Africa was made in 1866, by a Boer child who pocketed an attractive-looking pebble he had found on the banks of the Orange River. It turned out to be a diamond weighing $21\frac{1}{4}$ carats.

Two years later, prospectors rushed in when a shepherd boy picked up an even finer stone in the same area. He swapped it for 500 sheep, 10 oxen and a horse. The man who made the trade sold the stone in turn for £11,200. The stone, weighing $83\frac{1}{2}$ carats, was later cut into a flawless,

pear-shaped diamond for the Countess of Dudley.

When the prospectors moved in, they built a shanty town which they called Kimberley, after the British Colonial Secretary of the time. Some of the early diamond hunters quickly struck it rich, for the precious stones were lying in distinctive patches of yellow clay. Even when the topmost diamonds were harvested there were more underneath in a layer of 'blue ground'—the prospectors' name for kimberlite.

Eventually the adventurers gave way to commercial miners, who dug down thousands of feet to claw every available diamond from the ground. But after those initial simple treasure hunts, diamond mining became hard work. At Kimberley nowadays 1000 tons of ground must be moved to yield just an ounce or so of diamonds. But the stones are so precious, that even this vast turnover in waste material is still profitable.

The Koh-i-Nor

One of the most famous diamonds, and certainly the one with the longest history, is the Koh-i-Nor.

It was first reported in 1304 as being in the possession of the Raja of Malwa in India. For the next 400 years it formed part of the treasure of the Moghul emperors, until the Nadir Shah of Persia invaded India in 1739 and took the diamond. In 1849 the diamond was discovered in the jewel house of Lahore, capital of Punjab, when that province of India was annexed by the British.

The East India Company presented it to Queen Victoria in 1850, but she was disappointed with its lack of fire and had it recut from its original weight of $186\frac{1}{2}$ carats to 108·93 carats. It is now part of the British Crown Jewels.

One diamond that did not end up in the Crown Jewels, although it passed through London, is the Orloff, which weighs 194·8 carats. This stone is reputed to have been the eye of a statue of Brahma in Madras at the beginning of the 18th century. A French soldier is said to have risked his life in 1750 to prise it out and sell it for £2000 to the captain of an English ship. The stone came to London,

83

where a dealer bought it for £12,000, and in turn it was sold in 1773 for an unknown sum to a Russian, Prince Orloff. Revolutionaries found the diamond in Russia's Imperial Treasury in 1917, and today it is one of the prizes of the State collection in Moscow.

During the French Revolution a stone weighing 67·1 carats, and known as the Blue Diamond of the Crown, was looted from Louis XVI. It was never seen again, but in 1830 a diamond was sold in London to Henry Philip Hope. This stone, America's most famous diamond, weighs 44·5 carats and is certainly blue, like the one that vanished in France in 1792. The Hope Diamond is now owned by the Smithsonian Institution.

About 5 tons of diamonds are mined every year—but much of the production goes to industry, for diamonds are the only known natural material for cutting and fashioning hard metals.

As the mines run out of supplies, more attention is being paid to the possibility of getting diamonds from the sea-bed. South Africa's Marine Diamond Corporation recovered more than 2000 stones during its first ten months of dredging for diamonds in international waters.

STRIKING IT RICH

Liquid assets beneath the ground

When Edwin Drake retired from his job as a railway guard in America, in 1859, he sank his savings into drilling a hole in the ground . . . and became the owner of the world's first oil well.

A sticky, black mess bubbled to the surface at Drake's workings on the site of a former Seneca Indian village, 75 miles from Pittsburgh, Pennsylvania. The young John D. Rockefeller, sent by a bank to investigate Drake's well, reported that it seemed to offer no real prospects of profit—a prediction he was to disprove in his own lifetime, by becoming one of the richest men the world has ever known, with a fortune based on oil.

With or without Rockefeller's ap-proval, the Seneca Oil Company was in business, heralding the end of man's dependence on whales as a source of oil.

Within a year the lonely spot had become a thriving community, known to this day as Oil City. Prospectors sank thousands of 'wildcat' wells to cash in on the prospect of extracting oil for lighting and heating from the ground.

The hunt for oil in the ground had been launched to find a cheap substitute for whale oil in lamps. At first, petroleum was scorned as a valueless by-product, but by the turn of the century the emphasis was changed by the motor car.

Although the commercial exploitation of one of the world's most valuable and convenient resources is a modern pheno-

MEETING THE DEMAND *The City Field outside Los Angeles in 1895 was typical of the industrial congestion created by the world's new-found need for oil and its by-products.*

menon, oil has been known for thousands of years. The Sumerians, Assyrians and Babylonians used bitumen pitch in 3000 BC as a building mortar, and for fixing jewellery in place. The bitumen was formed after crude oil seeped through the ground to the surface and was weathered by the sun.

During their wanderings, the Children of Israel were guided by 'a pillar of cloud by day and a pillar of fire by night'—a perfect description of what happens when an oil seepage catches fire.

Later, the Persians and Arabs collected the oil itself and used it for lighting and for cleaning silk. By AD 300, oil was being used by the Chinese, who discovered it by accident when they dug salt mines in oil fields. Both the Chinese and American Indians used oil as a medicine.

In 1272 the Venetian traveller Marco Polo described oil springs near Baku on the Caspian Sea, where for 1200 years there had been a fire-worshipping cult around 'eternal fires'—oil seepages that burnt day and night. But it was not until the 19th century that the true potential of such oil finds was realised.

In 1850, James Young, a Scottish industrial chemist, patented a process for manufacturing crude oil from bituminous coal and shale. He refined this oil into paraffin, and the technique proved such a formidable competitor to whale oil that plants were set up rapidly near coal-mines in Britain and other countries.

The next step was inevitable. Some manufacturers successfully experimented with oil obtained from seepage swamps, to by-pass one of Young's production stages. The stage was set for Edwin Drake to start drilling to produce natural oil.

He was a fortunate man, for wherever oil is found, it is there only because of a series of accidents and geological freaks. The substance is believed to be derived from the decomposed remains of countless billions of tiny aquatic plants and animals.

Over the ages, they were crushed into oil by the weight of rock above them. Oil has been produced only in tropical latitudes. Deposits in Alaska, beneath the North Sea, and in other places far from the tropics, have moved to their present sites with the drifting continents.

Oil can be held underground only where there is a perfect seal of rock above to keep it in place, and these oil traps are the reservoirs prospectors hunt for. But even with the most sophisticated instruments, it is impossible to be sure that oil exists at a drilling site until a well is sunk.

At one time, a successful strike was often heralded by a 'gusher'—a huge jet of oil thrust to the surface by compressed natural gas. It could take days to get the jet under control. In 1901, for instance, one Texas gusher hurled 30 million gallons of oil to waste.

There were only 14 million gallons left underground when the well went into normal production. Modern drilling techniques have overcome this hazard.

But no matter how much waste is avoided, the amount of oil in the world is limited. Most land-based oilfields are now thought to have been discovered.

It took millions of years for the oil deposits to be created, but in not much more than 100 years since Edwin Drake made his strike, one-third of the world's known oil resources have been used up. It is unlikely that the demand can be satisfied for more than another 100 years, no matter how much oil comes from beneath the sea-bed.

AUSTRALIA'S ETERNAL FIRE

THE FIRE that never goes out has been eating away an Australian mountain for thousands of years. It is in the Hunter Valley region of New South Wales, 15 miles north of Scone. Early explorers thought that the column of smoke came from a volcano, but investigation showed that the cause was a burning seam of coal, 500 ft below the surface. It is thought that about 2000 years ago a tree, perhaps set on fire by lightning, fell on to the exposed face of the coal seam. This set light to the coal and, over the years, the fire has slowly smouldered along the line of the seam. Another theory is that the seam caught fire by spontaneous combustion—through the heat generated by the oxidation of sulphur pyrites. The local aborigines fear the place, yet associate it with the creator Bhaiami, and his earthly mediator Turramulan, who speaks from the smoke.

SENTINELS OF MILLENIA

Ancient trees that help to rewrite history

Before the foundation of Rome, before the golden age of Athens, and about the same time as the Pyramids were built, a seed germinated on a mountain in California. The tree that grew from that seed is still alive today—the world's oldest living thing.

It is Methuselah, a 4600-year-old bristlecone pine growing 9000 ft up in the White Mountains.

There was another bristlecone even older than Methuselah. When it was cut down in 1964 for scientific study, it was found to have 4900 rings.

Scientists estimate that a bristlecone can live for 5500 years, so Methuselah may be around for another 30 generations.

At the laboratory of Tree-Ring Research at the University of Arizona, scientists have compiled a calendar based on bristlecone rings and those of old remnants of the trees. In this way, every year dating back to 6200 BC has been specifically identified.

Researchers also discovered a fossil tree-line of bristlecone remnants above the current tree-line on Mount Washington, in eastern Nevada. By examining damaged cells, the scientists were able to pinpoint climatic conditions of years gone by, such as freak cold waves in the summers of 1453 and 1601.

Pollen grains trapped in the successive layers of growth have been examined, so that a picture of plant life of, say, 1300 BC could be compared with that of AD 350.

These pines are, in effect, organic computers which automatically record the changing conditions of life on this planet.

Paradoxically, the oldest bristlecones live in the poorest conditions; steep and rocky land, 9500 ft or more above sea level, with only thin soil and very little rainfall.

In better conditions, bristlecones grow faster, die earlier and decay more quickly.

The ancient pines have also helped to bring about some startling changes in our reckoning of prehistory.

Radio-carbon readings of bristlecone rings year by year showed up errors in the radio-carbon dating systems used to date archaeological finds. Basically, the radio-carbon dating system involves measuring the amounts of carbon 14 remaining in a fossil and, by estimating the amount of carbon loss, calculating its age.

But this system was based on the assumption that carbon in the atmosphere, caused by radioactive bombardment, had remained constant. The examination of the pines suggested fluctuations of the amount of carbon, creating discrepancies in the dating system.

A new, recalibrated system of dates, based on the bristlecone scale, was devised, involving date discrepancies ranging from a few centuries to 1000 years.

This is not simply a matter of correcting and reshuffling a few historical date inaccuracies. The revised system has weakened assumptions about the influence of ancient cultures upon each other.

NATURAL HISTORIAN *Studies of trees like Methuselah, a 4600-year-old bristlecone pine, are helping man to delve deeper into his past.*

Archaeologist Colin Renfrew, of the University of Southampton, England, has said that some of the great stone tombs found in north-western France and in Spain may be older than the Pyramids. It has also been suggested, using the new dating system, that important, evolutionary trends in building and engineering, and the use of metals, may have originated in Europe and not, as hitherto supposed, in the East.

The implications are that early Europeans were not less creative than advanced civilisations elsewhere. It could mean, Renfrew suggests, that textbooks of pre-history will have to be rewritten.

The usefulness of the bristlecone pine does not end there. It is also helping in the study of even more complex and fundamental aspects of science and human knowledge.

A Czechoslovakian geophysicist has been using samples of the pine's wood to investigate suspected fluctuations in the earth's magnetism.

At the University of California, a scientist has been using the tree as an aid in checking the effects of bomb tests.

The trees are also employed as monitors of air pollution from Pacific Coast industry and traffic.

Thus, a tree with a lifespan that exceeds the period of development of modern civilisation, is helping man to learn more about his past, present and, indirectly, his future.

THE MIGHTY AND MICROSCOPIC
Giants and midgets of the plant kingdom

The world's largest seeds resemble giant coconuts, and for centuries were thought to come from the sea. They were washed up on the shores of the Indian Ocean and, consequently, those who found them called them sea coconuts.

But with the discovery of the Seychelles Islands in the mid-18th century, the seeds, which weigh upwards of 40 lb. and are two or three times the size of coconuts, were found to come from tall nut palms which grow only on the islands.

For years, Eastern kings and Oriental potentates eagerly sought the seeds, thinking that they could be used as antidotes to poison.

The oldest and biggest

The largest plants in the world are the Big Trees (*Sequoia gigantea*) of California. It is believed these can live for as long as 6000 years.

The Big Trees live in groves between 6000 and 8000 ft high on the western slopes of the Sierra Nevada, and are also the world's largest living organisms. 'General Sherman' in Sequoia National Park, California, is 272 ft tall, has a base circumference of 101 ft 7 in. and is estimated to weigh 2145 tons.

Cousins of the Big Trees, the west coast redwoods (*Sequoia sempervirens*) are the world's tallest trees. These giants grow along the California coast and the tallest is the Howard Libbey tree in the Redwood Creek Grove, in Humboldt County. It is 367 ft $9\frac{1}{2}$ in. tall.

What was the tallest tree of all time is a matter for conjecture. In 1872, in Victoria, Australia, lumberjacks felled a mountain ash that was believed to have been 500 ft tall. But there is no official record of this.

There are claims that the tallest-ever title should go to a Douglas fir felled in British Columbia in 1940 and said to have measured 417 ft.

The tallest non-sequoia alive today is also a Douglas fir at Quinault Lake Park Trail, Washington. It is 310 ft tall.

The stoutest living tree is in the Mexican state of Oaxaca. It is a Montezuma cypress, called the Santa Maria del Tule, and has a girth of 112–13 ft at a height of about 5 ft from the ground.

In 1770 a European chestnut, known as the Chestnut of the Hundred Horses, measuring 204 ft in circumference, was found on the edge of Mount Etna in Sicily.

The seeds of all these tremendous trees weigh only about 1/6000th of an ounce.

The tiniest plants are, in fact, microscopic algae and bacteria which are found almost everywhere.

Algae live on animals, in soil, in hot springs, in salt and fresh water and on long-lying snow.

Bacteria are even more plentiful, and are found in the human body, feeding on cells and on each other. These are so small that about 25 million of them could fit on the head of a pin.

The world's smallest plants

There are viruses even smaller than this, which prey upon bacteria. But it is not clear, from a scientific standpoint, whether viruses should be classed among living things.

A virus cannot live until it gets into the cell of another living organism. It is not large enough to contain all the chemical information necessary to support its life processes, and uses the chemicals it finds in the cells of its host.

They are so microscopic that many hundreds of viruses can live in the smallest plankton—plants and animals that float on water. Plankton themselves are so small that 500 of them, laid side by side, would fit in a 1 mm. space.

But despite their size, some groups of plankton, such as a type known as *Coccolithophoridae*, are exotically beautiful. Each of these tiny plants has an outer armour of elaborately patterned scales made of chalk. They are the smallest known plants in the world—at the other end of nature's scale from the trees of California.

BEAUTY IN MINIATURE *One of the world's smallest plants,* Cyclococcolithus leptoporus, *has an elaborate outer shell of patterned scales. These plants are so tiny that 500 would fit on a pinhead.*

REACH FOR THE SKY *The Howard Libbey tree (second from right) in California, is the world's tallest known tree. It is 366 ft 2 in. high— about 90 ft taller than its near neighbours, the Big Trees.*

GARDEN OF EXTREMITIES

The largest and smallest flowers

The world's smallest flower, and also the world's smallest flowering plant is the Brazilian duckweed called wolfia. The whole plant can be less than $\frac{1}{16}$ in. across and the flower about half that. The rootless *Wolfia punctata* has fronds only $\frac{1}{50}$ to $\frac{1}{35}$ in. long.

These tiny plants were first discovered by the French naturalist Weddell, who found them growing among the leaves of the largest-flowering plant that lives in fresh water, the giant water lily *Victoria amazonica*. Named after Queen Victoria and the river on which it grows, this water lily is the fastest-growing flowering plant. Its massive leaves can grow from a very small prickly bud to over 3 ft across in as little as six days.

The world's largest flower is produced by the plant *Rafflesia arnoldii*, named after the two men who discovered it, Sir Thomas Stamford Raffles and Joseph Arnold. Rafflesia is parasitic on the roots of vines in the deeply shaded forests of Borneo, the Malay Peninsula and other parts of South-east Asia. It has no roots, leaves or stems to speak of, but the flower itself can measure more than 3 ft across and is $\frac{3}{4}$ in. thick. Resembling the heart of an enormous red cabbage, a bloom can weigh as much as 15 lb.

Rafflesia is marred by the nauseating smell, resembling that of rotting meat, which it emits. But the plant with the most repulsive smell is the tropical giant arum lily. The function of the smell is to attract flies to carry the pollen. Perhaps the most revolting variety is the swamp arum in whose flower flies lay their eggs. When opened, this flower reveals a mass of seething maggots surrounding the developing seeds.

NATURE'S MASS PRODUCTION

UP, UP AND AWAY A spore is a single cell or seed capable of redevelopment. Spores from an insignificant mould, *Cladosporium herbarum*—which have been caught by balloons as high as 90,000 ft above the earth's surface—are the most common.

Some of the larger bracket fungi, often found growing on old decaying trees, can keep up a daily spore production of 30,000 million for five months.

The pollen grains of the silver birch are here enlarged 300 times their natural size. These tiny spores cause most of the hay fever in Scandinavia.

Bracket fungus is especially common on oak trees. This picture, taken in England's New Forest, shows a sulphur polypore fungus, that causes rot in the heart of the trees.

THE FLESH-EATERS

The predators of the plant world

A fly hovered over a small, white-blossomed herb, whose open leaves revealed an inviting red centre. The fly descended to investigate, and that was a mistake—the last it ever made. For the open leaves sprang together, their comb-like edges interlocking to form a death trap. Slowly the trap tightened, and the Venus's fly-trap began to devour its latest victim.

The fly-trap, a native of North and South Carolina, is one of a number of carnivorous plants that live by digesting animal proteins in their simple soluble amino acids. Its leaves are hinged at the centre, and thread-like triggers set the trap. The moment an insect touches one of the triggers the trap is sprung, and the plant's digestive juices set to work.

The process usually takes about ten days, then the fly-trap opens its leaves again and ejects the indigestible parts, such as wings and scales. It then pre-pares again to receive its next victim.

A near relative of the Venus's fly-trap is the pitcher plant, found in Australia and eastern North America, which has small, pitcher-shaped containers hanging from its leaves. An insect is lured into the trap by the plant's exotic smell, and as it crawls over the slippery mouth of the pitcher it loses its footing and falls into an acid pool. Stiff, downward-pointing bristles prevent the victim from climbing out, and it soon succumbs to the poisonous bath of digestive juices.

Remarkable trapper

Perhaps the most remarkable of the animal-trapping plants is the bladder-wort, usually found in tropical regions. It grows in ponds and sluggish streams and has no roots, drifting at the mercy of winds and currents. It is a long, slender plant with many-parted leaves, each carrying about a dozen small bladders.

SETTING THE TRAP *A Venus's fly-trap opens its leaves and waits for a victim. Insects are attracted by its blood-red centre.*

THE TRAP IS SPRUNG *An unsuspecting fly has touched off the trap, and becomes a meal for the carnivorous plant.*

A LIVING SNARE *Two nematodes are caught in the stranglehold of* Dactylaria gracilis. *The one on the right is freshly caught, the one on the left is almost entirely consumed.*

A STICKY END *This eelworm has been caught by* Trichothecium cystosporium, *a fungus with adhesive networks. The creature's head is entangled with the fungal network.*

These are the traps, and the entrance is a door which can be pushed open from the outside but not from the inside. The insect does not enter from choice—it is sucked in.

Not all insect-catching plants use mechanical traps. Some employ a 'fly-paper' technique. The beautiful sundew of Australia and South Africa is a sweet-smelling plant, with a flower that spells death for any unwary creature.

Its pincushion centre contains a strong glue, and when an insect alights it becomes firmly stuck. Then the glittering heads of the pins curl over the victim—and the sundew commences its meal.

Similarly the leafy butterwort, lying flat on the ground in moist and mossy areas, usually in the Northern Hemisphere, waits for its insect prey. When a moth or bee alights to feed, the plant exudes a sticky secretion to hold the insect. Then it emits an enzyme which digests the proteins over which the leaves have curled, holding the victim in a deadly embrace.

DO PLANTS HAVE EMOTIONS?

Sensitive creatures in the plant world

In the fantasy world of Walt Disney cartoons the creatures of nature perceive more than mere man. At the approach of danger, trees draw in their branches, bushes shrivel, flowers close their blossoms, blades of grass send messages to fields far away.

Saucer-eyed children throughout the world anticipate the happy ending when the evil threat is overcome. Then the music surges, trees reach for the sun, flowers bloom and the audience applauds —the end of another make-believe episode. Or is it make-believe? Is it possible that plants know who loves them and who wishes them harm?

Within the past decade several researchers have reported that plants do know who their friends are, and react to threats, even going so far as to 'faint' in the presence of a dangerous person.

For example, Cleve Backster, an American lie-detector expert, attached one of his polygraph machines to the leaves of a philodendron and saw to his surprise that the tracing began to show a pattern typical of the 'Response you get when you subject a human to emotional stimulation of short duration'.

In search of other reactions, Backster decided to burn the leaf of the plant. While he was thinking about this, there was a dramatic upward sweep in the tracing pattern. He had neither moved nor touched the plant. He had apparently frightened the plant only by his thought of burning it. Not only can plants feel things, he decided, they can also anticipate actions by reading people's minds.

Reports of Backster's philodendron experience were made public early in 1966. Press coverage was extensive and most people seemed to accept the findings at face value. Owners of plants became in various ways servants of their botanical friends. Some devotees of the new cult even installed recorded-music systems so that their plants would not feel alone while they were away.

The belief that plants are capable of emotional response was not a short-lived fad. In 1973 Peter Tomkins and Christopher Bird published *The Secret Life of Plants*, which became a best seller. Enlarging upon Backster's thesis, Tomkins and Bird stated that plants respond to speech, thoughts and prayers. They claimed to have proved that plants could count and even alter their own behaviour.

The nature of their proof is what many scientists find questionable. Scientific evidence, they argue, is an accumulation of data derived from repeated experiments which can be controlled and recorded not only by the initiators of a project but also by researchers in laboratories anywhere in the world.

Backster, Tomkins and Bird have turned their backs on these requirements. Indeed, Backster was reported in *The Christian Science Monitor* as saying, 'Mother Nature doesn't want to jump through the hoop ten times in a row simply because someone wants her to'.

The three men maintain that 'some' people—very special, very sensitive people —might be able to obtain the very same results as they. In short—the character of the researcher determines the results of the experiment.

91

Strange and mysterious creatures that share our world

The surprising animal kingdom

---•---

THE LONG AND THE SHORT AND THE TALL
Laws and limits of size

A favourite theme of science-fiction films is that ants or other insects, mutated by radiation, will grow to gigantic proportions and terrorise mankind. But nature prevents this nightmarish fiction from becoming a reality; for the size of every living creature on earth is limited by immutable laws.

It would be just as impossible to produce an ant the size of a horse as it would be to shrink a man to the size of a mouse or a bird. In both cases, the change in size would alter the relationship between mass and surface area, producing entirely new problems for the new-sized creature.

As the diagram on this page makes clear, double the size of an animal and you reduce by half the rate at which it loses heat through its surface. Conversely, reduce its size by half, and it loses its body heat twice as fast. A man as small as a bird would have to do as birds do: spend the bulk of his time eating or looking for high-energy food—always supposing that, without feathers, he did not freeze to death in a matter of minutes.

The fact that large animals conserve body heat better than small ones explains why those that live in polar regions are generally bulkier than those that live in warmer climates. A polar bear, for instance, can grow 11 ft tall and weigh up to 1600 lb.—nearly twice the height and six times the weight of the Himalayan black bear.

Bulky animals that live in hot climates, such as elephants and rhinos, have to get rid of excess heat by wallowing in water and plastering themselves with cool mud.

An ant that reached the size of a horse, apart from overheating, would die of oxygen starvation, for insects have no lungs. Oxygen reaches their air sacs through tiny holes, called spiracles, in their bodies. In insects of normal size, the air simply seeps through to the air sacs, but with an ant as big as a horse it would take a wind of hurricane strength to force the air from its spiracles down to its internal tissues.

Even if the giant ant of science fiction somehow evolved muscle-powered lungs, that would not save it. For its shell would need to thicken immensely if it were not to buckle under air pressure, with the

THE PROBLEM OF SIZE *Imagine a man whose mass is one cubic unit (small figure). Double his height, and his mass increases eightfold, while his surface area increases only four times (large figure). His rate of heat loss through the skin will have been halved. Such an increase in size would cause overheating problems.*

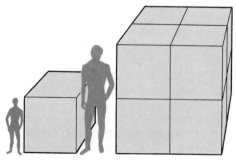

result that it would crush the body it was meant to protect.

Apart from considerations like these, there are many other factors that affect size. At one end of the scale, anything less than about 1/1000th of a centimetre in diameter is at the mercy of the molecules around it. Molecules of air, for instance, are in constant motion, colliding with one another and with objects in their way. With large objects, the collisions on one side are balanced by those on the other, producing the unfelt force known as air pressure. But if the object is infinitesimally small, the collisions are uneven, so that the smallest living organisms are kept in a permanently active state, thus making it impossible for them to have any control over their environment.

At the other end of the scale, massive bulk brings its own penalties, not the least of which is the difficulty of finding food. The largest animal the world has ever seen, the 100 ton blue whale, needs 4 tons of food a day. It obtains this by sucking in thousands of gallons of sea water and straining out krill and other tiny organisms from this liquid intake. No creature living on less widely available food could attain such a size.

The largest living organisms of all, the sequoia and redwood trees of California, get round the problem of finding food by manufacturing their own. Like almost all plants, they transform carbon dioxide into sugar and oxygen.

The drawback to being a plant, whatever its size, is again lack of control over the environment. No creature which has to move about can afford to be as large as these trees, for its appetite would then outstrip its food supply.

LARGEST, SMALLEST, FASTEST

The Goliath beetle, measuring 4 in. across and 5·8 in. in length, is the world's largest-known insect.

WHEN animal life first appeared on earth, some 2000 million years ago, it was in the form of single-celled creatures called protozoa. As more complex animals evolved, their need for an even greater number of cells brought about an automatic increase in size. A man, for instance, has about 60 billion cells: his very complexity sets a limit to how small he can be.

The largest and heaviest animals the world has ever seen are blue whales, some of which weigh more than 100 tons. The largest creature without a backbone is the Atlantic giant squid, which can weigh 2 tons and grow up to 55 ft long.

The largest land mammal is the African bush elephant, which averages 5·6 tons, while at the other end of the scale is the pygmy shrew of northern Europe, which is rarely longer than 1½ in. from nose to tail.

The flightless North African ostrich is the largest bird, weighing up to 345 lb. and growing to 9 ft tall.

The smallest is the bee hummingbird of Cuba: 2 in. long with a 1·1 in. wing span.

The fastest creature is the spine-tailed swift; it has been reported that it can fly at speeds in excess of 200 mph.

In the insect world, the Goliath beetle weighs in at 3·4 oz. and measures 4 in. across and 5·8 in. long. The South American bird-eating spider, with a leg span of 10 in. and 3½ in. body length, is the largest of all spiders.

THE SUPER-SENSES OF ANIMALS

Nature's amazing communication systems

To a sparrow, the human voice sounds something like the low rumbling of distant thunder, and the low notes produced by a bass singer may well be completely inaudible.

This is because the sparrow's hearing range is different from a human being's. Like most of the creatures in the world around us, it possesses the five senses of sight, hearing, touch, taste and smell, but these are heightened or diminished according to its way of life.

In birds, it is the sense of sight that has developed to a pitch of perfection. The high-soaring buzzard, which needs to be able to pick out a meal as small as a lizard or even a beetle on the ground below, has eyesight eight times as keen as a man's.

Animals that hunt by following a trail, on the other hand, often have poor eyesight but a keen sense of smell. Dogs, for instance, see a world that is blurred and devoid of colour, apart from shades of grey: for they are shortsighted and have no colour vision.

But a dog's sense of smell is to a man's what a symphony orchestra is to a penny whistle. An alsatian has 220 million olfactory cells, compared with a man's 5 million, and experiments suggest that this makes it a million times better at detecting odours.

This does not mean that the sense of smell in humans is rudimentary. Most of us are equipped with a far more sensitive nose than we need in the modern world. The average human being can distinguish between more than 10,000 different odours, and if put to the test could detect the presence of a single drop of musk inside a large concert hall.

Only one relevant smell

It is not always the ability to distinguish between a host of smells that is necessary to survival. There is a type of beetle larva which feeds on vine roots, and is sensitive only to a single smell—the odour of carbon dioxide, which is given off by the roots of vines. Any other smell is irrelevant to the larva, but it will pursue the scent of carbon dioxide unswervingly through the ground until it reaches its goal.

The characteristic scent of every living creature is carried in molecules which leave the body in the form of sweat, breath, bodily wastes and so on. With every step you take, you leave behind millions of sweat-borne molecules which lay a scent trail.

Creatures that spend most of their time in the air cannot mark the ground with a scent trail, yet butterflies, in the mating season, can attract a mate from miles away by scent alone. The female butterfly carries a store of perfume weighing only one ten-thousandth of a milligram and she squirts minute fractions of it into the air. These scent molecules can be detected by a male 7 miles away.

Echo-locating system

Just as remarkable is the echo-locating system used by bats to pinpoint their prey, or obstacles in their way. Contrary to popular belief, bats are not entirely blind. Most can see in twilight, but in pitch darkness they rely on sending out high-frequency squeaks, some audible to the human ear, others inaudible. The returning echoes tell them the exact position of any obstacles.

In this way bats can flit about in great numbers without colliding. Even when they fly out of caves in their thousands, they respond only to their own individual echo-signals, and are not confused by the noises of their neighbours.

How they manage to tune in so finely remains a mystery. Scientists have conducted experiments in which they tried to jam the radar signals of bats by drowning them with a volume of noise 2000 times as intense, and on the same frequency. It made no difference. Somehow, the bats managed to pick out their own echoes and ignore the foreign noise.

One of the oddest hearing systems in nature is that of a North American daddy-longlegs, the ichneumon fly. Its 'ears' are in its feet, and it uses them to listen for the noise made by the larvae of the horntail wasp when they are chewing wood.

The larvae of the fly, when they hatch, feed on the living bodies of the wasp larvae, and no other host is suitable. The female fly locates the wasp larvae with deadly accuracy, both by her sense of smell and by running up and down tree trunks, listening with the hearing cells in

A SNAKE'S SECOND SIGHT *The deep pits between the red eyes of this bamboo viper of Formosa are organs sensitive to heat. They help it to find its warm-blooded prey, even in darkness. These extra aids were first observed in the rattlesnake by two American zoologists in 1952.*

her feet for the sound of the larvae chewing inside.

Many of the senses of animals are switched on or off by a system of signals.

Bees, for example, are first attracted by the smell of flowers, they can also distinguish them from leaves by their shape and colour. But when bees have finished foraging, they are instinctively attracted to black dots—the flight holes of their hives—and no flower-shape can lure them.

Bees are also sensitive to ultra-violet light, invisible to humans, which enables them to locate the position of the sun even when it is obscured by clouds. This helps them to navigate. On the other hand, there are parts of the colour spectrum to which bees are insensitive. They can see red only as black.

The secrets of the animal world are being gradually revealed by patient observation and imaginative experiments. In 1952, two zoologists at the University of California discovered that rattlesnakes possess a 'third eye'.

When they taped over a rattler's eyes, they found that it could still locate mice with uncanny precision. The organs responsible appeared to be two small dimples located on either side of the snake's head, between the nostrils and eyes.

In these they discovered heat-sensitive cells which enabled the snake not only to locate living prey when its eyes were covered, or at night, but also to determine the size and shape of these creatures from the heat given off by their bodies.

Experiments have shown, too, that the frog has a completely economical and selective sense of vision, seeing only the objects necessary to its survival—a fly crawling within striking distance, or an approaching enemy.

The eyes of most creatures produce pictures of objects on a layer of light-sensitive cells called the retina. These are transmitted to the brain, which forms a mental picture.

But a shrimp-like creature, *Copilia quadrata*, in the Bay of Naples, has eyes which work on a different principle.

The animal has one lens in the front of its head, but no retina. Behind the lens is a single, light-sensitive spot which darts about, building up an image as a system of dots, rather like a television receiver. The 'receiving equipment' for these images is in the creature's waist.

HOW SNAILS HELP TO SAVE LIVES

THE COMMON garden snail lays about 30 eggs a year, each of them the size of a large pinhead and each one a potential life-saver. The snail's egg is a cheap, readily available and stable source of a chemical that is used to determine blood groups. Normally, this chemical is extracted from human blood, but it takes the blood from five donors to provide as much as is contained in a single snail's egg. The contents of the egg are extracted and dissolved in a saline solution.

LIVING LIGHTS OF THE ANIMAL KINGDOM
Creatures that produce their own illumination

Only 4 per cent of the energy output of an electric bulb is light. The other 96 per cent is given off as heat. The firefly, a tiny member of the beetle family, glows in the dark to attract its mate. It has an efficiency of over 90 per cent, producing light almost devoid of heat.

Fireflies, which are found in the tropics and parts of Europe and North America, produce their light through a chemical process in an organ near the tip of the abdomen. Light-producing chemicals and enzymes combine with oxygen to produce a bright glow. The insects, placed in perforated gourd lanterns, have been used in Brazil and China as a form of cheap lighting. The glow from six large fireflies would provide enough light to read a book. But attempts to produce artificially the 'living light' or bioluminescence of animal life have proved more costly than orthodox electric lighting.

The glow-worm, a member of the same beetle family, *Lampyridae*, also produces chemical light. The winged male possesses two tiny light-producing organs on the abdomen. The grub-like female has light organs in the tail segments of her body, whose powerful glow attracts the male. The larva of the glow-worm becomes luminescent only in defence when it is disturbed. Its light is a brighter green than that of the adult.

Many deep-sea creatures also employ bioluminescence, both as a mating signal and as a means of attracting prey.

In depths where light does not penetrate, sea anemones, sponges, coral shrimps, prawns and squids can produce their own light. Other fish act as hosts to colonies of luminescent bacteria which illuminate parts of their bodies from within. The bacteria emit continuous light, but the host often has a means of shutting off the light when danger threatens. Possibly this is done by reducing the oxygen supply. The Indo-Pacific fish *Photoblepharon* has a large white spot under each eye, rich in bacteria-filled blood vessels. A black fold of skin above the luminous spot can be lowered to shut off the light.

The bathysphere fish, so called because the pale blue, glowing spots along its sides resemble portholes of a diving bell, has two 3 ft tentacles with luminous

---

NEW LIMBS FROM OLD

IN THE PAST starfish were dredged up from oyster and mussel beds, where they are a severe pest, ripped apart and thrown back into the sea in the belief that they were dead and could do no more damage.

Far from it—the injured starfish merely grew new arms from the torn body parts, so that from one animal two or more arose.

Starfish are not alone in this curious habit of replacing bits of themselves. Crabs and lobsters are able to regrow a leg or claw they have lost in a fight. The earthworm can replace its head if it loses the first few segments of its body. Lizards can grow a new tail—though a somewhat stumpy one—if necessary.

Some of the simpler animals have the ability to regrow complete new bodies from a minute part of the old.

Planarian worms live both at the bottom of the sea and in fresh water under mud and stones. They are usually less than an inch long and look like small leeches. If the tail is cut off, a planarian will grow a new one. If the head is cut off it will replace that. If a piece is taken from the middle of the body a new head and tail grows on each end. The head develops at the original front end and the tail at the original hind end as if the piece 'remembered' its position.

If the head is cut down the middle each half replaces the missing part so that the flatworm ends up with two heads. If the head is cut several times and the cut edges not allowed to grow together then a monster with ten complete heads results.

Planarians can be trained to contract when an electric light is switched on. Trained worms cut in half and allowed to regrow their appropriate missing bits were tested to see if they too cringed at the light —they did. Even the tail that regenerated a new head cowered when the light was switched on. Hungry, untrained planarians were fed trained chopped-up worms. The hungry worms 'learnt' the light trick much quicker than worms fed on pieces of untrained worms. It was as if they had eaten the memory of their fellows.

ends which attract the fish on which it feeds. Its long glowing teeth are also an invitation to inquisitive prey.

The tiny hatchet fish, on the other hand, emits from its body ghostly, greenish-white lights which resemble a row of teeth, deterring would-be enemies while it feeds undisturbed on its diet of plankton.

The lantern fish uses the blue, green or yellow luminous 'buttons' along its body as a form of recognition and to attract a mate, while the angler fish actually uses luminous lures as fishing rods to catch fish whose usual prey is luminescent.

BEAUTY OF THE DEEP *Many types of deep-sea fish, such as the* Chauliodus, *employ luminescence to lure prey and attract mates.*

NIGHT LIGHTS *Both the male beetle and grub-like female glow-worms have light-producing organs which they use as mating signals.*

TRAVELLING LIGHTS *Light-producing chemicals combine with oxygen to produce the bright colours of fish like the* Ichthyococcus.

Starfish, regarded as a pest in mussel and oyster beds, were once dredged up, torn apart and thrown back in the sea. But since the starfish can regenerate lost limbs, the process was ineffective. Here, a painted prawn is carrying off the arm of a starfish, which will grow another limb.

97

THE SURPRISING ANIMAL KINGDOM

MARKSMEN AND TRAPPERS

Winners in a world where the unwary can end up as a meal

Many creatures have evolved ingenious ways of hunting and capturing their prey. The young ant-lion, before it changes into a type of dragonfly, uses its pincer-like jaws to dig a hole in the sand in its desert habitat. Then it sits in the hole and waits for its prey—ants and spiders.

When one of these creatures approaches the hole, it disturbs the sand on the rim, and the ant-lion goes into action. It places a grain of sand on its head and flicks it with unerring accuracy towards its target. This tumbles the creature into the pit, where it is quickly devoured. And the ant-

FISH-CATCHING FISH *The angler fish lures its smaller victims with a fleshy, wormlike growth at the end of its rod-like fin.*

lion resumes its position, ready for its next victim.

The archer fish also claims its victims by firing a missile. Swimming close to the surface in rivers of its native India and Australia, it seeks insects on the low-hanging branches of trees. When it spots a victim, the fish rises to the surface and fires a jet of water from its mouth, knocking the insect into the water.

This water-pistol effect is achieved by the shape of the fish's mouth. A groove runs along its roof, and when the tongue is pressed against it a narrow tube is formed. Closing the gill flaps provides the pressure to eject the water.

Fish that fishes

The deep-sea angler fish uses a more subtle method. A long fin like a fishing rod grows from its back, and the fish can bend this forward so that the tip is just in front of its mouth. On the end is the 'bait', a fleshy, wormlike growth which wriggles convincingly. When smaller fish try to take the bait the angler strikes.

A cunning trick is used by one species of jumping spider. It spins a web across the mouth of the carnivorous pitcher plant, which feeds on insects that fall into the pitcher-shaped flower.

The spider sits on its web and waits for insects to fall into the net. Thus it catches its prey—and robs the plant of a victim.

FLYING UNDERWATER

CLOSE to the rushing waters of mountain streams lives a sturdy bird, about the size of a starling, called the dipper.

Found in many parts of the world, it is a truly aquatic creature with the ability to 'fly' underwater. Using its strong wings, it has been known to dive into 20 ft of water and fly down to the bottom, staying down as long as half a minute while it searches in the grit and sand for food.

It is thought that the dipper is able to walk on the bottom by setting its body at an angle against the current to obtain a planing effect which prevents it from bobbing to the surface until it has finished its meal. A movable flap over the bird's nostrils keeps out the water, and the eyes are protected by a thin membrane that somewhat resembles a third eyelid.

ON THE DEFENSIVE

How nature survives by camouflage—or bluff

The law of nature demands that every creature must have some form of defence—or die. Some have developed fearsome weapons with which to defend themselves, others use subtle disguises to escape attention.

Insects are the staple diet of many predators, and so they have become particularly adept in the art of disguise. In forests and jungles all over the world, the foliage and branches of trees are not all they seem; the stick insects merge with the twigs, a piece of fungus may be the cricket-like katydid, tree-hoppers look like thorns, and the leaf insect sways its body to resemble a leaf that is blowing in the wind.

The caterpillar of the elephant hawk moth goes one better. When threatened, it retracts its legs and rolls over, revealing a pair of false 'eyes' that give it the appearance of the deadly pit viper.

One insect that can defend itself in a daunting and spectacular manner is the bombardier beetle. With a loud bang the beetle fires a jet of liquid, composed of hydrogen peroxide and quinol, at any would-be attacker. The European species is quite small, but in India they grow up to 2 in. in length, and their deadly jet could cause severe pain to a man if it entered his eyes.

The infamous skunk also uses a noxious fluid to repel attackers, but gives two clear

WALKING STICK *These stick insects are almost indistinguishable in shape and colour from the stems of the plants upon which they are feeding.*

NOW YOU SEE ME, NOW YOU DON'T *A praying mantis waits motionless, camouflaged against a twig background, ready to pounce on victims.*

BLOWING IN THE WIND *Leaf insects not only resemble leaves in their colouring and vein-like markings, but flap their bodies, imitating trembling, wind-blown leaves.*

FACE TO FACE *An elephant hawk moth caterpillar takes on the appearance of a miniature snake to scare off a toad that is threatening to eat it.*

warnings. It thumps the ground with its forefeet, and if this warning is ignored shakes its head from side to side in a disapproving manner. Finally, arching its black-and-white tail, it turns its back towards its adversary and fires a jet of blinding fluid. The sulphurous liquid, known as mercaptan, does not kill, but any animal that has been on the receiving end gives the skunk a wide berth in future.

When it comes to a stand-up fight, however, the musk-oxen use a formidable defence system. To protect their young from marauding wolves they form a ring, like the battle phalanx used by ancient infantry. With horns lowered, the ring wheels so that the adult bulls face the enemy, and any wolf that comes too close is caught on the horns and tossed over the ox's shoulder, to be trampled to death.

IF IT MOVES, IT'S MOTHER

VIENNESE zoologist Konrad Lorenz studied the behaviour patterns of newly hatched ducks and geese, and found that a greylag gosling will follow the first moving object it sees after hatching, and adopt it as its mother. Lorenz's goslings have adopted various mother-substitutes, including an Alsatian dog, a ball and a block of wood. Ducklings, on the other hand, reacted to sounds. Young mallards showed fear of anything other than an adult mallard, unless the call of the mallard was imitated.

KILLER THAT TIES ITSELF IN KNOTS

A hungry hagfish slides its tail into a knot around its slime-covered body and when it attacks, rolls the knot forward to press against its prey.

The hagfish's twisting knot can help it to escape if caught—although the slimy, rubbery creature has no known natural enemies.

A hagfish also uses its knot for leverage to tear flesh from its prey. Flexibility comes from a spine made of cartilage, not bone.

THE HAGFISH ties itself in knots to become a killer. This slimy, eel-like creature twists itself into a loop as it attacks another fish, then plunges its sharp rows of teeth into one of the fish's gills.

Once firmly attached, the tenacious hagfish begins a twisting action with the knot in its body, burrowing deeper and deeper into its prey until it is completely inside the other fish. Then the hagfish starts eating its captive while it is still alive—from the inside —until only the victim's skin and bones remain.

The creature's name is thought to be derived from its sheer ugliness—like a jagged-toothed hag.

HIGH-POWERED HUNTERS

Fish that generate electricity

The electric eel, which lives in South American rivers, can produce a burst of power strong enough to light more than a dozen household bulbs. It discharges up to 600 volts at a current of around 2 amps to kill prey, such as fish and frogs, and to ward off predators.

The shock, which lasts only a split second, is generated from thousands of linked cells in the creature's tail. The heavy discharge of energy drains the battery—but within an hour it is fully charged again for either attack or defence.

The electric eel, sometimes 6 ft long, is actually a knifefish more closely related to the catfish and carp than to the eel.

When it moves it sends out weak electrical impulses from two small pilot 'batteries' to detect unseen prey or enemies.

The impulses create an electrical field round the eel, and an intruder's size and position are betrayed when the eel senses changes in the field.

Electric fish are found in rivers and oceans in various parts of the world, but although they have the power to produce electricity in common they are not related to each other.

The freshwater electric catfish of tropical Africa kills or paralyses its prey with a shock of up to several hundred volts emitted from a membrane along its back.

Another shock producer is the disc-shaped electric ray, found in the Atlantic, the Indian Ocean and the Mediterranean. This member of the shark family can kill or stun smaller fish, but its shock is not powerful enough to harm humans.

THE MATING SEASON

Finding a partner can be a serious—or deadly—occupation

Courtship among the animals has many strange forms and rituals, and finding a mate can often be a perilous business, particularly in the insect world.

The female praying mantis will eat anything that passes by—including a potential mate. Fortunately for the male, she can spot prey only when it moves, so he approaches from behind and freezes in his tracks whenever she moves her head. As soon as the female is distracted by another insect, the male seizes his chance and mating takes place. Even then, however, his chances of escape are slim, for as soon as he moves away his partner turns and makes a grab for him—often with fatal results.

Insects that lead solitary lives have the problem of finding another of their species to mate with, and the senses of smell or hearing are used to attract a partner. The male bumble bee makes his presence known by leaving spots of scented chemical secreted from his mouth on leaves and twigs. When a female bumble bee finds one of these spots, she waits patiently for her lover to return. He then mates—and dies shortly afterwards.

The female moth also uses scent to attract the male. Glands at the rear of her body produce the scent, which she disperses by vibrating her wings. Carried on the breeze, this scent can be detected by a male as far as 6 miles away.

The mole cricket calls his mate with a chirping song made by rubbing his forewings together—and to make sure his song is heard he builds his own kind of stereo amplifier.

With his large, flattened forelegs he digs an underground nest with a twin-horned tunnel entrance. Then he sits at the junction of the horns and beams out his hi-fi message for any passing female to hear.

Nature's compensation

If speed is essential in finding a mate, the snail has a big disadvantage, but nature has compensated by making most species bi-sexual.

Banded snails meet by picking up each other's slime trails, and courtship begins as they rear up and press their bodies together. During this embrace each fires a love dart—a chalky needle—into the

FINAL TOUCH *With his mate already in the nest, the satin bower bird adds one final decoration.*

HIGH-SPEED SERENADE

These pictures show how the male fruit fly produces his courtship song—a serenade which lasts only 1/3000 of a second. By making incredibly rapid upward wing movements, he emits a high-pitched buzz that stimulates the female. If she accepts him, she buzzes in reply.

other. This powerful stimulant enables them to mate for several hours.

In the world of mammals and birds, courtship is often of a more gentle and considerate nature. Elephants spend weeks in gentle love-play before actually mating. A couple will stand for hours playfully entwining their trunks and engaging in a mock tug-of-war.

Females take the lead

Female mammals often take the leading role in courtship. The tigress parades before her potential mate, flicking her tail across his muzzle in a tantalising manner. The female giraffe canters with a peculiar gait that shows she is ready to mate. The gnu drops to her knees and gives a suggestive nudge to any male that happens to wander past her.

But for painstaking wooing, the Australian satin bower bird has few equals. His glossy, blue-black plumage would be enough to dazzle any female, but he also tempts her with a home, or bower. Every year he builds or renews his elaborate parlour, using twigs and sticks firmly interlocked. It has two parallel walls of sticks extending upward about 12 in., and averages 2 in. in thickness.

The bird then sets about decorating the interior.

First he paints the inside walls with a mixture of charcoal and saliva, using a wad of bark as a brush. Then he decorates the bower with brightly coloured objects: flowers, parrots' feathers, berries and man-made objects such as tinfoil and pieces of glass.

When a female arrives near the bower the male puts on a display, flashing his wings and emitting curious croaking sounds. Eventually the female enters the bower and, after she has made a few alterations to the 'furniture', the male enters and mating takes place.

Courtship and mating is the sole purpose of the bower. Once this has taken place, the female flies away, builds her own nest and brings up her young.

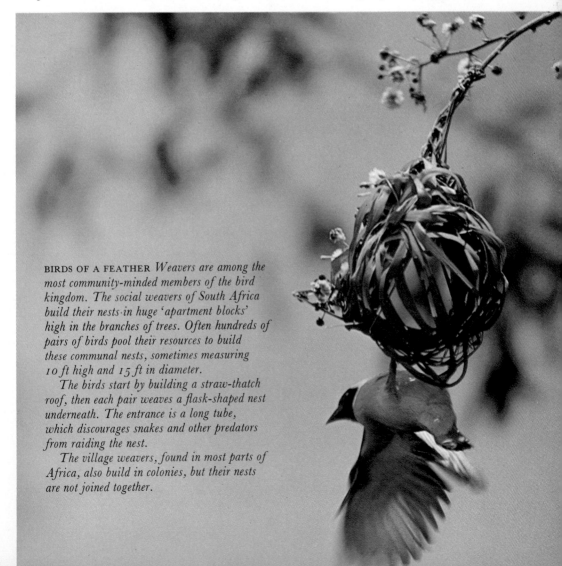

BIRDS OF A FEATHER *Weavers are among the most community-minded members of the bird kingdom. The social weavers of South Africa build their nests in huge 'apartment blocks' high in the branches of trees. Often hundreds of pairs of birds pool their resources to build these communal nests, sometimes measuring 10 ft high and 15 ft in diameter.*

The birds start by building a straw-thatch roof, then each pair weaves a flask-shaped nest underneath. The entrance is a long tube, which discourages snakes and other predators from raiding the nest.

The village weavers, found in most parts of Africa, also build in colonies, but their nests are not joined together.

TURNING BACK NATURE'S CLOCK

Animals in cave paintings are brought to life again

Standing uncertainly on spindly legs was the most unusual foal the two zoologists had seen. But they were delighted by its strange appearance.

For it was no ordinary foal—the zoologists, Heinz and Lutz Heck, had re-created an animal that had been extinct for 50 years.

The foal had all the characteristics of the wild tarpan, the Stone Age ancestor of the modern horse. These animals, mouse-grey in colour, had roamed the plains and forests of Europe and central Asia for thousands of years.

The Hecks were able to report after many years' research that an animal had been born which no man had hoped to see. They had their first primeval horse.

Unexpected characteristics appeared. When winter came, the foal's coat turned

PREHISTORIC WALL PAINTINGS *Artists who decorated cave walls at Lascaux in France, 10,000 to 30,000 years ago, recorded important details which were used by two Germans, Heinz and Lutz Heck, to breed the horses and cattle that once roamed Europe and central Asia. The tarpan (left) and aurochs (right) are shown, re-created.*

A SPECIES REBORN *By crossing strains, the brothers bred back to the tarpan, the tough wild horse from which modern breeds are descended.*

CATTLE OF THE FOREST *They also re-created the aurochs, cattle which inhabited the forests that covered Europe until the Middle Ages.*

white—just as the coat of the ancient tarpan was known to have done.

Then, after five more generations of foals, the animals developed another feature the Hecks had not expected— their hooves became much tougher than those of any horse in the world. This was the hoof of the wild tarpan—a hoof which, unshod, would not wear down.

The Hecks—Heinz was director of Munich Zoo and Lutz was director of Berlin Zoo—were confident they could put evolution into reverse and breed back to extinct animals.

Correcting past changes

Lutz Heck explained: 'We proceeded from the principle that no animal can be extinct whose heritable constitution still exists. This constitution may have been crossed with other animals, it may have suffered changes, but with the aid of our present-day knowledge of heredity it can be brought back as a whole. Crossings can be bred out again, and changes can be corrected by suitable selection.'

So they followed a process used by their father when he ran the Berlin Zoo. He had mated an ibex—a wild goat—with domestic goats.

Some of the goats' offspring had the colour of the ibex, some the colours of the mothers. But some had the exact colour-ing of the bezoar, the wild goat of the Middle East, which is the primeval ancestor of all domestic goats.

The last tarpan had died in captivity in 1887, and to build up an exact picture of the animal, the Hecks studied medieval records, fossil remains, skeletons—even the drawings of primeval horses made 10,000 to 30,000 years ago by Stone Age men on the walls of the Cap Blanc and Lascaux caves in France.

In the first breeding in Munich some 40 years ago, the brothers used stallions from Poland, known to be descendants of the tarpan. These they crossed with carefully chosen domestic horses from Iceland, Scotland and Scandinavia.

When the first foals were born, the brothers checked carefully for tarpan characteristics—then mated the most suitable animals. Heinz reported: 'In the second breeding there appeared our fabulous foal.'

Today there are herds of tarpan in zoos and sanctuaries in Europe and the USA.

Using the same techniques, the Hecks also set out to re-create the aurochs, the fierce ancestors of present-day cattle. Aurochs, which weighed up to a ton, died out in the 17th century. After ten years a calf was born that had all the characteristics of the aurochs. Today there is a complete herd in Munich Zoo.

THE SURVIVOR

IN 1938, fishermen working in the Indian Ocean brought up a strange, metallic-blue fish almost 6 ft long, with large, thick scales and strong fleshy fins.

When the catch was landed, the curious fish was spotted by Dr Marjorie Courtenay-Latimer, then curator of East London Museum. Although she did not know what it was, she realised it was quite exceptional. So she sent a rough sketch of the creature to Professor J. L. B. Smith, an organic chemist at Rhodes University, but also an eminent amateur fish expert.

From that sketch alone, he was able to identify it—a coelacanth, which is now called *Latimeria chalumnae* in Dr Courtenay-Latimer's honour.

Professor Smith commented: 'My surprise would have been little greater if I had seen a dinosaur walking down the street.' And indeed he was understating the case, for hitherto the fish had been known only as a fossil in rocks 400 million years old— 200 million years older than the dinosaurs.

Since then, several others have been caught. With hearts more primitive than those of any other vertebrate, and brains only 1/15,000th of their body weight, they belong to the era when the world was young.

GOING TO WORK ON AN EGG

Four stages in the process of getting a very small African egg-eating snake outside a very large egg. First, the snake sizes up the job.

This snake, which lives solely on eggs, opens its flexible jaws. They will distend, if necessary, to four times the circumference of its body.

The snake, only about 2 ft long, has engulfed an egg that is more than double its own diameter. Powerful muscles will now force the egg down.

The snake is ready to start digesting its food. Internal backbone spines are worked back and forth to break the shell, which will be regurgitated.

THE POISONERS

Fangs and stings can bring rapid death

In 1963 a Tasmanian woman was bitten on the foot by a small insect. Fifteen minutes later she was dead. The creature that inflicted the fatal wound was a black bulldog ant, one of the world's deadliest venom producers.

Venom is used by some reptiles, spiders, scorpions and fish to kill or paralyse their prey. In reptiles it is a modified form of saliva which also acts as a pre-digestive juice, enabling snakes to devour and digest animals larger than themselves.

The venom is usually injected into the bloodstream through hollow fangs like hypodermic needles. The poison is in sacs at the base of the fangs and is forced out by the reptile's biting as it attacks its victim.

Animal venoms fall into two groups; haemotoxic, which causes blood cells to clot and destroy the blood vessel walls; and neurotoxic, which acts on the heart muscles and breathing and nervous systems.

The paralytic venoms are generally used by creatures that wish to preserve their victim, either for consumption later, or as a food supply for their unborn young. Solitary wasps stun caterpillars and other larvae, then lay their eggs on the paralysed bodies, which will serve as food for the young after hatching. The amount of poison to be injected must be precise, to ensure that though immobilised the creature does not die.

Many spiders paralyse their prey, then wrap it in a silken shroud to be eaten later. But some are killers, and can be dangerous to man. The black widow is highly poisonous, though deaths from its bite are rare. Other spiders which have killed humans are the brown recluse spider of the southern and central United States, the funnel web spider of New South Wales, the red-back spider of Australasia and the South African· button spider.

Scorpion venom usually paralyses rather than kills but some scorpions, such as the *Androctonus australis*, can inject a lethal dose from the sting in their tails. Between 1936 and 1950, in Algeria, 377 people were killed by these creatures.

One of the strangest poisons is in the green maritime worm. The female carries a poisonous sticky substance on her skin. If the young worms swim about normally, they grow to become fat adults—and female. But if they happen to land on a female's skin, the sticky poison changes the young worms into microscopic males.

The deadliest snakes

An estimated 40,000 people die each year from snakebite, 75 per cent of them in India. Most of the deaths are due to the king cobra. This snake has been known to kill elephants by striking at the tender tips of their trunks.

Australia has some of the world's most poisonous snakes, though the average death toll is only six every year.

The Southern Australian tiger snake has venom so deadly that only ·609 milligrams will kill a man. The diamondback

rattlesnake of south-eastern United States produces sufficient quantities of venom to kill 30 people.

Yet one of the most powerful poisons is manufactured by a frog. The kokoà of Colombia, South America, keeps its body moist with a substance known as batrachotoxin. Though the poison is used neither for defence nor aggression, 0·1 milligrams would kill a man.

Blue-water killers

The deadliest of all animals live in the sea. One of the most terrifying is the blue-ringed octopus of the Pacific.

Its venom, injected through its horny beak, is so potent that a bite can kill a man within two hours.

Although scientists have discovered the chemical make-up of the venom, it acts so quickly that antidotes are useless. Many people presumed drowned are believed to have been victims of the octopus.

The sting of the sea wasp, a type of jellyfish, is even worse. It attacks the nervous system, and can cause a victim to break into a fierce sweat, go blind, gasp for breath and die, all within minutes.

Some biologists have classified this creature's poison as the most potent of all. In the last 25 years, 60 people have died from sea-wasp stings while bathing from beaches in Queensland, Australia.

The stonefish, found in Indo-Pacific waters, injects neurotoxic poison through 13 spines in its back. The stings cause excruciating pain, delirium and sometimes death.

In the same region lives the world's most venomous snail, the cone shell. At least five men have died from the effects of the paralysing fluid which the creature injects through a needle-like tooth.

ONE THOUSAND EGGS A DAY

THE QUEEN termite grows 100 or more times bigger than her subjects, as she develops into a massive egg-laying machine. She spends her entire life in a chamber in the most secure part of the nest where she is fed by worker termites. A mature queen, fertilised at intervals by her consort, may lay as many as 1000 eggs a day at the rate of more than one a minute.

Both queen and consort secrete an acid which other members of the colony lick to stop themselves developing the power to reproduce. If the queen becomes sterile she is denied food and dies of starvation. Her body is then devoured by her subjects. Deprived of the contraceptive fluid, a female of the right age develops the ability to reproduce and so becomes queen. If a consort becomes sterile, he is replaced in a similar way by a young male.

AS LIGHT AS GOSSAMER

How man has learnt to exploit insects

Gossamer threads spun by spiders are incredibly flimsy—about 1/5000th of an inch in diameter—and weigh so little, that if a spider could spin a single thread long enough to encircle the world it would weigh no more than 6 oz.

In 1710, French entomologist René Reaumur was asked to look into the practicalities of a spider-silk industry. He found that whereas it took 2500 silkworms to produce 1 lb. of silk, 265 times as many spiders would be needed to obtain a similar amount of silk.

In fact, spider silk is too sticky and fragile for most commercial purposes—but man still finds uses for it.

Spiders in war

The silk from two common European spiders, *Araneus diadematus*, the garden spider, and *Zygiella atrica*, was widely used to mark the centre of the field of vision on telescopic gunsights from the early 1930s until fine wire was introduced soon after the Second World War.

Some microscope manufacturers still use spiders' silk for the same purpose, although it has been largely replaced by wire or photo-etched lines.

The silk is gathered by holding the spider, gently pulling the thread hanging from its spinnerets, and winding the fibre on to a card. The thread is workable even after two years' storage.

The Papuans of New Guinea use the huge, flexible web of the tropical orb spider as a fishing net. The spider spins its web—up to 8 ft across—between trees, and the Papuan fisherman scoops it off with a pliable stick bent into a loop with a handle. A gummy substance coating the silken threads acts as a natural waterproofing and the ready-made net is strong enough to bear a 1 lb. fish.

Insects in industry

Many other insects provide raw materials for human use. Cochineal, the brilliant crimson dye used in medicines, cosmetics and confectionery, is obtained from the dried, pulverised bodies of the scale insect, *Dactylopius coccus*, which lives on cactus plants in Mexico and Peru. The insect's 'scale' is a body covering that protects its eggs, after the insect dies.

Another scale insect, *Laccifer lacca*, exudes a sticky resin that is made into shellac, an important industrial resin used in varnishes, polishes and sealing wax. It is also used for making inks, linoleum and electric insulation material.

The scale insect, *Trabutina*, may well have been responsible for providing the manna that the Israelites ate during their 40 years in the wilderness. The exact nature of this food cannot be established from its biblical description, but one theory among entomologists is that it was a sweet honeydew secreted by *Trabutina*.

Yet despite the many benefits that scale insects have unwittingly conferred upon mankind, they have their drawbacks. They live by sucking the sap from plant tissues, and are among the most destructive of crop pests.

HARNESSING A BIRD'S NATURAL SKILL

For centuries, Japanese fishermen have harnessed the remarkable food-hunting skills of the Japanese cormorant, to provide them with their catches. The bird is trained to swoop down on a shoal of fish and carry its prey back to the fishing boat. A leather collar fitted tightly round the cormorant's neck stops it from swallowing the fish it has snapped up for its masters. The fisherman gently

A WHIFF OF THE SEA

A whale's indigestion yields fabulous rewards

The sperm whale has been the principal target of the whaling industry for more than 200 years. Its great square forehead contains as much as 500 gallons of the purest oil, which, until the development of refined mineral oils, was the finest lubricant known. Early hunters believed the fluid to be the animal's sperm, and from this error the whale was named.

But useful as this oil is, it does not begin to compare in value to the evil-smelling black lump of matter which the whale occasionally regurgitates from its intestinal tract. Ambergris, or grey amber, as it is called, is thought to be produced from the irritation caused by the hard beaks of the thousands of squids that the sperm whale swallows whole.

Ambergris is most often found floating in the sea. After exposure to sun and air, it pales in colour and develops a pleasant fragrance of its own, though its chief value lies in its ability to fix other perfume ingredients and make them more long-lasting. Usually it is found in lumps of no more than a few ounces; in 1912, however, a record 1003 lb. was discovered in a whale's intestine. It was sold eventually in London for £23,000.

HUNTER OF EDEN

The whale that killed for man

One of the most remarkable partnerships between animals and man came to an end on a September morning in 1930, as the tide gently deposited the carcass of Old Tom the killer whale on to a beach in New South Wales.

Each winter, for almost a century, Tom and his companions had appeared off Twofold Bay and waited for their human allies—the whalermen of the little township of Eden—to row out and join them. Then the hunt would begin. The killer pack would seek out their gigantic quarry —usually a humpback or fin whale—and drive it into shallow water.

The killer whales worked with terrible

squeezes the bird's throat to release the catch. A contemporary photograph (left) and an eighteenth century print show how little the technique of men and birds has changed.

skill. With the boats standing by, two killers seized the victim's tail to stop it flailing about, while two more swam beneath its head to prevent its escape by diving. Then the remainder of the pack closed in, hurling themselves out of the water in turn on to the creature's sensitive blowhole. At last, stunned and breathless, it rolled on the surface until the whalermen plunged their lances home. Dying, it slid beneath the waves, and as it did so the killer whales fought over their reward —the tongue and lips of their victim. All the whalermen had to do was to wait for a few days until the carcass rose to the surface. Then they could tow it ashore.

Old Tom began his incredible reign in 1843, and almost from the start showed an uncanny understanding of the whalermen's methods. Even when there were no boats at sea, the pack would surround a whale, then detach two or three of their number to raise the alarm in Eden by slapping the offshore waters with their flukes. Then, as the boats put to sea, the killers would guide them to the fray.

After Tom's death, the pack forsook Eden for ever. In any case, more sophisticated whaling methods were replacing the old rowing boats and hand-held harpoons, and the industry gradually died out in the town. But Tom is not forgotten; to this day his skeleton is one of Eden Museum's proudest exhibits.

DEEP CONVERSATIONS

The dolphin's wonderful sonar system

For thousands of years, dolphins were known simply as playful creatures which seemed to have a fondness for human company, and were thought to save swimmers in distress by nosing them to the surface.

But it has recently been discovered that a dolphin's brain is as large as a man's, and that although it has no vocal chords it has a vocabulary of at least 32 distinct sounds, including clicks, whistles, creaks, barks, rasps, squeals and groans.

These sounds are produced by forcing air past valves and flaps located just below the blowhole. Every dolphin has its own distinctive voice.

Like a bat in a cave, this bottle-nosed mammal navigates by emitting sounds and picking up their echoes. In an experiment at the Oceanic Institute in Hawaii in 1950, blindfolded dolphins were able to determine the size, distance and rigidity of an object by listening to the soundwaves bounced off it.

They could also distinguish between two spheres differing in size by only $\frac{1}{4}$ in. when the objects were 10 ft away. A dolphin's hearing is so acute that it can pick up an underwater sound from 15 miles away.

With their ability to isolate, interpret and remember sound signals and the messages they represent, dolphins can deduce navigational information, discover the position of other members of the schools and discuss strategy with fellow hunters.

They have a strong herding instinct, living in schools of up to 1000 and showing a great reluctance to desert any member of the school that is in trouble.

Distress alarm

A dolphin in danger or distress will emit a short, sharp, high-pitched whistle that acts as an SOS. Its companions will nose it to the surface if it needs air, and there are cases on record of a dolphin being supported in this way for four days.

The instinct to nose an injured companion to the surface is probably maternal in origin, for when a baby dolphin is born it has to be nudged to the surface by its mother to take its first breath. It is from this behaviour, too, that the legend has grown that dolphins will try to save a drowning man.

Their extraordinary ability to communicate with one another has encouraged scientists to experiment with trying to teach dolphins human speech. But although they seem to recognise a few commands and can give a plausible imitation of human laughter, they have not yet mastered the intricacy and complexity of the human voice range.

HUNTING BY TRAP AND TRICKERY

The intuitive cunning in staying well-fed

Spiders are the favourite prey of the hunting wasp, but the trapdoor spider keeps itself safe from attack by digging an underground retreat with a tight-fitting door.

Using its powerful jaws it excavates a vertical shaft about 12 in. deep and $1\frac{1}{2}$ in. in diameter. The walls of the tunnel are lined with a sheet of silk, and the trapdoor is built up with layers of silk and soil.

Above the door, a layer of leaves and moss camouflages the entrance and, as an extra precaution, the spider holds the door shut from the inside with its claws. It even makes special holes on the inside of the door so that it can get a proper grip. In some species, the trapdoor is toothed so that it gives an exact fit.

In part, the trapdoor is undoubtedly a protection against enemies, but it also serves to shield the insect's burrow from dust and vegetable rubbish.

During the day the trapdoor spider remains in its hideaway, but at night it cautiously emerges to catch its prey. Any passing insect is quickly seized and taken below. The spider seldom leaves its home completely, preferring to stay just outside the entrance, holding the door open with its back legs to guard against being locked out. When it retreats to safety with its prey, it pulls the door closed behind it.

INTELLIGENCE OR ADAPTABILITY?

The monkey that could drive a tractor

A rough measure for comparing the intelligence of different animals is the ratio of the weight of the brain to that of the spinal cord.

The ratio for a cat is four to one; for a monkey eight to one; and for a human being 50 to one. The animal with the highest ratio after man is the marmoset, a South American monkey, with 18 to one.

Among mammals, primates (men and monkeys) are the most intelligent, followed by flesh eaters and grazing animals.

But, like human beings, individual animals can be brighter than their fellows. For instance, Johnnie, a rhesus monkey kept by Mr Lindsay Schmidt on his farm at Balmoral in Australia, learnt to drive a tractor and to follow simple driving instructions such as 'turn right' and 'turn left'.

Monkeys can also teach each other. Japanese scientists lured a troop of macaques to a supply of sweet potatoes. It was the monkeys' habit to remove sand sticking to the vegetable by rubbing it. One of the monkeys, however, found it was more effective to wash the potatoes in a brook. This practice soon spread to the other monkeys.

Other monkeys have learnt that the easiest and fastest way to separate grains of wheat from dust and sand is to throw handfuls of the dirt on to a stream or pond, and wait until the wheat grains float to the surface.

Among other animals with high levels of intelligence are dogs, horses, lions, tigers and elephants. Their ability to learn can be seen from the tricks they perform in circus rings.

CLEAN FOOD *A Japanese macaque finds that dipping sweet potatoes in a brook is the best way to wash off grit and sand.*

A QUICK MEAL *A monkey teaches its young how to separate wheat grains from sand and grit by throwing handfuls of dirt into a nearby pond.*

NATURE'S UNDERTAKER

ANOTHER creature with a strange job is the *Necrophorus* beetle, more popularly known as the sexton. When a small animal dies, the smell of death attracts the black-and-orange beetle, which then sets about its task. By lying on its back beneath the corpse, the male beetle moves it to a suitable burial place. Then, with the aid of the female, it digs a hole into which the body slowly subsides. Using some of the animal's fur as a nest, the female lays eggs in a tunnel from the burial chamber. When the eggs hatch, the grubs feed on meat from the scavenged body—until they themselves hatch, grow and become adult and go into the world to continue as nature's undertakers.

ANIMAL ARTISANS

Making up for nature's shortcomings

It has often been said that one of the most important distinctions between man and the rest of the animal kingdom is that he alone uses tools. This is not an accurate definition, however, because many animals use tools.

The chimpanzee, for example, strips a twig of its leaves and uses it to dig into an ant heap. The disturbed ants bite the twig, and the chimpanzee quickly pulls it out to lick off the insects clinging there. The chimpanzee also chews leaves into a kind of sponge, which it uses to soak up drinking water from shallow puddles.

Another tool-user is the woodpecker finch of the Galapagos Islands. It lives on insects from tree bark but, unlike the woodpecker, it does not have a long, sticky tongue to prise them out. So the finch snaps off a cactus spine and, holding it in its beak, digs out the insects.

Infant labour

Insects also use tools. The weaver ants of south-east Asia and Australia construct their nest by sewing leaves together with silk produced by ant larvae. One ant takes a larva in its mouth, while rows of workers hold together the leaf edges. Then the 'weaver' moves to and fro, joining the leaves.

Several animals use stones as tools. The European hunting wasp uses them to flatten the sand in which it has buried its eggs. The European song thrush holds the rim of a snail shell in its beak and hammers it against an 'anvil' stone to break the shell. The Egyptian vulture opens ostrich eggs by dropping them on to a stone, or by picking up stones in its beak and throwing them at the eggs. The dwarf mongoose of Africa throws eggs backwards through its hind legs against a rock.

The sea otter also uses stones to get at its food, and does so with considerable skill. It balances a stone on its chest while swimming on its back, and hammers shellfish against this anvil.

Further down the scale of marine life, the shrimp *Phronima* is a unique tool-user. It makes a baby-carriage for its young by scraping out the barrel-shaped body of another sea organism, the salp. The shrimp then lays its eggs in the pram, and pushes it around until the eggs hatch and the larvae are ready to swim off.

MOBILE HOME *This shrimp pushes through the sea the empty body of a salp that it has hollowed out to make a baby-carriage.*

LUNCH BREAK *The woodpecker finch snaps off a cactus spine to poke into tree bark for the insects on which it feeds.*

BACK-STROKE *A sea otter lies on its back in the water, hammering a shellfish against a stone balanced on its chest.*

THE DEMOLITION EXPERTS

Nothing is indigestible to the voracious termite

Frail and virtually blind, and no bigger than a grain of rice, the termite is one of the world's most extraordinary builders—and one of its most effective demolition experts.

Guided mainly by smell and touch, some species extend their nests above ground level to form giant ant hills.

Some of the largest of these termitaria are to be seen in northern Australia, between Mount Isa and Darwin. Here, millions of termites have produced a strange tourist attraction—thousands of 'cathedrals' with rock-like spires from 12–20 ft high and 10 ft in diameter.

In parts of Africa, such pillars built by termites may be anything up to 20 ft high and 100 ft in diameter. Inside is an intricate system of tunnels and connecting spaces spreading over several acres. To build on such a scale takes a termite colony at least eight years.

Virtually all termites, male and female, are sterile. But after the colonies have existed for some time, sexual forms of the species are produced. These 'nymphs' of both sexes have wings and the important function of ensuring that termite life survives by establishing new colonies.

How they judge when the moment for departure from the native colony has arrived is a mystery, but when it comes there is a flurry of activity. Workers bore tiny holes to the outside of the mounds and build minute take-off platforms.

One by one the nymphs flutter away. Probably only one in a million survives—lizards, frogs, birds and other insects eat the rest.

When a female, exhausted from a flight that may not have taken her more than 100 yds, touches down, she must find a mate. She releases a scent, and when a male appears a strange ritual begins. Both termites hunch up their bodies and break off their wings. Then they search for a nesting place in the soil or in rotting wood. The female selects the spot, and two days of frantic burrowing begins. A few days later a dark, humid nest is completed, and mating proceeds. A new termite city has been founded.

Appetites extraordinary

The destructive dry-wood termites burrow in wood above ground. They damage forests, and often cause wooden structures to collapse without warning. When termites tackle a joist, a rafter or a tree they gnaw away on the inside, without damaging the exterior surface of the wood or the bark. Only the shell remains.

Colonies of termites have been known to chew through tyres, lead sheathing on telephone cables and even billiard balls. They can also exude a liquid over tin which causes rust.

A termite colony may contain a population of 3 million, and is run on ruthlessly totalitarian lines. Ruled by a queen who may be more than 100 years old, most termites work 24 hours a day until death. And the strict conditions necessary for life for these specialised insects make death a daily proposition. Without constant warmth and moisture, the termite would die in a matter of hours. If all other dangers are avoided, they are eventually eaten by their kin. In the event of a food shortage, termites will cannibalise their own nurseries.

Gardeners in darkness

Most of the population are workers who look after the nest and the eggs, and collect food. Deep inside the nest, the workers tend a fungus garden that yields the cellulose essential to the termites' diet. Each night, columns of termites venture out to collect wood and grass which is pulped by the termites' jaws, mixed with faecal matter and spread on the garden.

TERMITE SPIRES *This 20 ft high 'cathedral' in Australia took a colony of termites about eight years to build.*

113

Vital heat is also generated as the fungus grows, absorbing excess moisture.

Soldier termites differ from the workers in that they are armed either with powerful mandibles for seizing and fighting, or with a mechanism in their foreparts which ejects poison.

Most of the time, soldiers patrol the maze of tunnels in the nest. But their most important role is to defend the colony against invasion by ants.

When marauding ants find an opening, they pour in and carry off hundreds of termites and eggs. But the sightless termite soldiers fearlessly and instinctively attack the bigger and more powerful ants.

Some will grab the enemy with their jaws. Others exude a gummy substance which irritates the ants' bodies and tangles their legs and antennae.

While the battle rages—a battle whose orders seem to be passed telepathically—thousands of termite workers go into action, sealing off the battle area from the rest of the nest.

The workers wall up the tunnels by cementing minute fragments of soil into place. The soldiers will fight to the death in their effort to shut out the enemy. The colony usually survives.

WEAVERS OF DEATH

Silken traps that are stronger than steel

Long ago, it is said, there was a girl named Arachne who wove so beautifully that she excited the envy of the goddess Athene. Despite divine warnings, she rashly persisted in her excellence, so Athene turned her into a spider. To this day the spider family is classed as *Arachnida*, and in the intervening years, they have lost nothing of their namesake's skill.

For sheer artistry, the spider's web is without equal. It is a home with food trap attached, made from silk sometimes only 1/12,000th of an inch in diameter. With this unbelievably fragile material, spiders are able to calculate stresses and strains on their intricate webs, measure angles and weld 'joints'.

Silk for all needs

They make silk to meet their every need —each one produced by a series of organs called spinnerets. A coarse, dry silk is used to create the permanent frame of the web, and a sticky type to form the wide carpet that traps insects. Then there are dry 'pathways' that the spider uses to run from its base at the centre of the web to inspect captured prey.

The spider also spins a thick, often brightly coloured silk in which it encases its eggs for safety.

Some silks are stronger than steel—supposing steel could be drawn out to the same diameter. They can also be stretched by as much as one-fifth before they snap.

Seven kinds of spider silk are known, and although no spider can produce all seven, every one can create at least three and most can create four.

Not all the 40,000 species of spider spin webs; of those that do, the best spinners are usually female. Frequently the males produce only temporary 'bachelor' dwellings of poor-quality silk.

There are thousands of types of web, the simplest being the cobweb—a shapeless, dingy mess made by the common house spider.

One of the most familiar, yet most spec-

BEES WITH A STING OF DEATH

AMERICAN SCIENTISTS have warned that swarms of killer bees are advancing up South America and approaching the US border. Their violent behaviour has proved fatal to animals, and human deaths have been reported. The bees were bred by accident in São Paulo, Brazil. Large African bees were being crossed with gentler European bees to improve productivity, when 26 European swarms escaped, each with an African queen. America is now trying to develop a vigorous but less aggressive strain of bees which can be released in central America to breed out the savage strain.

tacular examples of the spider's skill, is the orb web which is made by many species, including the garden spider. This has a central hub with a number of radial threads linking it to nearby plants.

Immediately surrounding the hub is a short spiral of silk, which joins the radials and looks something like the grooves in a gramophone record. After a short gap a second spiral begins, extending outwards in some places almost to the extremities of the radials.

It takes a spider about four-and-a-half hours to spin a web, including brief rests. When the web is completed, any flying insect that touches its sticky threads is doomed: no matter how the trapped creature struggles it can only become more and more entangled.

Monitoring vibrations

In the daytime, the garden spider stays hidden and uses a 'dragline' connected to the web to monitor vibrations created by its victims. In the evening, the spider moves to the web and lurks in its central lair, ready to run out along one of its safe paths when movements indicate that some prey has been trapped.

The spider immobilises a victim by injecting it with venom which causes instant paralysis. The insect is then either devoured on the spot, or wrapped in a silken shroud and carried to the centre of the web to be eaten later. The spider can take food only in liquid form, so it bathes its prey in digestive juices which turn the insect's inner parts to liquid.

Spiders are the best insect killers known, and will also prey on each other. Even mating is fraught with danger, for the larger female sees her suitor only as an advancing meal. For this reason, the male approaches courtship with a good deal of caution. First, he spins a small silken parcel and deposits sperm cells on it. Then he absorbs the cells into leg-like attachments near his head and sets out to find a suitable mate.

Avoiding death

Male spiders use various techniques to avoid being devoured during their brief courtship. Some vibrate the threads of the female's web in a particular way to establish recognition, then mate by depositing the sperms on to the threads. Fertilisation occurs as the female absorbs the sperms as she moves over the web—without contact with the male.

The males of some species placate the females by wrapping a fly in silk and presenting it to them. The male crab spider is even more cautious. He criss-crosses the female with threads until she is stuck helplessly to the ground. The silk he produces for this purpose is known as the 'bridal veil'.

The number of eggs produced varies according to the species—some lay ten, others as many as 2000. Most females live for a year and mate only once, but during this time produce several batches of eggs. These are laid on a small web and cocooned in silk.

When the spiderlings emerge, they travel considerable distances by a method known as 'ballooning'. Each one climbs to the top of a blade of grass and produces a long strand of silk, which is carried away by the wind with the spiderling attached. Some spiderlings have been carried as high as 14,000 ft on this journey to find a new home.

THIMBLE-SIZED IGLOO

The tiny false scorpion constructs an igloo-type nest little bigger than a thimble. The ¼ in. long creature, a remote relation of true scorpions, has no tail or sting and surrounds itself with sand grains and fragments of wood and stone which are cemented together with a coating of fine silk threads. The dome rises until only a small hole remains, out of which the false scorpion emerges to forage for new materials. Finally, this too is sealed, and the internal walls are lined with further quantities of silk before egg-laying or moulting begins.

TINY, BUT DESTRUCTIVE

When ant battalions go foraging for food

The ant is one of nature's busiest creatures. There are at least 10,000 billion ants in the world, constantly toiling to perpetuate their species.

This instinct for survival sometimes creates havoc in Africa and South America, where huge battalions of army or legionary ants march in search of food. They eat and devastate everything in their path with their enormous sickle-like jaws.

In one horde there might be 100,000 ants—most of them blind. They will strip a house and garden of everything edible, including domestic animals. Once, a tethered horse was reduced to a skeleton in three hours.

Aggression is also the hallmark of the Amazon ants, which raid the nests of other ants to capture slaves. The hunters, who are unable to feed themselves, spend days scouting an objective and marking out escape routes. Then they attack and carry off pupae. When these hatch out, they gather food for their masters.

The Argentine and fire ants prey even more viciously on fellow-ants. When they move to new areas, they exterminate the existing ant population for food.

Red wood ants are also killers, but they hunt other insects—and will sometimes slaughter creatures much larger than themselves, such as centipedes.

Other ants live on vegetable substances. The parasol ant of South America mixes saliva with finely shredded leaves to form a compost, on which a fungus is grown inside the nest. The harvester ant builds granaries and stocks them with grain collected from cornfields. This food is eaten in winter.

MINUTE BUT MIGHTY BUILDERS

LOOK at the White Cliffs of Dover or the 1000 ft thick chalk deposits of the Mississippi and you are seeing how the minute and apparently insignificant *Globigerinoides sacculisera* has changed the face of the earth—with a shell only about 1/60 in. wide. These creatures, called foraminiferans, are mere specks of protoplasm existing in shells perforated with hundreds of holes, through which strands of protoplasm project to trap food. When the creatures die, their empty shells sink to the bottom of the sea where, over millions of years, they combine to form vast chalk deposits.

HARSH START IN LIFE

Chicks that have to make a double breakthrough

A double obstacle faces an African hornbill chick of the *Tockus* species when it enters the world. First it must break out of its shell, then it has to demolish the walled-up entrance to its specially built 'nursery'.

The female lays between one and six eggs in a tree-trunk cavity, and blocks up the entrance from the inside with cement made from clay and saliva. The bird leaves a hole just big enough for her mate to be able to feed her.

For five weeks she incubates her eggs, and when they hatch she breaks through the wall, leaving her brood behind. The bird repairs the damage at once—often helped by the chicks on the inside.

When the chicks are strong enough, they attack the wall with their beaks and emerge into the outside world.

LABOUR OF LOVE

Birds that build their own incubators

Breeding chicks is a lifelong labour for the mallee fowl of southern Australia. The hen lays an average of one egg a week for six months, and she spends another five months of the year helping her mate to construct and tend their nest—an elaborate incubator.

The pair first dig a pit 2–3 ft deep and about 10 ft in diameter, then fill it with leaves, twigs and bark. After rain has soaked the debris, the birds cover it with soil or sand.

As the compost rots and heat rises, the cock regularly probes the mound with his beak to check the temperature. When this reaches 33°C (91°F) the hen lays her first egg. Her mate opens the mound, puts the egg into position, and carefully rebuilds the structure ready for the next laying.

He also has the job of keeping the incubator at an even temperature. In early spring, when the leaves rot rapidly, he uncovers the eggs each morning to let air circulate round them. In summer, he adds soil to the mound to insulate it from the sun's heat.

Later in the year, when the weather is cooler and the rotting ceases, he uncovers the mound early in the day to let the heat reach the eggs.

Recurring cycle

Each egg needs 50 days' incubation, which means that while the hen is still laying, other eggs are hatching out.

The chicks have to make their own way to the surface, tunnelling through almost 3 ft of soil to reach the open air. This may take as long as 15 hours; they then stagger to the nearest bush to rest and shelter.

The chicks have to fend for themselves from the day they hatch, for they are totally ignored by their parents. They can fly within 24 hours of leaving the egg.

When the nesting season ends, the cock and hen have just one month's rest before the whole cycle begins again—often resulting in the laborious building of a completely new incubator.

FINERY FROM THE SILK OF A SEAFOOD

THE FIELD OF THE CLOTH OF GOLD, meeting place in 1520 of Henry VIII of England and Francis I of France, was so named because many of the nobles assembled there wore golden tunics. These clothes were made from the 'beards' of mussels, bundles of short, tough threads secreted by a gland in the mollusc's foot. The threads are discharged as a thick fluid, which sticks firmly to the rock or gravel where the creature lives. They harden almost immediately, yet are loose enough to allow the mussel to swing round with the movement of the tide. The silky beards of the 12 in. long fan mussels *Pinna nobilis* and *Pinna fragilis*, found on the shores of the Atlantic and Mediterranean, were woven into cloth.

LIVING IN HARMONY

In sea and on land, some creatures exist by mutual consent

The laws of nature are often harsh and cruel, but some groups of animals have learnt to live together in peaceful co-existence. The zoologists call this 'symbiosis', from the Greek words for 'life together'.

The European hermit crab is one example. It uses a discarded whelk shell to protect its soft body, but often shares its home and meals with a ragworm. Sometimes another lodger, a parasitic anemone, attaches itself to the shell.

The ragworm is usually a reluctant guest, becoming trapped in the shell when the crab moves in, but the anemone chooses to live with the hermit and follows its host when the crab moves to a larger shell.

Strangely, the crab neither tries to eat the ragworm nor dislodge the anemone, and the latter's stinging tentacles form a useful protection against marauders.

Another sea creature that hitches a lift is the remora, a tropical fish that lives with the deadly shark. The remora attaches itself by means of a suction disc on its head, and lives on the parasites that attack the shark's skin. Sometimes it detaches itself to feed on scraps from the shark's kill, and is totally ignored by its fearsome host.

Interdependence is carried to extremes by the bitterling, a minnow-like fish found in European and Asian rivers, and the mussel. In April, when the female bitterling is ready to spawn, the male guides her to a mussel and she releases her eggs into the mussel's siphon, or breathing tube. The eggs are fertilised by the male, and are then hatched out within the mussel's shell.

The mussel, in turn, fosters its offspring on the fish. While the bitterling is spawning, the mussel discharges its larvae, which grip the fish's tail or fins. The bitterling's skin grows over these tiny passengers, and three months later they emerge as perfectly formed mussels.

On land, symbiosis is found among the tiniest and largest of creatures. Blue-

FIGARO OF THE OCEAN

THE CLEANER, or barber, fish make their living, as many humans do, by offering a service to others. And they find that it pays to advertise. Working in groups, the tiny fish base themselves in a crevice near a brightly coloured sea anemone or sponge.

This performs the same function as a barber's pole, attracting custom for their grooming service. Shoals of larger fish queue up to be cleaned, and the cleaner fish are rewarded with food. They eat through the patches of dead skin, parasites, bacteria and fungi on their visitors.

The larger fish co-operate throughout, raising one gill cover to let the cleaner in and opening the other to let it out when its work is done. Even sharks and other deadly species allow the cleaners into their mouths without harming them.

Fish that live far out at sea, such as the ocean sunfish, make long journeys inshore for this cleaning service.

bottles, dung beetles and ants are often inhabited by mites, which live on the food particles adhering to their host's mouth.

Riding pick-a-back is a favourite occupation of some birds, to the mutual advantage of rider and ridden. The carmine bee-eater rides on the kori bustard through the tall grass of the African savanna. The bustard, a bird which stands over 3 ft tall, disturbs flies and other irritating insects, and the bee-eater swoops down to capture them.

Similarly, the cattle egrets in Africa perch on the backs of buffaloes, antelopes, zebras or rhinoceroses and snap up the insects disturbed by the animals' hooves. The birds are thereby ensured of a constant supply of food, while relieving the animals of irritating pests. But they also give another service.

When anything that may threaten their safety approaches they fly up, and their flashing white wings act as a warning signal to the herd.

The oxpecker, or tick-bird, also stays close to a buffalo, living on the ticks that infest the animal's hide. Some birds become so attached to an animal that they will stay with it constantly, even to the extent of courting and mating on its back.

Perhaps the most remarkable example of co-existence, is that of the plover and the Nile crocodile. The crocodile is renowned as a voracious reptile that will snap at anything that comes within range of its powerful jaws. Yet the plover can enter that gaping mouth and act as a 'dentist'—cleaning the scraps of decaying food from between the crocodile's teeth.

The farmers

In most animal partnerships the relationship is one of mutual convenience, but in the case of ants and aphids, or greenfly, the ants act as 'dairy' farmers. When aphids suck the sap from plants they leave behind a sticky substance called honeydew, which is a favourite food of some species of ants. By stroking the aphids with their antennae the ants induce them to produce more honeydew, and to ensure a copious supply of the liquid they herd the insects together. In the autumn the ants collect the aphids' eggs and care for them in their nests. When the young hatch in spring, the ants carry them above ground to 'graze' on plants.

THE KAMIKAZE RODENTS

The lemmings' four-year death cycle

Everyone has heard the legend of the lemmings—how every four years frenzied millions of these little rodents hurl themselves from Norwegian cliffs and beaches into the sea to drown.

The lemming, a little hamster-like creature with a short tail, is normally shy and scarce. But their lives follow a strange four-year cycle. In the first year their reproduction is slow, but it builds up during the second and third years, and by the fourth the females are almost continually with young. And then panic —seemingly caused by overcrowding— takes hold, and they quit their habitat in millions in a desperate search for more living space.

The maniac rush goes on until the lemmings find their flight barred by a river valley or a fiord. Driven by desperation they plunge in madly, but although they are fair swimmers in calm water, even the smallest waves overwhelm them and they inevitably perish.

IS THIS HOW WE LEARNT TO WALK?

HOW was it that our far-off ancestors developed so large a brain and learnt to walk on two legs? Dr Sydney Britton, the zoologist, may have found the answer when he installed a chimpanzee named Bonga on a small island. When there was snow on the ground, Bonga walked upright, apparently to keep her body from getting cold and wet. Dr Britton believes that long ago our ancestors reacted in the same way. Their brains received more blood and grew bigger—and the long process of man's evolution began.

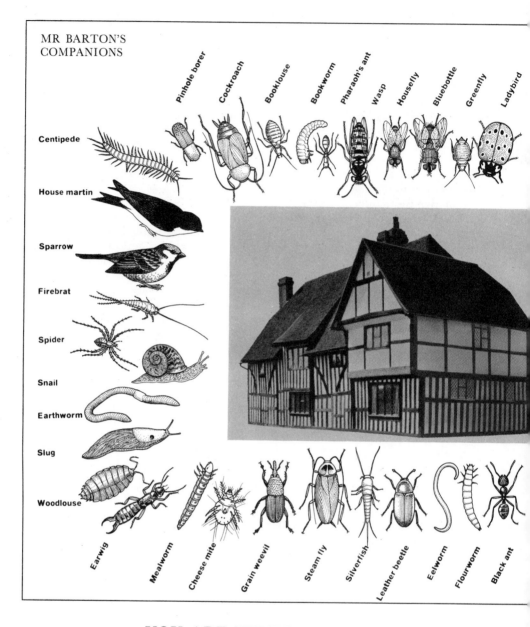

MR BARTON'S COMPANIONS

Pinhole borer · Cockroach · Booklouse · Bookworm · Pharaoh's ant · Wasp · Housefly · Bluebottle · Greenfly · Ladybird

Centipede

House martin

Sparrow

Firebrat

Spider

Snail

Earthworm

Slug

Woodlouse

Earwig · Mealworm · Cheese mite · Grain weevil · Steam fly · Silverfish · Leather beetle · Eelworm · Flourworm · Black ant

YOU ARE NEVER ALONE

The teeming life that shares our homes

Like most people, John Barton's son wanted a little privacy, so his kindly father cleared some forest land in Kent and built a secluded farmhouse for him. The young man moved in with his family and servants in 1555.

But they were not the first occupants. Pinhole borers and all kinds of wood beetles were already there in their hundreds, eating away at the beams and woodwork. Families of birds, bats, worms and insects were quick to move in too. Three years after the house was finished it had 1092 tenants—only seven human.

The history of the squatters of Barton's End, as the house was called, has been traced by zoologist George Ordish. He studied the many surviving documents relating to the house, its structural changes, and the varied lives of its human inhabitants. From them, and his knowledge of animal life, he could estimate the principal animals living there in different years and their numbers.

After the first wave of invaders, noctule bats and the smaller pipistrelle bats arrived in the loft. They ate some of the wood-boring beetles, but brought their

120

Carpet beetle
Moth
Wood beetle
Pipistrelle
Noctule bat
Mouse
Rat
Dormouse
Toad
Millipede
ck beetle
Mosquito
Cellar beetle

side the house. This proved a handy way in for toads, as well as more insects and spiders, although the toads fed on the spiders, keeping the numbers down.

On the other hand, the replacement of the thatch by tiles in 1660 reduced the volume of life in the house. Even so, by then earthworms, woodlice, snails, centipedes, millipedes, slugs and greenfly were all thriving, and there were more than 3000 living creatures in the house.

The larvae of moths devoured the family's furs and woollens, the carpets and upholstery, the stuffed birds in glass cases, leather harnesses, book-covers and even the corks in the wine bottles. Many things had to be shared with the carpet beetle, leather beetle, cellar beetle, earwig and pharaoh's ant.

When books in the library grew slightly damp, bookworms, booklice and silverfish arrived to eat them—and the wallpaper. The kitchen, of course, swarmed with life—cockroaches, silverfish and their relatives, the firebrats. The larder housed and fed grain weevils, mealworms, flourworms, black beetles and steam flies; eelworms wriggled in the vinegar and cheese mites gave savour to the Stilton.

By 1860 the population of Barton's End had reached its peak—119 species plus *Homo sapiens*. More people now came to stay, which meant that many of the rooms were kept warmer for longer periods. The total population rose to 3287, including common houseflies, mosquitoes, black ants, bluebottles, ladybirds and various wasps. And this total refers only to visible creatures. It omits the tens of thousands of mites to be found in any house.

The changing natural history of Barton's End is typical of country houses. Because of central heating, synthetic fabrics, vacuum cleaners and pesticides, nature is now kept largely at bay. At the last census of Barton's End, only 452 inhabitants were estimated—an average number for a well-scrubbed modern home.

own insect parasites to keep up the numbers. Sparrows nested under the eaves and house martins built on the walls.

Mice moving in from the fields were the only rodents, but rats and dormice visited occasionally for meals. A cellar was dug in 1630 with a loose-fitting trapdoor out-

THE BIRDS THAT WENT TO WAR

ONE of the heroes decorated in the First World War was a pigeon which carried vital messages through the artillery fire round Verdun in 1916. The bird—one of thousands used by the French—died after a hazardous trip, and was awarded a posthumous Legion d'Honneur for its courage. In the Second World War, British aircraft dropped boxes of homing pigeons behind enemy lines by parachute. The birds were used by resistance fighters to fly messages to London.

HARDY PERENNIALS

Huskies—the toughest, most faithful dogs of all

The eskimo sled-dog, or Husky, is one of the hardiest animals on earth and is still the most reliable form of overland transport in the 2 million square mile frozen wastes of Canada's North-West Territories.

Without the Husky, the rich fur and mineral resources of the north could never have been developed, and the nomadic Eskimo might never have survived. Doctors, missionaries and the Royal Canadian Mounted Police still have to depend on the sturdy creatures in the more remote areas.

The Husky belongs to three breeds: the pure, original strain of northern Canada, the Malemute of western Alaska and the Siberian Husky, imported when the Russians occupied Alaska.

They stand about 25 in. high, are 44 in. long from nose to bushy tail, weigh between 60 and 100 lb. and have coarse hair under which is another coat of oily wool 2-3 in. thick. This enables the dogs to endure immense cold (temperatures as low as −50°F) without shelter.

Eerie howling

Both the male and female are built for hard work, with deep, wide chests, muscular necks and powerful legs. Their tough, padded feet can negotiate jagged rock and broken ice that would split the hooves of a horse.

The dogs' eerie, long-drawn howls tend to make people think they are domesticated wolves and, although the Husky did branch out from the wolf's family tree thousands of years ago, it is the wolf's bitter enemy. Even when starving, Huskies will not eat wolf flesh.

Huskies will, however, mate with wolves. But a male will be killed by the rest of his pack if he returns after doing so; a female will be unharmed.

The dogs have immense strength—a team of 12 to 15 Huskies will pull the average Eskimo's sled weighing about 1100 lb. fully loaded. So long as the nomadic Eskimo can move from one hunting ground to another, he can live well. If not, he will perish, so his life depends on the faithfulness and efficiency of his Husky team.

An Eskimo will rarely part with his pack and will frequently risk his life for them. Many Eskimos have died trying to free their dogs when thin ice has broken under a heavy sled.

Pups are trained by introducing them one or two at a time to the sled team. With tough competition from its veteran teachers, an eight-month-old pup will learn quickly. Although the dogs may have toiled together for years as a team, they will fight over food and for the favours of the females.

Boss dog

Eskimo Husky teams are usually harnessed in a 'fan-hitch'—each dog being separately tethered to a 6 ft walrus or seal-hide pull rope, and hauling abreast of each other in a fan formation. A 'boss dog' runs backwards and forwards around the formation, nipping the legs of shirkers and urging the team forward.

The lead dog, often a bitch, works with a quiet determination, feeling out thin ice and sometimes leading the team back to base when the driver has lost his bearings in a blizzard.

Food is the team's greatest incentive because it is always scarce. The dogs need rich fats, muscle-building meat and plenty of vitamins, all of which are available in the flesh of the Arctic seal. But when the dogs are let loose to fend for themselves in the two-month Arctic winter, they readily return to camp when the weather turns cold because they have had to exist on a scanty diet of shrimps, mussels and birds' eggs, or any dead creatures cast up by tides.

The Husky's apparent ferocity at feeding times is countered by its amazing devotion and self-sacrifice. Often, the dogs can cover 25 miles a day at about 7 mph without feeling it. Sub-zero gales can freeze the dogs' faces or lungs, slushy snow can harden and cripple their feet and sometimes the animals have to be destroyed.

Now, however, Eskimos are taught to feed their dogs a full ration all year round, to breed them properly for strength and intelligence, to inoculate them against sickness and to isolate them when they fall sick—the kind of care inherited by the breed that has helped develop the vast Arctic wastes.

part 2

Contents

The marvels of science

———————•———————

MOON VOYAGER

The awesome complexities of Saturn 5

Blasting off a Saturn 5 rocket is the equivalent of setting off an explosion under a naval destroyer balanced upright on its stern and blowing it more than 30 miles into the air—but so smoothly that no fragile object on board is broken.

The rocket, the biggest operational one in the world, was designed and built to get man to the moon. It has 2 million working parts and—for a launching—each is monitored electronically from a control centre 3 miles from the launching pad. At the control centre, 400 men and women sit watching television screens and instrument panels. But the final word rests with three small computers on board the rocket. Two of them must vote 'yes' before a clock starts ignition in the engines and the rocket lifts off.

The stages assemble

The Saturn 5 is constructed in three sections, each made in a different part of the United States and transported, by barge, road or air, to the John F. Kennedy Space Center in Florida to be put together. Final assembly and check-out is done in the vast vehicle assembly building and takes at least four months.

The first stage, 138 ft tall, 33 ft in diameter and weighing 130 tons without fuel, is placed upright on a six-legged platform alongside a servicing tower. The second stage, 81 ft 7 in. tall and weighing 43 tons, is lifted on top by crane.

Stage Three, 58 ft tall and weighing 16 tons, is hoisted on top. Finally, the spacecraft itself, which might possibly carry three astronauts to the moon, is placed on the very top. An Apollo spacecraft is 82 ft high and gives a total height of about 360 ft. Only when the spacecraft nears its destination will Stage Three be jettisoned.

The whole rocket is fitted together vertically and moved to the launching pad, with its service tower clamped to it.

The 'crawlers' that carry out this huge task are the world's biggest land vehicles. There are only two, both at the Kennedy Space Center. Everything about them is colossal. They weigh 3000 tons each, are 131 ft long and 114 ft wide, have a crew of ten in a driving cab at each end and do the nine-hour journey to the launching pad at a majestic 2 miles an hour, tackling gradients of 1 in 20.

Each crawler has 18 engines, including two which develop 2750 hp. Then there are generators, hydraulic power units and electric motors for driving the tracks. Starting up a crawler takes 90 minutes; the manual on how to do it is 39 pages.

Each link of the eight caterpillar tracks weighs a ton, and the special roadway to the firing pad sinks an inch each time a laden crawler passes over it.

As the crawler and rocket move slowly towards the pad, a complex jacking and levelling system keeps the ungainly load level. When the rocket is at last unloaded it is filled with 12 million gallons of liquid hydrogen, liquid helium and liquid oxygen. The fuel is poured into cold-storage tanks so well insulated that ice cubes would take eight years to melt in them. With the fuel loaded, the weight of the rocket is increased to 3000 tons—heavier than a destroyer—and it sinks 16 in. into the brick-lined pad.

There are 11 main engines on a Saturn 5 for upward thrust and another 22 for steering. Each of the five engines in the first stage weighs 10 tons, and consumes 3 tons of fuel a second, pushing with the combined power of 30 diesel locomotives. Together they generate 160 million hp. They take the rocket about 38 miles up and boost its speed to more than 6000 mph. Then the second stage engines ignite, raise it to an altitude of more than 100 miles, and increase its speed to 15,000 mph or more. The fuel pumps need turbines generating 300,000 hp—twice the engine power of a liner.

The third stage contains only one engine, but it can be re-started. This engine is used for putting a Skylab space station into orbit, or sending a spaceship to the moon. It can boost speed to 25,000 mph. The conical command module has no propulsion system of its own, but it does have small control jets to position itself for re-entry to the earth's atmosphere.

So far Saturn 5 has made 13 almost perfect flights. The first men to land on the moon were lifted off earth by Saturn 5.

But when the next flight of this gigantic rocket will be is uncertain. The Americans are keeping two rockets 'in mothballs' for when they are wanted.

BLAST-OFF *A Saturn 5 rocket rises from the launching pad at the Kennedy Space Center.*

A WORM'S-EYE VIEW *of the world's biggest land vehicle, the 3000 ton crawler that moves Saturn 5 to its launching pad at a speed of 2 mph.*

HEAT FROM THE SEA
Uses for hydrogen fusion

There is enough hydrogen in 1 gallon of sea water to provide as much heat as 10,000 single-bar electric fires burning for one hour.

Scientists all over the world are now trying to harness this energy by a process similar to one that occurs on the surface of the sun. This is called continuous thermonuclear fusion and involves causing hydrogen atoms to rush together and release vast amounts of energy. The process is vastly more powerful than the energy created by nuclear fission, which involves breaking uranium atoms apart, and was used in the first atom bombs.

Safely harnessed

The fusion has already been achieved to a degree in the hydrogen bomb. But H-bombs, like the sun, are an example of uncontrolled thermonuclear fusion. What the scientists are seeking is a way to harness the energy safely for peaceful purposes.

Hydrogen nuclei do not fuse readily, but if the temperature of their surround-ings is increased sufficiently, they rush together and fusion takes place.

But raising the temperature is not easy. About 100 million degrees Centigrade is required, and has to be maintained for about one second to start the reaction.

Once the hydrogen atoms are fusing, the reaction has to be contained so that it does not explode and allow the energy to escape and be wasted.

So far, the nuclear scientists have been unable to maintain the reaction for more than a fraction of a second, but they are confident that the problems can be overcome, and that by the year 2000 the first thermonuclear power station will have begun operation.

The sea will provide an almost unlimited supply of hydrogen and it can be simply and cheaply extracted.

While a modern coal-fired power station needs ten trainloads of coal a day, a thermonuclear station could operate for a day on the hydrogen from one single water-truck.

FUEL CELLS—LIGHTWEIGHT ALTERNATIVES TO BATTERIES

A MAJOR problem in space travel is providing power to use inside the spaceship. It is needed for instruments, heating and cooling systems, computers, radios, TV cameras and other equipment. A trip to the moon would call for something like 40 tons of conventional car batteries and a generator.

The hydrogen-oxygen fuel cell is a lightweight alternative that also provides drinking water as a by-product. Three of the cells were installed in each Apollo spaceship which went to the moon.

A fuel cell is a type of battery which makes electricity instead of storing it. A hydrogen-oxygen mixture, or oxygen acting on a fuel such as carbon, creates current at two terminals. As long as the gases are fed in, the cell continues to produce electricity. In a spacecraft both gases can be produced from water, and they recombine to form water again as they produce current in the cell. It is a cycle that can, in theory, go on indefinitely. However, since the energy released in the cell is less than the energy required to produce the gases from water, in practice cells are normally powered from gas cylinders.

Fuel cells, developed by Francis Thomas

The layout of a typical fuel cell—hydrogen and oxygen combine in a chemical solution, releasing electrical energy through the terminals.

Bacon, an English engineer, offer many possibilities: electric trains that need no overhead wires or trackside live rail; buses and cars that do not emit fumes; silent generators and lightweight power packs for spacecraft.

The main problem in adopting the cell for use in everyday life is cost. Although hydrogen and oxygen are cheaply available, catalyst materials—which help the reaction—are expensive. The market price of platinum—the most efficient catalyst—is about £80 for just over an ounce.

BOATS ON CUSHIONS OF AIR

Christopher Cockerell reversed the vacuum cleaner

In 1950 an electrical engineer had an idea to make boats go faster, by using a vacuum cleaner.

Working from his boatyard on the Norfolk Broads, he first borrowed his wife's cleaner, then cut a slot in the bow of a punt, reversed the motor of the vacuum cleaner so that it blew instead of sucked, and squirted air beneath the punt.

The result was that the friction of the water flowing past the punt was decreased.

Some months later, he found that by blowing air through open-ended tins of different sizes on to kitchen scales he got vastly different readings. The same mass of air through a narrow tin exerted up to three times as much thrust as when it was blown through a wide tin.

The British engineer's name was Christopher Cockerell—and in that moment he laid the foundation for the first new form of transport since the jet plane. He called it the Hovercraft.

Cushion of air

Eleven years later, the first experimental Hovercraft—the SR–N1—was launched at Cowes, Isle of Wight. It amazed the world by skimming over the water at 40 knots, and moving effortlessly between land and water because it rode on a cushion of air. Today, more than 140 of the machines are in operation, some of them as large as ships.

Many of the early problems of the Hovercraft—noise, high running costs, limitations of use during rough seas—have been largely overcome. The challenge to designers of the future will be to develop a more efficient propulsion unit than the aero engines which are used in most Hovercraft at present. One suggestion is that very large Hovercraft may be driven by atomic power.

Cockerell knighted

In 1969, Christopher Cockerell was knighted for his invention, the principle of which has now been applied to other spheres of activity. Engineers have developed a strange assortment of vehicles for carrying people and cargoes where no other transport can go, and for lifting heavy objects.

Hover trailers have been used to lay pipelines across swamps in Holland and Germany, and for carrying heavy machinery across paddy fields in Bangladesh. Other equipment has been developed for moving crashed aircraft off runways, while hover platforms are being developed to carry oil-drilling rigs over difficult terrain such as the Alaskan tundra.

Small Hovercraft are also proving reliable for high-speed shallow-water surveys, in places as far apart as the dykes of Holland and the Amazon River. Others are undergoing trials as coastal patrol craft, police patrol launches and fire-fighting tenders.

HOVER-BEDS FOR SEVERE BURNS

ONE OF THE most unusual applications of the Hover idea is the Hover-bed, which is used to support badly burnt hospital patients on a cushion of air.

It was designed by a British bio-mechanical engineer, Dr J. T. Scales, and a team of engineers, who thought it would be a good idea to turn the Hovercraft upside-down and blow air upwards so that a patient could be supported on air.

Until new skin begins to form on his raw flesh, a severely burnt patient can suffer agonies from the contact of his bed under the pressure of his own weight. If only he could be floated, his new skin could form without being rubbed.

After many experiments, a bed was designed to support a patient indefinitely and at the same time blow sterile air over him. Trials at Mount Vernon Hospital, London, proved this was a particularly effective way to treat patients who had been badly burnt.

The Hover-bed lifts patients into the air and is especially useful in treating burns.

MAN AND SUPERMAN?

Steel muscles can give men the power of giants

One day you may see a motorist in a traffic jam get out of his car, go to the boot, take out a large metal frame, strap it around himself and use it to carry his car off.

In theory it is already possible, because of 'mechanical muscles' which engineers are developing to give men the strength of giants. These are frames with a system of levers and linkages which a man can strap to his arms, waist and feet to amplify his own movements. This technique mimics the man's actions but feeds back extra strength, so that he should be able to lift over half a ton with ease.

Another mechanical muscle, the Uni-mate, does not work from the human frame, but needs to be taken through a series of operations only once to remember and repeat them. It can store 200 separate actions in its magnetic tape memory, and it works tirelessly for 24 hours a day, with a consistency and an accuracy far beyond that of the best human worker.

Learning by mistakes

Some Unimates used in diecasting have been given the first vestiges of senses—a system which checks the temperature of a casting. If it is not right, the machine starts an alternative series of operations.

Other robots with sensory equipment have been devised, but they have so far not been programmed for elementary tasks. It seems incomparably easier to design a computer which will solve problems beyond the reach of the most brilliant mathematician than to design one which will empty ashtrays, because ashtrays come in so many shapes.

Ordinary robots can do only what they have been told in a programmed set of instructions. But another and more advanced type, the automaton, can actually learn by its mistakes.

Driving a robot mad

Few have been built, but one that seems extremely promising is the American-designed Perceptron. When the machine is completed it will have no instructions built in, but will have a sense of logic and an instinct to solve problems.

The possibilities for a successful machine of this type are enormous. Already psychiatrists envisage a time when Perceptron could be driven mad, so that in curing it they could learn how to treat the human mind.

IN ACTION *Mechanical muscles mimic and amplify the driver's arm and leg movements.*

POSSUM—THE BREATH OF FREEDOM

IT IS POSSIBLE to dial a telephone number, open a front door, switch on a light or fire without lifting a finger by using Possum, electronic equipment made to help severely disabled people. A sequence of lights on a display board is operated by blowing on a stem pipe. When the light flashes on over the panel designating the desired appliance, the user stops blowing and sucks. The release of pressure activates the gadget. A code of sucks and blows enables disabled people to operate an electric typewriter at up to 40 words a minute.

SOUNDS OF SILENCE

Engineering's invisible tool—ultra-sonics

Some of the world's most interesting and useful sounds cannot be heard at all. Ultra-sonics—the 'too high to hear sounds'—can be used to drill, cut, weld, clean, and inspect for cracks and flaws. Like all sounds, they travel in waves through the air or any other medium, but they have a far higher frequency than the sounds we can hear.

Human ears can detect sound waves which vibrate from 20 to 20,000 times per second. Bats can hear up to 50,000 vibrations per second. But when scientists talk about ultra-sonics they can mean as many as thousands of millions of vibrations per second.

A crystal sandwich

Special vibrators produce such high-frequency sounds. One, the transducer, is made by sandwiching a thin slice of quartz crystal between two metal plates and passing an alternating electric current through it. When this happens the crystal alternately swells and shrinks by a tiny amount—but enough to generate the pressure waves needed.

Ordinary sound waves spread in all directions, but because of their high

SOUND PICTURE *Twins (outlined) are revealed in the womb by an ultra-sonic beam.*

frequency, ultra-sonics can be directed into a beam and made to do useful work.

They can clean weeds and barnacles from the hulls of ships just as a car engine will vibrate off a loose nut. They can be used to detect invisible cracks in metal because the sound waves travel at a different speed through the crack than through the metal. You can wash dishes and clothes with them because of the pulsations they set up in liquid. And, perhaps the most exciting development of all, doctors can use them to examine the unborn child in its mother's womb.

CROWNING TRIUMPH

An American scientist, Dr Harold Edgerton, took this remarkable photograph of a drop of milk splashing into a bowl in 1937, at a flash exposure of 1/10,000th of a second. Through his researches into stroboscopes, or flashing lights, Edgerton helped bring about high-speed photography techniques.

ANCIENT MYSTERY *A fragment of the Dead Sea Scrolls subjected to infra-red photography.*

MODERN REVELATION *Infra-red photography clearly reveals the centuries-old text.*

ARTFUL DODGES

How science can restore great works of art

In 1965 a Liverpool art gallery had a 19th-century painting of Dante's meeting with Beatrice flown to Rome for an exhibition. But the painting, by Henry Holiday, was placed in an unpressurised hold, and on arrival the canvas was half-bare and a pile of tiny flakes of paint lay in the crate. The canvas had shrunk due to the changes in air pressure.

Fortunately, Rome boasts one of the world's top centres for restoration and, after months of intricate work, the jigsaw puzzle of paint fragments had been re-glued on a new canvas.

Rome's Central Institute of Restoration was set up by the government because it was felt that many private restorers did more harm than good.

Paintings can be damaged by fungus, mould, smog, insects and moisture. When a painting arrives at the Institute, black and white, infra-red and ultra-violet photographs are taken of it.

Infra-red photography allows the restorers to see through the thin, outer layers of paint, occasionally disclosing signatures. Ultra-violet shows up the retouching and repaints.

If it is suspected that there are previous compositions under the surface, the painting is X-rayed. Torn canvases are glued and ironed on to new fabric backings.

Wooden-panel paintings are treated with deadly methyl bromide gas in a sealed chamber to kill off any lice or eggs.

After cleaning, missing parts of the surface of paintings are filled in and retouching is done.

BLUE MOON ... AND SUN

BOTH THE MOON and the sun can appear blue, as happened with the sun in 1883 after the volcanic eruption of Krakatoa near Java, and in 1950 when the moon appeared blue throughout the Western Hemisphere after a forest fire in Alberta, Canada. The reason is that if individual molecules in the air—particularly dust —come between the source of light and the observers, the light scatters and becomes richer in shorter wavelengths (blue and violet) than in the longer, yellow or red wavelengths.

130

A MACHINE has been developed that can take three-dimensional X-ray photographs of the human brain. It allows doctors to see for the first time a living brain in cross-section.

Developed by Godfrey Hounsfield, an English computer engineer, the machine has the added benefits of providing fast, more accurate and detailed diagnosis (which should reduce hospital costs), and lessening radiation risk to patients.

A wide variety of disorders can be detected by the machine, which scans the brain with X-rays and is linked to a computer and a Polaroid camera. The effects of a stroke, the presence of tumours, cysts or skull injuries can be diagnosed within minutes.

By comparing segments of the brain at different levels, the depth of a tumour can be determined. In addition, the machine is capable of identifying tumours as small as 1·5 mm. in diameter, which means that surgery can be performed quickly, before the tumour grows.

The scanning unit takes only four minutes to rotate around the patient's head in 180 steps of one degree each. At each step, 240 readings are taken from a narrow beam of X-rays.

Then, the 43,200 readings from each 'slice' are fed into a small computer, and from these a picture is formed on a television monitor screen. The picture is available a mere six minutes after scanning, and may be studied either immediately on the screen or later on a photograph or computer print-out.

The patient remains fully conscious throughout the procedure, and merely lies flat on his back with the top of his head in the scanning aperture.

The process, which is completely painless, does not entail any of the discomfort of other tests, which involve injecting air and chemicals into the head. These can result in considerable discomfort, and the patient must be kept in hospital for at least 24 hours. Perhaps the greatest advantage to both doctor and patient is that the system eliminates a great deal of exploratory surgery.

THE WHOLE PICTURE

Lasers are the key to 3-D television

Holography, a system of creating pictures to give a three-dimensional effect, is being developed in Britain and America. Literally meaning the 'whole message', it has been described as the photographic equivalent of hi-fi in music.

Its development was made possible by the invention, in 1960, of the laser, which turns ordinary light—a jumble of wavelengths or colours radiating in all directions—into a single, intense wavelength.

In holography, light from a laser is split into two beams. One is pointed at the scene to be recorded and the other, called a 'reference' beam, at a mirror.

The light reflected from both beams mixes to form a hologram which is captured in emulsion on a special photographic plate. To the naked eye, it is a meaningless blur, but when another laser beam is shone on to it from the back, it springs to life: a perfect 3-D reproduction of the original.

But a hologram is more than just a striking picture. It contains many optical details too fine for the human eye to take in. Holographic pictures can even be taken through a microscope, which is why scientists envisage many different applications for it.

One is for processing information. A hologram the size of a postcard could store all the information in 3000 telephone directories. At present, engineers are striving to develop *moving* holography—and when that becomes practicable, so do 3-D films and television.

A LEAP IN THE DARK

A HUMAN being can now see better in the dark than a cat or an owl—thanks to a device known as an image intensifier. It consists of a tube through which the images of objects at night are made brighter by electrons focused on a phosphor screen, on which is built up a brighter reproduction of the original picture. The device can be used for military operations at night, for driving at night without headlights, to observe the habits of nocturnal animals and to intensify X-ray pictures.

CLEAR AS GLASS
New uses for one of man's oldest discoveries

Since man first began to explore the ocean depths, one of the major hazards has been the enormous pressures that exist in the sunless world beneath the sea. For every 33 ft of descent, the pressure increases by 15 lb. per square inch. The record depth reached in a steel bathyscaphe is 35,082 ft, by a US Navy team in 1960. To have descended much further would have been to run the risk of the bathyscaphe, *Trieste*, being crushed by the weight of water above it.

But a new era in undersea exploration is promised by submarines made of glass. For glass can withstand much higher pressure than steel. The reason is that the microscopic faults and scratches on the surface 'knit together' under pressure.

This principle is being exploited by scientists such as Taylor Pryor, director of the Oceanic Foundation in Hawaii. His aim is to use glass vessels to put men 20,000 ft below the surface of the Pacific to study prospects for ocean farming— aquaculture. At this depth, the pressure is almost $4\frac{1}{2}$ tons per square inch, but the explorers will run no risk of being crushed, and they will have perfect all-round vision. Fine glass filaments are used to twist

light through any direction. This concept, known as fibre optics, enables doctors and engineers to see round corners inside the human body or machines.

The flexible filaments—no thicker than a human hair—transmit light along their entire length. When hundreds of them are bundled together like a strand of spaghetti, it is possible to look through one end and see out of the other even if the glass cord is knotted.

These vision tubes are used in medicine for inspecting lungs and stomach walls. In industry they allow engineers to study inaccessible parts of engines.

Fibre ends can also be placed in spots where it is inconvenient to mount electric bulbs. For instance, some traffic signs mounted high above motorways have their bulbs at ground level where they are easily maintained, and the light is carried aloft through the glass tubes.

Technologists are experimenting with a telephone cable made up of glass strands which will carry thousands of conversations, transmitted along a light beam.

Glass has been manufactured for 4500 years, and its extraordinary qualities are constantly being put to new uses.

Soft as silk

Glass can be spun into fibres fine enough to produce material as soft as silk. It can also be made so tough that it is six times stronger than steel, or so heat-resistant that in the nose cone of a missile it will withstand the intense heat of re-entry into the atmosphere.

The flight-deck windows of the Concorde supersonic airliner must cope with temperatures ranging from $-70°$ to $-150°$C ($-94°$ to $-238°$F). The crew sit behind $1\frac{1}{2}$ in. thick glass pressure panels which are protected by an outer shield made up of six $\frac{1}{4}$ in. thick glass panes. Each pane is coated with gold two-millionths of an inch thick, to deflect dangerous ultra-violet rays.

The Leonardo da Vinci cartoon in London's National Gallery is protected by the sort of anti-bandit glass that has become a standard fitting in many banks, post offices and jewellers' shops. Two sheets of glass are bonded together with a tough plastic filling that resists intense

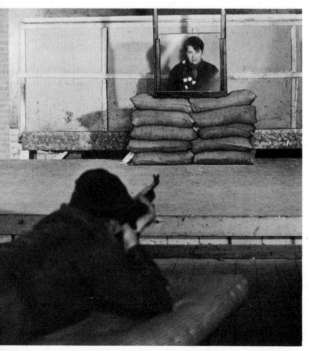

TARGET PRACTICE *Soldiers demonstrate the bullet-resistant Triplex glass.*

ALL-GLASS BATHYSCAPHE *Ocean scientist Taylor Pryor and an assistant try out a glass vessel which Pryor hopes will allow his team to investigate depths of up to 20,000 ft in the Pacific.*

shocks—such as an attack by a smash-and-grab raider or a bullet. A fierce blow will shatter the glass, but not the plastic.

Reaction to light

Photochromic glass is clear in darkness but turns dark in daylight—a characteristic that may be exploited in future house and car building, with windows being made to act as automatic shades, depending on the sunlight. Moulded glass fibre has been used to replace damaged 1812 stonework in Brighton Pavilion and in the choir school of St Paul's Cathedral.

Some architects are now designing glass-walled houses which would never need painting because the colour would be baked into the glass.

GETTING 300,000 MESSAGES ACROSS

SO MUCH information has to be exchanged at high speed in the modern world that the airwaves and telephone lines are being stretched to the limit of their capacity. A new communications system called Waveguide promises to help solve the problem, by using a simple copper tube.

At present, information is transmitted electronically either through the air or along wires. Both systems are limited by the number of separate channels that can be used before messages start interfering with each other and become garbled.

The copper tube in Waveguide has a diameter of only 2 in., yet it can cope with up to 300,000 two-way telephone conversations simultaneously, or 200 television programmes, or a mixture of both. A conventional cable of the same diameter carries only 4000 calls at once.

Speech and pictures are automatically changed into an electronic code at one end of the tube and converted into radio waves of super-high frequencies—up to 1000 times higher than ordinary VHF (Very High Frequency) radio.

The tube is filled with dry nitrogen, allowing the radio signals to travel much more easily than in the outside air, where moisture and oxygen create resistance. The result is that even in such a confined space many different frequencies can be used to stop messages becoming jumbled and indecipherable.

At the far end of the tube the transmissions are decoded, reverting to their original form to be either heard or viewed.

Waveguide tubes are laid along ducts that travel as far as possible in straight lines, because the coded radio signals could lose power and become distorted at sharp bends. When a tube changes course it takes a gentle bend.

At present Waveguide is used only experimentally, but the copper tubes cost less than conventional cables capable of carrying the same number of messages. The system could be in wide use by 1990.

ALTERNATIVE TO MEAT *Kesp, made by Courtaulds Ltd in England, is a nutritious natural vegetable protein. It tastes like beef and does not shrink when cooked.*

YOU ARE WHAT YOU EAT
'Artificial' protein may sustain life

A revolution in food production has made it possible to walk into a restaurant and sit down to a steak which has been spun and knitted, like thread, out of beans. It looks like meat and even tastes like meat.

The population explosion has stimulated intensive research in Europe and the United States to develop new sources of protein, the body-building compound found in meat, fish, eggs and cheese.

About two-thirds of the world's natural protein-bearing food is eaten by about 1000 million people in advanced countries, while only a third goes to the 2500 million people in poorer countries.

Worse is to come. By the year 2000, the world population will have grown from the present 3600 million to an estimated 7000 million. The production of animal protein, however, is increasing by only 2 per cent a year, so by the end of the century shortages will threaten even the richer countries.

The first of these protein foods has already reached the tables of Europe and America. It is derived from soya beans and is properly called textured vegetable protein, but often referred to as 'knitted' or 'spun' meat because, during part of the process, it goes through a spinning machine in the same way as rayon and other textile fibres.

Flavourings, usually beef, pork or chicken, colouring and animal fat are added before the solution is forced through the tiny holes of the spinning machine. After being stretched to give them the consistency of tender meat, the fibres are bound together either as 'meat chunks' or as mince.

The process is so successful that 30 per cent of school meals in the US consist of textured vegetable protein, which costs about a third of the price of fresh meat.

The United States alone grows more than 1200 million bushels of soya beans a year. But the need for still more protein is so urgent that American scientists are searching for untapped supplies from such sources as sugar cane waste, potato stalks, pea vines, beet and carrot tops, water hyacinths, and even wood pulp.

Already one factory produces commercially a drinkable high-protein juice by passing lucerne, a plant resembling clover, through modified sugar rollers.

In Britain, the National Research Development Council is backing research into a high-quality protein produced by a fermentation process similar to brewing beer. The protein is to be used to enrich bread, breakfast cereals or biscuits, and to create new foods made to look and taste like meat.

But scientists are already preparing the day-after-tomorrow's menu. It will include high-protein dishes with no animal or vegetable basis at all. Instead of coming from traditional farmlands these foods will be from gas and oil fields.

The first of these protein foods is a microscopic organism, a form of which feeds on paraffin wax. The discovery was made in the late 1950s when scientists, employed in the oilfields at Lavéra, in southern France, began using the yeast as a means of getting rid of the excess wax in crude oil.

Two plants set up at Lavéra and Grangemouth, Scotland, are now producing it to fortify animal fodder.

Meanwhile, scientists of Imperial Chemical Industries have been feeding a micro-organism called pseudonomads on methanol, which is made from natural gas or naphtha. The resulting protein is also being used in animal foods.

In both processes the protein could be more efficiently used by feeding it directly to people, rather than to animals. The reason why this does not yet happen is that despite what the scientists tell us, humans still prefer meat, eggs and cheese. By AD 2000, however, hunger may change our minds.

MICROBES IN MAN'S SERVICE

A revolutionary answer to pollution

One of the 20th century's major problems—pollution—may soon help scientists to find a solution to one of mankind's greatest needs—how to feed our over-populated world.

Researchers in microbiology believe that human and industrial waste from large towns and cities can be converted to food for animals.

The researchers have found that certain kinds of microbes can be stimulated to exceptional growth by feeding them a mixture of oxygen and phosphorus. When treated in this way, the microbes develop the ability to live on almost any 'foodstuff' available to them. It is the scientists' plan to develop large factories where armies of microbes would be kept in special tanks into which would be dumped waste of many kinds.

As the microbes attack the waste material, a kind of fermentation process is started and the first beneficial side-effect is that the fermentation produces gases—especially methane, which can be used either as an ordinary domestic fuel or can be used to power the 'factories' in which the microbes grow.

Later in the fermentation process, when the waste material has been largely disposed of, scientists find that the water remaining is rich in many kinds of minerals which can be used to support the growth of plants, such as algae.

These plants may in turn be used directly as animal foodstuffs or may be fed to such creatures as earthworms which can themselves be used to fatten fish and chickens for human consumption.

The use of microbes in this way is a never-ending process, for as long as some form of waste is available microbes will go on reproducing and will never die. The more they are fed, the more they reproduce themselves.

Microbe miners

Scientists who have been engaged in research work in this field have also found that selected strains of microbes can be developed to eat certain kinds of rock or mineral and to ignore others. It is possible that before the end of this century armies of microbes can be pumped down mine-shafts where they will eat up bedrock and leave behind only the required minerals.

NEW USE FOR OLD BODIES

MAN'S NEW-FOUND ability to keep bodies functioning with the use of heart, lung and kidney machines, has led to a startling proposal by Columbia University sociologist Amitai Etzioni. He wants 'cadaver farms' set up, using bodies that are technically dead—with no brain-waves being registered over a prolonged period, but with the other organs intact. Machines would keep the organs functioning in order to produce vaccines and blood for transfusion.

MILLION-DOLLAR BRAINS

Machines man devised to do his thinking for him

Computers of one sort or another have been around for nearly 5000 years. The Babylonians invented the first about 3000 BC. This was the abacus, a sand-covered slab. About 600 BC the Chinese developed the bead-frame type. But the first automatic calculating machine did not appear until 1833 when an Englishman, Charles Babbage, invented his 'analytical engine', which was able to calculate logarithms and the position of the moon.

The Second World War gave impetus to computing, and the first computers using modern principles were developed at the University of Pennsylvania and at the German Aircraft Research Institute, to calculate the trajectories of shells.

It was not until 1951 that the first commercial computer was put to work on the US census. Shortly afterwards, the International Business Machines Corporation (IBM) began producing computers for the commercial world.

Every computer has five basic units which enable it to perform vast numbers of complex calculations at fantastically high speed. The input unit 'reads' information fed into the machine; the data store holds the information—usually on magnetic tape—until it is needed; the arithmetic unit selects stored information and performs calculations; the control unit co-ordinates all the processes; and the output unit produces the results.

The world's most powerful computer is the Control Data Corporation's CDC 7600, which can perform 36 million flawless operations a second.

Computers have been used to compose music, create designs, play chess . . . and work out that Shakespeare used the word 'love' 2271 times in his writings.

At the Massachusetts Institute of Technology computers are sorting waste materials to decide what can be recycled. And at the University of Texas a computer has been programmed to simulate human behaviour. It responds to objects with fear, anger or attraction, and simulates actions of withdrawal, approach, attack or indifference.

Computers do have limitations. They have no intuition, and can work only by sheer logic. They are incapable of solving a problem that is beyond human intelligence, because humans must provide the information for every calculation and give the instructions for working it out.

Nervous breakdowns

Several hard-working computers have had 'nervous breakdowns'. One clicked and clacked all night trying to do an impossible task. Finally it 'collapsed'. It had been trying to divide by zero.

Another computer which has shown sensitivity is the British ERNIE, the Electronic Random Number Indicator Equipment that picks Premium Bond winners. One day, as a film star was about to perform ERNIE's monthly switching-on ceremony, bagpipes were heard in the street. ERNIE showed every sign of switching himself on, and engineers leapt forward. Apparently the pipe music had struck some sympathetic chord deep in ERNIE's 'heart'.

LANDING GEAR

Ingenious devices that keep aircraft on the right track

An RAF Varsity transport plane touched down at a Suffolk airfield in 1949—and made flying history. For the pilot had not laid a finger on the controls. Instead, he used the first automatic landing device.

The search for a way of landing 'blind' began in earnest during the Second World War. Too many bomber pilots and crews, their missions accomplished and fuel tanks low, were at the mercy of the weather when they came in to land. So a team of scientists was set up at Ipswich, Suffolk, to try to find a solution.

They took as their starting point a method called Instrument Landing System. Twin radio beams, transmitted from the ground, gave an aeroplane its angle of descent and relative position to the approaching runway.

However, the system needed the pilot's unswerving concentration, and was useless below 200 ft. So the scientists developed a radio altimeter coupled to the automatic pilot, which levelled the aircraft just above the runway.

Even after the 1949 demonstration, it took years before automatic landing was reliable enough to be used regularly and accurately. Only in 1962 was the system considered safe enough to build into an operational aircraft.

Another electronic miracle, the Decca Navigator, helps a plane thread its way through the world's crowded skies.

The Navigator also grew out of a wartime need—guiding a ship safely and accurately through a sea full of peril.

The Navigator was invented in Britain by an American, Chicago-born William O'Brien He got the idea just before the Second World War, and the British Admiralty gave him backing.

Life-saving ripples

Radio navigation beacons then in use had one big snag—they told a navigator he was on the right path, but they did not tell him exactly where he was on it.

O'Brien's idea ran something like this. Suppose three men were stationed around a pond, with a fourth suspended over the centre, and at the same moment each dropped a pebble in the pool.

The four ever-widening circles of ripples would form an orderly lattice, and anyone on the pond, if he were a good enough mathematician, could fix his precise position by using the ripple intersection pattern on a chart.

O'Brien planned to do the same with radio beacons. Three set up at the corners of a triangle, with the fourth 'master station' in the middle, would produce a similar grid of radio waves.

The Admiralty was intrigued. A test of the system in 1942 proved that the beacons did everything O'Brien said they would. By D-Day in June 1944, the navy had set up beacons along the south coast, and O'Brien had produced 27 receivers, made largely from old gas-meter parts.

The success was phenomenal. Thanks to the first Decca Navigator, not a single ship was lost in the landings.

Today, the Decca Navigator system is worldwide. Forty chains of radio beacons cover 7 million square miles of the earth's surface. The receivers, too, have come a

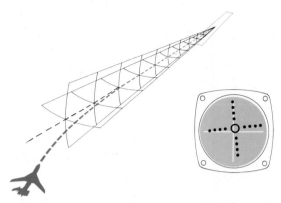

HOW IT WORKS *If the plane stays on the path formed by the crossing beams, it will be guided home. The instrument shows divergences.*

long way. Using a computer the size of a shoe box they pick up and instantly digest as many as 4000 instructions, continuously plotting an aircraft or ship's course on a map which unrolls automatically.

The advantages for aircraft are enormous. Because of the lack of precision of most navigational systems, huge amounts of airspace must be allotted to each plane. Aircraft over the North Atlantic, for example, must stay at least 110 miles apart. Approach paths to major airports must be 10 miles wide.

But the fantastically accurate Decca system is not obstructed by mountains or buildings and can locate a runway to within 40 yds.

Now, because of this precision, it is possible for planes to fly both ways down a 10 mile air corridor, thus doubling the capacity of existing airlanes. And 12 aircraft fitted with the Navigator could fly safely in airspace at present used by one.

CRASH REGISTER *'Black' boxes, or flight recorders, are sensitive but tough devices containing multi-channel wire or tape machines that store vital information about aircraft performance. When an aircraft crashes, the black box—which is often bright orange for easy location—helps investigators find out what happened, and why.*

137

THE FIRST TRANSISTOR *The original electrical circuit (pictured twice its actual size) assembled at Bell Telephone laboratories in 1947. Its inventors were awarded the Nobel Prize.*

THE MINIATURISATION of electrical circuits—and everything that depends on them, from tiny hearing aids to computers, slimline television sets and spaceships—would not have been possible without the invention of transistors in 1947.

The three Americans responsible, William Shockley, John Bardeen and Walter Brattain, were all awarded the Nobel Prize. They worked for the Bell Telephone laboratories in New Jersey and had been researching ways of switching calls through an exchange more quickly.

Their basic discovery was that a small piece of germanium, or of silicon, could be made to amplify speech 40 times.

The atoms of some substances—such as metals—hold their electrons loosely, and an electrical current is easily induced. Other materials—such as glass and rubber —hold their electrons tightly.

Germanium and silicon are between these categories and are known as semiconductors. The three researchers found that several layers of germanium or silicon, treated with specks of chemicals, boost an electrical impulse passed through them.

PINHEAD ELECTRONICS

Here is the news . . . on a radio cufflink

It is now possible to listen to the radio —on your cufflinks. A British electronics firm makes the tuned-in cufflinks as a gimmick to give to visiting VIPs. But the technology that makes this miniaturisation possible has more practical uses—including sinister ones.

Miniaturisation has made possible a radio set that will fit into a matchbox . . . a television set with a 5 in. screen . . . a computer that will go into your pocket . . . and a pill containing a tiny radio transmitter, which can be 'fed' to a suspect and will then give out signals so that he can be constantly tracked.

The secret of such minute devices is the development of integrated circuits.

The process starts with electronic engineers designing a circuit which is drawn on a chart and then reduced photographically to, say, the size of a pinhead. The 'picture' of the circuit is then printed on a slide which is made into a mask. This is put over a tiny sliver from a crystal of silicon, and through lines cut in the mask the silicon is etched to reproduce the lines of the circuit. The transistors and other components are deposited on the circuit. Then girls using binocular microscopes solder fine gold wire less than 1/1000 in. thick on to the ends of the circuit, so that it can be connected to other components in the finished article.

Using this technology, a computer, which 20 years ago occupied a room and needed refrigerators to keep it cool, can be reduced to the size of a typewriter.

RADIO LINK *This cufflink is a radio amplifier. When it is connected to a power supply the wearer can listen to broadcasts.*

BOOK IN MINIATURE *Actual size (16 mm.) of pages in this book as they would appear in a retrieval system. But by using micro-film, it would be possible to photograph the entire book on just two of the frames shown in this picture.*

MICRO-DOT PIGEON POST

First miniature photographs failed to save Paris

Napoleon III had been captured, France was in chaos and the invading Prussian army had surrounded Paris. It was then, at the height of the 1870 siege, that the first practical use of micro-photography was conceived.

The hard-pressed garrison holding on in Paris needed to get messages to the French Commander-in-Chief outside the capital. But the information was too bulky to smuggle through the army lines.

Then an inventor named Prudent Dagron remembered the work of an English optical manufacturer, John Dancer. In 1853 Dancer had reduced a page of *The Times* to a dot, $\frac{1}{16}$ in. across.

Dagron suggested that the vital messages should be printed, then photographed and reduced. How would the film be carried? Dagron's answer to this was less of a technological breakthrough. 'Pigeons,' he said.

The idea worked although, in the event, it did not save Paris from capitulation.

Dagron used the collodion process invented by Dancer. (Collodion was a liquid used to cover photographic plates.)

When the messages had been photographed the negative was reduced and printed on to plates. The processed emulsion was stripped off and wound into a thin tube which was fastened to the tail of the pigeon. Up to 3000 messages were recorded on one plate, and 18 of the emul-

sion films could be carried by one pigeon. When the pigeon landed at its home loft, outside Paris, the films were transcribed, using a lantern projector.

Sixty years later, Kodak began working on a semi-automated method of photographing documents for filing.

By the 1930s, banks and some newspapers were keeping records on film and, in 1938, under the threat of war, the British Museum stored 35 mm. films of some of its most valuable books. Espionage, too, found the process useful.

War, and the threat of war, led to another advance in the 1950s. Research into materials that could shield the eyes of troops exposed to the glare of an H-bomb, led scientists to a number of compounds that change colour when exposed to radiant energy.

The compounds, called 'photochromic', form the basis of one of the most effective micro-film systems presently in use.

Molecules of light-sensitive organic dye are integrated into the film emulsion, so that when images are transferred on to it they can be read as soon as light falls on them. The film does not need developing.

Using this system, a bank clerk can, at the press of a button, flash on a screen in front of him any one of 160,000 signatures.

Reductions in size of 40,000 to 1 are possible, reducing a 300 page book to postage-stamp size.

NEW SOURCE OF ENERGY *A laser beam, at 10,000°F, eats its way through a thin razor blade.*

THE DEATH RAY THAT SAVES LIFE
Widespread uses being developed for laser beams

A beam which was once thought to have potential as an invisible death ray has turned out to have countless peaceable uses. It can measure the distance between earth and moon to within 6 in.; burn holes in a piece of metal in a few seconds; transmit a three-dimensional television picture—or cut a man's suit from a length of cloth.

The beam can even be used in the most delicate eye surgery to weld back detached retinas or to destroy tumours. It can even remove tonsils.

The beam is shot from a 'laser', a device named from the initials of its title, Light Amplification by Stimulated Emission of Radiation. Much of its development in the 1960s was secret because defence scientists thought it could be used as a weapon of war.

But, happily, the amount of energy needed to project a powerful beam any distance ruled it out as a means of destruction. Laser beams are used to guide bombs to their targets and as rangefinders for artillery, but they are not practical enough to be lethal in themselves.

The laser is a device which stimulates the atoms of the substances fed into it to give out radiation in an intense beam of energy—it may be a light or it may be invisible. All the rays are of the same wavelength or colour. They remain concentrated and are able to penetrate objects or be beamed great distances with very little spreading.

Excited molecules

The idea first occurred to Professor Charles Townes, of Columbia University. In 1950 he found that he could excite the molecules of ammonia gas by bombarding the gas with microwaves at a frequency of exactly 23,890 megacycles a second. The molecules jumped about so that they gave out a very much greater

AN END TO PAIN *Laser beams can pinpoint and painlessly destroy decayed areas of a tooth.*

amount of energy than they had taken in.

Townes and his research team built a device which they called a 'maser', standing for Microwave Amplification by Stimulated Emission of Radiation. It was a highly sensitive, interference-free radio amplifier, of the type used in radio telescopes and space radio communications.

But masers operate in only one part of the energy spectrum. Townes and others turned their thoughts to the part bordering the frequency of light.

Potential of light

Light is made up of all the colours of the rainbow. At one end there is blue; at the other red; and at the extremes there are ultra-violet and infra-red, which cannot be seen but can be felt as warmth.

Townes reasoned that, if he bombarded a few atoms of a material to make them give off light, it might be possible to direct this energy into other atoms to make them give off light too. If he made the whole thing take place between two mirrors, the light might not scatter but might bounce backwards and forwards until it eventually built up into an intense beam.

Success in 1960

He published this theory in 1958, and engineers competed to make the first working laser. The race was won by Theodore Maiman, a young electronics engineer working at the Hughes Research Laboratories in California, in 1960.

He used a ruby as the heart of his laser. It was not, in fact, very efficient and now other substances are used, notably gases such as helium and neon.

THE COLOUR NO ONE SEES

Infra-red warning meant no landing on Mars

New developments in the study of infra-red rays have enabled astronomers to measure the density of the atmosphere around Mars, doctors to make earlier diagnoses of cancer, and explorers to devise better equipment for polar expeditions.

Infra-red rays are the invisible light that emanates from beyond the red of the visible spectrum. Their existence became known in 1800 when the English astronomer, Sir William Herschel, measured the colours of the spectrum with a thermometer. He found that the bands of light became warmer as he approached the red band at the end of the spectrum. When he placed the thermometer beyond the visible red streak, into an area where no apparent light existed, the temperature rose higher still.

Herschel had found a new kind of light which could not be seen but which could be detected by its temperature. He named it infra-red, meaning below the red.

Practical use of his discovery came about only in recent years.

Space officials scrapped plans for parachuting instruments on to Mars when measurements of the planet's infra-red radiation showed the atmosphere was too thin to permit a soft landing.

British doctors found in 1961 that breast cancers were slightly warmer than normal tissues. This led to the first medical infra-red camera, or thermograph, which is now widely used to aid cancer diagnosis, indicate the depth of burns, detect hidden bruises in unconscious patients, and pick up early signs of one type of stroke before it occurs.

Scientists testing the efficiency of Arctic clothing found that body heat loss soared where clothing wrinkled near the thin metal of zippers. Thanks to the lessons of heat-photography, Arctic workers are now more warmly clad.

OUT OF THE DARK *An infra-red 'heat' camera reveals the face of a man hidden in darkness.*

LIQUID CRYSTALS, a scientific oddity, switch colour like chameleons according to the heat, electricity and chemicals around them. Sprayed on the body they can reveal what is going on inside. The hand on the left has an even blood flow after 24 hours without cigarettes. Smoking, however, cools the blood and turns the crystals green.

CHEATING DEATH BY FREEZING
The remarkable science of ultra-coldness

In an underground storage site near Los Angeles, a dozen men and women lie in capsules that look like giant vacuum flasks. Their bodies are wrapped in aluminium foil. Remove the foil and a thin layer of frost covers their faces. An icy mist of liquid nitrogen clings around each body.

These people have been dead for some years. But centuries from now, attempts may be made to bring them back to life again. They chose this odd method of entombment in the hope that, at some time in the future when medical science has improved far beyond today's standards, they will be thawed from their deep-frozen state and cured of the disease that killed them.

In their lifetimes, these men and women were pioneers of cryogenics—the science that paved the way for the first serious attempt to conquer death by the use of freezing. It is based on the study and application of very low temperatures.

Though cryogenics began as more of a craze than a science, it may one day enable man to travel to the distant stars, and help him to discover a cheap, almost limitless, supply of energy.

The first known example of cryogenics, in 1626, had an unhappy ending. The English philosopher Francis Bacon stuffed a chicken with snow, so that he could observe the effect of the cold in preserving its flesh. Unfortunately, Bacon caught a chill from the snow and died from it soon afterwards.

In the 19th and early 20th centuries, scientists found that if gases were sufficiently cooled they turned into liquids. If these super-cooled liquids are applied to metals, the metals become brittle; steel shatters to powder at one blow of a hammer. In addition, metals in this state are better conductors of electricity.

The discoveries lay unexploited for 50 years. But with the space age came the need to build rockets which could carry enough fuel for journeys hitherto unimagined. Cryogenics supplied the answer. Oxygen, hydrogen, nitrogen and helium in liquid forms were all needed in the space industry—and as they were tested more uses were found for them.

Near absolute zero

Several of the most far-reaching discoveries have been in the use of liquid gases to cool metals to near absolute zero, $-273°C$ $(-459.6°F)$—the lowest temperature that can be recorded anywhere in the universe.

One such use of cryogenic cooling is in the food industry. Liquid nitrogen, which has no taste or smell, gets fresh farm produce into a frozen state far faster than conventional refrigeration methods and so preserves the flavour better. Meat, shellfish and bread are now being preserved in this way.

So, too, is blood, for cryogenics has meant that blood can be banked indefinitely. The blood cells, if soaked first in an anti-freeze agent, are undamaged by rapid freezing to −196°C (−320°F), which is the temperature at which all molecular activity stops.

Research into the rapid freezing of blood, as well as human sperm and skin tissue, led to the craze for freezing bodies in the hope of bringing them to life again —and to those corpses lying in their beds of liquid nitrogen near Los Angeles.

Hundreds of years

Some of the corpses have been there since 1967. They could be there for hundreds of years because, if the person died from a particular form of cancer, it could take that long before an effective cure is found.

Apart from a cure for cancer (and the hope of such a discovery accounts for several of those bodies awaiting a new life), adherents of cryogenics are also believers in the possibility of rejuvenation. It is little more than a dream now, but future scientists may make it come true. In that hope, some of the bodies will be left in limbo until their inhabitants can be not only cured, but also be made young again.

The cost of dying-to-live-again is high: anything from £3000 to £6000 to be put in a state of 'cryogenic suspension' and about £300 a year for 'storage' costs.

Scientists say the chances of these people having cheated death are slim. For cryogenics is just not advanced enough to freeze the entire brain and other tissue fast enough to avoid the destruction of vital cells. Even so, science may well learn to conquer that problem, too.

NEW LIFE AHEAD? *Inside the capsule—a corpse, deep-frozen. It may some day be brought back to life, perhaps rejuvenated and, if possible, cured of the disease that killed it.*

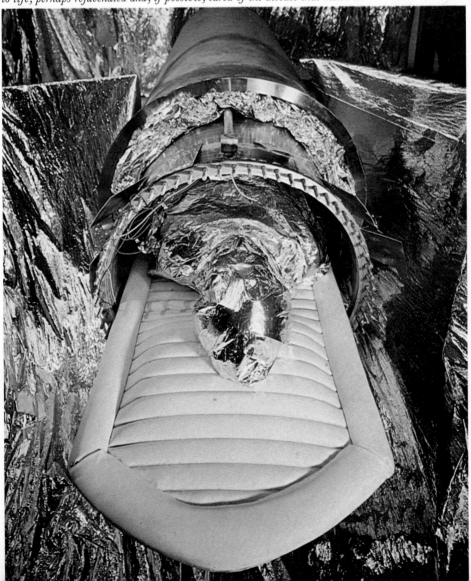

Immortal milestones of civilisation

Feats of building and
engineering

THE SHOWPLACE OF FRANCE *The Palace of Versailles was built at the expense of the nation. It typified the vanity and arrogance of Louis XIV, who satisfied his whim with complete disregard for the cost in money and human misery. Its influence ended with the Revolution. Louis, when not fighting wars, personally supervised the building of the palace and gardens which took 50 years to complete. More than 30,000 workmen were employed at any one time, many of whom were unpaid or forced labour. The gardens alone cover an area of about 250 acres.*

THE GREAT PALACE

France's monument to a king's vanity

A king's vanity helped to bankrupt a country—and gave the world one of the most beautiful follies. The king was Louis XIV of France. The folly was the Palace of Versailles.

The palace, which became the centre of the French court and government, started as a humble hunting lodge where Louis' father, Louis XIII, could retreat from the rigours of the French court. In 1627 Louis XIII built a modest château at Versailles. After his death his son determined to replace the château with a lasting monument to his own vision of himself as the 'Sun King'.

The work began in 1661, and the place chosen for 'the greatest palace on earth' was an architect's nightmare. The fine, sandy soil caused some foundations to sink, and the whole of the surrounding area was wild and inhospitable.

Louis XIV was obsessed with Versailles. For 50 years, when not engaged in fighting wars, he personally supervised the building of the palace and gardens, undeterred by the cost, human misery and loss of lives involved in the project.

At any one time, more than 30,000 workmen were employed at Versailles, and many of them were unpaid or forced labour. The conditions in which they worked and lived led to epidemics, and hundreds died. Fatalities on the building sites were frequent, and the fevers emanating from the marshes took a heavy toll. Even Louis was embarrassed by the death roll, so he expressly forbade his courtiers to discuss the subject.

Nothing but the best

Time, ingenuity and expense were never spared. The area became the workshop of France. Large forests were planted, and statues of marble and bronze were brought to the site to embellish the magnificent formality of the gardens.

Occasionally, Louis brought the entire French court from Paris to Versailles to admire the progress of the buildings. The courtiers had to sleep on half-built floors or wherever else they could find accommodation in the area.

To fulfil his ambition, Louis employed the best architects in France. Le Vau began by improving the original Louis XIII buildings. Then, in 1678, Mansart took over and remodelled the main body of the palace, building the two north and south wings, creating a façade of 667 yds embodying 375 windows.

The task of finding the money was allotted to Jean Baptiste Colbert. He tried to recoup some of the money invested in the project by building factories to manufacture the many elaborate trappings for Versailles.

Colbert appointed Charles le Brun, the king's favourite artist, as director of the factories which turned out furnishings not only for Versailles but also for the other royal palaces in France. Le Brun prepared the designs, which ranged from the painted ceiling of the Galerie des Glaces (The Hall of Mirrors) at Versailles to the design of metal door locks.

The linen, silks, furniture, carpets and other luxuries were displayed to the foreign visitors who flocked to Versailles.

Flowers for the king

The gardens, which cover an area of about 250 acres, were the work of Le Nôtre. Louis had a passion for flowers. He imported 4 million bulbs every year from Holland—when he was not at war with the Dutch.

Two star attractions were the Grotto de Thetis and the Menagerie. The grotto was encrusted with pebbles and shells and contained an organ which worked by water power. Another feature, less enjoyed by visitors, was the concealed water jets which sprayed the unsuspecting admirers. The Menagerie was contained in a small château and housed a collection of exotic animals and birds.

In the gardens Louis built the Grand Canal, 200 ft wide and a mile long, where ornamental gondolas and other boats were kept. Between 1684 and 1686 Mansart built the Orangerie, importing fully grown orange trees for the purpose.

But the most splendid features of the gardens were the fountains and waterfalls. These required an enormous water supply and a huge pumping station. The Machine de Marly was built between 1681 and 1684 to bring water from the River Seine. It was not a success, and an effort was made to divert the course of the River

Eure. The cost in lives and money was vast, and the project was halted by the war of the Grand Alliance in 1686.

Eventually, the waters of the plateau between Versailles and Rambouillet were collected and fed to the gardens through a system of channels.

Magnificent, but unsuitable

The entire court moved to Versailles in 1682, and it became the capital of France until 1789. Louis' court was as grandiose as his palace. It consisted of 20,000 people, including 9000 soldiers who were quartered in the town of Versailles. One thousand courtiers and 4000 servants lived in the palace, but the magnificent rooms and galleries were unsuited to ordinary human needs. The building was virtually impossible to heat and had practically no sanitation.

After Louis XIV's death, his great-grandson, Louis XV, made further additions to Versailles. He built the Petit Trianon, which became a favourite retreat of Louis XVI's queen, Marie Antoinette.

Louis XVI added a suite of apartments for Marie Antoinette, but the power and influence of the Palace of Versailles ended with the French Revolution of 1789. After the Revolution the furniture and fineries were sold or stolen and the palace was neglected. Restoration work was carried out in the middle of the 19th century by Louis Philippe, with help from the United States.

Versailles became a museum, dedicated to 'All the Glories of France'.

THE MACHINE DE MARLY

THE LACK OF a water supply was always a problem at Versailles. There was never enough to slake Versailles' insatiable thirst.

In the gardens Louis XIV demanded water for 1400 fountains. The volume of water required exceeded the amount available to the whole of Paris.

Whenever the king walked in the grounds of Versailles, numbers of servants had to operate the controls so that wherever Louis happened to be, the fountains were playing. The overseer was liable to a fine if any of the fountains failed to work.

Louis' search for an adequate supply of water inspired amazing schemes and inventions—of which the best known was the enormous Machine de Marly.

Work started on the machine in 1681. Its purpose was to raise a constant supply of water from the Seine.

Fourteen enormous waterwheels, each 36 ft wide, moved 221 pumps to bring water 162 metres up the hillsides from the Seine.

But after its completion in 1684, work began on an aqueduct to carry the water to two reservoirs near Versailles.

The machine suffered frequent breakdowns and required costly repairs.

IMMORTALITY FOR A PHARAOH

All Egypt toiled to build Cheops' tomb

Egypt is a treasure house of engineering miracles, both ancient and modern. No two feats demonstrate this 5000 year link more dramatically than the building of the Great Pyramid of Cheops around 2700 BC, and in the 1960s the internationally organised rescue of the massive rock temples of Abu Simbel from the rising waters of the Aswan High Dam.

The Great Pyramid rises as high as a 42 storey modern building and covers 13 acres of desert.

Within this solid stone structure there is room for St Paul's, Westminster Abbey, St Peter's in Rome and the cathedrals of Florence and Milan. It contains enough stone to build a 10 ft wall round the whole of the boundaries of France.

Channels in the rock

When the ancient Egyptian engineers began to build this massive structure, they had first to establish a truly horizontal surface for the foundation. They did this by cutting channels in the rock, filling them with water, and then, on a calm day, sticking in rods and measuring the waterline.

With the aid of this giant spirit level they then cut the surface of the rocks down to the waterline.

Countless thousands of masons, quarrymen and labourers toiled for 20 years to build the tomb on the Gizah Plateau for the pharaoh, Cheops.

Its stones range in weight from $2\frac{1}{2}$ to 15 tons; and in total they number an awesome $2\frac{1}{2}$ million.

Yet the men who quarried these stones and raised them into position used no mechanical aids except the lever, the roller and the inclined plane (even the wheel was to remain unknown in Egypt until 300 years more had elapsed).

Without possessing any fine measuring instruments, the Egyptians achieved an astonishing degree of accuracy.

The corners of the pyramid are almost perfect right angles, and the sides precisely face the four main points of the compass—north, south, east and west.

The ancient architects almost certainly managed this remarkable feat with the use of astronomical observations.

Originally, the building was encased in blocks of white, polished limestone. A few casing stones which survive near the base are so exquisitely cut that a piece of paper cannot be inserted between them.

The building of the Great Pyramid was a highly organised and co-ordinated effort.

From the Nile, half a mile away, a great stone causeway was built, sloping gently upwards to the lip of the plateau.

This construction alone took almost ten years. Along its slope, work gangs hauled huge chunks of stone on wooden sledges, using thick, strong ropes made from plaited reed.

Central core

Quarrymen worked at three widely separated parts of Egypt. The stone for the massive central core of the pyramid was cut from the coarse desert sandstone of the Giza region itself.

From the east bank of the Nile came the limestone for the casing. The granite that lined the inner galleries and burial chamber was hewn from rock at Aswan, at the first cataract of the Nile, and was floated 600 miles downriver on huge barges—an enormous operation.

The Aswan quarrymen used mallets of dolerite, a stone harder than granite, to roughly cut the blocks.

At the pyramid site, masons accurately trimmed the blocks to their final shape, using abrasives to give them their final high polish.

Liquid mortar

Gangs hauled the stones up a long supply ramp, to put them in place. At the lip of the ramp where the last layer of stones had been laid, each block was slid into position on a bed of liquid mortar, which also acted as a lubricant.

As the pyramid rose, the ramp was lengthened, for the slope had always to remain the same to ensure that the building's dimensions were correct.

Skilled craftsmen were employed all through the year. But the unskilled men could only work for three months at a time, in the autumn, when the Nile had its annual flood.

While these agricultural workers—

147

Channels in the rock and mud walls round the base held water that acted like a spirit level.

The causeway was built for hauling construction materials above ground level.

With the core of the pyramid finished, the causeway touched the apex, providing a gradient.

The ramp was dismantled progressively as the stonework was dressed from the top down.

about 100,000 of them—waited for the flood to subside before planting their crops, they were put to work on the building of the pyramid.

The names of some of the gangs and overseers have survived, painted roughly on the limestone surfaces.

Started from the top

By the time the entire inner core was laid, the pyramid had become totally hidden, surrounded by ramps.

The final task of facing the pyramid with its overlying skin of limestone was begun at the top.

As the casing stones were fitted, the ramps were gradually removed until the moment arrived when the great building stood revealed on the plateau in its glistening white coat.

In the heart of the pyramid more than 140 ft above the desert floor, but still far beneath the peak of the building, is the King's Chamber, a cell which is lined with polished granite.

At one end of the room, let into the floor, was a stone sarcophagus, intended to be the last resting place of the mummified body of the pharaoh, Cheops.

Cunning engineering

The Grand Gallery, adjoining the King's Chamber, is an extremely cunning piece of engineering, which was intended to solve the problem of sealing the royal burial place permanently.

Huge 'plug blocks' were stored on the floor of the gallery, resting on temporary timber supports.

After the immense and colourful funeral procession had followed Cheops' body to the pyramid, workmen released the blocks which slid down the gallery's slanting floor and jammed the entrance.

The workmen escaped down a near vertical tunnel which was then sealed. Cheops' body seemed safe from intruders for all time.

The plundered tomb

In fact, man was to prove over the centuries that his ability to plunder burial places of ancient kings matched his ability and skill in constructing them.

In the 9th century AD, Arab workmen tunnelled through the pyramid and found only a rifled sepulchre. Later, Arab rulers stripped away most of the limestone casing to use in the building of their mosques.

Nevertheless, the Great Pyramid is the only one of the 80 or so pyramids which were built that stands almost in its original state, despite many hundreds of years of plunder and exposure to extremes of weather.

The Great Pyramid of Cheops remains today as an enduring monument to man's skill—and to his longing for immortality.

HOLDING COURT

Removals on a royal scale

Three enormous statues of the god-king Ramesses II now gaze across the 20th-century man-made Lake Nasser from their original 3200-year-old rock temples. They survive because of the world's most spectacular removal job.

In 1963 these and other antiquities faced destruction from the rapidly rising water behind the Nile's new Aswan dam. Of all the priceless treasures, the most important were the two Ramesses temples.

A Swedish engineering firm devised a plan to move the Small Temple with its statues of Queen Nefertari and the Great Temple with those of Ramesses—three complete and the 67 ft seated, but broken, fourth one. The engineers managed to cut away some 330,000 tons of cliff and shift most of the temples.

The total operation cost £16,666,666. It took four and a half years to cut the temples into 1050 pieces—some weighing 33 tons. This mass of material had to be reassembled piece by piece 690 ft further up the sheer rock face.

Egypt then decided to raise the waterline, so all the Small Temple blocks already rebuilt had to be dismantled and resited 7 ft higher. The engineers beat the rising waters with three months to spare. At the same time, other engineers were concerned with imitating the original cliffside background. A dome with a span of 195 ft was built over the Great Temple and, above it, a man-made mountain of rocks and rubble.

By the end of 1967 the Great Temple dome was in place. The rock-fill was made from ground level.

There remained one important task—a special treatment to camouflage the mile-upon-mile of cutting on the joints along the surface of the temples.

Today, the colossal stone guardians of the temples have been expertly restored to match their former majesty.

MOVING A ROYAL FAMILY *Colossal statues of the god-king Ramesses II (above left) were cut into blocks (above right), moved to another site and reassembled (below) in a £16·6 million scheme to save two ancient temples from the rising waters of the new Aswan dam on the River Nile.*

CHINA'S ANCIENT BULWARK

The wall that has stood for 2000 years

Of all man's achievements, the one that qualifies for the title of the greatest building work attempted by human hands is the Great Wall of China. And it certainly is great, stretching 1684 miles from the Yellow Sea westwards to the Jade Gate, where the ancient Silk Road crosses into the wilderness of Central Asia.

The Ch'in emperor Shih Huang-Ti began the wall in 214 BC to protect his vulnerable northern border, where the frontier was open to raids by the fierce Mongol horsemen of the Hsiung-Nu—the Huns who, centuries later, were to topple the Roman Empire. Tens of thousands of criminals slaved in relays to complete the defence, and Chinese legends say that more than a million died before it was finished.

Branch lines

A defensive wall was not a new idea. Centuries before, kings and princes had built walls around their cities. What Shih Huang-Ti did was to join up three sections of these old border walls to form one continuous defence system surrounding his whole empire.

In places, branches leave the main wall for local defences—sometimes there is a double or triple line of defences. In some areas the wall is simply earthen, in others it becomes a rampart of rubble faced with brick or stone.

Did it work? In an age without artillery, walls would and did keep invaders at bay. But the wall had to be garrisoned, and maintaining a steady defence force was almost impossible—even in the China of those times.

Universal fame

Shih Huang-Ti died only four years after the work was begun, but his successors carried on the task. The wall was repaired and extended, giving it a height of 30 ft in places with 40 ft towers every 200 yds, and ramparts 32 ft thick.

So, after more than 2000 years, the zigzag climb through the hills to the north of Peking still presents a daunting spectacle to the observer on this earth—and perhaps beyond—for the Great Wall is the only man-made object big enough to be visible from Space.

BORDER BARRIER *The magnificent ramparts and watch-towers of the Great Wall which winds over desolate northern China.*

CITY OF THE MAYAS

The splendour of a little-known civilisation

Little known, but barbarously magnificent, the Central American empire of the Maya Indians flourished at a time when Europe was still weltering in the bloodshed and chaos of the Middle Ages.

The Mayans' great stone cities, now often overgrown by the encroaching jungle, were joined by a network of magnificent paved roads. The longest ran 62 miles in an arrow-straight line from Coba in Mexico to Yaxuma, accurately surveyed and carefully laid on a raised causeway, like all Mayan roads. The method of construction was simple but effective—a central core of rubble was laid between thick stone borders, and pressed down with heavy stone rollers.

Three great cities formed the basis of the empire—Mayapàn, Uxmal and Chichén-Itzá. Of the three, Chichén-Itzá grew into the greatest of all.

Slow beginnings

In the dry, waterless country of Yucatan the discovery of two natural underground wells led to its founding in the 6th century, yet its beginnings were slow. A century later, the city was abandoned, and remained deserted for more than 300 years. But in 987 Chichén-Itzá was occupied again, and a complex of strange, unexplained stone palaces sprang up.

Soon Mayan power began to crumble before the attacks of warlike tribes, and about 1200 Chichén-Itzá was conquered by the Toltecs and Aztecs. Nevertheless, Mayan tradition and design were in many ways retained by the new lords.

The city reached the undoubted height of its fame, glory and prosperity in the 13th century, when splendid temples and halls were built. The Thousand Columns, ranked around a 5 acre plaza containing a huge temple covering an acre, date from this period. Round about are columned halls, sunken gardens, terraces and pyramid temples.

Heads you lose

Like all Mayan cities, Chichén-Itzá also had its Ball Court, a rectangular enclosure 448 ft long and 120 ft wide, where two teams played tlachtli, in which they struggled to force a heavy rubber ball through their opponents' goal. The goals were vertical stone rings on elevated pedestals. Tlachtli was played at a furious pace, sometimes so violent that players died during the game.

Reliefs carved in stone walls of the Ball Court show the decapitation of a ball player, and along a nearby platform are carvings of skulls skewered on sticks. It may well be that the losing team had their heads chopped off for display on the platform.

The city is also famous for its Well of Sacrifice, a deep pool linked to the Grand Plaza by a 900 ft causeway. Into this pit

SERPENT GUARDIANS *These enormous columns stand at the entrance to the vast Temple of the Warrior at Chichén-Itzá in Mexico.*

STEP PYRAMID *The El Castillo pyramid is made of huge blocks of cunningly worked stone. It was abandoned in the 15th century.*

men, women and children were thrown alive to propitiate the gods in time of drought. Precious objects were also thrown in as offerings. Many skeletons have been recovered from the well, as have the most exquisitely beautiful golden ornaments and carvings of jade.

Chichén-Itzá's end came suddenly. For 200 years the city survived as the Mecca of the Mayan world, but in the middle of the 15th century it was abruptly and inexplicably abandoned by its inhabitants, who never returned. They left only the massive ruins to mystify future visitors to an otherwise forgotten corner of Central America.

SPLENDOUR IN THE JUNGLE

The fabulous home of a god-king

In 1861 a French naturalist, Henri Mouhot, was marching along a forest path in the jungle of northern Cambodia when, high above the treetops, he saw three tall stone towers. They were the pinnacles of Angkor Wat, one of the most splendid temples in all Asia, and the first sign of the fabled lost city of Angkor Thom. This, the capital of the great Khmer Empire, had been abandoned 500 years before, to lie hidden and forgotten in the folds of the all-embracing jungle.

Even in ruins, Angkor has a disconcerting impact. Surrounded by a wide moat once stocked with crocodiles, backed by a high defensive wall with earthen ramparts, the city was founded by the 9th-century Emperor Jayavarman II.

Declaring himself a god-king, he set out to build a capital to declare his power and the wealth of his empire.

Each side of the square moat is 2 miles long, and the area inside the walls could contain all of ancient Rome, with room to spare. Yet few people lived there—it was simply the royal, religious and administrative centre of the capital. The people of the city had their homes in two huge suburbs outside the walls, beside artificial lakes along the banks of the nearby Siem Reap River.

Four broad causeways cross the moat, leading into the city through huge triple-towered gateways. The arch of each gate was built tall and wide enough to allow the royal elephants to pass, each beast carrying a howdah and large ceremonial sunshade to protect imperial heads.

Terrace of the Leper King

The four roads meet in the very centre of the city, in a great square bounded by two carved terraces, the Royal Terrace and the Terrace of the Leper King. Opposite them are ranged the 12 elaborately carved Towers of the Cord Dancers. Flights of steps lead through the terraces to the lawns and pavilions of the royal gardens and tombs.

PARADISE LOST *The noble towers of Angkor Wat climb towards the sky, their image reflected in a shimmering pool. For 500 years the temple lay forgotten in the Cambodian jungle.*

The chief glories of Angkor are the wonderful sandstone carvings: each causeway is bordered by parapets carved in the shapes of gods and giants supporting mythical creatures. Every gateway is covered in elaborate sculpture, the towers crowned with triple-headed heraldic elephants.

The royal terraces are crowded with figures of kings and queens, princes and princesses, lions and elephants and figures from Hindu religious epics. Other carvings portray almost every kind of activity of a highly civilised society, in a style so lifelike that movements seem interrupted only for an instant.

Noble monument

Yet perhaps Angkor's most noble monument lies a mile outside the walls of the city—Angkor Wat, one of the most beautiful and famous shrines in the world. Built by the 12th-century Emperor Suryavarman II, under whose rule the empire and city reached their height of prosperity, it is surrounded by a mile-long moat in an almost perfect square. The temple is a bewildering complex of lakes and libraries, cloisters and galleries, shrines and stairways. Behind the central sanctuary wall,

the lowest gallery contains a frieze of vivid carvings from legends and Hindu holy books. It stands 8 ft high and stretches right round the gallery's half-mile circumference. Above this the pyramid-shaped temple climbs in three stages to the central cluster of five towers, the tallest of which is 215 ft high—these were the signposts that guided Henri Mouhot to the city's ruins.

Not defensible

What happened to Angkor? Less than 30 years after Suryavarman's death it was captured and sacked by Cham invaders from Laos in 1177.

The Chams were eventually conquered by Emperor Jayavarman VII, but the city's days were numbered. In the following century and a half, the empire was invaded by the Thais from the west and the Mongols from the north. The Thais captured Angkor in 1369, 1388 and again in 1431. Despite its forbidding ramparts, the city was indefensible.

Finally, the elaborate rice-producing irrigation system on which Angkor depended was destroyed, and in 1434 the capital was moved to a site near Phnom Penh, and Angkor was left to the jungle.

STREETS AHEAD

The road network that lasted 2000 years

The Roman Empire, at its height, stretched from the Persian Gulf to the Humber in Britain. Fifty thousand miles of first-class roads linked Britain and Europe, and a quarter of a million miles of local roads connected forts, legionary camps, towns, villages, harbours and signal stations with the main road system.

The main roads carried the postal services, set up by Emperor Augustus, as well as government decrees and all the commercial traffic of the empire.

Five-day mail

The regular postal services could cover 50 miles a day, so a letter from the garrison on Hadrian's Wall could reach London in less than five days. Vital messages carried by relays of mounted dispatch-riders travelled up to 200 miles in a day and a night. An order from Rome, for example, could reach the legionary

headquarters at York in just one week.

The Roman legions were responsible for road-making, backed up by the enforced labour of the local inhabitants, but the cost of building the roads was high. One Roman mile of road, nine-tenths of the present mile, cost the equivalent of £5500 to build, whereas today a mile of modern motorway costs £1 million.

Military surveyors planned the routes. Using a simple type of theodolite lined up with smoke signals, straight stretches could easily be plotted. There were no maps to help the surveyor, so careful surveys had to be made. But there were few towns or dwellings along the route and any detours could take the shortest natural routes.

The design of the roads was complex. The width was defined by ditches, on average 84 ft apart. Wide stone embankments 4 or 5 ft high provided the roads

153

HIGHWAYS OF AN EMPIRE *The Roman Empire covered most of Europe and parts of North Africa and the Middle East. An intricate network of roads linked the furthermost outposts with Rome.*

RECOVERED FROM THE ASHES *The excavated ruins of Pompeii have revealed some fine examples of Roman road-building. The ruts worn by chariot wheels can be seen on the left.*

with drainage. The embankments bordering the roads have helped to maintain them in good condition for many centuries. The roads themselves were usually 14 to 16 ft wide, enabling two legions, each marching six abreast, to pass. The topsoil was removed, the foundation of heavy stones fitted by hand, then layers of small stones, broken tile, brick and chalk held together with mortar were laid. The surface, cambered for drainage, was of flat stones cemented into place and bordered by kerbs on each side.

Along the road, milestones were erected giving the distance to the nearest town. At regular intervals along the route were posting houses where relays of horses were stationed, and inns for overnight stops. The local communities, with great resentment, paid for the upkeep of the roads.

The Roman road network was so efficiently planned, and the roads so well built, that the system lasted for nearly 2000 years, and was the fastest transport system until the coming of the railways.

Rome's race — Rome's pace

A traveller between London and Rome during the height of the Roman Empire would take only 13 days for the journey. About 1700 years later, on his recall to England from Italy to be Prime Minister, Robert Peel took exactly the same length of time, although he travelled post-haste all the way.

In the United Kingdom, several of the old Roman roads are still in use. Watling Street, which runs from Dover to London and on to Wroxeter, is built on Roman foundations. Dere Street runs from York to Melrose in Scotland, via County Durham. Sarn Helen East runs through majestic Welsh countryside and was built to serve the Dolaucothi gold mines.

The road system which was originated by Britain's conquerors, to enable them to maintain control over her hostile native population, continues to benefit the British 19 centuries later.

THE GLORY THAT WAS ROME *The arena floor has long fallen in, but the rows of storerooms and wild beast cages underneath the Colosseum are still well preserved.*

BREAD AND CIRCUSES

Rome's mighty stadium, where games were played to the death

Towering above the bustling traffic of Rome, the enormous bulk of the Colosseum still stands as a link with her mighty Imperial past. The games held there dominated social life in the ancient city—a cruel and spectacular mixture of wild beast hunts, gladiatorial combats, mock battles and fights between condemned men and wild animals.

It was the policy of Rome's rulers to provide such circuses—and bread—to keep the unruly citizens quiet.

At first the games were held in a stone amphitheatre with wooden seats built in 29 BC. This was destroyed in Nero's great fire, and the Colosseum was built on the site of Nero's own Golden House by his successors, the emperors Vespasian and Titus. Despite legend, Nero never saw the Colosseum, which was opened in AD 80, many years after his death.

The oval arena, nearly 100 yds long, was built over a complex of underground passages and animal cages. Flanking it, tiers of stone benches rose to a height of 160 ft and provided room for 50,000 spectators. The lowest row of seats was for senators and high-ranking citizens only, and in the centre stood the Imperial box, with boxes near by for the consuls

and vestal virgins. The higher tiers were for the patricians, and above them sat, or stood, the plebeians—the common people.

During wild beast fights a strong fence was erected round the arena; and to protect spectators from the sun, the seats could be screened by awnings, which were swung into position as they were needed by sailors of the Imperial Navy.

The great opening ceremony lasted 100 days. Nine thousand wild beasts were killed as well as gladiators and sailors who took part in a naval battle. The arena could be flooded to a depth of 5 ft for these naval *naumachiae*, but it was difficult to keep it watertight. However, there is no record of Christians ever being put to death at the Colosseum.

The glory crumbles

During the 6th century the amphitheatre fell into disuse, and earthquakes in the 13th and 14th centuries badly damaged it. The stone was used for other buildings, and many of the statuettes which stood in niches in the walls were stolen.

Restoration began in the 19th century; but all that remains now is an empty shell of stone and brickwork—and the memory of the blood-lust of ancient Rome.

IMPOSING AND IMPREGNABLE *Krak des Chevaliers dominates a vast area of the Syrian desert. This was the formidable obstacle in the way of invaders on the road from Damascus to Tripoli and Jerusalem. Perhaps this Crusader fortress was impregnable; it was never taken by direct attack.*

MIGHTIEST CRUSADER FORTRESS
It fell to the guile of a Muslim sultan

Krak des Chevaliers—Crag of the Knights—a fortress of astonishing strength, with towering defences and walls dozens of feet thick, yielded at last in 1271 . . . to a humble pigeon.

The castle was built by the Crusaders on a spur in the Syrian Desert for the strategic purpose of guarding the road between the Muslim city of Homs and the Christian city of Tripoli on the Mediterranean coast. A small castle, occupied by a Kurdish garrison, had stood on the site when the Crusaders arrived in the 1090s. This passed into the hands of the Christian counts of Tripoli, who in turn sold it in 1142 to the Knights of the Hospital of St John of Jerusalem. In the next 150 years the knights constructed an edifice of such immensity and ingenuity that it withstood at least 12 Saracen attempts to storm it.

Krak des Chevaliers was built in two stages. The outer curtain of walls and an inner castle of small, square buildings came first. In 1202 an earthquake damaged many of these inner buildings and a massive redesign was undertaken. This included the huge inner or second series of fortifications, plus the distinctive round-house look of many of the buildings. Wherever possible the plunging contours of the spur were used to tactical advantage.

Weak points

But two weak points needed special treatment: the main entrance and the exposed south side, which opened on to a plain. The knights solved the second problem with a formidable wall of masonry composed of three huge linked towers, further strengthened by an apron of rubble and masonry, in places 80 ft thick, that made mining almost impossible. The problem of the entrance was met in an even more ingenious way. The path leading to it was made to zigzag up the steep escarpment, so that any invader had to cross and recross a concentrated line of fire. A hairpin bend, followed by the fortified main gates themselves, compounded the invaders' misery.

If, then, attack was a waste of life and limb, siege was equally futile. Like all great Crusader castles, Krak was provided with vast storage spaces for food and water; enough to keep a full-strength garrison of 2000 men alive and fighting for at least a year, while a relieving army marched to the rescue.

Fall of the fortress

Krak seemed impregnable. Even the great warrior Saladin had turned away. In 1271, however, another Muslim conqueror stood at the gates of the castle. He was the Sultan Baybars (the name means panther) with an Egyptian army, and Krak was the last defence in his way toward total domination of what had been the Crusaders' kingdom.

By this time, the castle was seriously undermanned. A year before the Eighth Crusade had failed, and reinforcements from the West were out of the question. Nevertheless, the handful of fighting monks left in command of the garrison's

mercenaries were tenacious fighters, and Baybars still had to pierce layer upon layer of defence to get to them.

The sultan set to work with fanatical determination. After weeks of heavy mining the south-west tower of the outer curtain collapsed and the attackers rushed in, only to find the huge inner defences towering above them.

Baybars, refusing to accept defeat or the probability of a lengthy siege, turned to trickery. Arab historians record that he used a carrier pigeon to send a forged letter into the castle. The message purported to come from the Grand Masters of the Hospitallers in Tripoli and ordered the garrison to surrender since no help could be sent to them. The order was obeyed and Krak had fallen at last, but her strongest fortifications had never been put to the test. Baybars chivalrously permitted the garrison free conduct to Tripoli.

Today, the castle stands in a remarkable state of preservation and is considered one of the finest examples of military architecture. In the words of Lawrence of Arabia, Krak des Chevaliers is 'the most wholly admirable castle in the world'.

NO PLACE TO HIDE

The strongest walls have proved no match for ingenuity

Fortifications have played a vital part in military history, from the earthen ramparts of Iron Age hillforts to the steel-and-concrete emplacements of the 20th century. Yet however impregnable these fortresses may have been, a wily enemy has always found some way of breaching their walls.

In Biblical times the Assyrians were particularly skilled at walling cities and battering down enemy fortifications. Later the Romans perfected the art. When the Roman general Silvius Flavius attacked the Jewish rebels at Masada in AD 73, for example, his engineers built a 3800 yard siege wall and then erected 12 towers upon it.

Constantinople, greatest city of Europe in the Dark Ages, had three sets of walls, with a moat 60 ft wide and 20 ft deep. Behind this was a row of battlements, 60 ft further back was another wall, studded with 96 towers at 200 ft intervals,

and inside this was a third wall with another 96 towers, each set between a pair of towers of the middle wall and reaching twice the height. A daunting obstacle for any enemy. But the warriors of the Fourth Crusade penetrated the defences by throwing bridges across from ships to the battlements, and setting fire to as much of the city as they could reach.

The art of fortification reached its peak in the Middle Ages, when the great stone-walled castles sprouted like mushrooms all over Europe. Before the advent of gunpowder, these fortresses could hold off an attacker for months, sometimes years, but even the strongest fell to a determined foe.

The Château Gaillard, built by King Richard the Lionheart near Rouen in Normandy, had three lines of defence consisting of ditches and walls studded with towers. The castle stood overlooking the town of Les Andelys, and is considered

STRIFE WITHIN THE FORTIFICATIONS *The fortified city of Constantinople fell partly because of internal strife during the Fourth Crusade. The best troops mutinied because of arrears in pay, and the city surrendered when the moat, walls and towers were breached by invaders.*

to be one of the most powerful built in the Middle Ages.

In 1203, Philip II of France laid siege to the castle, then held by Roger de Lacy for King John of England, and having taken Les Andelys began to seek ways of making life uncomfortable for the defenders.

Trenches were dug to cut off the castle's water supply, and siege engines were brought up to batter the outermost wall. In time the wall was breached, and the attackers poured through. A party of men climbed the castle's drains and emerged behind the second wall, where they were able to lower the drawbridge between the middle and outer defences. Finally, they started digging under the inner wall. The defenders dug counter-tunnels and furious battles took place underground. But at last the wall, now thoroughly undermined by both sides, collapsed into the moat and the castle fell to the French.

The emergence of gunpowder spelt the beginning of the end for the stone-built castle. Forts became steel-and-concrete emplacements, sunk deep into the earth and invulnerable to direct hits by the heaviest of shells—until the invention of the aeroplane and tank changed the pattern of war once again.

CHÂTEAU GAILLARD *These few remains can still be seen near Rouen. The long siege staged there in 1203 reduced the castle to a ruin.*

HEART OF THE VATICAN

Centuries of craftsmanship created perfection

Few of the world's great buildings can have had so many fingers in its architectural pie as the Basilica of St Peter in Rome.

From the time it was conceived by Pope Nicholas V in the 15th century, it took nearly 350 years to complete. During that time, a succession of popes and architects left their mark on it.

Although it was Nicholas V who first decided to replace the original basilica built by Constantine the Great in honour of the apostle Peter, the first tangible move did not come until 1505. In that year Pope Julius II thought of building close to the basilica a mausoleum to contain a vast monument to himself. He had already asked Michelangelo to execute it, and expense was no object.

Building demolished

After changing his mind several times Julius abandoned the idea of a separate tomb and decided that the old basilica must be completely rebuilt. He brought in the architect Danato Bramante, who first demolished Constantine's building— and everything in it. Bramante threw out tombs, statues, mosaics, icons and altars, and employed 2500 men for weeks on the work of destruction. But although he was an architect of genius, Bramante was too hasty to be thorough and too casual to supervise his workers properly. After his death, faults appeared in the building which were costly to put right.

When Pope Julius died, his successor, Leo, appointed Raphael as his new architect. He made radical changes to Bramante's design, but when he died, six years later, he had done little more than erect one or two columns and continue the correction of Bramante's faults.

Delay, then new life

In 1521 Leo died, and the new pope, Clement, made Peruzzi chief architect. He built much in Rome, but almost nothing in the neglected St Peter's. Grass and weeds grew in the crevices of Bramante's piers and arches, but the next pontiff, Paul III, breathed new life into the project. He pilfered funds given by Spain for a crusade against the Turks, and appointed first Antonio da Sangallo and then Michelangelo as architect. The great Florentine was then 72 and had long ago finished his ceiling in the Sistine Chapel.

Michelangelo produced his first model for St Peter's in 1547 and soon began building. But when Paul died in 1550, however, the zest which Michelangelo had inspired in the builders began to fade. The next pope encouraged Michelangelo, but the great architect's age was beginning to tell and he made many mistakes. His death, in 1564, led to another spell of confusion and little was done to the building during the rest of the pope's reign. His successor, Gregory XIII, made progress but, like so many before him, not so much as he had hoped. Then Sixtus V (1585–90) ascended St Peter's throne, and work on the great project began to move again.

He did far more than any of his predecessors, and was almost entirely responsible for building the dome designed by Michelangelo.

It was Sixtus who ordered the construction of the Sistine Hall and Vatican library—built by Domenico Fontana in 1588. The library was originally founded between 1447–55 by Nicholas V, with a nucleus of more than 300 volumes.

At last the finishing touches

In 1594 Pope Clement VIII celebrated the first mass at the new high altar. Then came another unproductive period, until Pope Urban VIII (1623–44) brought in the architect Bernini, who built the canopy over the papal altar, put up the bell-towers and decorated the naves.

The last addition was the sacristy—in 1784—and, with that complete, St Peter's was finished. But it was then nearly 200 years since Sixtus built the dome; 238 years since Michelangelo worked on the great piers that support it; and 338 years since Nicholas V set out to replace the ancient basilica of Constantine.

Considerably expanded during the 17th and 18th centuries, the library suffered severely when numerous manuscripts were taken to France in 1798.

Today it contains some 60,000 manuscripts, 7000 incunabula, 100,000 engravings and maps, and more than 900,000 printed books.

MR PAXTON'S WONDROUS PALACE

The glass and iron symbol of Victorian ingenuity

Although the name survives today only as that of a sporting centre, a soccer club and a district of south London, Crystal Palace was one of the great design and engineering feats of the Victorian era. It was the brain-child of a man who had previously built greenhouses, bridges, reservoirs and a gasworks.

In 1850 the organisers of the Great Exhibition under the royal patronage of Prince Albert, had been looking for a suitable building in which to house the event, and most of the 250 plans submitted had proved too costly or impracticable.

Master innovator

Then Joseph Paxton, a self-taught architect who specialised in buildings of glass and iron, was consulted. He promised to design and plan the construction of a building of 33 million cubic feet within nine days. He spent the first two days watching the construction of Robert Stephenson's Britannia Bridge over the Menai Strait. On the third day he produced, on a blotter, a rapid sketch of the building which was eventually constructed in London's Hyde Park, to house the many thousands of exhibits of 'the Work of All Nations'.

There were no established methods for building in glass at that time, yet Paxton quickly delivered a design for a structure 1848 ft long and 450 ft wide. Materials required included 205 miles of iron bars, 3300 columns, 2150 girders, 293,655 panes of glass (total surface area, 900,000 square feet) and 600,000 cubic feet of timber. No scaffolding was used in assembling the iron framework. The girders supported each other, rising up from the first, ground-level, skeleton.

Work on the Palace proceeded at an amazing pace. Paxton reported the assembly of three columns and two girders in 16 minutes. By the end of the year, the work force had grown from 39 to more than 2000.

Trolleys, designed to run along the grooves of Paxton's guttering, were used to carry out the glazing. By this method 80 men fitted more than 18,000 panes of glass in one week. One man fitted 108 panes in one day.

The total operation took only eight months. After the exhibition, in 1851, the whole structure was removed to South London, where it was used for concerts, festivals and exhibitions until 1936 when it was destroyed by fire.

NINE-DAY DOODLE *Joseph Paxton's rough sketches, scribbled on a blotting pad. In nine days the plans were completed.*

THE PRIDE OF LONDON *The Crystal Palace, left, erected in Hyde Park, housed exhibits in the Great Industrial Exhibition of 1851.*

GLAZIERS AT WORK *Specially constructed trolleys travelled along the guttering to allow the glaziers to work comfortably.*

THE BIG MOVE *The Crystal Palace was moved from Hyde Park and was re-erected at Sydenham in South London in 1854.*

SKELETON OF IRON *This general view shows the simple girder construction employed by Paxton. The simplicity of the design made it possible to dismantle the building for reconstruction.*

ON THE RIGHT LINES

The railway system that showed the way to safety

Right from its opening in 1841 the Great Western Railway was different from other British railways—thanks to its brilliant, but unorthodox, engineer, Isambard Kingdom Brunel.

In a pioneering age, Brunel had his own personal style. Faced with the necessity of boring Box Tunnel for the Great Western's main London to Bristol line— a difficult, dangerous and expensive undertaking—he did it on a precisely calculated alignment. It is said that on one day a year the sun shines right through the length of the 1¾ mile tunnel—on April 9, Brunel's birthday.

To carry the line across the Thames at Maidenhead, he built a shallow-arched brick bridge—which his colleagues insisted would never carry the weight of a train. Yet more than 130 years later the bridge is coping with trains ten times the weight, travelling at twice the speed of the ones that crossed it in Brunel's time.

While all the other railway companies laid their lines with the rails 4 ft 8½ in. apart (a measurement inherited from the early coal-wagon ways on Tyneside), Brunel had other ideas. He set the Great Western's tracks 7 ft apart, wide enough for engines and carriages to be slung between the wheels, giving them much greater stability. This broad gauge served the company well, and for half a century, while derailments were commonplace on other lines, they ran expresses at top speed, almost without a hitch. For many years the Great Western Railway expresses were the fastest in the world.

Even when mishaps did occur, the broad gauge proved its worth. In 1847 a driving wheel on the Exeter to London express collapsed at speed as it roared on to an open viaduct near Southall. Yet not a single wheel jumped the rails.

Brunel's problems in building the line were enormous, but he was undaunted. A cutting through Sonning Hill, Berkshire, had defeated two contractors, but despite torrential rains which flooded the excavations the tireless engineer urged on his team of 1220 navvies and 196 horses until the 2 mile long, 60 ft deep cutting was completed.

The last and probably the greatest of his railway engineering triumphs was the Royal Albert Bridge at Saltash, Cornwall, over the most formidable River Tamar, 1100 ft wide and 70 ft deep at high water. Because the river was used by shipping, Brunel had to give ample clearance—and an assurance that he would not obstruct the channel with scaffolding.

His final design was for two 455 ft spans, supported by one central pier, at a level of 100 ft above the high-water mark. When the railway company ran short of money, Brunel decided to put only a single stretch of line across the bridge. Today, although the track has been replaced by standard gauge, the bridge remains a one-line crossing from Plymouth to the West.

In May 1859, after the opening of the bridge, Brunel had his first and last sight of the finished structure. Seriously ill from overwork, the engineer was carried across his bridge, lying on a platform truck.

ALL CHANGE *A print from 1846 shows the chaos as passengers and luggage are shifted from Brunel's broad-gauge express to the narrow-gauge train at Gloucester, the end of the line.*

CANADIAN PACIFIC

The track that created a nation

The Canadian Pacific Railway was not only a great construction achievement, linking the western and eastern seaboards of Canada—it was a project which created a nation.

In 1867 the eastern provinces of Ontario, Quebec, New Brunswick and Nova Scotia formed the Federation of Canada, to offset the threat of invasion from the south. But British Columbia on the Pacific coast remained vulnerable, while Saskatchewan and Alberta were still part of the North-west Territories. As an inducement to get British Columbia into the federation, the Canadian Parliament guaranteed a trans-continental railroad in ten years.

Six millionaires formed Canadian Pacific and for $25 million, 25,000,000 acres of choice western land, a 20 year exemption from tax and other guarantees, they promised to build the railroad. William Cornelius Van Horne, a railway superintendent from Chicago, was appointed construction boss. He urged work gangs into rapid progress across the prairies, and then took 12,000 men and 5000 horses into the icy wastes north of Lake Superior to begin digging, blasting and bridging.

When dynamite supplies ran out, Van Horne built three emergency factories. At one stage, 3 miles of granite had to be excavated to make 900 yds progress; swampland swallowed up three locomotives, and one particularly difficult mile cost $11 an inch.

Soon Van Horne had spent $27 million over his budget, and creditors began clamouring for cash. An application for a fresh grant of $35 million was ignored by Parliament. The CPR seemed on the verge of ruin when, inadvertently, Louis Riel, a half-Indian anarchist saved it— by stirring up a rebellion in Saskatchewan.

Van Horne guaranteed to transport 4000 soldiers to the scene on his unfinished railway, within 11 days. He did it, and they crushed the rebellion.

The speed of the operation awakened the nation to the value of Van Horne's project, and fresh funds were raised.

As work gangs moved east and west towards each other, a scouting party found the final link in the chain—the north-west land passage, avoiding four ranges of impassable mountains. Tunnels were blasted, valley walls were shored up and on November 7, 1885, four and a half years after taking over the job, the gangs drove in the last spikes.

At the western terminus Van Horne ran his tracks to a spot on Burrard Inlet and called it Vancouver, after Captain George Vancouver who had explored the area a century earlier. A CPR team dragged a post-office shack to a spot in Alberta, and the bustling cattle town of Calgary grew around it.

The official opening date of the railway was June 28, 1886, when the Pacific Express, the first through passenger train, made the 2905 mile journey from Montreal to Vancouver.

Today Canadian Pacific is an industrial colossus, embracing an airline (C. P. Air), shipping fleets, hotels and resorts. Its subsidiary operations reach into practically all aspects of the nation's life.

THE ROARING U. P. TRAIL

The workmen who won the West

It was not the best time or place to build a railroad. The American Civil War was being fought, and marauding Indians roamed the central plains. Yet in 1862 Congress passed an Act for building the Union Pacific, the railroad that opened up the West.

It was agreed that the Central Pacific Railroad Company of California should work east from Sacramento, and the Union Pacific west from Omaha, Nebraska. Work began in 1863.

The Central Pacific men, under the supervision of dry goods store owner Charlie Crocker, were faced with the solid granite slopes of the Sierra Nevada only 80 miles from their starting point. The Union Pacific gangs, under General Grenville Dodge, had to cross the territory of hostile Sioux and Cheyenne Indians who were already resentful of the white man's 'talking wire' telegraph network, and convinced that the railway would ruin their hunting grounds.

Supplying materials for 1 mile of track at Dodge's end meant 40 wagon-loads of supplies from the Missouri River, about 50 miles away. Oak sleepers, at a cost of $3·50 each, had to be brought from Pennsylvania 800 miles away.

But by the end of 1866 Union Pacific had laid 300 miles of track and Central Pacific, although only 90 miles from their starting point, had conquered the 7000 ft Sierra.

Most of Dodge's men were Irish. Crocker's gangs were mainly Chinese, of whom he remarked: 'They built the Great Wall of China and that's the biggest run of masonry in the world.'

In the severe winter of 1866–7, many workers froze to death or were killed in avalanches in the Sierras. In February 1867, a 12 day blizzard buried a shack of workers in 60 ft drifts.

The two lines eventually met at Priomontory Point, Utah. The eastbound team had covered 690 miles and the westbound gang 1086 miles. And so, by an eventual link-up of the Union Pacific with the railroad network in the East, a coast-to-coast service was established.

On May 10, 1869, a ceremonial mahogany sleeper with a silver plaque was laid at Priomontory Point—only to be quickly broken up by souvenir hunters. Two locomotives met at the site to mark the occasion and commemorative spikes, including one of gold, were hammered home—and quickly withdrawn for safety.

Dodge's Irishmen and Crocker's Chinese had truly won the West.

CHARGE OF THE HEAVY BRIGADE
How an army of navvies saved the British army at Balaclava

Who were the real heroes of the Crimean War? Not the Light Brigade, whose famous charge threw away Europe's finest cavalry on a worthless objective because of a mistaken order. They received the glory, but the unsung heroes were a bunch of railway navvies who rescued an army one hundred times their number from defeat and death.

In the early winter of 1854 Lord Raglan's forces were laying siege to Sevastopol, but delay and bungling had allowed the Russians to reinforce the city's defenders, and Raglan's 30,000 soldiers were suffering from cold and disease.

As the Russian winter tightened its grip, the single road to the port of Balaclava broke up. Deliveries of food, water, clothing and medicine petered out.

Fortunately for the army, the great railway builder Morton Peto was a Member of Parliament. Peto, his brother-in-law Betts, and his greatest rival Brassey offered to build a railway to supply the troops without making a penny profit. They proposed a force of 250 navvies, 30 gangers and masons, 80 carpenters, 20 blacksmiths and 10 enginemen. All were to be formed into a Civil Engineer Corps, entirely separate from the army.

The Prime Minister, Lord Aberdeen, agreed, and the party of volunteers left Liverpool on December 21. During the following month, 23 other ships carried more men and supplies to Balaclava.

They took everything, from picks and shovels to cranes and piledrivers, wagons and engines to ropes and rails.

The bleak Russian winter was nothing new to many of the navvies—fresh from railway building in Canada and the USA. They built an encampment of warm, solid huts and laid 5 miles of track, all in the first ten days. The army were amazed. In the words of Captain Henry Clifford, they could do 'more work in a day than a regiment of English soldiers do in a week'.

Within six weeks they laid a double-track main line from the harbour to the hills overlooking Sevastopol, 7 miles away. But with branch lines to outposts the total network covered 29 miles. Once finished, it was handed over to the army.

The trains, drawn by horses, steam locomotives and stationary engines hauling wagons by wire ropes, carried 112 tons of food a day, plus ammunition, clothing and medical supplies.

By April the army was saved, and in September the Russians abandoned Sevastopol. For the railway navvies, saving an army from disease and starvation was, very nearly, all in a day's work.

CLEOPATRA'S NEEDLE

The priceless piece of Egyptian flotsam

The strange-looking vessel, abandoned and wallowing in the Bay of Biscay, carried a priceless treasure—Cleopatra's Needle, a 3500-year-old Egyptian obelisk.

The British public had subscribed £15,000 for the needle—actually made for the Pharaoh Thotmes III—to be shipped from Alexandria to London, but it looked now as if it would end up at the bottom of the sea.

The obelisk's specially designed cigar-shaped container ship, the *Cleopatra*, seemed in danger of sinking. The steamship towing her, the *Olga*, sent six volunteers in a boat to take off the *Cleopatra's* crew. But the boat was swamped and the volunteers drowned. Eventually, the *Olga* drew alongside and rescued the *Cleopatra's* five crewmen and their skipper—then cut the tow-rope, leaving the vessel adrift.

Everything now depended on the buoyancy of the *Cleopatra*. In Britain, the nation held its breath. Five days later a steamship spotted the *Cleopatra* floating undamaged off the northern coast of Spain and towed her to the port of Ferrol.

The brothers John and Waynman Dixon designed and built the *Cleopatra* around the 70 ft long, 200 ton obelisk at Alexandria. When completed, the *Cleopatra* was a 93 ft long iron cylinder, 15 ft wide and divided into ten watertight compartments. Bilge keels, a cabin, bridge and rudder were riveted on and she floated.

After the *Cleopatra's* narrow escape, the steamship *Anglia* was sent to fetch her. In January 1878, the two ships sailed up the Thames. Crowds cheered, and artillery salvoes roared a welcome.

That September, the needle was winched into position on the Thames Embankment to commemorate Britain's victory over Napoleon, 63 years earlier.

COSTLY SHIPMENT
Cleopatra's Needle (left) was shipped from Egypt to London . . . at a cost of £15,000 and the lives of six seamen, drowned in the process.

MOMENT OF TRIUMPH
Made for Pharaoh Thotmes III in 1460 BC, the obelisk was placed on the Thames Embankment (right) in 1878 to commemorate Britain's victory over Napoleon.

CLEOPATRA'S BARGE *A specially designed cylindrical ship, the* Cleopatra, *was built around the needle to float it from Alexandria to London. After the operation, the vessel was sent for scrap.*

DITCH ACROSS THE DESERT

De Lesseps achieved what others had dreamt

Almost 4000 years ago, the ancient Egyptians built waterways across the Isthmus of Suez, a neck of land 100 miles wide separating Western Asia from Egypt. But they fell into disuse and were filled in AD 775 after an Arab invasion.

Napoleon discovered the remains and dreamt of improving trade routes by linking the Red Sea and Mediterranean.

It was in 1859, due to the genius of a French diplomat and politician, Ferdinand de Lesseps, that work started on a new waterway. Though he was not a trained engineer, he had been haunted by the idea of the canal since his youth.

From striking the first blow with a pickaxe, de Lesseps spent ten dedicated years supervising the massive operation that involved the excavation of about 97 million cubic yards of earth.

De Lesseps first established an artificial harbour at Port Said as a base, and had a canal dug from the Nile to the isthmus to provide fresh water for the 20,000 labourers.

Working from north to south, de Lesseps' scheme involved carving a 24 ft deep channel across the land, connecting up lakes en route. The Great and Little Bitter Lakes in the south were reconnected with the Red Sea and flooded with sea water. The canal joined these with Lake Timsah.

Three thousand camels carried drinking water for the workers across the desert to Lake Menzala, where it was sent by barge to Port Said. Local fishermen were recruited to scoop out a channel through the lake by hand, working by day, sleeping on rafts at night.

At the height of the operation, an estimated 80,000 fellaheen, or peasants, were employed, each being paid up to three piastres (about 3p) a day.

From 1863 until 1869 when the canal was opened, the labour force was gradually withdrawn, in favour of mechanical dredgers and digging equipment.

During October 1869 a French steamer, *Louise-et-Marie*, became the first ocean-going vessel to sail through the canal. But the official opening was on November 17, when representatives of almost every European royal family attended an inauguration fête.

A little before midnight on opening day, an unfortunate accident occurred. An Egyptian frigate ran aground, 30 kilometres from Port Said, and threatened to prevent the ceremonial sail-through of ships from many nations, including France, Russia, Austria, Italy, Britain and America.

Dispatches from Paris published the news that the opening would have to be postponed. Next day, the fleet of ships was only five minutes from the site of the incident when de Lesseps was informed the canal was clear.

The total length of the canal is 103 miles, 21 of them through the lakes. It is 500 ft wide at the top, sloping to 196 ft at the bottom, and the total cost of the project was an estimated £20 million.

This was more than twice the original estimate, but it was a tiny sum compared with the value of the canal to world trade.

SHIPWAY TO THE PACIFIC

First a battle had to be won against yellow fever

As early as 1517, the Spanish explorer Vasco Nunez de Balboa saw the possibility of a canal across the narrow waist of Central America, connecting the Atlantic and Pacific oceans.

But 400 years passed before the sea journey from New York to San Francisco was cut from 13,000 miles to 5200. The French in 1879 tried but failed to build a canal, and within ten years the French Panama Canal Company collapsed due to bankruptcy, lack of planning and the deadly yellow fever.

It was not until 1898, during the Spanish American War, when the US had to send the battleship *Oregon* nearly 13,000 miles from San Francisco to Cuba, that the value of a trans-continental waterway was appreciated.

In 1903 the US gained permanent

control of a 10 mile wide canal zone, after paying $10 million to the new Republic of Panama, plus, from 1913, $250,000 a year. In return, the US guaranteed Panama's independence.

The greatest obstacle to building the canal was disease, and in 1904 Colonel William C. Gorgas, who had successfully combated yellow fever in Havana, took charge of improving sanitary conditions.

The first two years' work consisted of clearing vast areas of brush and grass where disease-carrying mosquitoes swarmed and bred.

The Americans excavated about 184 million cubic yards of earth, apart from the 78 million cubic yards the French had already removed.

More than 43,000 men were employed at the peak of construction and the main work was completed in 1914. On August 15 of that year, the SS *Ancon*, a passenger-cargo vessel, made a complete trip through the canal, from the Atlantic to the Pacific. But landslides prevented any further use for a time. President Woodrow Wilson opened the canal on July 12, 1920.

The canal, with its approaches, is 50·72 miles long. There are three steps at the Pacific end and three on the Atlantic side, equipped with locks 1000 ft long and 110 ft wide.

Because the Isthmus of Panama runs east-west and the canal cuts across it diagonally, a ship going from the Atlantic to the Pacific emerges about 20 miles *east* of the Caribbean entrance.

Some 14,000 ocean-going ships travel through the Panama every year, each paying a toll of around $4000 to $5000.

A ship usually takes 15 hours to go through the canal. Experts estimate that the waterway may reach a capacity of 25,550 ships a year by 1990.

EXCAVATING AT MIRAFLORES *At the height of construction of the Panama Canal, more than 43,000 workers were employed.*

SURVEYING *Work on the Panama Canal was difficult and hazardous in swampy jungle infested with disease-carrying mosquitoes.*

GIANT WITH A JINX

The Great Eastern *seemed doomed from the start*

Isambard Brunel had successfully designed two ships, the *Great Western* and *Great Britain*, when he began to consider the idea of a ship large enough to steam to Australia and back without refuelling.

He found a backer in the Eastern Steam Navigation Company, which had been formed in 1851 to trade with India, Australia and countries of the Far East.

Everything about the ship was of staggering proportions. The overall length was 692 ft, the breadth of the hull over the paddle-boxes, 118 ft. Two sets of massive engines drove the 56 ft diameter paddle-wheels and the 24 ft screw. Her displacement was 32,000 tons.

Brunel applied his bridge technique

THE GREAT EASTERN *Designed by Brunel to carry 4000 passengers, the ship became a success only when converted into a cable-layer.*

to the hull. It was constructed in the form of a huge box girder, with a double frame and skin. Watertight bulkheads divided the hull into ten compartments, each 60 ft long.

The ship was built at the yards of John Scott Russell in Millwall, London. The Thames at that point was too narrow to permit a lengthways launch, so the hull was built broadside on to the river. This created a problem that kept the ship high and dry for many weeks, while the costs escalated and Brunel became ill through worry and overwork.

The first launching attempt, on November 3, 1857, was abandoned when a man working on one of the checking drums was killed by a winch handle spinning suddenly and hurling him into the air. The second attempt, on November 19, was a little more successful, and by the end of the month the ship had moved a total of 33 ft 6 in.

Eventually the ship was eased into the water, on January 31, 1858, with the name *Great Eastern*. But her troubles were not over. On her trial run to Weymouth a steam pipe burst, wrecking one of the funnels and killing six stokers. When the news reached Brunel, who was by then extremely ill, it proved too much for him and he died a few days later on September 15, 1859.

The Eastern Steam Navigation Company were unable to bear the heavy costs of the delayed launch, and the ship was taken over by a new concern, the Great Ship Company. They tried, unsuccess-

fully, to use the *Great Eastern* on the trans-atlantic route. Her accommodation for 4000 passengers was never filled, and on two voyages she suffered severe damage, once in a mid-Atlantic storm and again when she hit an uncharted rock outside New York harbour.

These two accidents cost £130,000 in repairs, and the ship was put up for sale. She was bought by three former shareholders of the Great Ship Company who chartered her to the Telegraph Construction Company for use as a cableship.

Successful career

So, at last, the *Great Eastern* embarked on a successful career. In July 1865 she left Ireland to lay a new cable across the Atlantic. After 1200 miles the cable snapped, and all efforts to retrieve it failed. The following year she set out again, this time to succeed, and then went on to recover the cable lost the previous year.

Having proved herself in her new role, the *Great Eastern* laid cables from France to America, Bombay to Aden and along the Red Sea.

When her cable-laying days were over the *Great Eastern* was used for a time as a floating exhibition and funfair at Liverpool. Oddly enough this ignominious fate had been predicted by a cartoonist when she was launched.

In 1888 she was broken up on Merseyside, and nearly 20 years passed before another ship, the *Lusitania*, exceeded her displacement.

PLUTO AND MULBERRY

Two ideas that helped win a war

In spite of Hitler's succession of lightning victories in 1940, one prize still lay beyond his grasp. For all the toughness and efficiency of his troops, the English Channel was a formidable barrier—even though the British forces were so painfully weak that resistance could have been easily overcome once his troops were ashore.

Yet when the Allies faced the same task in reverse four years later, the opposition they faced was even more daunting; heavy fortifications and an army which, though stretched to its uttermost, was still one of the most efficient in the world.

Given command of the Channel, and the air above it, the problems of landing the first wave of troops on enemy soil were straightforward enough. But once the Germans woke up to what was happening, and mounted a full-scale counter-attack, then everything would depend on landing masses of reinforcements and—even more important—keeping them supplied.

But all the harbours were strongly defended. Capturing even one would divert men and equipment from the main invasion, and even if the attempt succeeded, it was recognised that the Germans would destroy the installations so thoroughly before retreating that the port would be unusable for weeks.

Only one answer

The Allied planners searched for an answer, but the conclusion remained the same. The invaders had to have a harbour —and if capturing one would take too long, then they would have to take one with them.

And so it was that the harbours, code-named 'Mulberry', were born—pre-fabricated ports of breakwaters, jetties and pontoons where ships could tie up to unload, and floating ramps where lorries could be driven on to the beaches.

As the invasion fleet of more than 1000 ships headed towards the coast of Normandy in the early hours of June 6, 1944, the components of two Mulberry harbours went with them. Tugs towed caissons and sections of concrete-and-steel pontoons, making up 7 miles of piers and jetties. Sixty blockships, which would be manoeuvred into precise positions and

then scuttled to build an outer harbour wall, followed the invaders. Each harbour weighed 750,000 tons, and each had the capacity of the port of Dover.

Avalanche of men

In the first six days of the invasion, the Allies managed to land a third of a million men on French soil, backed up by 54,000 vehicles and more than 100,000 tons of stores. On June 19 a storm in the Channel wrecked the American Mulberry harbour and severely damaged the British port at Arromanches. Swift work by engineers soon had them operational again and, a week after the storm, the Americans captured Cherbourg.

Although the port was extensively damaged, more blockships were sunk outside the harbour to extend the port area, and it was soon able to take over

ELABORATE CAMOUFLAGE *Care was taken to disguise the British end of the Pluto pipeline. Bungalows 1 and 4 are pump houses.*

MULBERRY SUCCEEDS *Allied war vehicles drive on to a Normandy beach from a steel roadway supported on concrete floats.*

as the major supply port. By the end of the first three months, two million Allied troops had been landed, with three and a half million tons of ammunition and half a million vehicles.

Invaders' lifeblood

These, however, were only part of the lifeblood of a modern army—without fuel, any offensive would soon grind to a halt. But tankers and petrol lorries were extremely vulnerable to accidents and enemy action, and they tended to monopolise harbour space.

So the planners came up with another idea—Pluto. The initials stood for Pipeline Under The Ocean, and the idea was astonishingly simple. Specially modified tugs towed huge drums wound with continuous lengths of flexible piping, and as the drum rotated the pipe unwound to sink to the sea-bed.

Eleven pipelines were laid across the Channel, mainly between Dungeness and Boulogne, and by April 1945, a total of 3100 tons of fuel was being delivered every day—without a single conventional tanker being necessary.

TUNNELS OF DANGER

Men faced death to drive new pathways beneath the ground

For merchants and military conquerors alike, climbing over mountains is a long and laborious business, and for centuries the Alps formed an almost impassable barrier between France and Italy. It was not until the middle of the 19th century that a successful attempt was made to link the two countries by tunnelling, and even then many engineers predicted that such a feat was impossible.

The idea of an Alpine tunnel had occurred to the spice merchants of Genoa and Turin as long ago as the 15th century. Their project was a 2 mile dig through the Col di Tende, the main mountain barrier between Genoa and Nice, which would speed the progress of their mule trains. Explosives were not then in use, and the only method of cutting through the mountains was to light fires under rock to heat it, then to pour on cold water to crack it. This was an ingenious method, but the rock still had to be removed by pick and shovel, and progress was painfully slow.

Finally, history overtook them; Vasco da Gama sailed round the Cape of Good Hope to the Far East and pioneered the way for Portuguese ships to smash the Italian spice monopoly.

Abandoned for 300 years

The partially dug tunnel was abandoned for 300 years, until the King of Piedmont ordered work to start again. This time, it was the French Revolution and the rise of Napoleon that brought the work to a halt.

Twenty years later the arrival of the railways changed the picture dramatically, and once again it was the Kingdom of Piedmont which took the initiative with a scheme for a 7 mile tunnel under the Mont Cenis Pass.

Miles of fumes

A French engineer, Sommeiller was given the task of drawing up the plans, and his problems were many. The tunnel would be nearly a mile under ground at its deepest point, where the temperature of the rock would reach $47°C$ ($117°F$) and the choking fumes from the gunpowder would have to diffuse through miles of tunnel.

Sommeiller found the answer with the introduction of the compressed-air drill, which would blow away the fumes and even help to cool the rocks.

Volcanic mountains

In 1857 digging started from both sides of the Alps, but until the compressors were ready the men had to use the old methods. The rate of advance during the first few years was 9 in. per day.

When compressed-air drills at last went into action they were even slower, until Sommeiller installed compressors that were driven by water. Above the compressor station a dam was built, and water descending from it drove water wheels which in turn operated the compressor.

At last, on Christmas Day 1870, the two tunnels met, and when the final breakthrough was made the misalignment was less than 18 in. The cost of the project was £3 million, and 28 lives.

Tunnel building is still difficult and dangerous, even with modern aids. The

Tanna tunnel in Japan was planned to take the Tokyo-Kobe main line of the Imperial Japanese Railway through the volcanic mountains of the Atami peninsula, 60 miles south-west of Tokyo. Work began in 1918, and was to be completed within seven years.

In fact the project took 16 years, during which time 70 men died. Flooding was the major problem, and drainage tunnels had to be dug on either side of the bore.

On November 26, 1930, the mountain was hit by an earthquake, and for three years work was held up while the torrents of water drained away. But, eventually, in 1934 the two bores met.

Under rivers

Mountains were not the only barriers to man's progress. Rivers divided the land, and before modern bridge-building techniques were developed the only way to link the banks of a wide river was by tunnelling.

In 1825 it was decided to join the north and south banks of the Thames by digging the first-ever underwater tunnel. The work was entrusted to the engineer Marc Brunel, famous father of an even more famous son, Isambard Kingdom Brunel. He had patented a tunnelling shield in 1818, the principle of which occurred to him when he observed the action of ship worms in ships' timbers.

The shield consisted of cast-iron frames 21 ft high and 2 ft wide, with three platforms on which the excavators worked. Six frames were placed side by side against the workface, and as the men dug away at the soft earth the frames were moved forward $4\frac{1}{2}$ in. at a time. Behind the excavators, bricklayers lined the semi-circular tunnel with brickwork.

As the tunnel progressed, water seepage caused grave problems. The foul waters of the Thames—then an open sewer—carried disease and death. In May 1827 the river burst through the tunnel roof, miraculously without loss of life.

Financial difficulties beset the Thames Tunnel Company from the beginning, and the flooding delayed the operation disastrously. But eventually the work was completed, and in March 1843 the first horse-drawn carriages passed through the tunnel. Later it was used by the railway, and today it still forms part of London's underground railway system.

EARLY PLANS TO TUNNEL UNDER THE CHANNEL

THE FIRST proposal to link England and France by tunnelling under the Channel was made in 1802 by the French engineer Albert Mathieu. He suggested that relays of horses could pull coaches through a candle-lit tunnel between Dover and Calais in under an hour.

A start was made near Folkestone, in 1881. The remains of this venture can still be seen; a dank, 7 ft high, 879 yd long tunnel behind a locked wooden door on a sea-swept ledge of Kent.

Design suggestions for the Chunnel, as the newspapers have christened it, have been many and elaborate, including the cast-iron submarine railway (above) with steeple-like observation and ventilation towers put forward by French engineer Hector Horeau in 1860.

A modern project to build a Chunnel—financed equally by French and English companies—was to be completed by mid-1980 at a projected cost of £846 million. It was abandoned in 1974.

SPANNING THE WAVES

The problems of bridging troubled waters

Water has always been one of the most formidable barriers to the progress of land transport; and bridges have been one way of taking a short-cut.

Stone bridges go back to prehistoric times, but with 18th-century iron technology, bridge-builders could design spans of unprecedented length.

MENAI BRIDGE *The 1850 bridge, between Anglesey and North Wales, was one of the world's strongest tubular iron structures.*

The advent of the railways in the mid-19th century brought an urgent need for long bridges of great strength, and one of the most impressive was the Britannia Tubular Bridge over the Menai Strait between North Wales and Anglesey.

Designed by Robert Stephenson and William Fairbairn, it consisted of two continuous 1500 ft wrought-iron tubes which carried the railway tracks. Placed side by side, these tubes formed a rigid and immensely strong structure, which eventually carried trains 12 times heavier than those for which it was designed.

There were four spans, supported by three towers, and the two main sections were 459 ft long and each weighed 1500 tons. The total length of the bridge itself was 1380 ft and it stood 100 ft above the water. When it was opened in 1850 it was the longest railway bridge in the world. It was destroyed by fire in 1970. The tubular sections were removed, and after rebuilding the bridge was re-opened in 1972.

In the mid-19th century, US engineers began building bridges of steel.

The famous Brooklyn Bridge, which carries traffic over New York's East River, was completed in 1883 and has a span of 1595 ft. The bridge is suspended from four steel cables, and its designer, John A. Roebling, devised a cable-spinning method used on all big suspension bridges subsequently built in America.

Demands of the motor car

With the coming of the motor car, bridges were required to carry all kinds of traffic, but for sheer carrying capacity few can equal that of the Sydney Harbour Bridge. Not only is it the world's largest steel arch bridge, but also it has the widest carriageway. Two railway tracks, eight lanes of roadway, a footpath and a cycle track soar 172 ft high, spanning 1650 ft.

Of all civil engineering challenges, the bridging of Lake Maracaibo in Venezuela must rank as one of the most difficult. A bridge of more than 5 miles in length was required and, to allow shipping to pass through, the central spans would have to be 150 ft above the water.

To complicate matters, the whole area was affected by tropical storms, torrential rainstorms and earthquakes.

Designed by R. Morandi of Italy, the bridge was finally completed, on schedule, in 1962. In three years a structure of supreme complexity had been built under the most arduous conditions. It consists of a quarter-mile of embankment, 20 spans of 40 yds apiece, another 77 spans of 50 yds each, the main spans of 80 yds in the centre and five high spans of 260 yds, each slung from 300 ft towers.

In the USA the desire to get there quicker led to the building of yet another bridge in New York harbour. The Verrazano Narrows Bridge runs from Staten Island to Brooklyn, and at 4260 ft is the longest suspension bridge in the world.

But to satisfy the demands of the motorist, no structure can beat the complicated bridge-tunnel system at Chesapeake Bay in the United States. Not only does it stretch for a total of $17\frac{1}{2}$ miles, but it contains 12 miles of low-level bridgework, two high-level steel bridges across shipping channels, four man-made islands and two mile-long tunnels. All to save one and a half hours of driving time.

RESERVOIR BELOW THE SEA

How Hong Kong tapped a salt-water inlet

A large part of Hong Kong's water supply is stored below sea level. A sea inlet, Plover Cove, was blocked off to make a reservoir holding 37,000 million gallons of drinking water.

This gigantic reservoir was the brain-child of Hong Kong waterworks engineer, Tommy Morgan. His department faced a serious problem. The colony's water supply was hopelessly inadequate for its growing population and water was already rationed to eight hours a day. While sailing in Plover Cove Mr Morgan suddenly saw the mountains and peninsula surrounding him as three of the four sides of a natural reservoir.

Within two years the £40 million project was launched. Engineers had to dig a trench in the sea bottom 7000 ft long and 600 ft wide, at depths of 60 to 95 ft.

Nearly 15 million tons of rock and rubble were dropped into the underwater trench for the dam's foundation.

There was one moment of anxiety. When the last few yards of the dam's rock-fill were left to be closed, the escaping waters surged through at a rate of nearly 7 mph. Any greater velocity would sweep the fill away. Luckily, the rocks held and the gap was closed.

Within three months about 25,000 million gallons of salt water were pumped from the cove, leaving a mud-cake desert. Drought slowed the build-up of fresh water in the new reservoir and for some time the water from Plover Cove remained unpleasantly salty. But the project later proved to be so successful that the reservoir's capacity was greatly enlarged to 50,000 million gallons.

MOON POWER AT ST MALO

The world's first major tidal power station

For centuries men have dreamt of harnessing the power of the rising and falling tides. Now, near the ancient French town of St Malo, on the English Channel, the dream is a reality. The St Malo site, spanning the estuary of the River Rance, tempted power experts because some of the world's highest tides —raising the sea level as much as 44 ft— occur there. Twice a day the waters surge up the estuary and then back again, reaching a maximum volume of about 280 million gallons a minute.

In the early 1940s a French engineer, Robert Gibrat, saw St Malo's potential for producing hydroelectric energy. He was influenced by documents and patents going back to 1737, showing ideas for utilising the tides.

Gibrat spent 20 years researching the project, finally persuading colleagues in Electricité de France of its worth.

In 1961 engineers began the formidable task of building a half-mile barrier across the Rance. They had to overcome a unique problem. When building a conventional river dam, the stream is simply diverted around the site. At St Malo the engineers had to contend with a tremendous two-way daily flow.

To cope, they built two coffer dams, one on each bank of the river and each with its own system of locks which allowed the tide to pass. In the middle, they constructed a temporary lake.

The lake was then drained, and over the dry river bed was built the central dam wall. The wall contains 24 uniquely designed turbines which work also in reverse—so that they are driven by both the incoming and outgoing tides. Each turbine can supply the electrical needs of about 15,000 people.

After five years' work and an expenditure of £35 million, the station was opened in November 1966. It now functions for at least 14 hours a day.

This braking action on the tides has had one strange side effect. Scientists have calculated that it has imperceptibly slowed the earth's rate of revolution.

Throughout the world there are only a few sites where the differences between low and high tides are great enough to produce power on a large scale. At one of these, the Bay of Fundy, on America's eastern seaboard, plans are well advanced to build a St Malo-type station.

SUPER SCULPTURE
Man's attempts to immortalise himself in effigy

The building of giant statues has a long and awe-inspiring history, leaving us with a permanent record of man's efforts to immortalise himself, or to pay homage to his gods or his country in stone or metal edifices.

The Colossus of Rhodes soared 117 ft and stood guard astride the entrance to the harbour on the Greek island of Rhodes. It was justifiably classed as one of the Seven Wonders of the Ancient World.

Work on the great bronze statue, by the sculptor Chares, a pupil of Lysippus, was begun in 292 BC, and this unmistakable landmark and guide to shipping took 12 years to complete.

It was so gigantic that the ships entering or leaving the harbour sailed through the arch of its legs. But, tragically, its very size was its downfall.

The island of Rhodes was ravaged by an earthquake in 224 BC, and the huge statue toppled and was smashed to pieces. The massive fragments lay where they had fallen for almost 900 years until, in AD 653, the chunks of bronze were finally sold for scrap and carted away by the buyers to be melted down.

An emperor's vanity

The Romans, too, thought on a large scale, and never did anything by halves. Predictably, they were lovers of giant statues; none more so than the megalomaniac Emperor Nero.

He summoned the sculptor Zenodorus, who was then working on a statue of Hermes in Gaul, and ordered him to drop everything and come to Rome to start work on an enormous statue of the emperor to satisfy his vanity.

When it was finished, the effigy measured 106 ft from top to toe. However, Nero's bid to create a permanent reminder of his greatness did not survive his suicide in AD 68—when the statue was promptly dedicated to Apollo, chosen as a personal god by Emperor Augustus.

But, no matter how grand a scale on which the Romans and ancients thought, the biggest statues of all have been built in modern times.

The Statue of Liberty—officially called 'Liberty Enlightening the World'—stands at the approaches to New York Harbour,

an enduringly impressive first sight of America for the seagoing traveller.

It is by the sculptor Auguste Bortholdi, and measures an awesome 305 ft from the base of the pedestal to the tip of the torch's flame. The pedestal is a granite and concrete structure, but the figure itself, which measures 151 ft 1 in., is made of copper sheets over an iron and steel framework. It was built by Gustave Eiffel, creator of the most famous of all Parisian landmarks.

It was presented to the Americans by the French people to commemorate the

FRENCH GIFT *The building of the Statue of Liberty in New York Harbour. Engineered by Eiffel, it was given to America by the French.*

birth of the United States and the friendship between the two countries.

Dedicated in 1886, the statue incorporates viewing galleries in the torch and head. However, the torch gallery has been closed for several years.

The head can be reached by a lift which runs inside the body . . . or, if the visitor is particularly energetic, he can walk up the steps.

But the prize for sheer height goes to the figure 'Motherland', which is the tallest statue in the world, and stands on Mamayev Hill, outside Volgograd in Russia. It was designed in 1967 by Yevgeyi Vuchetich to commemorate the Battle of Stalingrad. The female figure measures 270 ft from its base to the tip of the sword clenched in its right hand.

Just to prove that the rivalry of the two Great Powers extends beyond weaponry and sporting events, the American sculptor, Felix de Welton, is now working on an ambitious plan to build a replica of the Colossus of Rhodes—with one big difference. De Welton's version will stand 308 ft—191 ft taller than the original version.

Faces in stone

The desire to carve figures in stone is an inherent part of man's nature that has its roots back in the days of the cavemen. But no one has taken this desire to such satisfying and impressive lengths as the American sculptor Gutzon Borglum.

In 1916 Borglum began to carve a gigantic head of General Robert E. Lee on the sheer rock face of Stone Mountain in Georgia. The work, commissioned by the Daughters of the Confederacy, was intended to include the figures of Stonewall Jackson, Jefferson Davis and 1200 Confederate soldiers.

The head of Lee was unveiled in 1924, but Borglum then had a difference of opinion with the Daughters of the Confederacy and quit the project.

The work was taken over by Augustus Lukeman. He worked on until 1930, but made little progress during this time—and actually destroyed the gigantic head.

In the meantime, Borglum had moved on to better things and had begun work on the mammoth project for which he is most famous.

Into the craggy rocks of Mount Rushmore, in the Black Hills of Dakota, he carved the heads of four great Presidents of the United States of America—Washington, Lincoln, Jefferson and Theodore Roosevelt. Each of the massive figures measures 60 ft from the chin to the top of the forehead.

Before the great work was completed, Borglum had patched up his quarrel with the Daughters of the Confederacy and had agreed to resume his work on the Stone Mountain carvings. But he died before this could be achieved.

GREAT PRESIDENTS *Borglum's giant carvings in the craggy face of Mount Rushmore. Each face measures 60 ft from chin to forehead.*

INFLATING THE BUBBLE BUILDING BOOM

THE HANDYMAN of the future may have not only to check the air pressure in his car tyres—but also in his house, garage, greenhouse and, in the case of the more affluent, swimming pool. All this could come about if the present boom in bubble building continues. Instead of a rigid structure, a skin of thin fabric is held in place by internal air pressure, created by a blower. If the blower stops running, the building slowly goes flat.

The idea is not new, for it was patented in 1918 by Frederick William Lanchester, one of the pioneer British car-makers. But it was developed only in the Second World War when engineer Walter Bird, of Cornell University, was asked to find a solution to the problem of protecting radar antennae in northern Canada from frost. The cost of bubble building can be as little as one-fifth that of traditional structures. Versatility is the main attraction. They can be used to cover tennis courts, and as warehouses and greenhouses. The first couple to move into a bubble house were Americans, David and Vicki Schumacher.

SHORTAGE OF SPACE has led the inhabitants of America's great skyscraper cities to live literally on top of each other.

But the beginnings of the skyscraper can be traced back to the days of the Roman Empire, when architects designed five-storey blocks, with shops open to the street at ground level and balconied homes above.

Most famous of the modern skyscrapers was the Empire State Building, completed in 1931. At 1250 ft it towered above New York until it was overtaken in 1970 by the twin 1350 ft towers of the World Trade Center.

In 1973, the World Trade Center was knocked into second place by the Sears Tower in Chicago, 100 ft higher at 1450 ft.

The Sears Tower has 110 storeys and provides office space for 16,500 employees on 101 acres of floorspace. More than 17,000 tons of refrigeration equipment maintain a year-round temperature of 22°C (72°F). It has its own electricity substation below ground level which not only provides power for the building but boosts the entire system in the surrounding city centre.

A five-storey Roman block, 2nd century AD (model).

WHITE ELEPHANT OR A WONDER?

The story of Sydney's controversial opera house

Australia's Sydney Opera House, in its magnificent harbour setting, is the biggest and probably the best piece of abstract architecture in the world. It is the world's most expensive building and has been called a white elephant, a king's palace, an unjustifiable extravagance and a wonder of the world.

Its original estimated cost, when work started in March 1959, was £5 million, and it was planned to be completed in two years. By the time it was opened by Queen Elizabeth II in October 1973, it had taken longer to build than any other modern building and its costs had soared to £50 million—and were still rising, for union troubles had delayed other work. Access roads and car parks had yet to be built and the site's $5\frac{1}{2}$ acres paved. Money is still being spent and the final cost may be about £55 million.

Sculpture in the round

The story of the Opera House began with an international competition for its design which was won by Danish architect Joern Utzon. He envisaged it from the beginning as a piece of sculpture which, to use his own phrase, could be seen in the round.

It stands on a peninsula jutting into Sydney Harbour, just in front of the famous bridge, and can be seen from every side. Since the shore slopes steeply behind it, the Opera House can also be

GRACE *Designed as a sculpture, the shells of Sydney Opera House sit majestically over the waters of the harbour, like a ship at sea.*

Lower New York . . . from a 1911 painting by Richard Rummell. *Sears Tower, 1973.*

seen from above. The most striking features of the building are probably the ten shells which make up the roof. The highest of the shells soars 221 ft above the surface of the harbour.

Self-supporting concrete

When Utzon first conceived the idea of them he saw them as true shells—thin skins of self-supporting concrete. But when work started, he found he had to design massive arches to support them.

The result was that the cost of the building rose dramatically, and the shells took on a heavier appearance. Not surprisingly—since their total weight when finished amounted to 26,800 tons—it is the heaviest roof in the world.

Utzon never saw the shells completed. He resigned from the project in 1966 in the midst of a furore over rising costs.

His place was taken by a consortium of four Sydney architects, with Peter Hall as design architect. Hall faced the awesome task of designing the great glass walls which close in the shells at each end, for

when he took over only the first stage of the building had been completed. But perhaps his biggest task was the interior, which in $4\frac{1}{2}$ acres had to accommodate a concert hall, a theatre for opera and ballet, a drama theatre, a recording room for the Sydney Symphony Orchestra, and a cinema which could also be used for chamber music recitals. He solved most of the difficult problems well, but the opera theatre turned out to be too small for its purpose and is not expected to make a profit.

More expense on the way

Utzon's white shells sit majestically over the harbour as he conceived them, despite gloomy predictions by his critics that they might fall down. Visitors standing on the terrace below them feel they could be aboard a huge yacht at sea.

Public lotteries paid for the building, but more money may still be needed, for the magnificent, but controversial Opera House promises to be almost as costly to run as it was to build.

RECYCLING RUBBISH

RUBBISH IS being used as a valuable raw material in the production of energy for the city of Nashville, Tennessee.

A plant that cost $16·5 million (£6·8 million) went into action in February 1974, to start converting hundreds of tons of rubbish at a time into enough energy to provide heat and air-conditioning for 38 Nashville office blocks. Lorry loads from the city tip are fed into an incinerator-boiler, where they are burnt to convert water into high-pressure steam. The steam is then used to spin the rotors of turbines, and so generate electricity.

Man's amazing inventions

ANCIENT PENNY-IN-SLOT MACHINE

The Greeks had a drachma for it 1900 years ago

The coin-operated machine—almost a symbol of our own age—was first designed by the Greek scientist Hero, who lived in Alexandria during the century after Christ.

It was planned as a holy-water dispenser in temples. The water was contained in an urn with a short dispenser pipe leading out from the bottom. The upper end of this pipe, inside the urn, was closed by a plug fixed to one end of a horizontal bar that pivoted like a see-saw. When a coin was put into a slot at the top,

STEAM ENGINE *With this design, which spun the sphere by feeding steam into the jet, Hero beat James Watt by 1700 years.*

it dropped down a chute on to the other end of the see-saw. For a few seconds the see-saw would tip and, lifting the plug from the pipe, allow the water to pour along a trough into a goblet. As soon as the coin—a 5 drachma piece—fell into the bottom of the urn, the see-saw would return the plug to the end of the pipe and shut off the water flow.

A similar principle is used to this day in the simpler coin-operated machines, such as chocolate-bar dispensers.

Hero's extraordinary genius made him a prolific inventor in the fields of music, religion, war, engineering and industry.

The author of important books on geometry, he had a mind that soared away from figures on paper to practical applications of science. He showed how to calculate the distance from Rome to Alexandria by observing an eclipse, and devised many useful machines.

He designed a beam press for crushing olives to make olive oil, and a screw press to squeeze the juice out of grapes.

Screw-cutting device

He also built a screw-cutting machine to make wooden bolts, and a machine to make the wooden nuts to screw on them. An indication of how far he was ahead of his time, is the fact that 1600 years passed before the turnscrew came into general use, with the modern screwdriver following 100 years later.

To the military field, he contributed a powerful crossbow, called a gastrophetes, incorporating a pair of animal horns for the bow, and spring power from stretched and twisted animal sinews.

His contributions to music were two semi-automatic organs. One had an air-pump, which could be driven by a water-wheel or a windmill. The other was operated by pumping water into a tank of air.

Most advanced of his inventions was a steam reaction engine, an aeolopile, in which steam was generated in a boiler and led into a hollow sphere. The steam escaped through a pair of jets and caused the sphere to spin round. The world had to wait for the 18th century and James Watt before this power was harnessed in a practical way.

Remote control

But his most spectacular design was one to open and close huge wooden temple doors by remote control. The idea. was that a priest would light a fire on the temple altar, and this would activate the doors before the mystified congregation. The secret was that when the fire ignited on the altar, it heated air in a chamber inside. The expanding air would be forced down a pipe into a water-filled vessel below. This pushed water out of the vessel, along a tube, and into a bucket attached by rope to spindles connected to the base of the temple doors. Weighed down by the water, the bucket descended, so turning the spindles and opening the doors. With the priest nowhere near, it would have seemed to the congregation that the doors had been opened by divine intervention. When the altar fire was put out, the air in the chamber cooled, contracted, and

SLOT MACHINE *Coins fed into an urn tilt a see-saw, displace a plug, and allow a few seconds flow of water. Designed as a holy-water dispenser for temples, it was similar in principle to today's slot machines.*

reversed the whole operation, sucking the water from the bucket and allowing a counterweight to fall and close the doors—again, apparently unaided by human hand.

It is not known how many of Hero's inventions were actually used, but the details of them, contained in his books, leave no doubt that he was a gifted inventor, centuries ahead of his time.

THE DOOMWATCH DRAGONS

THIS ornate and fanciful object is not a tea urn, but an early earthquake alarm, invented in AD 132 by the Chinese astronomer Chang Heng. It was indirectly the forerunner of the modern seismograph, which measures earth tremors.

When a shock occurred, a free-swinging pendulum inside the 8 ft high vessel would dislodge one of eight horizontal arms, opening the jaws of one of the eight dragons around the outside. A ball would then fall from the dragon's mouth into the mouth of one of the eight frogs around the base of the vessel.

The dragons and frogs were aligned along points of the compass, and the ball would indicate the direction of the earthquake.

GUNS WITHOUT GUNPOWDER

Deadly weapons that devastated cities

MEDIEVAL MISSILE LAUNCHER *Besieged troops use a petrary, powered by plaited human hair, to bombard an assault tower with boulders weighing up to 5 cwt, while tunnellers attack from below.*

Long before the days when the western world used explosives, armies had a whole range of devices for hurling missiles at enemies.

One of the most powerful was the ballista which was used by the Greeks and Romans. Built like a huge crossbow on a frame, it could fire a 5 lb. bolt more than 500 yds.

At the siege of Rome in AD 537, a Gothic chief was pinned to a tree by a ballista bolt, and when Paris was besieged by the Vikings three centuries later, another bolt passed clean through three Norsemen in succession.

Backing up the ballista was the catapult—the equivalent of the modern mortar—which lobbed rather than fired missiles. The catapult's arm, with a cup for a missile at one end, was wound back and held under tension by twisted animal sinews. When it was released, the arm flew upwards and struck a crossbar, sending the missile 500 yds or more.

The ballista and catapult continued to be used until the 12th century. However, the ancient method of twisting animal sinews to provide the necessary tension had long been forgotten, and ropes were used instead. This meant that the Crusader's machines, for example, were not nearly as powerful as those of the Romans.

The solution was a new engine of war —the trebuchet. This machine was similar to the catapult, except that it used a counterweight to swing the arm and fire the missile.

Some trebuchets were colossal. With throwing arms 50 ft long and counterweights of 10 tons they could hurl 300 lb. boulders more than 600 yds.

Stones were not the only missiles fired. Trebuchets were used to throw Greek Fire—a highly inflammable mixture of sulphur, bitumen, resin, naphtha and tow with sprinklings of turpentine, charcoal and saltpetre. This fearful concoction was regarded as the ultimate weapon in the early Middle Ages. Its most alarming property was that water only caused the flames to burn more fiercely. For centuries, the secret of how to manufacture Greek Fire was known only to the Byzantines.

It made their fleets invincible, but during the 9th century the Arabs discovered how to make it and were soon using it against the Byzantines.

Other tactics were more subtle. Sometimes trebuchets were used to terrify the enemy by throwing dead opponents and live prisoners over the defender's walls. The rotting carcasses of horses were also fired into besieged cities in an attempt to spread pestilence among the enemy.

At the siege of Carolstein in 1422, the garrison was showered with 200 cart-loads of manure.

One of the last recorded uses of a trebuchet was at the siege of Rhodes in 1480, when the Turks brought up heavy guns to batter the defenders. In desperation, the beleaguered Christians built a trebuchet, and with it they managed to silence the Turkish siege artillery.

But the days of the trebuchet were over. Gunpowder, first used by the Chinese in the 4th century BC, became known in the western world, and the first guns, which were appallingly unreliable, were invented early in the 14th century.

CREATURE OF WAR *A siege machine designed in 1472, with drawbridge, 'gun' and turret.*

FIRE POWER *The man aiming the catapult (top) is lifted off his feet by the weapon's force.*

HOW ARCHIMEDES SET THE ENEMY ON FIRE

ARCHIMEDES, the mathematician and inventor who lived more than 2000 years ago, may have used solar energy as a weapon.

According to several ancient writers—including Plutarch and Anthemius of Trailles—he reflected sun rays on to the Roman fleet, when it sailed against his home town of Syracuse between 215 and 212 BC, and set it on fire.

But their descriptions were garbled, and historians tended to discount them. In 1973, however, Dr Ioannis Sakkas, a Greek engineer, carried out a series of experiments which proved it could have been effective.

He focused 50 bronze-painted mirrors on a small rowing boat and reflected the sun's rays on to it. Within seconds the craft began to smoulder, and after two minutes it burst into flames.

Professor Evenghelos Stamatis, a Greek authority on Archimedes who saw the experiment, said later he had no doubts that the inventor had used solar energy.

In a 1973 experiment to prove that Archimedes, the Greek inventor, had used the sun's power to defeat the Romans, 50 Greek sailors were given oblong mirrors which they focused on a small boat, setting it on fire. When Archimedes carried out the same operation, he probably used shields of polished bronze. The Roman ships are reported to have been routed by Archimedes' device.

THE GENIUS OF LEONARDO

Tanks and aircraft designed 500 years ago

The many-sided genius of the 15th-century artist and engineer Leonardo da Vinci produced schemes for a host of modern inventions, hundreds of years before their time—including road vehicles, aircraft and weapons.

Leonardo (1452–1519) was a man of many talents—painter, sculptor, musician, architect, town planner, military engineer and scientist. But it was as an inventor that his ideas were most prolific.

He produced designs for a vehicle propelled through a system of gears, which foreshadowed those on the modern car. He planned a tank with sloping sides to shield it against artillery.

His military inventions included a rapid-firing cannon, exploding shot and a giant crossbow.

He worked on plans for several flying

MACHINES OF WAR *Leonardo's design for a system of military flails (top); the revolving blades would have swept the horseman's enemies from his path. Below: an armoured vehicle, driven by operators turning cranking handles and protected from artillery fire by steeply sloping sides.*

FLYING MACHINE *A pair of flapping wings, powered by the flyer's legs and arms, were intended to get this strange craft into the air.*

machines. His proposed 'ship of the air' had four flapping wings which the pilot was supposed to operate by pushing against a pole. It would have been too heavy to get off the ground, but showed a grasp of the principles of flight.

So, too, did Leonardo's ideas for a vertical take-off aircraft using an aerial screw similar to the modern propeller.

Leonardo also designed a basic parachute and tackled the problems of underwater exploration. He produced schemes for a diving bell and suit.

His ingenuity was irrepressible, and sometimes resulted in bizarre contraptions. He even drew up detailed instructions for making stink bombs.

Sadly, Leonardo lacked the temperament to carry through most of his schemes. His designs for new machines, and his scientific observations, were set down in thousands of pages of drawings, carefully annotated in mirror writing (he was not only left-handed; he wrote from right to left).

He died with his work unpublished, leaving his conclusions to be rediscovered by others—often hundreds of years later.

GIANT CROSSBOW *This massive machine dwarfs the operator (bottom right), who was to load and fire it using cogs and pulleys.*

RAPID-FIRING GUNS *Alternative designs for semi-automatic weapons. Each employed several barrels firing in quick succession.*

IRREPRESSIBLE INGENUITY *Leonardo's inventive powers even extended to articulated chains. The drawings anticipated much later inventions leading to the familiar bicycle chain.*

ON VICTORY'S TRACK

How the modern tank was developed

The tank, as we see it smashing through defences in war films or in news programmes, seems a brilliant example of modern inventiveness and military engineering. Yet the concept of a vehicle strong enough to carry guns or missiles, while protecting its own crew from enemy fire, is far older.

An armoured battle car was first proposed by Guido da Vigevano in France in 1335, and sketched by Leonardo da Vinci in 1484.

But even before Leonardo, armoured wagons had proved themselves in battle, and with devastating effect. Their innovator was Jan Zizka, leader of the Protestant Hussites of Bohemia. In 1420 Sigismund, the Holy Roman Emperor, invaded the Hussites—and Zizka was waiting with his secret weapon, the wagon-fort. This was a heavy wagon drawn by a team of horses and armoured with sheets of iron. The crew fired crossbows and guns through loopholes pierced in the side.

The galloping fortress

Zizka's tactics were astonishingly original. His wagon-forts carried out complicated battle manoeuvres at full gallop, shattering their opponents by speed and mobility. If forced to defend, Zizka used the wagon-forts in much the same way as modern generals deploy their tanks. Dug in behind a ditch, linked together by chains, the wagon-forts made a formidable obstacle to any advance.

Zizka, with a mere 25,000 men, crushed

FIRST TRUE TANKS *Armoured wagon-forts with crews firing through loopholes helped the Hussites to repel a vastly superior army.*

Sigismund's invasion force of 200,000. For the next 14 years the Hussites ravaged Central Europe, winning 50 battles. It was over 400 years later, in 1855, that the armoured car evolved a stage further when a British inventor named Cowan patented a turtle-shaped vehicle based on a steam tractor. In 1899 a Mr F. R. Simms fitted a Maxim machine-gun to a four-wheeled armoured motorcycle; and three years later a boat-shaped armoured vehicle carrying machine-guns was exhibited at the Crystal Palace.

Stalemate in the trenches

The ultimate battle-wagon, the modern tank, with its caterpillar tracks and heavy armour and guns, was invented by Ernest Swinton in 1915 to be used against the Germans during the First World War. It was the obvious way to break the stalemate in the trenches, but too few were built to make much difference.

The first tanks went to France in August 1916, and they were given their name because—for security reasons—the crates in which they were sent were labelled WATER TANKS.

BATTLE-WAGON *Horse-drawn carts carried crews armed with pikes, bows and early guns into battle in the 15th century.*

THE SQUARE-SHOOTER

A machine-gun that dealt two sorts of death

One of the world's first machine-guns fired two types of bullets: round ones for shooting at a Christian enemy; and square ones, which were more damaging, for killing Turks.

The inventor, a London lawyer named James Puckle, designed the flintlock machine-gun in 1718 for use on board ships, claiming in his patent application that 'it discharges so often and so many bullets and can be so quickly loaded as renders it next to impossible to carry a ship by boarding'.

The gun was not the most portable of weapons, however. It was heavy, with a bore of $1\frac{1}{2}$ in. and a barrel nearly 3 ft long. The barrel, mounted on a tripod, had a firing drum that held 11 pre-loaded chambers, which could be hand-revolved by the gunner.

At a public demonstration in 1722, a Puckle gun discharged 63 bullets in 7 minutes. The impressed authorities put the weapon into production, but it proved cumbersome and hard to load in action, and the Puckle gun was soon no more than a military curiosity.

Three examples survive, one in Copenhagen and two in the Tower of London. Both London models, one of brass and one of iron, are fitted with the square firing chambers.

THE MIGHTY, VULNERABLE MOUSE

THE HEAVIEST tank ever built weighed 180 tons and stood almost 20 ft high. Its armour at the front was 12 in. thick. Code-named the Mouse, it first appeared in 1944, after the German Army's tank divisions had been badly mauled on the Russian front.

Hitler had realised he could never hope to match the masses of Russian tanks now ranged against his forces, and the huge output from the Soviet factories meant that the gap was widening every day.

So he briefed Dr Porsche—designer of the Volkswagen Beetle—to produce a land battleship, a tank that would pack a heavier punch than any enemy tank, yet remain completely invulnerable, thanks to its own massive armour protection.

To shift this enormous bulk, it had a 1500 hp diesel engine driving an electric generator which fed the power to two motors mounted in each hub of the monster's giant caterpillar tracks.

The Mouse was completely watertight with its hatches closed. It could cross the bottom of a river 40 ft deep, with its engine switched off to conserve power and its motors fed by cable from another tank on the river-bank. Once the tank was safely across, the roles were reversed for the second tank to cross.

But its size and weight were the Mouse's undoing. Its top speed was only 12 mph, and when it drove along roads on test the vibration cracked foundations, smashed cobblestones and shattered windows in all the towns and villages it passed through.

Although its tracks were each 1 yd wide, the pressure on them was enough to cause it to sink on anything but the driest ground. So finally, the project was dropped.

MOUSE WITH A WEIGHT PROBLEM *It was supposed to be an invincible land battleship, but the tank ordered by Hitler wrecked roads, shattered windows and sank in damp land.*

THOSE MAGNIFICENT MEN

The uncertain struggle for the skies

STRICTLY FOR THE BIRDS *Design for a flying machine submitted to an American magazine anonymously in 1865. So far as is known, the ten eaglepower device never flew.*

The ascent of man has always been a precarious affair, particularly in the early days when most attempts to get off the ground were clumsy efforts to emulate the action of birds in flight. A Benedictine monk is said to have jumped from a tower, wearing wings, about AD 1000. He broke both his legs, and there is no record of a further attempt.

Examples of Leonardo da Vinci's studies in the 15th century include drawings of a parachute and a helicopter model.

Looking forward to lift-off

A hundred years after da Vinci, inventors began thinking in terms of using other power sources to obtain lift-off. In 1670

Francesco Lana Tetzi designed an airship with four vacuum cylinders 'to wreck ships at sea, or houses could be set on fire by fireballs dropped from the sky'. Since he was a peaceful man he abandoned the idea, which was just as well, for he had overlooked the fact that vessels emptied of air would need to be strong enough to resist the external air pressure, and so would be too heavy to fly anyway.

It was another century before man finally rose triumphant, borne aloft by the hot-air balloon of the French Montgolfier brothers. Joseph Montgolfier is said to have conceived the idea of using hot air when watching smoke from a fire curl up the chimney. He took paper bags—

FLIGHTS OF FANCY

Magnets were supposed to help lift this aircraft off the ground. It was designed by Barthélemy Laurenço de Gusmão in 1709.

Rubber bands acted as springs on the wings of this birdman's design by Bréant in 1854. The rest was up to the energy of the would-be flier.

A highly sophisticated failure by M. G. de la Landelle in 1863. It combined propellers, inclined planes, parachutes—and hope.

ANIMAL ASCENTS *The Frenchman, Margat, rode his white stag, Coco, aloft in Paris during 1798, in a gondola beneath a hot-air balloon.*

JET POWERED *This Steam Kettle machine toured England in 1790—but never flew.*

he was a paper manufacturer—held them over the flames, and watched them rise gently to the ceiling.

On November 21, 1783, two Frenchmen, Pilâtre de Rozier and the Marquis d'Arlandes, soared to 300 ft in the Montgolfier balloon and made a journey of 5 miles.

Balloons across the Channel

In 1785 the first crossing of the English Channel was achieved, with rather less dignity than such an historic occasion deserved. The balloonists, Jean-Pierre Blanchard and his American backer, Dr John Jeffries, sat in a car slung beneath the giant balloon. It was hoped to propel it by an arrangement of flapping wings and a propeller.

The launch from the cliffs of Dover went without mishap, but 6 miles off the French coast, the craft began to lose height. The aeronauts first shed their equipment and finally most of their clothes. These desperate measures worked, and the happy pair landed in a forest 12 miles inland, clad only in their underwear.

It is unlikely that the flapping-wing arrangement on the Blanchard balloon contributed in any way to its progress, but it was one of the earliest attempts at air propulsion. As soon as balloon flight had become a reality the designers turned their attention to controlled flight, and some very remarkable and quite impractical devices were proposed. These ideas ranged from Blanchard's hopelessly small

UP AND AWAY *German glider pioneer Otto Lilienthal tested his models from 1891 to 1896. He made many hundreds of successful flights of up to 250 yds in his graceful craft before he was killed in 1896 when his glider stalled and crashed.*

propeller to hot-air jets, steam jets and even gunpowder.

Possibly the most eccentric idea came from an anonymous American designer who wrote to a science magazine in 1865 suggesting that eagles could be used to carry a man. He designed a harness for the birds, each tethered to the rim of a circular frame, with the passenger seated in a basket in the centre. Ten sets of reins were provided to steer the birds, with a set of cords to make the birds fly higher or lower. The inventor did not say where one would find ten eagles obliging enough to co-operate with this scheme.

An idea that comes a close second in the eccentricity stakes was that proposed in 1885 by another American, W. O. Ayres. This was a forerunner of the 'flying bed-stead' and was driven by seven propellers, six for lift and one for propulsion. Foot pedals provided the drive for two of the lifting propellers, and compressed-air motors drove the other four. The propulsion screw was operated by a hand crank, as were the rudder and elevator controls.

Inevitably, steam power was considered as a power source by some inventors and one, Hiram Maxim, inventor of the machine-gun, built a biplane test-rig in 1894. The wings were 125 ft across, and two propellers were driven by powerful steam engines that consumed 12 gallons of water a minute. At its first, and only, trial the machine left its rails briefly before being brought to a stop.

Tragedy after soaring success

In contrast to Maxim's snorting giant were the silent, graceful gliders built by the German, Otto Lilienthal. In 1891 he started his serious gliding experiments. He made many hundreds of successful flights of up to 250 yds before he died in 1896. His glider stalled and sideslipped into the ground, breaking his back.

Another silent spectacle was the first parachute descent, made on October 22, 1797, by a young Frenchman called André Garnerin. He hitched a car and a parachute to a hydrogen balloon, rose to 3000 ft and then released his device

PEDAL POWER *Dr Ayres hoped to use pedalling, cranking and compressed air.*

FLYING BEDSTEAD *A 1953 rig designed by Rolls-Royce to test vertical take-off.*

navigation. He had realised that an aircraft must have fixed wings and a separate propulsion system, and his work between 1799 and 1809 laid the foundation for the whole of modern aerodynamics. He designed and flew models and full-sized machines, proving that fixed-wing aircraft were possible.

The Wright brothers

One hundred years later the Wright brothers made the first powered, sustained flight in an aeroplane at Kill Devil Hill, Kittyhawk, USA, on December 17, 1903. And Wilbur Wright wrote: 'Sir George Cayley carried the science of flying to a point which it had never reached before, and which it scarcely reached again during the last century.'

The Wright brothers made four flights that first day at Kittyhawk. The first lasted only 12 seconds, but the last was 59 seconds and took them 852 ft.

Wilbur Wright later went to Europe where he greatly stimulated interest in aviation, and by 1908 he had made more than 100 flights.

With the initial powered flight problems now behind them, aviators began to look for new uses for planes. As the threat of the First World War loomed, the race for air power began in earnest.

from the balloon. The canopy, 23 ft across, opened perfectly, but the descent proved uncomfortable. Garnerin swung like a pendulum and he was violently sick, but he landed safely.

Progress on more satisfactory lines was taking place in other directions, however. The airship began to emerge from the balloon, and in 1852 Henri Giffard, a French engineer, built the world's first working dirigible. The airship had a capacity of 88,300 cubic feet of hydrogen, and was driven by a steam engine developing 3 hp. Giffard made his first flight from Paris on September 24, 1852, and travelled 17 miles at 6 miles an hour.

Aeroplanes around the corner

Almost 50 years later, the Brazilian Alberto Santos-Dumont popularised airships by flying his cigar-shaped airship, powered by a small petrol engine, from Saint-Cloud to the Eiffel Tower and back.

In the field of heavier-than-air machines the groundwork had been done by Sir George Cayley, truly the father of aerial

MADONNA AND HELICOPTER

A 15th-century French Madonna and Child shows the infant Jesus holding what looks like a toy helicopter that works by pulling on a string. It may have been simply a toy windmill, but it may have been a flying top— surprising for about 1460.

TOPS FOR IDEAS

How a child's toy revolutionised navigation

Airliners fly on automatic pilot and navigate with great precision around the globe, ships keep a relatively even keel in rough seas and submarines find their way around the ocean depths . . . all thanks to a child's toy and an imaginative American, Elmer Ambrose Sperry.

While watching a child's spinning top on a summer's day in 1905, Sperry was asked by one of his children: 'Why does it stand up when it spins?' It gave him the inkling of an idea which, eventually adapted as the gyro-compass, revolutionised sea and air navigation.

Sperry borrowed an electrically powered gyroscope from a technical school, which was used to demonstrate the rotation of the earth on its axis, and studied it. He began to wonder if the gyroscope's action—whose axis retained its position whichever way the frame was moved—could be put to practical use by modern engineers.

Later, on a sea voyage to Europe, he was thrown out of his berth during a storm, and thought that the gyroscope could be used to steady a ship. After three years of tests, he produced the first, full-scale stabiliser for the United States destroyer *Worden*.

Constant axis

Basically, the principle involved in the use of a gyroscope as a stabiliser, is that the gyro's constant axis helps compensate for the movements of a ship and, to some extent, reduces its tendency to roll.

In 1908, using the same principle, Sperry produced the gyro-compass, which stayed on true north and was unaffected by any magnetic influences.

Further developments from Sperry's ideas followed: the automatic pilot which, through a system of tiny gyroscopes, can keep a plane on course in clouds or darkness; a direction finder for use in drilling, and a bank indicator, which indicates whether a plane is following a straight course or turning, and by how much.

On his death at the age of 69 in 1930, Sperry had nearly 400 patents in his name.

SEEDING THE RAINCLOUDS

When cannon fire failed to start a downpour

In the 18th and 19th centuries it was noted that it frequently rained after battles in which there had been heavy cannon fire. This was taken to mean that the loud bangs had sent shock waves into the clouds and caused the rains to form and fall.

So early attempts at rain-making, aside from the rain-dances of primitive societies, involved the firing of artillery, or the launching of explosive grenades into the clouds, fired from a large cannon.

Inflated claims

Some exponents of this technique, lending an authentic air to an otherwise scientifically unproven theory, made inflated claims for their efforts. They suggested that their methods would cause only rain and prevent hail, high winds and forest fires.

Daniel Ruggles, an American inventor, used a hot-air balloon in 1880 to lift an explosive charge into clouds, but his attempts were made usually before an obviously imminent downpour.

Rainfall is naturally caused by ice particles combining in clouds until they are heavy enough to fall. In 1946, Vincent J. Schaefer, now one of the world's leading cloud physicists based at New York State University, began experiments in 'seeding'—trying to create rain by introducing chemicals into clouds. He let winds carry particles of dry ice (solid carbon dioxide) into clouds.

In 1947, another General Electric scientist, Bernard Vonnegut, developed a more economical rain-making technique—spraying clouds with silver iodide crystals, which then serve as nuclei for snowflakes.

Other nations such as Australia and Israel are also trying to 'make rain'. Israel has claimed that it has substantially increased its annual rainfall.

SMOKE SIGNALS OF DISASTER *Full speed ahead for a K-boat, one of the steam submarines built by Britain in the First World War. Designed to operate with the battle fleet as a combination of destroyer and submarine, they proved a disastrous failure in both roles.*

THE DEADLIEST WARSHIPS OF ALL

K-boats killed the men who sailed them

Performing sea lions and fruit salts are unlikely partners in any venture. Yet both figure in the bizarre story of submarine development, along with such failures as the British steam submarine or K-boat—which cost 270 lives, without ever going into action—and the one-man submarine used against the British in the American War of Independence.

The sea lions, fruit salts and K-boats each had a role in Allied attempts to beat the German U-boats, which were sinking British merchant ships in the First World War and threatening to starve Britain into surrender.

The sea lions, once circus performers, were trained to locate submarine propeller noise, and rewarded with fish when they reacted correctly. Unhappily, most of the sea lions tended to follow every ship, without discriminating between surface and submarine noises—and soon realised how easy it was to catch their own fish anyway.

The fruit salts were to be used by the barrel-load. The idea was to dump the barrels on the sea-bed and blast them open by remote control when submarines were known to be around.

The resultant effervescence, it was thought, should blow the U-boat to the surface in a stream of bubbles and leave it as a sitting target for waiting warships.

The results of this strategy, if recorded, have never been published.

The five-minute crash dive

It was at about this time—the summer of 1915—that the British Admiralty decided to increase its own underwater striking force by building a new type of submarine. What they required was not only a commerce raider but a vessel big and fast enough to operate with a battle fleet in action. And so the K-boats were born.

They proved to be the most deadly warships ever built—but only for those who sailed in them.

The K-boats were 330 ft long and heavier than the navy's biggest destroyers. Before they could dive, the crew had to shut off steam, douse the boilers, lower the two funnels and shut nine watertight doors or hatches.

It meant that the crash dive, the submarine commander's most effective defence when attacked on the surface, was impossible. While a well-drilled U-boat could dive in 90 seconds, the K-boat crew were doing well to get below in less than five minutes. And then their troubles were only just starting.

The K-boat's length and weight made it difficult to trim properly. The slightest error could send it diving out of control, and the story of the early K-boats was a catalogue of disasters.

K-13 crashed to the bottom of Gareloch, in Scotland, on her diving trials, with the loss of 32 lives. K-2 caught fire on her first dive. K-3 plunged to the bottom of Stokes Bay on a test dive; among the survivors of K-3 were the Commander-in-Chief Portsmouth and the future George VI, then a midshipman.

K-4 ran aground; K-5 vanished—with her crew of 57—on an exercise; K-6 got stuck on the bottom of Devonport dockyard; and K-14 sprang a leak in Portsmouth harbour.

Despite these setbacks, and the mounting loss of life, naval chiefs pressed ahead for three years with the K-boats, even though the plan for their eventual use—in close formation with the battle-fleet—was fraught with danger.

Battle of May Island

Proof came on the evening of January 31, 1918, when two flotillas of K-boats sailed from Rosyth as the Grand Fleet's advance guard. The resultant shambles became known as the Battle of May Island —the spot in the Firth of Forth where the leading K-boats, running at top speed on the surface, had to swerve to avoid a pair of minesweepers. The helm of K-14, the third boat in line, jammed, and K-22 ran her down. As the crew sent up distress signals, the battle-cruiser HMS *Inflexible*, bearing down in the darkness at 18 knots, ploughed into the wreckage. She tore away 30 ft from the bow of K-22 and bent it through a right angle before vanishing at top speed into the night.

HMS *Ithuriel*, the light-cruiser leading the first flotilla of K-boats, turned back to help and her flock of submarines faithfully followed . . . right into the path of the battle-cruisers, their escorting destroyers and the light-cruiser HMS *Fearless*.

Fearless ran down K-17; K-4 swerved to avoid them both; K-3 swerved to avoid K-4 and was run down by K-6. Then K-7 hit the sinking K-17.

In those two hours, on their first and last major exercise with the fleet, the lesson of the K-boats came home: two of them sunk, three crippled, a light-cruiser damaged and the K-boat death roll up to 270.

EARLY SUBMARINES

Rowing 15 ft below the surface of the Thames

Despite Britain's experience with the K-boat, it was during the First World War that the submarine became one of the most effective war machines ever invented.

The first submarines, however, were in existence 200 years before, and the theory of the submarine vessel goes back even further—to ancient Greece. Aristotle, Archimedes and others all mentioned attempts to build diving bells.

The idea lapsed, but in 1578 William Bourne, a British author and mathematician, designed what might have been the first submarine—a contraption of waterproof leather over a wooden frame. It was to have been propelled by oarsmen, but it never left the drawing-board.

The next move also came in England, from Cornelius van Drebbel, a Dutchman. In 1620 he built a wooden boat, covered with greased leather to make it watertight. He rowed it, successfully, 15 ft below the surface of the Thames.

In 1776 an American, David Bushnell, built the first submarine to be used as a weapon of war. It was the *Turtle*, and was used in an unsuccessful attempt to attach a gunpowder bomb to a British ship, in the American War of Independence.

The next development was also American, also anti-British. In 1800 Robert Fulton produced the submarine *Nautilus*, which he hoped to sell to the French, then at war with England. Despite an impressive demonstration, complete with exploding mine, the French were not interested.

Development continued in America, and the first successful use of a submarine in wartime took place there. In 1864, during the American Civil War, the Confederate states built a submarine called the *H. L. Hunley*. Armed with a mine, attached to a boom that projected from the bow, it engaged and damaged the Federal ironclad warship *Housatonic*.

Most of these early craft had a limited underwater range, because they quickly ran out of steam or air. The solution came with the development of reliable electric motors in the 1880s.

SHIPS WITH ROTATING SAILS

In the 1920s, the Germans planned to return to wind propulsion

In 1925 the nautical world was startled by the appearance of ships apparently propelled by gigantic cotton bobbins. Their German inventors believed that these vessels were a major breakthrough in sea transport.

Experiments at the University of Gottingen in 1922 gave Anton Flettner, a German engineer, the idea for the revolutionary rotor ship. He had found that wind pressure on a revolving disc was very much greater than pressure on a conventional sail. Rotor ships operated on this principle of propulsion.

The ships had two rotors, each turned by a small engine at its base. When turned at four times the speed of the wind, the pressure exerted was 15 times greater than that on a sail of the same size.

Idea from sport

Long before anyone thought of applying the principle to ships, players of ball games had noticed the phenomenon and had even turned it to their advantage. In cricket a bowler spins the ball and takes advantage of the effect of the wind upon the spinning surface to produce a deceptive flight. Tennis players spin the ball to deceive their opponents, and so do many other sportsmen.

The Flettner rotor ship was said to be faster than sailing ships, cheap to run and efficient to crew. It could fight its way through storms using only the power of tiny petrol engines, no bigger than those used in small cars. An ordinary sailing vessel is required to take down all canvas in a hurricane while the rotor ship could continue sailing.

On transatlantic voyages, rotor ships reached speeds of 17 knots. They were small vessels—about 600 tons—with their two rotors looking like enormous funnels, 65 ft high and 10 ft in diameter.

Cheap to run

Rotor-ship enthusiasts predicted that all the world's shipping would soon be using rotor power. The advantages the rotor ship had over conventional sailing ships were simplicity, and economy in handling. The Flettner was 80 per cent cheaper to run than sailing ships. Whereas several dozen men would be required to handle the sails, a single man could control the speed of the rotors. The rotor ship could also be turned or reversed simply and quickly.

But less than 20 years later, the revolutionary new ships were broken up for scrap. The ships had all developed serious mechanical problems because of the rotor's incessant vibration. And they had proved unreliable because of their dependence on wind power.

ROTOR IN MANHATTAN *Anton Flettner's rotor ship, the* Baden-Baden, *weathered several heavy gales on its transatlantic voyage from Hamburg to New York. Propelled by two rotating yellow towers, the ship caused a sensation in America.*

193

SIR HENRY BESSEMER, the inventor of a revolutionary steel-making process, was a constant traveller to the Continent—and a very poor sailor. So he designed a 'swinging saloon' which, with the help of a naval architect, R. J. Reed, was incorporated in a new cross-channel steamer, the *Bessemer*. The saloon was balanced amidships on a central pivot, and was supposed to remain on an even keel regardless of the ship's motions. In the event, it rolled violently and the passengers fared worse than those on the upper deck. So Sir Henry introduced a hydraulic brake, operated by a man who sat watching a spirit level. Every time the ship rolled, the brakeman was supposed to check the motion of the saloon. This worked even worse than the pivot. So the saloon was locked in position and the ship was used as a conventional steamer. Unfortunately she was virtually unsteerable. On her first trip she collided with the pier at Calais and repeated the performance on her return to Dover. Sir Henry sold her for scrap, but the saloon found a home at the Horticultural College in Hextable, Kent. It was finally 'sunk' there by a German bomb in the Second World War.

ALARM TO THE ADMIRALTY

Glass-shutter signals from Portsmouth to London

At the end of the 18th century, bad food, inhuman treatment and appalling living conditions roused more than 50,000 men of the Royal Navy to mutiny.

On April 13, 1797, an informer on HMS *Sovereign* at Portsmouth told an officer that mutiny was imminent, and only minutes later the authorities in the British Admiralty were handed a message: 'Mutiny brewing in Spithead.'

The signal had been flashed the 70 miles from Portsmouth to London in three minutes, by means of a remarkable signalling system devised by George Murray in 1795. Coded messages were sent along a series of relay stations, about 7 miles apart and manned by teams who were equipped with telescopes and a special signalling apparatus.

The signalling apparatus was a large, wooden frame divided into two columns of three shuttered apertures, rather like a window with six panes of glass. When the operator pulled a lever, the shutter it controlled was opened to reveal a square of daylight.

Different combinations of opened shutters represented a letter of the alphabet, or even a complete word. At night, lanterns were used to replace shutters.

The relay stations were on the tops of church towers or hills, with each one in sight of those on either side in the chain. The system linked London with Deal, Portsmouth, Plymouth and Yarmouth.

ICEBERG AIR BASES

Cold feet only in the Treasury

In the early years of the Second World War, German U-boats were sinking thousands of tons of shipping every month. Convoys escorted by warships were the usual form of protection, but the best defence of all against submarine attack was aircraft patrol.

Aircraft did not have the vast flying ranges and flight-refuelling techniques of today, so air cover was limited to within only a few hundred miles of friendly Atlantic coasts.

Then, in 1942, an English inventor named Geoffrey Pyke put forward a possible solution: giant, man-made icebergs which could be used as floating, mid-Atlantic airstrips. These might also be used as halfway refuelling stops when ferrying new war-planes from America.

Pyke's ice-ship would be 300 ft wide and 2000 ft long—a hollow ice hull like a rectangular box. Aircraft would land on the upper surface, beneath which would be hangars, workshops, crew's quarters and a refrigeration plant.

The project was named 'Habakkuk', after an Old Testament minor prophet. Habakkuk 1, verse 5 says: 'For I will work a work in your days, which ye will not believe, though it be told you.'

Secret research work was begun on lakes in the Canadian province of Alberta. There, during the construction of small-scale prototypes, it was discovered that the addition of 10 per cent wood pulp made the ice as strong as concrete and as easy to work as wood.

But there was a snag. When it was found that Habakkuk would cost at least as much to build as a conventional aircraft carrier, enthusiasm waned and the project was abandoned.

READING FOR THE BLIND

System devised for military use at night

Until 1819, lettering for the blind consisted simply of raised characters of the alphabet made of wood, lead, twigs, or even pins and needles arranged in pin cushions. Valentin Hauy, founder of the Institute for the Young Blind in Paris, experimented with 3 in. deep letters from cloth which he stuck on paper.

In 1819, the same year that a ten-year-old blind boy named Louis Braille enrolled at the Institute, a French artillery captain tried to interest the Academy of Sciences in Paris with a new system which he described simply as 'night writing'.

Captain Charles Barbier de la Serre had devised an alphabet of raised dots and dashes on strips of cardboard which soldiers could 'read' with their fingertips when in action at night.

He eventually took his method to the Institute, but, because his system consisted of a complex arrangement of 12 dots to each letter, it was not a success.

Braille, now a teenager, became interested in de la Serre's system and simplified it. From this he developed the now internationally used Braille system.

FLOATING SERPENT

THE 'FLOATING SERPENT' is a flexible barge—an alternative to tankers and pipelines as a method of carrying crude oil from wells to distant refineries. It was invented in 1956 by a British scientist, W. R. Hawthorne, who called it 'Dracone' —the Greek word for serpent. The huge vessel, made of rubber-proofed cloth, could be filled with oil and towed, just beneath the surface of the water, by a tanker. The idea was later adapted as a means of taking fresh water to remote Greek islands. But as an oil-carrier, the 'Dracone' was abandoned. It had two drawbacks: it could be towed only at slow speeds and was not suitable for large shipments—quite apart from the pollution risk if it should burst.

PEDAL FOR THE SHORE

An invention to prevent that sinking feeling

Once the bicycle had developed to the stage where it was powered by pedal cranks and a chain drive, many inventors adopted this form of drive for other vehicles.

One of the most remarkable of these was a one-man, pedal-driven lifebuoy for use in case of shipwreck. It was invented in 1895 by a Frenchman, Francois Barathon, and consisted of a saucer-shaped metal dish containing an inflatable rubber bag and some complicated machinery.

The survivor sat on the bag—which kept him and the machine afloat—and worked two sets of cranks, one with his hands and the other with his feet. The cranks turned two propellers, one placed vertically to keep the craft stable and the other to push from behind.

RESCUE IN SIGHT *Suitably dressed for the occasion, a shipwrecked victim pedals to safety, helped along by a small sail.*

THE FIRST HOT-ROD

An idea that ran out of steam

The first steam carriage to run on English roads was designed by Richard Trevithick in 1800. Despite warnings by James Watt that the boiler would explode, the engine ran on a steam pressure of 60 lb. Watt was opposed to high-pressure engines—his engines seldom ran on more than 7 lb.—and said that Trevithick deserved hanging for introducing such a device.

The vehicle had its first outing on Christmas Eve 1801, and three days later Trevithick invited some friends to take a ride. The journey ended abruptly when the carriage broke down, so the travellers made for the nearest hostelry where they warmed themselves with mulled ale. But the boiler fire was still burning merrily, and when the party returned the carriage was a smouldering wreck.

A WATERTIGHT CASE

Saving life at sea was an obsession with the Victorians. Many bizarre and impractical ideas were put forward, but one with possibilities was the suitcase/life-jacket.

Invented by a German named Krenkel in the 1880s, the case had circular panels in the lid and base which could be quickly removed. The user then fitted a watertight rubber seal into the hole, and pulled on the case to encircle his body.

Such a device would probably have kept its wearer afloat for several hours. Moreover it had the added advantage that a gentleman could politely raise his hat to any lady who happened to be floating by.

HOW MANY MILES TO THE GALLEON?

IN THE AGE of invention, one thing that the innovators knew all about was harnessing the wind. Several road carriages were designed to use this form of power, and one of the most efficient was the sail carriage invented by a Frenchman.

The vehicle was tried out in Paris in 1834, and required a crew of sailors to man the rigging in addition to the usual coach-man and postillion.

The carriage was called *L'Eolienne*, after Aiolos the Greek god of the winds, and on its first run showed an impressive turn of speed. Steering the carriage must have been a terrifying experience, as the 'driver' had no control over its speed. Stopping the vehicle seems to have been entirely over-looked by the inventor.

Devices such as this were never practical, and soon gave way to the steam carriage, and later the motor car.

HORSE OF A DIFFERENT COLOUR

When the first steam trams were introduced in San Francisco in the 1870s, horses panicked at the sight and sound of these snorting monsters. For a while, chaos reigned in the city streets as horsedrawn vehicles careered in all directions whenever a tram came into sight. But an inventor named S. R. Mathewson provided the answer. He built a steam tram in the shape of a horse, which could travel at 8 mph. The engine, patented in 1876, was gas-fired so that there would be no belching smoke to frighten the horses. Apparently the idea worked, and order was restored.

197

FIRST CAR—FIRST CRASH

And the inventor lands himself in court

Nicholas Cugnot, a French artillery officer, was the world's first motorist. Within minutes of starting, he had the world's first motoring accident. A year later, he became the world's first convicted dangerous driver.

His three-wheel vehicle appeared in 1769. A steam-driven, two-cylinder engine drove the front wheel and Cugnot said his contraption would carry four people at a speed of just under 2 mph.

But the weight of the huge copper boiler on the front of the carriage made it almost impossible to steer. On its maiden run, the machine demolished a stone wall.

Undismayed, Cugnot spent the next year building a larger version as a gun carriage for the French War Ministry. He demonstrated the new machine in a Paris street. The military observers were impressed, particularly as Cugnot promised that it could carry 5 tons.

But the steering again let him down and, as he tried to turn a corner, the carriage overturned. The ministry lost interest—and Cugnot lost his freedom. Magistrates sent him to jail and impounded his machine.

By the time he was able to think of modifications, France was in the grip of the Revolution. Cugnot moved to Brussels, where he died in 1804.

Cugnot's ill-fated gun carriage was later rebuilt, and remains his only monument —in the Paris Conservatoire des Arts.

THE IMPOSSIBLE DREAM

Man's quest for free power

The first law of thermodynamics says, in effect, that you cannot get something for nothing—but that has never stopped people from trying. It is scientifically impossible to build a machine that will run without an external energy supply, yet for centuries inventors have persisted with designs for perpetual motion machines.

One of the most common was a gravity-operated overbalancing wheel. If a weight is attached near the top of an upright wheel, the wheel will rotate until the weight reaches the bottom. If it were possible to arrange a series of weights around the wheel so that those on the way down were further from the wheel's centre than those on the way up, the result would be an overbalancing wheel which should keep on turning.

Leonardo's attempt

Such a device was designed in the 13th century by the French architect Villard de Honnecourt.

His wheel had seven pivoted hammers which stuck out on the falling side and folded in on the rising side.

Even Leonardo da Vinci designed one in the 15th century using four radial arms. At the end of each was a metal sphere containing a little mercury. The shifting weight of the mercury was supposed to keep the wheel turning.

A balanced wheel will keep turning for some time, simply because it slows down very gradually. This explains the apparent success of an overbalancing wheel, 14 ft across, built in the 17th century by Edward Somerset, Marquess of Worcester. It was started by hand, then rotated on its own for the few minutes that observers were permitted to watch. But once they had left, friction began to slow it down until it eventually came to a complete halt.

And back to square one again

Other 'perpetual motion' machines used liquids. One naïve effort, proposed by the Abbé de la Roque in 1686, consisted of a funnel with its long stem curved around and upwards in such a way as to discharge any liquid in it back into the funnel. The inventor hoped that the weight of the water in the funnel would force liquid up round the stem and back into the funnel for ever.

The fact is that the only way to force water up from such a funnel would be to install a pump—which would defeat the idea of perpetual motion.

DELIVERING THE MAIL—BY AIR

A practical use for the air-tube railway in February 1863. The first mailbags are sent speeding on their way from the Post Office's North Western District Office at Eversholt Street, London, through a pneumatic tube, to Euston Station. Inset: A 1914 variation of Brunel's system—the prototype of the electric train which now moves the mail around London in a similar way.

TRAINS THAT COULD RUN ON AIR

Early attempts to develop tube trains

Trains have been powered by steam, diesel oil, electricity and, experimentally, jet and rocket engines. But in 1847 Isambard Kingdom Brunel, the great British inventor, built a train which was driven by air.

His plan was to pull a train along a tube between the tracks. The leading coach was attached to the 15 in. diameter pipe by a piston arm.

Huge pumping engines every 3 miles along the track extracted air from the pipe in front of the train, and the pressure behind the piston forced it along.

Brunel built an experimental section of pipe on the South Devon Railway. But the copper and leather pipe valves corroded in the salty air and were chewed away by rats.

Seventeen years later, another British inventor, T. W. Rammell, designed a system in which the whole train was blown and sucked along a tube. But the idea of huge tubes criss-crossing the country was unrealistic, and in 1870 pneumatic railways went underground where they have remained to this day. .

That year a pneumatic underground system was built beneath New York. The coach, seating about 20 people, was pumped along by a 100 hp steam engine.

But within 10 years electric trains appeared, and the long search for a railway which could run on air was abandoned.

CYCLING ON AIR

JOHN DUNLOP, a Scottish veterinary surgeon living in Ireland, wanted to find a way to protect his son's tricycle from damage on cobbled roads. Robert Thomson, a civil engineer of Middlesex, had already designed and patented a hollow rubber tyre filled with air or horsehair in 1845. But Dunlop was looking for something better and, in 1888, he made a pneumatic tyre with a rubber outer casing and an air-filled inner tube, inflated through a valve. This was the first inflatable tyre containing air under pressure. André and Edouard Michelin first used the pneumatic tyre on motor vehicles in 1895, and five years later the Dunlop Rubber Company produced its first motor tyre.

WORDS ALONG A WIRE

The telephone evolved from attempts to make a deaf aid

By an odd coincidence, the first message transmitted by telephone, an instrument which has proved such a great boon in emergencies, was a cry for help from its inventor.

At the moment Alexander Graham Bell was ready to test his invention for the first time, he accidentally spilt some acid on his clothes.

So the first words his assistant, waiting in the basement of Bell's home, heard over the receiver from his employer who was in the attic were: 'Mr Watson, come here! I want you!'

Bell, born in Edinburgh in 1847, had been trying to design a machine for communicating with the deaf when he stumbled on the basic principles for a telephone. He found that when an iron diaphragm was vibrated by the human voice, close to a magnet around which was a wire coil, a weak current was created. This could be transmitted along a cable to a corresponding diaphragm.

Although Bell is generally acknowledged as inventor of the telephone in 1876, ten years later the US Supreme Court admitted a prior claim by an Italian, Antonio Meucci, who had perfected a similar device in Havana.

Also, a German, Johann Philipp Reis, made one in 1861.

It is thought that Bell may have been influenced by Reis, but almost certainly developed his telephone without knowledge of Meucci's experiments.

Bell later went on to invent the gramophone record, the photophone—which was the forerunner of film soundtracks—and the electric eye.

BELL'S ORIGINAL TELEPHONE ... *and one of the ad-man's early attempts to sell it to the public. An extract from the material accompanying this high-powered advertisement reads : 'Its employment necessitates no skilled labour, no technical education and no special attention.'*

FIRING RANGE

THE SIDEWINDER missile, developed for the United States Navy, is reputed to have such terrifyingly sensitive detection devices that it is capable of spotting and homing in on a lighted cigarette from a distance of 100 yds. However, these lethal devices have now been given a more peaceful—and life-saving—role to play. Technologists have successfully adapted the invention to give firemen the means of discovering and dealing with a potential blaze, long before it reaches killer proportions. A new device, which can be held in a fireman's hand, is able to detect sources of fire which are hidden from view behind walls. It then pinpoints the source of danger and tells the fireman where to break through the wall so that he can immediately deal with the seat of the blaze.

SIR JOHN HARINGTON'S LEGACY

The world's first w.c. was used by Elizabeth I

As an amateur poet John Harington was not a success, but when he turned to inventing and designed the world's first water closet, he won the approval of royalty.

He was a godson of Elizabeth I, but was banished from court for circulating a risqué story. During his exile—from 1584 to 1591—he built a house at Kelston, near Bath, and installed the first flushing lavatory, which he named Ajax.

Eventually, the Virgin Queen forgave him, and in 1592 visited Kelston. She tried the invention and ordered one.

Harington wrote a book about his water closet, describing the pan with an opening in the bottom sealed by a leather-faced valve. A system of handle, levers and weights poured in water from a cistern and opened the valve.

But the public did not share Elizabeth's enthusiasm. It preferred the chamber pot. These were often emptied into the street from an upstairs window, and in France it was customary to cry 'gardez l'eau' before pouring. The English nickname 'loo' may have derived from this.

It was not until 1775 that a flushing water closet was patented. Alexander Cummings, of London, took it out for a device similar to Harington's Ajax.

But water seeped through Cummings' primitive valve; not until 1777 did the notion of the ball valve occur to one Samuel Prosser.

The development of water-closet technology received a boost from Parliament in 1848, when a Public Health Act ruled that every new house should have a 'w.c., privy or ash pit'.

BOWL OF FLOWERS *Chrysanthemums were the favourite decoration in the 19th century—this 'Itonia' set was on sale in 1890.*

ATHLETE'S REST *This magnificent ruin was the latrine enclosure of the 2nd-century Roman Gymnastic Palace at Salamis, Cyprus.*

BEAST OF BURDEN *The Victorians often chose bizarre designs, and this Lion Closet was illustrated in a catalogue of 1890.*

201

TEMPLE OF VESTA

Forerunner of the automatic lighter

No one knows whether fire was first produced by rubbing sticks together or by striking sparks off iron pyrites, but for thousands of years getting a light was an uncertain business. The Chinese had 'fire sticks' by AD 1000, but in Europe matches were unknown until the 17th century. Then phosphorus was discovered in Germany and a number of primitive matches could be made.

The first modern friction matches were sold by John Walker of Stockton-on-Tees in 1827. Lucifers—a stick dipped in gum arabic, antimony sulphide and chlorate of potash—appeared in 1833, and within a year they had made the long-used tinderbox obsolete.

The friction match was not the only type experimented with, and some of the others were highly ingenious. The Promethean match, invented in London in 1828 and named after the man in the Greek myths who stole fire from heaven, consisted of a glass phial containing a drop of sulphuric acid and wrapped in a brown paper spill soaked in gum arabic, potassium chlorate and sugar.

To light the match, the end of the phial was nipped off with a pair of pliers, and the chemical reaction between the acid and the impregnated paper produced a vigorous but choking flame.

By then, automatic lighters were already being produced.

An elegant German model of 1807, made of porcelain and brass, was called the Temple of Vesta after the ancient Roman temple where the Vestal Virgins kept a sacred fire forever burning. Its 19th-century namesake contained an apparatus for producing hydrogen and a resin disc charged with static electricity. A button which released the hydrogen also completed an electric circuit. A spark leapt from the mouth of the lion reclining outside the temple and ignited the hydrogen.

Modern lighters may be more portable, but they could hardly be more spectacular than the Temple of Vesta.

THE TEMPLE OF VESTA *An electrostatic spark ignited a hydrogen jet, causing a blue flame to spurt from the lion's mouth.*

NEXT TO GODLINESS

The inventor who took a deep breath to success

The vacuum cleaner is considered to be a recent invention, but the Victorians had a machine which used bellows to suck up the dirt. Two people were needed to operate it, one to hold the nozzle and the other to operate the bellows. Often it would blow dust out again, but one successful model used water as a filter. This type was so well made that some of them are still in use.

In 1901 a new railway-carriage cleaner was demonstrated at St Pancras Station, London. It worked on the principle of blowing out the dirt, rather than sucking it up. The demonstration did not impress the choking, dust-covered onlookers. But one of them, Hubert Booth, was set thinking. When he got home he lay on the floor with a handkerchief over his mouth and sucked hard. The dust trapped in his handkerchief convinced him that sucking up dirt instead of blowing it out was the right principle; all he needed to introduce was an efficient cloth filter which would trap dust but let air through.

Booth's first practical machine was so big that it had to be drawn by a horse. It stood in the road and sucked dirt from houses through a long hose, but the inventor had difficulties with the police because his 'noisy serpent' caused passing horses to bolt in terror.

To this day, however, all cylinder vacuum cleaners rely on Booth's principle.

His vacuum cleaner came just 25 years after the first practical carpet sweeper had been marketed by an American china-shop owner named Bissell. Mr Bissell suffered terribly from headaches and, convinced they were caused by the dusty straw in which his china was packed, he invented a sweeper.

It was a huge commercial success—but it did not cure his headaches.

EARLY CLEANER *This 1905 machine had electrically driven pumps to provide the suction. The cylinder on the end contained the filter.*

THE PYRAMID SHARPENER

Mysterious way to put the edge back on a razor blade

When a Czech engineer, Karel Drbal, took a model pyramid to the patent office in Prague and told them it would sharpen blunt razor blades left under it, the staff refused to believe him. Only after their chief scientist tried it himself and found that it worked was Drbal's 'invention' registered, Patent No. 91304.

That was in 1959. But the idea was as old as the ancient pyramids of Egypt.

Drbal got his idea after reading about the experiments of a Frenchman named Bovis who, on a visit to the Great Pyramid, found that small desert animals which had wandered into the pharaoh's chamber and died, had not decayed. Bovis wondered if it had been the pyramids themselves which had somehow preserved bodies so well, rather than the mummification methods of the ancient Egyptians.

Bovis experimented with a scaled down model of the pyramid, placing inside it a number of highly perishable foods. They were preserved far beyond their usual span, and he came to the conclusion that this must have something to do with the pyramid's actual shape. Hearing of Bovis's experiments, Drbal wondered if the same principles might also apply to corrosion in metals. Apparently they did,

for out of his own tests was born Patent No. 91304.

Today there is a flourishing factory in Czechoslovakia, where razor blades are scarce, turning out plastic-foam models of pyramids for sharpening blades.

Why they work and how they work, no one knows. A razor-blade edge is made of a fine layer of crystals—so fine it is believed that the mere pressure of moonlight can rub them off and blunt the blade —and it could be that the pyramid shape somehow focuses or concentrates energy on to them.

To test Drbal's sharpener, make a cardboard pyramid. The four sides should be 15·7 to 14·94, whatever units of measurement are used.

Fix the sides together with adhesive tape so the height is 10 units. Place the pyramid so that the base lines face magnetic north–south and east–west. Make a stand 3·33 units high, and place it in the centre of the pyramid.

The sharp edges of a double-edged razor blade should face east–west when placed on the stand. Keep the device away from any electrical equipment.

The pyramid should also preserve perishable materials such as meat or eggs, but only for a short period.

MIGHTIER THAN THE SWORD

Blot was blessing in disguise

Fountain pens were born out of sheer exasperation. In 1884 Lewis Edson Waterman, an insurance salesman, had just won an important contract from several rivals. Waterman handed his client a fine quill pen and a bottle of ink to sign the contract. The pen spattered the document... Waterman hurried away to find another form . . . and a rival stepped in and completed the deal.

This incident spurred Waterman to design the forerunner of the modern fountain pen. He applied the principles of capillary attraction—by which sap defies gravity and rises in plants. In the piece of hard rubber linking the pen's ink reservoir and the nib, Waterman cut a hair-thin channel. This admitted a small amount of air into the ink chamber, keeping the internal air pressure in balance, so that the ink leaked out only when pressure was put on the nib.

The first Waterman pens were filled with an eyedropper, a technique soon replaced by the development of flexible rubber sacs which drew in ink after the air had been squeezed out.

The modern fountain pen, only slightly modified since 1884, is the descendant of a long line. The ancient Egyptians used a simple reed stem filled with ink, and a nib of copper. The Romans made pens not only out of quills, but also of bamboo, which could be worked to carry a reservoir of ink.

The term 'fountain pen', indicating that the pen contained a reservoir, was first used in England in the 17th century.

ZIP GOES A QUARTER OF A MILLION

SADLY, the original zip-fastener, invented in 1893 by Whitcomb L. Judson, a Chicago engineer, did not live up to its trade name, C-Curity. Its system of interlocking teeth would frequently spring open or jam.

Then, in 1913, a Swedish-born engineer, Gideon Sundback, turned Judson's unreliable brainwave into a multi-million dollar industry. Sundback devised a refinement of a series of cups on the backs of the interlocking teeth (left) that allowed them to be enmeshed more firmly and reliably.

Sundback's modified zipper has been used in many trades and professions—from agriculture to medicine. It has been fitted on boots for sheep in foot-and-mouth infected areas, and an Austrian surgeon sewed one into a patient's stomach for easy examination. Today more than a quarter of a million miles of zips are manufactured every year.

CUPS THAT CHEER

THE NEW YORK débutante who invented the brassière in 1914 was paid $15,000 for the patent. In the years since, the invention has made untold millions of dollars for manufacturers all over the world, and at least $15 million for the corset company that bought the patent. The débutante, Mary Phelps Jacob, had an inventive mind and a deep resentment of the corsets that imprisoned women of her time. One night, she and her French maid constructed a brassière out of two handkerchiefs and some ribbon. Her friends liked the idea, but she failed in her own attempts to market the bra commercially.

DINNER-TABLE RAILWAY

'THE MEAL now standing at platform. . . .' Things never quite went this far in the home of Frenchman Gaston Menier in the 1880s. Nevertheless, dinner was a strange and wonderful affair. Meals were brought straight from the kitchen to the table by the electric railway pictured below. Car- riages bearing the food ran on a four-rail track and were controlled by the host. No servants were needed, nor did guests have to pass the dishes from hand to hand. The train could carry 50 lb. of food at up to 2 mph. It gave the meal 'particular live- liness and intimacy', said one guest.

ELECTROPATHIC BELT

Shock-therapy, Victorian style

Victorian England was obsessed with the idea of a 'sound mind in a healthy body'. Especially the latter! Health gadgets, few useful, some harmful, most useless but harmless, abounded.

Girls with prominent ears wore 'Claxton's Ear-Cap' as they slept. Rheu- matic sufferers underwent excruciating treatment on 'Zander's Mechanical Exercisers'. Children were harnessed, sometimes painfully, to make them grow 'correctly'.

But one of the oddest inventions was 'Mr C. B. Harness's Electropathic Belt'.

This battery-operated appliance, strap- ped round the midriff, delivered a series of mild electric shocks. An advertisement at the turn of the century proclaimed that the belt 'acts upon all organs of the body, rarely failing to alleviate most of the dis- orders resulting from local or general debility'.

It could also 'improve the figure and prevent chills', not to mention that it renewed 'exhausted nerve form'. The one thing it could not do, apparently, was ensure its own survival in the face of advancing medical knowledge.

HOW 'GOOD MORNINGS' BEGAN

WHEN safety razors were introduced in 1903, the public bought 51 razors and 168 blades. The following year, 90,000 razors and 12,400,000 blades were sold. The first step towards safer shaving had been taken by a Frenchman in 1771 and in 1828 the Sheffield Company produced a razor with a guarded cutting edge. In 1895, King C. Gillette, a Boston salesman, hit on the idea of using wafer-thin slivers of steel that were held in a safety clamp and were so cheap they could be thrown away instead of sharpened. It took eight years to solve the difficulties of mass-production—then the shaving revolution was on.

THE CHESS-PLAYING TURK

Ingenious robot or elaborate joke?

Baron Wolfgang von Kempelen was a mechanical genius who intrigued 18th-century Europe with his automaton, which—dressed as a Turk—could not only play chess, but win every match it played.

It was never revealed at the time that the Turk was a fake—and the Baron a trickster with a dazzling sense of the outrageous to match his considerable mechanical ability.

The Turk was built in Vienna in 1769, and sat behind a chest, 4 ft long, 2 ft wide and 3 ft high. In front of him was a chess board on which he challenged all-comers, shifting the pieces with unerring movements of his left hand.

Touring Europe's courts

Before each game, the Baron would open all the chest's compartments, revealing levers, gears, drums and cylinders.

Emperor Joseph II of Austria sent the Turk on a tour of Europe's courts where it duly beat its royal opponents, including Empress Catherine of Russia and Napoleon—whose chess does not seem to have equalled his military strategy.

A widely held belief was that the chess was actually played by a series of talented, chess-playing midgets!

The truth was that a man squeezed into the chest and manipulated the Turk. He kept in touch with the game through a series of magnets attached to the base of the pieces. Below the board, small iron balls were suspended by threads. The balls stuck to the roof of the chest because of the magnets above them. When the chessmen were moved, the hidden player could follow the game by watching the balls also moving.

The facts about what the Baron always regarded as a 'mere trifle' to amuse the Austrian court were not known until after Von Kempelen died in 1804, when the automaton was taken to the United States. It was eventually bought by the Chinese Museum in Philadelphia—where it was destroyed by fire in 1854.

MACHINE OR MIDGET? *Von Kempelen's chess player in all his Eastern glory. The opened doors reveal the Baron's puzzling array of levers gears, drums and cylinders. But sceptics alleged that the chess was played by talented midgets.*

OPEN THIS END

Today's can-opener has a long history

Acan of veal, taken on Sir William Parry's Arctic expedition in 1824, was labelled 'Cut round on the top near to the outer edge with a chisel and hammer'. The can was the product of Britain's first cannery, set up at Bermondsey, London, in 1812, but the pioneers of canned foods had given little thought as to how their product should be opened.

AN ARCTIC SURVIVOR *This can of veal was once part of a ship's 'iron' rations. The problem of opening it was solved by the carpenter.*

It was Bryan Donkin, a partner in John Hall's Dartford Iron Works, who adapted the idea of Nicholas Appert, a French confectioner who is generally regarded as the 'father of canning'. Appert had sealed food in glass jars, then boiled it. This process won him a French government award with which he established the world's first cannery—the House of Appert—in 1812.

Donkin used iron cans coated with tin, and by 1818 had supplied 27,779 lb. of preserved meat to the British Admiralty. As an alternative to the hammer and chisel, a Frenchman, Angilbert, proposed in 1833 to modify the can so that it could be opened by melting the solder around the lid. Another French inventor, Bouvet, suggested a steel wire soldered between the lid and the body of the can, which could be removed by applying heat.

First openers

The first can-openers were elaborate mechanisms, used by shopkeepers before the can was handed over to the customer.

The introduction of tinplate in the 1860s made the cans easier to open, paving the way for small can-openers.

The earliest of these was the bull-head type, still used today, which had a steel blade attached to a cast-iron handle.

After that, a variety of different shapes and sizes were patented—from scissor-handled types to the familiar butterfly-screw models still used in many homes.

HATS OFF TO THE INVENTORS

THE VICTORIAN male's custom of raising his hat to ladies had its drawbacks. A gentleman laden with parcels, for example, would first have to set them down. But in 1896 James Boyle of Washington State invented a self-tipping hat. The wearer simply nodded to activate a clockwork lifting mechanism in the crown. Boyle noted that the device could also be used for advertising; a sign or placard could be placed on the hat and the novelty of its movement would attract attention. In 1912 the Canadian Patent Office recorded another self-raising hat, but it was no use to the parcel-laden man, being worked hydraulically by squeezing a rubber bulb.

TEETHING TROUBLES
Once, only the upper set could afford upper sets

False teeth are at least as old as the Etruscans, the rulers of central Italy before the Romans. Human skulls with false teeth carved from bone and ivory and with gold bridge work have been discovered, dating back to 700 BC.

But for centuries, the dental skills of the Etruscans were forgotten, and generations of men and women suffered agonies from toothache, and looked old before their time because of the sunken cheeks that resulted from losing their teeth. When England's Queen Elizabeth I lost her front teeth, she stuffed layers of cloth under her lips to fill out her face.

For many years, medieval quacks preserved the myth that worms in the gums caused toothache and decay, and often made a public entertainment of their 'treatment' and extractions—without anaesthetic. Usually, a clown capered and gestured to keep the crowds amused, while an assistant held down the patient and the quack yanked out teeth.

Sometimes, an assistant would bang a drum to drown out the cries of agony.

Hand-carved dentures

By the end of the 17th century, crude dentures, hand-carved in ivory, were available to the rich. The mouth was usually measured with compasses, and individual false teeth were tied to their neighbours with silk threads.

Full sets for the lower jaw were made, but top sets were difficult to keep in place.

As the demand for new teeth increased, the poor would often sell their teeth to the rich to buy food and clothing. But some of the more flamboyant figures of the English Court commissioned ornamental teeth in silver, gold or agate.

Even at this stage, however, the teeth had to be removed when eating.

Teeth transplants

Some fashionable women had their gums pierced with hooks to keep their dentures in place. But early in the 18th century, a Parisian dentist named Fauchard made upper and lower sets, coupled together with steel springs. This kept the upper set in position, but closing the mouth required quite an effort.

For a time during the 18th century, transplanted teeth became popular, with donors' teeth being wedged into sockets made in the recipients' jaws.

Shortly before the French Revolution, an Italian dentist, Guiseppangelo Fonzi, practising in Paris, manufactured individual porcelain teeth mounted on gold or platinum plates. These were introduced to England by a Frenchman, Dubois de Chémant, late in the 18th century.

In 1817 Anthony A. Plantou is reputed to have introduced porcelain teeth to the United States and, shortly afterwards, J. Leon Williams improved the appearance of artificial teeth by moulding the plates to the contours of the face.

Sets became available in three basic face-shapes: square, tapering and oval.

Teeth from the dead

Even with the introduction of artificial teeth, human teeth continued to be used. Ageing dandies wore 'Waterloo teeth'—extracted from skulls dug out of the 1815 battlefield of Waterloo. Teeth from the dead of the American Civil War (1861–5) were also shipped to England.

From 1845, a much-improved type of porcelain tooth was made by Claudius Ash, an American dentist who disliked handling dead men's teeth. Ash introduced vulcanite—a composition of sulphur-hardened rubber—to the casting of gums in which the teeth were set.

As moulded plates fitted better and were firmer, suction-pads and coil-springs were eventually discarded.

At one stage before the turn of the century, cheap celluloid teeth were introduced. But they were highly inflammable, and at least one man is said to have suffered when his teeth caught fire while he was smoking a cigarette.

Modern denture plates and teeth are made from plastic acrylic resin, although porcelain is still sometimes used.

In the late 1950s an American chewing-gum company, which was trying to solve the problem of its product sticking to false teeth, produced teeth to which their gum would not stick, by coating the dentures with polytetrafluorethylene (PTFE), the substance now widely used in many ways—from the coatings on non-stick frying pans to artificial arteries.

QWERTY—THE TYPIST'S BURDEN

The machine with the deliberate flaw

The job of the typist is made unnecessarily difficult by a deliberate flaw in the basic design of the typewriter itself—the curious layout of its keyboard letters.

As long ago as 1714, Queen Anne granted a patent to an Englishman called Henry Mill for the manufacture of a machine 'whereby all writings whatsoever may be engrossed on paper or parchment so neat and exact as not to be distinguished from print'.

No one knows how Mill's invention worked, or even what it looked like, but there were others throughout the world who worked on the same idea.

The first American patent for something like a typewriter was granted in 1829 to William Austin Burt, of Detroit, for 'Burt's Family Letter Press'. Four years later, Xavier Projean, of Marseilles in France, produced a 'Machine Criptographique'. It would, he said, record words 'almost as fast as one could write with an ordinary pen'. Credit for the first modern typewriter, however, belongs to Christopher Sholes, a newspaper editor who lived in Milwaukee in the 1860s. On the Sholes model, as on present-day manual typewriters, each character was set on the end of a metal bar which struck the paper when its key was pressed. The keys were arranged alphabetically.

Keys to success

But there was a snag. When an operator had learnt to type at speed, the bars attached to letters that lay close together on the keyboard became entangled with one another. One way out of the difficulty was to find out which letters were most often used in English, and then to re-site them on the keyboard as far from each other as possible.

This had the effect of reducing the speed and, by doing so, lessened the chance of clashing type bars. In this way was born the QWERTY keyboard, named after the first six letters on the top line.

Sholes was delighted with it. 'A blessing to mankind—and womankind,' he wrote.

THE FATHER OF QWERTY *'It is a blessing to mankind—and womankind,' Christopher Sholes said of his invention, the modern typewriter.*

BRAMAH'S LOCK

ONE OF THE 18th century's most prolific inventors was a Yorkshire farmer's son, Joseph Bramah. Among his brain-children were beer pumps, a water closet, a machine for numbering banknotes—and his famous lock. He patented the lock in 1784—11 years after he walked 170 miles from Yorkshire to London to seek a living. Bramah's lock was a revolution in safety measures. Until then, any lock—cheap or costly—could be picked by anyone with a little skill. Bramah claimed that his barrel-shaped lock, with 494 million possible combinations of notches, was totally burglar-proof. He was so confident that he offered a 200 guinea prize to the first person who could pick it. The prize went unclaimed for 67 years until an American locksmith, Alfred Charles Hobbs, finally picked the lock—after a month's work. Nevertheless, the design was so effective that the Bramah lock and variations on its design are used to this day.

Tales of courage and high endeavour

Daring
and epic journeys

---•---

SOUTH OF THE MID-DAY SUN

How the Phoenicians rounded Africa—and proved it

Nobody believed the Phoenicians when they claimed—2000 years before the Portuguese discovered West Africa—that they had sailed right round the Dark Continent from Suez to the Straits of Gibraltar.

They were laughed to scorn when they insisted that as they had rounded the southern tip, the midday sun had been to the north of them. Every man in the ancient world knew that the sun was *always* in the sky's southern half. And so it is—in the northern hemisphere.

Even the great Greek historian Herodotus, who reported their story 150 years later, dismissed the tale as a hoax. Yet the Phoenician adventurers did in fact make the journey they claimed. And what proves it to modern scholars is the very detail that convinced the ancient world they were telling a pack of lies: the report of the sun on their right at midday as they sailed west round the Cape of Good Hope.

The pharaoh's idea

Not even the exploring Phoenicians could have guessed that what was always true of the sun's position in the temperate northern waters of the Mediterranean was never true south of the Tropic of Capricorn. It would never have crossed their minds to invent such an unlikely piece of evidence unless they had actually seen it. The voyage itself was planned by an Egyptian pharaoh, Necho, around 600 BC. He became intrigued by the possibility

of sailing from Egypt's east coast on the Red Sea to Alexandria on its north coast. Rather than build a canal across the desert (as Ferdinand de Lesseps did 2400 years later when he built the Suez Canal), Necho thought it would be a fairly simple journey to follow Africa's southern coast round to Morocco.

Because his own people were not great seafarers, he hired crews of Phoenicians together with a small flotilla of their own 50-oared sailing ships. He ordered them to sail down the Red Sea and round Africa to the Pillars of Hercules, now known as the Strait of Gibraltar.

Rowing into the unknown

The Phoenicians were happy enough to be hired, because they were anxious to find a new route to their western markets avoiding waters controlled by their Greek rivals. But neither they nor Necho had any idea of the shape or the vast size of the continent that lay on their route.

According to modern reconstructions of their voyage, the Phoenicians set off in November—rowing to the eastern tip of Africa at Cape Gardafui before turning south-west with the monsoon winds.

For month after month, they pushed on down the coast—further than anyone before them—constantly expecting the coastline to sweep round to the west and north and point the way home. But to their dismay it did not.

Instead, they noticed anxiously that the sun was slipping down the sky to their north. Their 'compass' was wrong. And the pole star vanished altogether. The explorers were ready to give up when, finally, the coast swung west.

They ploughed slowly on along the 500 mile tip of the continent until, in May of the year after they set out, they rounded the Cape of Good Hope and the coast dropped away to the north.

The relieved crews stopped to plant some of the wheat they had taken with them. In December they sailed homewards with the harvest—and each day the sun climbed higher and higher in the sky.

It took them at least ten more gruelling months to fight their way round Africa's huge north-west bulge, and another long stopover somewhere in Morocco to restock their food supply, before they sighted the familiar Straits of Gibraltar.

More than two years and 16,000 miles after they cast off in the Red Sea, the Phoenicians sailed triumphantly up the Mediterranean to Egypt—and to 2000 years of ridicule.

SUN TO THE NORTH *A map of Africa showing the relation of the sun to Gibraltar and the Cape of Good Hope. The sun never moves north of the Tropic of Cancer or south of the Tropic of Capricorn. Thus, to the observer in the Mediterranean the sun is always to the south, while at the Cape of Good Hope it is to the north.*

OVER THE EDGE OF THE WORLD
The men who shone a light on the Sea of Darkness

Beneath the towering cliffs of Cape Bojador, just south of the Canary Islands, the Atlantic boils and foams in constant fury. Shoals of sardines flashing in the tumult give the water the appearance of molten metal. Seas crash into unseen gullies and explode like geysers into spume-laden columns.

This to the seamen of old was the gateway to hell. Beyond it lay the Sea of Darkness, peopled by monsters and the spirits of dead mariners . . . the end of the world.

The maelstrom raging along the 15-mile reef provoked such terrifying legends, that from 400 BC to early in the 15th century it slowed the pace of exploration down the west coast of Africa. The Pillars of Hercules—the Straits of Gibraltar—marked the western limit of the Mediterranean, and beyond them the discoverers advanced timorously, at an average rate of less than a mile a year.

Then, in 1434, Prince Henry of Portugal, who chafed and scoffed at the superstitions, persuaded one of his captains, Gileannes, to find out what really did lie south of Bojador. The spectacular fury which had terrorised seamen for so long

was caused, he believed, by nothing more sinister than rough seas pounding against the cliffs. He could not explain—for the knowledge was ahead of his time—that the effect was heightened by a northerly swell coming into collision with an off-shore wind.

Gileannes answered the fears of his crew with reason and common sense. He set course for the end of the world—and plunged over the edge.

The result must have surprised the fainthearts among his crew, for in 24 hours—not a long time by early sailing standards—they cleared the sinister Bojador barrier and broke out into calm waters, with not a monster in sight. Their fears now behind them, they steered east and were rewarded with a sight of a new unexplored coast reaching out before them.

It had taken Europeans 1000 years to reconnoitre 900 miles southwards from the Gates of Hercules. Gileannes's bold dash into the dreaded Sea of Darkness opened a door to a new surge of discovery, and the remaining 5000 miles of West Africa's coastline were mapped in less than 70 years.

THE MAN WHO DISCOVERED BRITAIN

He described frozen seas—but no one believed him

On his return from a sea journey north to the Atlantic, the Greek explorer said of Britain: 'The island is thickly populated . . . has an extremely chilly climate . . .' Of its people, he wrote: 'They are unusually hospitable and gentle in their manner . . . Their diet is inexpensive and quite different from the luxury that is born of wealth . . . It (Britain) has many kings and potentates who live for the most part in a state of mutual peace . . .'

Yet no one believed him. It was the year 304 BC, and the explorer was Pytheas of Marseilles.

For 2000 years historians labelled him a charlatan, although they enjoyed his accounts of his travels as masterpieces of fabrication.

Yet Pytheas was the first Greek to visit and describe Britain and its people and, possibly, to sail within sight of the Norwegian coast.

He wrote: 'The people of Britannia are simple in their habits and far removed from the cunning and knavishness of modern man . . . they do not drink wine, but a fermented liquor made from barley, which they call *curmi*.'

At the time of his epic journey, the northern waters of the Atlantic were unknown to Pytheas's contemporaries. How could they—familiar only with the warm waters of the Mediterranean—believe that he had seen chunks of floating ice

larger than his ship? Or that further north the sea was entirely frozen and the sun never set?

Pytheas was discredited, and although later Greek historians included references to his travels in their books, their attitude was typified by Strabo (born about 63 BC). He wrote: 'Pytheas tells us that Thule (believed then to be an undiscovered northernmost land) is one day's sail from the congealed sea . . . and this Pytheas saw with his own eyes—or so he would have us believe.'

What Pytheas might have seen was the coast of Norway, shrouded in mist. The 'congealed sea', some scholars think, may have been a huge shoal of jellyfish.

No fragments remain of Pytheas's own two books: *The Ocean* and *A Description of the Earth*. But his contemporaries wrote enough about him for his accomplishments to be reconstructed.

Pytheas's journey from Marseilles is thought to have taken six years, during which time he circumnavigated Britain and in various places went ashore, where he saw people harvesting grain and tending cattle. In Cornwall he visited tin mines.

On his return to Marseilles, he said that Ireland lay to the west of Britannia. Strabo disagreed, placed it north of Scotland and was believed.

Pytheas apparently spent the rest of his life trying in vain to convince his contemporaries.

THE TRAVELS OF MARCO POLO

A 25-year adventure to the empire of Kublai Khan

The sight was breathtaking for a young man barely in his twenties. There before him was a city more magnificent than any he had ever seen before. He considered that its beauty might lead an inhabitant to imagine himself in paradise. There were elevated highways, public parks, marinas, canals with hundreds of arched bridges, many of them so high that ships with masts could pass beneath. There were underground drainage systems, police and fire brigades and an efficient postal service.

Quite staggering . . . especially for a

youth who lived 700 years ago. He was Marco Polo, one of history's great adventurers, and the magnificent Hangchow was just one of the cities within the mighty empire of Cathay, the ancient European name for China.

Marco Polo wrote in his diary of Hangchow's pre-eminence over all other cities in the world. To him it was even more beautiful than the emperor's capital of Peking.

Marco was one of a widely travelled family. Before he actually arrived in Cathay himself in 1275, his father, Nicolo, and uncle, Maffeo, had already made the trip 11 years before, and before they had started back to Venice, the emperor had made them promise they would return. They did, and took the then 17-year-old Marco with them.

Their three year journey was arduous, sailing down the Adriatic to Ayas, a small town on the Gulf of Iskenderun, and riding overland to Hormuz on the Persian Gulf. Then, through Persia, they went to Balkh, and from there ascended the upper Oxus to Wakhan and across the plateau of the Pamir. From Pamir they travelled towards Kashgar, Yarkand and Khotan, crossed the Gobi Desert and entered China at Su Chou.

Marco, who kept a diary, described their fight to climb frozen mountain ranges, and their battles against torrential rain, sandstorms, floods and avalanches. In Afghanistan they were delayed for a whole year when Marco became ill. Bandits and local wars forced them to make many detours and new plans, but throughout Marco kept records in his treasured notebooks.

Stones that burned

He wrote of the wondrous sights and strange people they encountered. He was amazed by the 'veins of black stones which, when lighted, burn like charcoal and give out a considerable heat'. He saw 'a substance spurting from the ground and used for burning in lamps', and examined 'a material which could be spun into thread and woven into a cloth that would not burn when thrown into a fire'. He described crocodiles as 'huge serpents ten paces in length with jaws wide enough to swallow a man' and yaks as 'wild cattle that may be compared to elephants'. Coconuts were 'nuts the size of a man's head, pleasant to taste and white as milk'.

The emperor was so impressed with his young guest that he took him on hunting trips on royal elephants, and gave him the freedom of his opulent marble palaces and summer holiday resorts. Marco was dazzled by the gilded carvings, art treasures and the elegant courtiers of the emperor's world. He wrote that emissaries were sent out every two years to find 100 or more beautiful concubines to keep the harem well supplied.

But Marco had little time for dalliance and preferred to study the ways of Cathay. He was the first Western man to describe

ADVENTURER EXTRAORDINARY *Marco Polo wearing the Tartar costume in which he reappeared in Venice after 25 years of wandering. On his death-bed he said 'I have not told half of what I saw'.*

the empire and its bordering countries in detail, and the first to map a route across the Asian continent.

While his father and uncle amassed a fortune by trading, Marco spent 17 years working for the emperor, who first made him his personal emissary and sent him on missions across the empire. He visited such places as Cochin China, Burma and India during this period. Later he served three years as governor of the rich city of Yangchow, a centre of arms manufacture, with 24 towns under his jurisdiction. And, finally, he became commissioner in the emperor's imperial council in the capital. By then, however, the ruler was past 70 years of age, and the Polos decided they might not be safe under any of his rival successors if he should die. Early in 1292, in boats specially fitted out on the emperor's instructions, they sailed for home—after an absence of 25 years.

FLOURISHING TRADE CENTRE *The Polo family set off from their home in Venice (shown here in a 1338 manuscript) for China, spurred by the already thriving trade in goods from the Orient.*

When they arrived in Venice, no one recognised them, not even their own servants who refused them admission to their own villa. They and the family's friends had long ago given the travellers up for dead.

To convince people that they were not impostors, the three Polos threw a banquet and after their guests—who still doubted the identity of their hosts and the accounts of their adventures—had been wined and dined, the Polos donned their travel-torn Tartar clothes then dramatically cut the seams to let a shower of precious gems fall out. This was considered to be conclusive evidence of their claims, for who, they thought, but the Emperor of Cathay could have provided such riches?

For three years, life in Venice was good for the Polos. But then a fierce trade rivalry between the republics of Venice and Genoa broke into open war and it was not long before Marco became involved. But while serving as a 'gentleman commander' of a galley, he and his ships were captured and he was thrown into a Genoese gaol.

Yet he still managed to turn the time to good account. Using his travel-stained diaries to refresh his memory, he dictated his memoirs to a fellow prisoner. When the volume of his travels was first published—*A Description of the World*—it was denounced as a tissue of lies.

Even on his death-bed in 1324, a priest urged him to retract some of his tallest tales. But Marco remembered still. With his last breath he declared: 'I have not told half of what I saw.'

MASTERS OF THE PACIFIC

The Polynesians navigated the great ocean by sense of touch

Throw a stone into a large lake, and the pattern of ripples set up will be disturbed by any rocks that break the surface. Given a chart of the ripples, it would be possible for someone with a knowledge of mathematics to calculate the positions of the rocks.

Enlarge the pond to the size of an ocean, substitute waves for ripples and islands for rocks, and it is still possible to apply the same principles to pinpoint the location of an island 100 miles away.

Some 3000 years ago, the ability to read the messages of the waves in this way helped a race of master navigators to reach and colonise almost every inhabitable island in the vastness of the Pacific.

The Polynesians had no wide-ranging maps to guide them, no compasses, no sextants, no telescopes, not even a written language through which to hand down the lessons of experience. Yet over a period of 1000 years they populated a huge triangular area covering more than 12 million square miles from Easter Island in the east, to Hawaii in the north and New Zealand in the south.

They were able to do so by means of intelligent observation. They noticed that when waves hit an island, some were reflected back in the direction from which they came, while others were deflected at angles round the island to continue in altered form on the other side. Investigating the phenomenon further, they acquired sufficient knowledge of the behaviour of the waves to be able to judge accurately the position of an island 100 miles away.

When the Polynesians first showed them their *mattangs*, odd-looking webs of interlocking bamboo sticks, European sailors thought they were a primitive sort of map. But they were something quite different —devices for instructing boys in the principles of wave motion. The *mattang* demonstrated all the basic patterns that waves can form, and with its help a young navigator could learn the implications of the different wave formations.

Sense of touch

It was an intricate science and an intimate one, for it was not possible to read the waves from afar—from the top of high cliffs. The Polynesian sailor had to be so close to the waves that he could feel their motions through touch.

He would go to the bow of his canoe, crouch down in the hull and literally feel every motion of the craft. Within minutes he would be able to determine the positions of the nearest island, of intervening reefs and of other islands near by.

Of course, the Polynesians did not ignore the visible signs of a tropical island, which appear long before the island itself comes into view. Birds and flotsam indicate land—and often the direction in which it lies. And a stationary cloud on the horizon means there is an island anything up to two days' sailing away.

For local use, maps were made of individual islands and groups, showing islands with shells or pieces of coral fastened to shaped sticks.

Mysterious origins

Using these methods, the Polynesians explored most of the Pacific, yet where they came from originally is a mystery, for their culture cannot be traced back to the Asian continent and they were definitely not South American. It is known that nearly 3000 years ago they passed through Fiji, in Melanesia, settled in Tonga and then moved on to Samoa.

In the restricted space of an island, immune to plagues that swept the mainland, populations would explode.

So soon they were off again—their women, children, animals, fruits and seedlings as carefully guarded as possible against the elements—this time to the Marquesas, where they were said to be living 2000 years ago. From there they made spectacular voyages to Easter Island, Hawaii and New Zealand.

They travelled these vast distances in pairs of 80 ft dugout canoes made with stone and shell tools, and lashed together with a deckhouse between them. Although they spread their culture throughout the Pacific they remained a single people, so that to this day a Maori visiting Hawaii can understand the local language.

AID TO NAVIGATION *Interlocking webs of bamboo sticks*—Mattangs—*were used by the Polynesians to teach the science of wave motion.*

THE WESTWARD URGE

The men who discovered America

Few lands have been discovered as often as America. Before Christopher Columbus reached the Caribbean in 1492, voyages to the New World had been made, so it is said, by the Phoenicians, Irish, Vikings, Welsh and, on the Pacific coast, the Chinese.

As long ago as 800 BC, the Phoenician navigator Hanno was reported to have sailed to a land 'thirty days westwards from the Pillars of Hercules' (Gibraltar).

The Chinese claim was made recently by a Peking University professor who asserted that five Chinese had sailed the Pacific to Mexico in AD 459.

There is also documentary evidence to suggest that Irish monks explored the Atlantic coast of North America in the 6th and 7th centuries AD, penetrating as far south as the Bahamas.

The *Navigatio Sancti Brendani*—a clerical manuscript recording voyages made by the Irish St Brendan about AD 570—was thought for centuries to be no more than a collection of fanciful yarns. But modern scholars now believe that although the *Navigatio* was written two centuries later it is an account of voyages that actually took place, whether or not Brendan led them all in person.

In those days, when the old frontiers of the Roman Empire had crumbled, Ireland was in grave danger from the pagan Teutonic tribes invading Western Europe. And the tough, seafaring monks may well have set off to search for a refuge for their Christian flock.

Early doubts of their ability to cross the Atlantic in frail-looking curraghs have now been dispelled. Though only 30 ft long with a hull clad in greased animal skins, the Irish curraghs were sturdy and seaworthy vessels.

Study of the *Navigatio* suggests that Irish priests and monks landed in North America about 900 years before Columbus was born. Possibly they landed somewhere near Chesapeake Bay, marched inland across the Appalachian Mountains, and reached the Ohio River.

Their voyages also took them to what appear to be the Bahamas and even fur-

LANDFALL? *The 30 miles of sand at Cape Porcupine in Labrador may be the 'wonderful beaches' beyond the sea described in Viking sagas about the Norse expeditions to Vinland.*

ON COURSE *This steering oar on a restored long ship is 1000 years old.*

ther south. However, the abrupt ending of the *Navigatio* leaves doubt on this point.

About 400 years later, towards the end of the 10th century, intrepid seamen from Norway and Denmark began their voyages of exploration which led them to discover—and probably colonise—the coast of North America.

The Viking longboats were built for speed. They were narrow boats with a very deep keel, and clinker built of thin oak planking. This made them much lighter and more manoeuvrable than other ships of similar size. They had a single square sail, and about 16 pairs of pinewood oars jutting through small portholes that could be closed in rough weather and high seas.

Navigation by sea-birds

They had neither maps nor compasses. Instead they navigated by the sun and stars, and used their knowledge of the behaviour of sea-birds to estimate where and how far the nearest land was.

According to ancient Norse documents, it was Vikings led by Bjarni Herjulfsson who first reached America in AD 985. Fifteen years later, an expedition led by Leif Ericson—'Leif the Lucky'—set out to establish a colony there.

From the description of the voyage in the Icelandic record known as *Flateyarbok*, Leif and his men seem to have landed on the coast of Labrador, then worked their way south to the Cape Cod region. According to the *Flateyarbok*, they found wild grapes growing there and called the country Vinland.

Curiously, there is little trace of any Viking community on the American coast, although some of the Norse explorers are known to have settled in parts of Greenland.

They may perhaps have been driven out of Vinland by the Indians. The *Flateyarbok* describes a pitched battle between the Norsemen and an Indian tribe. But the Vikings kept up their visits to Vinland for about 300 years, using it as a source of timber for their settlement in Greenland.

But after the 14th century the records contain no further mention of Vinland. If there ever was a permanent Viking settlement in North America, it had vanished into oblivion.

Meanwhile, a discovery is said to have been made by a Welshman, Prince Madoc

ap Owain Gwynedd. In the words of a plaque at Fort Morgan in Alabama, the prince 'landed on the shores of Mobile Bay in 1170 and left behind, with the Indians, the Welsh language'.

So far as is known from the sketchy evidence that has survived, Madoc was driven into exile in North Wales by his brothers after his father, Owain Gwynedd, died. There he built the *Gwennan Corn*, a tubby wooden single-master—using horn instead of nails because, like other early sailors, he feared that magnetic rocks might tug a metal-using ship to disaster.

Tired of fighting and with no estates of his own, Madoc launched his ship somewhere between Abergele and Conway on Wales's far north coast and, with perhaps one other ship, sailed into the sunset.

He is thought to have made two crossings of the Atlantic, each time following the great sweep of the North Equatorial Current and the Gulf Stream to the coast of the Gulf of Mexico. On the second trip he disappeared.

End of the Welsh Indians

All that remained to mark Madoc's voyages are the ruins of three medieval Welsh-style fortresses near Chattanooga in Tennessee, and mysterious similarities between the Welsh and the now virtually extinct Mandan Indians. The fair-haired Mandans lived along the upper reaches of the Missouri River and used boats very like Welsh coracles, quite unlike those of any other Indian tribe.

But if the Mandans were in fact the descendants of America's first European colonists then, ironically, they were destroyed as a nation by their own successors—invading white fur-traders who started a smallpox epidemic among them in 1838. The few survivors of the Mandans became slaves to another Indian tribe—and died of hunger and despair.

And then came Columbus

Finally, in 1492, Columbus sailed the Atlantic and claimed the pioneer's crown. But even here the facts in every schoolbook are being challenged. Perhaps Mark Twain hit the nail on the head when he observed drily:

'The researches of many commentators have already thrown much darkness on this subject, and it is probable that if they continue we shall soon know nothing at all about it.'

NEW WORLD WAS FOUND BY MISTAKE

The arrogance and stubbornness of Columbus showed the way

As Ferro, the most westerly of the Canary Isles, faded astern, the crew of the square-rigged little sailing ship piously crossed themselves. Before them lay the open Atlantic—the great and terrifying unknown.

Only the captain was undismayed. He ordered his men to sail due west day and night for 700 leagues and, in case land was not sighted by then, kept a false second log to show his crew. In it he deliberately underestimated the distance sailed.

Four days later the compass needle began to veer west of north. The crew were confused and asked questions about the route. The captain was as unsure as they, but he covered his doubts by saying that the Pole Star was causing the needle to fluctuate. The earth's magnetic variations were then unknown, and he did not know that the compass was, in fact, working perfectly.

The ship sailed on with its two attendant vessels—to reach, inadvertently, the New World. The name of the ship was the *Santa Maria* and its captain was Christopher Columbus.

Many days passed and the crew became increasingly dissatisfied and worried about their future. Sometimes they were becalmed for days at a time. On other occasions storms and high waves battered the wooden hulls. But Columbus sailed onwards, despite threats of mutiny.

Driftwood and birds

Thirty-three days after setting sail from Palos in Spain on Friday August 3, 1492, the lookout spotted some driftwood and a few birds. It was a sure sign that land was not far away. On October 12 the small fleet arrived at an island, called Guanahani by its dark-skinned natives. Columbus renamed it San Salvador, or 'Holy Saviour', and claimed this Bahamian island for Spain.

To the end of his days, Columbus firmly believed that the islands he found were off the eastern coast of Asia.

But he remains in history as the man who, against great odds and with little support, opened the New World to European adventurers.

Many of the so-called facts popularly accepted about Columbus are untrue.

For example, he was not the only man of his day who believed that the earth was round and not flat. Many scholars and men of science also shared this view.

Nor was it the belief that the world was flat that at first made King Ferdinand and Queen Isabella of Spain refuse to back the Genoa-born sailor's project of trying to find new sea routes to the Indies.

Spain had been fighting constant wars with the Moors when Columbus asked for royal patronage, and they were not anxious to spend more money on a purely speculative venture.

Extravagant demands

Then, in 1491, when Columbus made another approach—he had already been rejected by John II of Portugal—it was his extravagant and audacious demands that made Queen Isabella reject him. Columbus had asked to be named Admiral of the Ocean Sea and viceroy of all lands he discovered, with the right to 10 per cent of all treasure he might find on the voyage.

It was finally only the jealous rivalry for discovery between Spain and Portugal that prompted the queen to change her mind and give him all he asked.

So, with 87 men, including three doctors and a man to record any treasure found, the *Santa Maria* and her attendant ships, the *Pinta* and *Nina*, set sail on the world's most famous voyage of discovery, heading westwards.

On reaching the New World, Columbus spent three months sailing among the beautiful Caribbean islands, giving the ones on which he landed Spanish names in honour of his sponsor.

He made three more voyages to the New World—on the fourth he steered along the coast of Central America, although he never landed.

Eventually, through ambition and arrogance, he fell out of royal favour and, racked with arthritis, he died on May 20, 1506, an almost forgotten and a very disappointed man.

Ironically, the huge continent he had discovered was named after his friend, Amerigo Vespucci, a little-known Italian merchant adventurer, the year after Columbus died.

LAST VOYAGES OF CHRISTOPHER COLUMBUS

was reverently re-interred in Santo Domingo, now the Dominican Republic. Then, in the 18th century, a descendant of Columbus's is thought to have removed him to Havana. But when Cuba gained its independence in 1902, the admiral was disturbed once more and returned to Seville—or so it was thought. In 1877 another vault was discovered beneath Santo Domingo Cathedral, containing a coffin bearing the initials 'C.C.A.', believed to represent 'Cristóbal Colón, Almirante (Admiral)'. Within, an inscription read 'Illustrious and famous gentleman, Don Cristóbal Colón'. Dust from this coffin was enclosed in two lockets (above) and was eventually put up for sale in 1973. But bidders were sceptical; the far-wandered dust did not reach its reserve price.

COLUMBUS, adventurer-extraordinary, died and was buried at Valladolid in 1506. Later his remains were moved to Seville monastery, and 30 years were to pass before his achievements were recognised, and his body

THE WORLD'S WORST CORNER

Sailing men who have lived to tell the tale of Cape Horn

On all round-the-world voyages, one frightening, natural obstacle looms ominously—the worst corner of the world. Cape Horn, the bleak, southernmost tip of the American continent, was once the only ocean passage between the Atlantic and the Pacific, and is a focus for the worst nautical weather of the Southern Hemisphere.

Winds blowing across the wide wastes of the South Atlantic for thousands of miles are deflected by the mountain wall of the Andes through the narrow gap between Cape Horn and the South Shetlands. Waves blown along by endless westerly gales, backed by a steady east-going current, force a huge volume of

water through the same narrow cleft in the opposite direction. As the sea bed rises sharply, rollers build to frightening heights—to 120 ft or more.

Heavy seas and strong headwinds might last for months on end. In the days of sailing ships, the Horn was a terrible challenge—men froze or fell overboard, ships ran on to rocks or collided with icebergs. In December 1905, a ship called the *British Isles* took more than ten weeks to fight her way through these waters, a time that was by no means unusual.

For yachts and other small sailing ships these remain the most dangerous seas in the world. Certainly yachtsmen have braved them: Chichester, Rose, Blyth,

Knox-Johnston. But, as they have freely acknowledged, they were lucky in not meeting the Horn at its worst. However seaworthy, however well-handled a yacht may be, there comes a stage where waves are simply too big for a small ship to cope.

In January 1957 Brigadier Miles Smeeton, his wife, Beryl, and their friend John Guzzwell set out from Australia in the 46 ft ketch *Tzu Hang* to round the Horn the 'easy way'—from west to east. It was a venture that nearly cost them their lives. After seven weeks running hard before strong westerlies, they were approaching the Cape.

Increasing violence

By St Valentine's Day (February 14) the sea was white with breakers and the wind so strong that all sails were taken in, and the boat ran on under bare masts with 60 fathoms of rope trailing astern to hold her in check.

The barometer had begun to rise, signalling better weather, but the wind continued strengthening and the waves started breaking with increasing violence, until one higher and steeper by far than all the rest caught *Tzu Hang* from astern, hurled her end over end, snapping both masts off at the deck, tearing away the cabin roof, half filling her with water and hurling Beryl Smeeton into the sea, despite her safety harness and lifeline.

Yet all three survived. Beryl managed to swim back to the waterlogged yacht, and the three were able to bail out most of the water and patch the hole with planks from a bunk, a locker door and spare sails. Then, with the weather improving, they improvised a makeshift mast and sail and ran for shelter towards the Chilean coast. After 1500 miles they reached Talcuanho, where the damage was repaired.

In December, Miles and Beryl Smeeton set sail again. By Christmas Day they were well on their way to the Horn for the second time. But once again the barometer dropped and the wind and sea kept rising as *Tzu Hang* raced southwards. This time the white breakers were hitting her beam on. Once again the barometer stopped falling when the storm reached its peak, but at 4 a.m. on Boxing Day the yacht was hit by another monstrous wave and rolled over, this time sideways.

Once again the masts were snapped, the cabin hatches torn away. Yet once again the Smeetons survived. Just as before they bailed out the water, rigged emergency sails and headed for shelter— this time 1100 miles away at Valparaiso.

The *Tzu Hang* had been savaged by Cape Horn weather twice in succession —yet the Smeetons were running with the wind and sea behind them, in the middle of the summer.

Bravery in a small boat

To sail against such violent winds and mountainous waves is well-nigh impossible in a small boat. Yet a Frenchman, Marcel Bardiaux, sailed single-handed round Cape Horn in a tiny, 30 ft home-built boat from east to west in mid-winter.

On May 7, 1952, Bardiaux approached the Horn by Le Maire Strait, between Staten Island and the coast of Tierra del Fuego. When the wind blows against the tide, the breakers in this wild stretch of water are big enough to threaten steamers, so Bardiaux hoped to time his entry at slack water, when conditions would be at their calmest. But strong winds had held him back. It was 14 degrees below freezing and there was a storm on the way. He was desperately tired and decided to rest. The only possible anchorage was Thetis Bay, on the mainland coast. There was a heavy sea running, and the bay was swept by fierce currents—the only shelter was a small pool at the end of a narrow channel, studded by rocks. It was pitch dark and the tide was rushing Bardiaux's boat out of control towards the waiting reefs. All he could do was heave three anchors overboard and tie a mooring rope to a nearby rock.

Frozen sails

When the weather calmed, he ran his boat on a sandbank, so that he could sleep for the first time in three days. After ten hours, he was off again—but after heavy snowfalls during the night, his sails were frozen stiff and he had to soak them in seawater to make them pliable.

Without warning, hurricane-force winds battered his vessel, and when Bardiaux went below to fetch a sea-anchor, two huge waves rolled his yacht over.

Sails, cabin shelter and everything breakable was smashed or swept away, the hull was full of water and Bardiaux soaked to the skin—a serious problem with the temperature well below freezing.

But before changing into dry clothes,

Bardiaux trailed his mooring rope astern as a makeshift sea-anchor while he bailed out the water. He hoisted spare sails but it was another ten hours before he could anchor properly. By then, he was suffering from severe frostbite and exposure.

Freezing spray

After a two-day halt the Frenchman returned to the attack on the Horn—blinded by freezing spray and hail. He tacked for 48 hours against snow-swept wind and sea, and on one occasion conditions became so bad that he had to boil water, kettle by kettle, to thaw out his sails.

Then, at 12.30 p.m. on May 12, Bardiaux looked astern through half-closed eyes and saw a headland through the driving snow. It was a steep land mass streaked with snow running down into narrow gullies.

Bardiaux realised that he was looking back at Cape Horn. He was safely round the corner at last.

AUSTRALIA'S FIRST SETTLERS
Mutinous and fugitive murderers

Australia's first European settlers may have been two Dutch mutineers who were set adrift off the western coast in 1629—159 years before the first English fleet arrived in Sydney Cove on January 26, 1788.

In 1628 the Dutch merchant ship *Batavia*, commanded by François Pelsaert, had left Holland with a fleet of United East India Company ships, bound for the East Indies. She carried a valuable cargo including 12 chests of money, jewels, silverware and rich merchandise.

The ships became separated in a storm, and just before sunrise on June 4, 1629, the *Batavia* struck a coral reef in the Wallabi group of islands in the Abrolhos Archipelago off Western Australia. She broke into pieces a week later.

Her complement of about 300 people—some of them adventurous men and women bound for the Indies in search of fortune—struggled ashore on two of the low, barren islands. Most of the provisions were salvaged but there was an acute shortage of water and Pelsaert, after a vain search, sailed in the small ship's boat to seek assistance in the East Indies.

With him were the skipper of the *Batavia*, the chief mate, other officers and men, two women and a baby. They made the dangerous 2000 mile voyage in about a month, arriving on July 5, 1629.

The Governor of Batavia (now Djakarta) lent Pelsaert the yacht *Sardam* to go back and rescue the castaways.

But during Pelsaert's absence one of the *Batavia*'s crew, Jerome Cornelius, had assumed command of the survivors, who were scattered over three islands. With several accomplices, Cornelius planned to seize the rescue ship and, taking the money chests and jewels, embark on a career of piracy. Those who would not join him were to be disposed of.

Meanwhile, one party of survivors, led by Webbye Hayes, had found water on a distant island and lit three fires to signal their success. The same day Cornelius ordered a general massacre in which 125 men and women were brutally killed. Some had their throats cut, others were hacked or clubbed to death, or drowned.

Wearing gold-and-silver-embroidered velvets and elegant silks, the mutineers drank great quantities of rum and wine. Cornelius, who had appointed himself 'Captain-General', wore a red jacket, richly trimmed with gold.

Warned by refugees

But he realised that he would not be safe until Webbye Hayes and his men had been eliminated. However, refugees from the massacre, who had escaped by swimming or on rafts, warned Hayes, and he was able to beat off two attacks.

Cornelius then tried to negotiate a peace treaty, to which Hayes agreed on condition that he and his party were allowed to leave the island unmolested. In return, he agreed to surrender a small boat to Cornelius. Cornelius immediately broke the treaty and secretly sent letters to men on the island, trying to persuade them to desert Hayes.

These men showed the letters to Hayes, and when Cornelius visited the island with a handful of followers to discuss terms, he was attacked and captured.

The fight between the loyalists and the mutineers was still raging when Pelsaert returned in the *Sardam*. Hayes alerted him, and when the mutineers tried to board the *Sardam*, they were seized.

Each was tried by the officers of the *Sardam*, put in irons and tortured. Cornelius had both his hands cut off before being hanged on Seal Island.

Two mutineers, however—Wouter Loos and a boy named Jan Pelgrom de By—were set adrift in a small boat. Neither was heard of again, but rumours arose that they had landed on the mainland. Certainly, light-skinned Aborigines who might have been descendants of the marooned Dutchmen were seen in the various coastal areas of Western Australia.

For many years it was believed that the site of the *Batavia*'s wreck was on the extreme tip of the Abrolhos, but in 1963, Dave Johnson, a cray fisherman, discovered the wreck 45 miles to the north.

On the islands, divers found coins, a seal, sword hooks, keys, glassware, and two macabre relics—a human ankle bone, and a male skeleton with a twisted jawbone and sword cleft on top of the skull.

A FAMILY'S BID FOR FREEDOM

Fear and desperation sowed seeds of hope

Famine swept through New South Wales. The harvest had failed, grain stocks were low and there was strict rationing among the convicts in the penal settlement at Sydney.

Many of the hungry convicts—transported to Sydney Cove in 1788 to found the colony—tried to escape. Some thought they could walk to China, which they believed was connected to the Australian

AUSTRALIA BOUND *Mary and William Bryant were among the first lot of convicts to be sent by ship to the colony which was 12,000 miles away.*

mainland. They either died from exhaustion or were killed by hostile Aborigines. Others took to the sea and few of these were ever heard of again.

But among those who chose the sea route and who succeeded in making one of the most daring escapes were William and Mary Bryant.

They had been convicted, independently, at Exeter in 1786: she of stealing a cloak and of street robbery with violence: he for 'interrupting revenue officers in the execution of their duty'.

Mary Broad, as she was then known, was condemned to death at the age of 21, but the sentence was commuted to seven years in the colony. William Bryant, 27, a Cornish fisherman, was also transported for seven years.

They sailed on the *Charlotte*, and during the eight-month-long journey she gave birth to a daughter whom she named after the boat. Four days after their arrival, the couple married. A year later she gave birth to a boy whom she named Emanuel.

Inspired by Captain Bligh

Frightened of impending famine, they decided to make a bid for freedom by sailing to the island of Timor 3254 miles away. Bryant was inspired by Captain William Bligh's amazing feat of rowing across the Pacific in an open boat after a mutiny aboard his ship the *Bounty*.

Through his job with the harbour fishing fleet, Bryant acquired a small single-masted boat and with their children and seven other convicts, set sail on March 28, 1791, under cover of night.

They steered north along Australia's eastern coast, navigating through mountainous and gale-whipped seas with amazing skill. Often their attempts to land to carry out repairs or look for food were thwarted by hostile natives.

Crossing the Arafura Sea, the escapees skirted the coast of Timor and more than two months later, on June 5, arrived at Kupang. There, Bryant told the governor that they were survivors of a brig wrecked off New South Wales.

But the party began to quarrel and the governor became suspicious. Then in the September of 1791 a Captain Edwards and some of the crew from HMS *Pandora*, which had been wrecked in Torres Strait while searching for the *Bounty* mutineers, reached Kupang and the governor had Bryant, his wife and companions arrested. They were taken, in irons, to Batavia on the island of Java and there both Bryant and his baby son died. On the way to Cape Town three more of the party died, worn out by their adventures.

The remaining four convicts and the daughter were then transferred to a London-bound ship. The child died on route, and when the ship reached Portsmouth in June 1792 the survivors were sent to Newgate prison.

Nearly a year later, and on the insistence of writer James Boswell who heard of their plight, Mary Bryant was given a pardon. Six months later the men were given their freedom.

THE COCKLESHELL HERO

Doctor 'shipwrecked' himself to prove a theory

Robinson Crusoe was lucky. When he was shipwrecked he found a desert island which enabled him to stay alive until rescue came.

Thousands of seafarers have been less fortunate. In peace and especially in war, men have pulled away in lifeboats from sinking ships only to die of thirst or starvation.

Their plight so appalled a French doctor, Alain Bombard, that he resolved to do something about it. Many of these deaths, he believed, were unnecessary. A castaway adrift without food or water, with only an open boat and his own resources, should be able to keep himself alive far beyond the known limits of human endurance in such a situation.

The method he chose to prove his theory was one that scientists have used for centuries: he made himself the guinea-pig. On October 19, 1953, he set off from the Canary Isles in a 15 ft rubber cockleshell of a boat to cross the Atlantic to the West Indies. To make the experiment as realistic as possible he took no provisions: not a scrap of food, not a drop of water.

Bombard did not accept the popular belief that drinking seawater sends a thirsting castaway mad and hastens his death. His theory was that shipwrecked men who suffered this fate had made the mistake of not drinking seawater until their bodies were already dehydrated.

From the time he set off he was careful to drink a pint-and-a-half of seawater every day, supplemented by water squeezed from fish caught with a makeshift harpoon. To ensure he did not fall a victim to scurvy, he trailed a net of close-woven cloth in which he scooped up plankton. One or two teaspoonsful a day of these tiny organisms which float on and near the surface provided the vitamins to reinforce his meagre diet.

Almost at the start of his voyage a storm nearly wrecked his tiny craft. His sail was ripped and his spare was torn away, so that he had to repair the original with needle and thread.

After a fortnight, his poor diet combined with constant drenchings brought him out in a painful rash.

Hair raising

The storm led to the most hair-raising experience of all. Diving overboard one day to retrieve his single comfort, an inflatable cushion, which had blown away, he was horrified to discover that his sea anchor, a parachute-type canvas gadget used to slow the boat down, had fouled in its trailing ropes and the dinghy was rapidly drifting away. Suddenly, the contraption righted itself; the 'brake' worked, and he managed to haul himself back on board.

But his biggest disappointment came when, on the 53rd day, he hailed a ship to ask his position—and found that he had another 600 miles to go.

He thought of giving up. His experiment in survival had already been vindicated. But a meal on board the ship revived his spirits and he decided to press on.

He reached Barbados on Christmas Eve, having sailed more than 2750 miles in 65 days. He had lost 56 lb., but he was alive and well. He had proved his point.

SEND IT BY BOTTLE

Messages can cross the world sealed with a cork

Paolina and Åke Viking were married in Sicily in the autumn of 1958, thanks to a far-travelled bottle. Two years earlier Åke, a bored young Swedish sailor on a ship far out at sea, had dropped a bottle overboard with a message asking any pretty girl who found it to write.

Paolina's father, a Sicilian fisherman, picked it up and passed it to his daughter for a joke. Continuing the joke, Paolina sent off a note to the young sailor. The correspondence quickly grew warmer. Åke visited Sicily and the marriage soon followed their first meeting.

Surviving hurricanes

Fragile as it is, a well-sealed bottle is one of the world's most seaworthy objects. It will bob safely through hurricanes that can sink great ships. And for most practical purposes glass lasts for ever. In 1954, 18 bottles were salvaged from a ship sunk 250 years before off the Kent coast. The liquor in them was unrecognisable, but the bottles were as good as new.

But it is impossible to predict the direction a bottle will take. Of two bottles dropped simultaneously off the Brazilian coast, one drifted east for 130 days and was found on a beach in Africa, and the other floated northwards for 190 days reaching Nicaragua.

Speed is also bound to vary according to wind and current. A bottle might be completely becalmed or, if caught up by the Gulf Stream at its raciest, might bowl along at four knots and cover as much as 100 miles a day.

The longest voyage

The longest bottle voyage ever is thought to have been made by a bottle known as 'The Flying Dutchman'. It was launched by a German scientific expedition in 1929 in the South Indian Ocean. Inside was a message, which could be read without breaking the bottle, asking the finder to report where he found it and throw it back into the sea.

It apparently caught an east-going current which carried it to the tip of South America. There it was found, reported and thrown back again several times. Eventually it moved out into the Atlantic, then again into the Indian

Ocean passing roughly the spot where it had been dropped, and was cast ashore on the west coast of Australia in 1935. It had covered 16,000 miles in 2447 days— a respectable average of over 6 nautical miles a day.

Charts compiled from bottles

When he was postmaster-general for the North American colonies, Benjamin Franklin realised that, because their whaler captains knew the currents much better, American ships were crossing the Atlantic much quicker than the British mail packets. He therefore compiled a chart using both the whalers' lore and information he obtained by loosing bottles into the Gulf Stream and asking the finders to return them. The information he recorded is still used today.

Since then both the British and US navies have used bottles extensively to compile intricate current charts. And the movement of oil slicks, mines and even fish have been predicted with the help of seaborne bottles.

Of course, a number of bottles have been dispatched containing strange messages. Elizabeth I once received an intelligence report by this means, and was so disconcerted to find it had been opened by a boatman at Dover that she appointed an official Uncorker of Bottles, and decreed that no unauthorised person might open a message-carrying bottle, on pain of death.

In 1875 the crew of the Canadian barque *Lennie* mutinied and murdered their officers. A steward who was spared because he could navigate, steered them to the French coast telling them it was Spain, and surreptitiously dropped several bottles over the side telling the whole story. The French authorities found one, boarded the ship and arrested the surprised mutineers.

Torpedoed destroyer

And a message found on a beach in Maine, USA, in 1944 read: 'Our ship is sinking. SOS didn't do any good. Think it's the end. Maybe this message will get to the US some day.' It was identified as coming from the USS *Beatty*, a destroyer torpedoed with heavy loss of life some-

FÜHRER'S END?

This message floated in a bottle in the North Sea for a year before being found on the Danish coast on November 26, 1946. It claims that Adolf Hitler did not die in the bunker in Berlin, but lost his life aboard the German U-boat Nauecilus, *which sank on November 15, 1945, after colliding with a wreck near Gedser lightship on the way from Finland to Franco's Spain. The message, probably a joke, is written on a page allegedly torn from the* Nauecilus's *log-book.*

where off Gibraltar on November 6, 1943.

In 1953 a bottle was found in Tasmania 37 years after it had been dropped overboard by two Australian soldiers on their way to France in a troopship.

The mother of one of the soldiers recognised the handwriting of her son who had been killed in action in 1918.

The strangest case was perhaps that of Chunosuke Matsuyama, a Japanese seaman who was wrecked with 44 shipmates in 1784. Shortly before he and his companions died of starvation on a Pacific coral reef, Matsuyama carved a brief account of their tragedy on a piece of wood, sealed it in a bottle and threw it in the sea.

It was washed up 150 years later in 1935, and at the very seaside village where Matsuyama had been born.

HORSEBACK TREK FOR HELP

Farmer's ten-day ride brought relief to besieged town

Shortly before midnight, Dick King and his Zulu servant boy stole softly into the darkness and crept unseen to Durban harbour. There they were rowed out, swimming their horses behind them, to Salisbury Island.

Behind them lay a beleaguered British garrison fighting desperately for their lives. Ahead stretched ten days of hardship and hazard; ten days that helped to shape the history of South Africa.

The date was May 24, 1842. Durban was then little more than a sprinkling of scattered homes and farmsteads occupied by British settlers who had founded the town in 1835.

But in August 1841 a group of Boer farmers, trekking away from British-ruled Cape Colony, proclaimed their own Republic of Natal. They were followed by a force of 250 soldiers sent by the Governor of the Cape to re-occupy the territory and reassert British control. Furious, the Boer farmers threatened to drive them out of

Durban. The British, outnumbered by more than six to one, fought back fiercely and dug in for a siege. Chivalrously, the Boers allowed the women and children to be evacuated to a cargo ship in the bay. Meanwhile, supplies and food for the fighting men left behind to defend the town were running out.

Only a hunter could make it

The situation was desperate. Somehow word must be got to Grahamstown, a British base 600 miles away across a wasteland of wild, mostly undeveloped country.

Dick King, a 30-year-old farmer, knew that only a man with his hunting skills and knowledge of the country could stand a chance of getting through—and even his chances were slim.

But he volunteered, and with his servant boy, Ndongeni, saddled up on Salisbury Island, in Durban Bay—chosen because at low tide the sea swept out and exposed a wide stretch of sand which he might cross and so outflank the Boer lines where they thinned out towards the coast.

The route to Grahamstown was crisscrossed by creeks and rivers. There were no railways or bridges or roads. Snakes and crocodiles infested the low-lying areas, and there were lions and savage warrior tribes on the veld.

Worst of all, Boer patrols might turn up anywhere. So, for safety, King and his companion slept and rested during daylight and travelled by night. Sometimes they had to dismount and swim across rivers, leading their horses behind them.

After 200 miles Ndongeni could take no more. Then King himself, hungry, weary and sick, became too weak to sit in the saddle and had to take two days to recover his strength.

He struggled on alone. But his horse reached the limit of endurance. At Butterworth a friendly trader exchanged it for a fresh mount.

The last great hazard of King's ride was Kaffirland, a bush territory peopled by hostile natives. Fortunately King spoke their language and was able to persuade them to allow him safe conduct.

On June 4, 11 days after he had set out, he rode up the main street of Grahamstown to the military headquarters and

CITY'S HERO *Durban's tribute to Dick King, whose epic ride saved the town's British garrison from disaster in 1842.*

delivered his message to the commander. A month later he was back in Durban with the seaborne troops who relieved the beleaguered settlement.

DR LIVINGSTONE'S DARK CONTINENT

He took faith and science to the ends of the earth

The man who opened up more of the world's surface than anyone else in history owed his success to a burning faith, a medicine chest and unfailing good manners.

Wherever Dr David Livingstone travelled in unexplored Africa he always treated the Africans with courtesy—even the witch-doctors, whom he called his 'professional brothers'.

It was only by chance that Livingstone

ever came to Africa. Born in 1813 in Blantyre near Glasgow, he was sent to work in a local spinning mill at the age of ten. By working 12 hours a day he paid his way through medical school in Glasgow to become a doctor-missionary in China.

But his hopes were dashed by the Opium Wars, which made it impossible for him to work in China. In 1840, at the age of 27, he decided to go to Africa instead.

In the 19th century most of the 12

million square miles of Africa were still totally unknown to civilised peoples. It was the Dark Continent, a place of impenetrable jungle, of ferocious animals, bloodthirsty black savages and disease.

Livingstone did not go to Africa to explore: the habit grew on him. At first he travelled only to establish his Christian missions and to bring medical assistance to those in need. But as the years went by he was gripped by wanderlust.

On foot, by canoe and sometimes on ox-back, he travelled thousands of miles from the Atlantic to the Indian Ocean through the territories that are now South Africa, Rhodesia, Zambia, Zaïre, Angola, Mozambique, Tanzania, Rwanda and Burundi.

With him he always carried a Bible, a magic lantern, a compass and a sextant. He had learnt to use the sextant in Cape Town, and he never failed to record his precise location each day.

Nor were his journeys those of a man whose sole purpose was to spread the Gospel. He charted all the regions he visited, making detailed and intelligent observations of the natural life, geography, geology and medical cases he witnessed. These painstaking reports he sent to the Royal Geographical Society in London. As much as a man of God, he was a man of science.

Nevertheless it was the Christian faith that drove Livingstone on, fighting superstition and cruelty, establishing churches and schools, and teaching elementary hygiene and sanitation.

He could survive where others had perished because, in the first place, he had sufficient medical knowledge to keep himself alive in malaria-infested regions. With his penetrating mind, he once noted: 'Myriads of mosquitoes showed, as they probably always do, the presence of malaria.' He did not reach the conclusion that mosquitoes *caused* malaria, but at least he invented an anti-malarial pill of jalap and quinine, with which he managed to survive his own bouts of the disease.

Secondly, unlike so many other white travellers, he journeyed among people for whom he felt compassion and respect, people who admired and respected him in return, not only as the doctor who helped them, but as a man.

Above all, as soon as he became aware of the horrors of the slave trade run by the Arabs, he resolved to fight slavery as long as he should live.

Livingstone married the daughter of a fellow-missionary and they had six children. When his baby daughter died on a journey in 1850, Livingstone sent his family home to Britain, but he stayed in Africa with the wider family of his African peoples.

In 1856 he returned to London and found himself a national hero. He could easily have rested on his laurels, but that was not for him. Soon he went back to his beloved Africa.

Then, in 1866, he started out from Zanzibar on a quest for the Royal Geographical Society—to track down the source of the River Nile.

This time everything went wrong. His bearers fell ill, his oxen died, many of his servants ran away rather than face the warlike tribes of what are now Tanzania,

THE DRAMATIC MEETING *America's Henry Stanley (left) greets the Scotsman who explored the Dark Continent. But Dr Livingstone was an exhausted man, and two years later he was dead.*

Rwanda and Burundi. Livingstone himself suffered agonies from several diseases—malaria, ulcers and rheumatic fever.

Then came the bitterest blow of all. Two more servants ran off, taking with them his medicine chest and quinine.

His supplies exhausted and with almost no hope left, his little party lay up in the village of Ujiji, on the eastern shore of Lake Tanganyika.

Meanwhile, the civilised world was wondering what could have happened to the celebrated Dr Livingstone. Rumours abounded, but nobody knew if he was alive or dead.

Nearly five years after his disappearance, the *New York Herald* decided to send its leading reporter, Henry Morton Stanley, to search for the great doctor.

Stanley himself was a remarkable character. A penniless Welsh waif, he had shipped to New Orleans as a cabin boy, then drifted into journalism and had become one of the greatest reporters in the United States.

In 1871, at the head of an expedition of 192 men, Stanley set off from Zanzibar, pushing through the wild country of East Africa and following up all rumours of the missing white doctor.

The search lasted eight months. On November 10, 1871, his party reached Ujiji village.

There, standing in a clearing before his tent, Stanley saw the emaciated figure of the explorer, staring in astonishment at the search party that had come so far to

his rescue. The meeting between the two men has since become legendary—and something of a music-hall joke. Much speculation has taken place as to what was actually said at the time, but perhaps some of the controversy is cleared through Stanley's notes in his autobiography. He wrote:

'I walked up to him, and, doffing my helmet, bowed and said in an inquiring tone—"Dr Livingstone, I presume?"'

'Smiling cordially, he lifted his cap and answered briefly, "Yes".'

'This ending all scepticism on my part, my face betrayed the earnestness of my satisfaction as I extended my hand and added,—"I thank God, Doctor, that I have been permitted to see you".'

'In the warm grasp he gave my hand, and the heartiness of his voice, I felt that he also was sincere and earnest as he replied,—"I feel most thankful that I am here to welcome you".'

Stanley's rescue came none too soon, for Livingstone had been without medicine for two years and was very ill. Nevertheless, he refused Stanley's invitation to return to the certain triumph that awaited him in London. 'I still have much work to do,' he said. So Stanley turned back and Livingstone, now supplied with medicine, equipment and servants, pressed ahead in his search for the Nile.

But he was a dying man. In the coming months he found the headwaters of a river—the Congo and not the Nile. He was never to know his error. At Chitambo village on the morning of May 1, 1873, his bearers found him kneeling by his bedside in an attitude of prayer, his head resting on his hands. They could not rouse him.

Journey's end

From village to village the message was spread. His converts came in their thousands to pay their last respects. They knew that far away in Britain the doctor's friends would want his body for burial. So they embalmed it. But first they removed his heart and buried it where it belonged, in the soil of Africa.

Then began a funeral march that took nine months to reach Zanzibar, the remains borne across the wild lands by relays of Africans chanting the hymns that Livingstone had taught them. From Zanzibar a British steamer brought the body home, where it was laid to rest in Westminster Abbey.

AFRICAN ODYSSEY *Livingstone, found by Stanley at Ujiji, died at Chitambo.*

THE FLOATING SCOTSMAN

Canoeist who opened up Canada

While his companions watched in silence, the 29-year-old Scot mixed vermilion pigment with grease and scrawled across a rock his title-deed to the most prodigious feat of exploration in North America's history: 'Alexander Mackenzie, from Canada, by land, the twenty-second of July, one thousand seven hundred and ninety-three.'

Though the words would soon be expunged by the Pacific gales, they proudly proclaimed that for the first time, white men had crossed the continent.

Mackenzie was born at Stornoway on the Isle of Lewis in the Hebrides, but grew up in America where his father took him after his mother died. He went to school in New York and Montreal and then joined the North-West Company, a firm of Montreal-based fur traders, who sent him to their most westerly outpost at Fort Chipewyan, now in Alberta.

HOW THE WEST WAS WON *Mackenzie's route (arrows) across the unmapped continent.*

Lure of the West

Having travelled there by canoe his enthusiasm for exploration was aroused. He shared his company's ambition of reaching the Pacific and reaping the harvest of sea-otter pelts then being monopolised by Russians from Siberia.

Poring over the vague, chaotic charts drawn by other pioneers from Red Indian legend and their own wild guesses, Mackenzie reckoned that the rivers flowing northwards must eventually turn west and empty into the sea. So, on June 3, 1789, with 13 companions in three canoes, he started north on a stream ending no one knew where. His surmise was false; the stream did not turn west. Instead it took him to the Arctic Ocean. The vast Mackenzie River system was now on the map of Canada.

This discovery—a voyage of nearly 3000 miles in 102 days—should have been sufficient achievement for one man's lifetime. It only tormented Mackenzie. His road to the Pacific still evaded him.

In the summer of 1792, while Mackenzie was studying navigation in England, his men were building a camp on the bank of the Peace River.

That winter he rejoined them and, as soon as spring broke, all ten of them set off in a single fragile birch-bark canoe.

The going was easy until the party encountered the furious waters of the Peace River canyon, which runs for 25 miles into the Rocky Mountains. The 25 ft long canoe could not be paddled, but had to be poled, dragged by rope or carried along the slippery cliffs.

Mackenzie's choice

Soon after they had passed the canyon and relaunched the canoe, the party was faced with a huge fork in the river—flooded when the Williston Lake dam was built.

Should they turn north-west along the wide and safe-looking main channel, now the Finlay River, or strike south on the narrow, swift and dangerous tributary, now the Parsnip River? Mackenzie remembered the words of an old Indian who had told him that the fork to the north poured out of impenetrable mountains where no man could travel. Against the unanimous advice of his crew, he chose the tributary.

It was very hard going and the men were again grumbling when the canoe was stopped by a party of Sekani Indians. Through his interpreters, Mackenzie discovered that the river went south and

229

joined another which flowed into the 'stinking lake'.

Across the Great Divide

This was the party's first rumour of salt water. They pushed on until the river dissolved into a maze of small brooks. On June 12 the canoe was lifted from the water and carried over a low hill to a small lake. White men had at last surmounted the Continental Divide.

After wrecking the canoe on a rock and patching it up with bark, the pioneers at last reached the Fraser River, which bore them safely west.

Suddenly a flight of arrows showered from the bank. Mackenzie ordered his crew not to shoot and stepped ashore alone. His daring gamble succeeded, and the Indians accepted presents of beads and knives from him.

Mackenzie had discovered the warlike Carriers, a people whose widows carried their dead husband's bones on their backs. From them he learnt that the Fraser did eventually reach the ocean, but that there was a quicker route due west overland to another river.

Though it was midsummer the men shivered as they left the canoe to cross the snow-packed Rainbow Mountains on foot, and it was 13 days before they descended into the warm valley of the Bella Coola River. Friendly Indians lent them two canoes and, on July 20, the ten men paddled through a labyrinth of islands into Dean Channel, a coastal inlet north of what is now Vancouver.

Two days later Mackenzie scrawled his message on the south-east face of one of the rocks, and began the return journey. This took a mere 33 days, and on August 24 he completed a unique double. He had beheld both the Arctic Ocean and the Pacific Ocean, and he had come back without the loss of a single life.

GATEWAY TO THE WEST

Two men who opened up the route to the Pacific

Wagons roll! Accompanied by a volley of whipcracks, those two evocative words started many an adventure along the Oregon Trail as families pulled up their roots and set off in search of a new life and prosperity in the unexplored West. But it was a single shot fired on the bank of the Missouri River on May 14, 1804, that signalled the beginning of the most famous trek of them all, the first expedition to find an overland route to the Pacific.

It took two years and four months, covered some 8000 miles and eventually added vast new territories to the emergent United States.

President Thomas Jefferson had asked Congress for $2500—about £500—to equip an expedition to follow the Missouri to its source, cross the formidable Rocky Mountains and descend the Columbia River to the Pacific. To lead it, Jefferson chose his private secretary, Captain Meriwether Lewis, a veteran of the North-West Territory, who was both a naturalist and an experienced navigator, and Lieutenant William Clark. Their instructions were to record geographical information and take note of mineral resources, Indian tribal customs and languages, animal and plant life and climate.

During the winter of 1803-4, the expedition camped on the Mississippi near St Louis. They recruited 43 men, mostly rugged frontiersmen, to go along with them, and accumulated 6 tons of supplies and ammunition, which were loaded into three boats.

The diaries of Lewis and Clark record that they set off to the firing of a shot to mark the occasion.

They sailed through rich lands, well stocked with game, especially buffalo and elk. Lewis noted that 'two good hunters could conveniently provide a regiment with provisions'.

After five months of pleasant journeying they reached the Mandan Indian country, now central North Dakota. The Mandans welcomed them, and the explorers spent the winter in their territory.

In April 1805 they set out again, keeping to the Missouri as far as Three Forks, near the site of Butte, Montana.

Before them lay the Rocky Mountains. Fortunately, a French Canadian trapper called Toussaint Charbonneau and his Indian wife, Sacagawea, had joined the party as guides. Although she had a baby

THE WIDE MISSOURI *Clark (left) and the expedition leader, Lewis, spent the winter of 1804–5 in this Mandan settlement on the banks of the frozen Missouri. Though decimated by smallpox introduced by white trappers, the Indians were friendly and helped the explorers on their way.*

with her, Sacagawea was tough and happened to be a member of the tribe through whose territory the route now led.

Thanks to her, the Indians were co-operative and provided horses for the journey over the Rockies, though the way was so steep and tortuous that the horses could be used only to carry supplies.

Then food ran short and the mountain cold became so bitter that the half-starved expedition was in constant danger of frostbite.

The journals record: 'We camped near a bank of snow, three feet deep. Some of this we melted and supped on the colt killed yesterday. Our only game today was two pheasants; and the horses on which we calculated as a last resource began to fail us, for two of them were so poor and worn out with fatigue that we were obliged to leave them behind.

'The road was like that of yesterday, along steep hillsides, obstructed with fallen timber, and a growth of eight different species of pine, so thickly strewed that the snow falls from them as we pass, and keeps us continually wet to the skin, and so cold that we are anxious lest our feet should be frozen, as we only have thin moccasins to defend them.'

The adventurers gritted their teeth and plodded grimly on.

Eventually their courage paid off. They reached open plains again. And finally they camped on a westward-flowing stream, where they built canoes for the final journey to the sea on the Columbia River.

Their triumph on reaching the Pacific was dampened, however, for it hardly stopped raining all winter.

In the spring of 1806 they started on their journey back, this time splitting into two groups to extend their explorations further. Reassembling at the junction of the Yellowstone and Missouri Rivers, they set off for the easy voyage downstream to St Louis. On September 23, 1806, they arrived back to a tumultuous reception.

The expedition had failed in one objective—to find an easy water passage across the northern United States.

They had encountered grizzly bears and rattlesnakes; they had overcome hardship and starvation; and Lewis had received a gunshot wound in the thigh when someone mistook him for an elk.

But they had lost only one man. They had shown that the dangers of the route could not deter capable and determined men. For years yet, as the wagons rolled to the far West, the way would be full of danger, hardships and disasters. But the door was open.

ACROSS THE WORLD IN 112 DAYS

The race that proved the motor-car had come to stay

Six awe-inspiring contraptions were lined up across 43rd Street, New York, and their combined din was overpowering. They were recognisably automobiles although one had a mast and sail, and another carried ski-like runners. As well as pneumatic tyres, most had high steel-studded wheels and all carried food and medicine chests, picks and shovels, repair tools and spares, and firearms.

Perched on top of these remarkable machines were men in fur coats, bearskin caps, arctic boots and goggles. Three of the vehicles bore French colours, one German, one Italian and one American. It was February 12, 1908. This was the start of the first round-the-world motor-car race.

Route without words

The route was across the northern United States and then by boat to Alaska, where it was planned to drive across the Bering Strait on the ice. From there the cars were to cross Siberia and Eastern Europe and finish up in Paris. It was a race which only supreme optimists were likely to enter, for there were virtually no tarmac roads in America outside the cities, and Siberia was almost devoid even of tracks.

But though the automobile was only 18 years old, the manufacturers were eager to show what it could do. Two newspapers were co-sponsors, the *New York Times* and *Le Matin* of Paris. The *Times* was particularly enthusiastic and proclaimed: 'Over this route, the traffic of

the world will some day move.' But sceptics were even more numerous, and among them was the London *Daily Mail*, which said: 'The motor-car, after woman, is the most fragile and capricious thing on earth.'

Of the six contenders, Germany's *Protos* looked the most formidable—a 60 hp monster manned by army engineers. Next biggest was the American *Thomas Flyer*, also 60 hp. Italy's *Zust* and two French cars, *De Dion* and *Moto-Bloc*, had 40 hp. The other French entry was the tiny 12 hp *Sizaire-Naudin*, whose drivers predicted that they would skim over snow and mud.

Substitute mechanic

Each car had two drivers and a mechanic. And perhaps of all of them the most unprepared was the young mechanic aboard the *Thomas*, George Schuster. He had never intended to enter the race. He had been sent by the Thomas factory to deliver the *Thomas* to the starting line. But when at the last minute the chosen mechanic withdrew, Schuster eagerly changed his clothes and climbed aboard.

Some 200,000 people crammed into Times Square to see the start of the race at 11.15 a.m., in a crescendo of banging motors, horns, cheers and brass-band music. Escorted by 200 cars, the racers swung north into Broadway. For 8 miles cheering crowds lined the streets. Then the escort dropped away, and the six cars roared off up the Post Road towards Albany.

THE GREAT CAR RACE
In the background, a contemporary illustration of the intended route from New York to Paris. Foreground: The massive De Dion, one of the French entries.

At Hastings, 18 miles from the start, the *De Dion* ploughed into a snowdrift, and it took half-an-hour's shovelling by all the crews to clear the road. At 8.20 p.m., the *Thomas* rumbled into Hudson, 116 miles from Times Square, trailed by the *De Dion* and the *Zust*. The *Protos* managed only the 74 miles to Poughkeepsie, while the *Moto-Bloc* and *Sizaire-Naudin* were at Peekshill, just 44 miles from the start.

The next day the *Thomas* and the *Zust* established themselves in the lead, while the little *Sizaire-Naudin* made a net loss of 4 miles, having taken a wrong turning and headed south. Then it tore out its differential gear on a rock and withdrew from the race.

West from Albany the drivers, despairing of the mapped route, took to the Erie Canal Towpath. The crews filled ditches, reinforced a bridge and rolled away 80 huge logs that blocked their progress. On the fourth day the *De Dion* and *Thomas* pulled the *Zust* out of a swamp.

Sleds to the rescue

South of the Great Lakes snowdrifts made the road impassable and Montague Roberts, out in front in the *Thomas*, paid $1000 to have ten teams, dragging sleds, harden the route for 100 miles.

The *Thomas*, *De Dion* and *Zust* were crossing Illinois, while the *Protos* and the *Moto-Bloc* were still struggling through Indiana. The road across Iowa was a ribbon of mud, sometimes 2 ft deep, and this ultimately proved too much for the *Moto-Bloc*.

News of the crazy adventure had captivated America. People lined the route to cheer and give aid. Straw fires lit the way at night. Boucier St Chaffray, driver of the *De Dion*, wired his backers: 'I can't spend money. They give me everything.' And Omaha's militia turned out to welcome the leading *Thomas* with a salute from eight guns.

In the mountain states, though, the crews were on their own and sometimes had to spend hours scouring the rocky, snowswept surface for possible routes. Eventually, on March 24, behind a raucous parade of local motorists, the *Thomas* rolled through the decorated streets of San Francisco. The 3836 miles from New York had taken 42 days. But the second-place *Zust* was still groping through the mountains of Utah; the *De Dion* was

in Granger, Wyoming; and the *Protos* was undergoing repairs even further behind.

Quicker by rail

When the *Thomas* arrived in Alaska by ship, the locals guffawed at its crew's plan to cross the Bering Strait. Not one of them could remember the Strait solidly frozen. Back in New York the red-faced committee sent out frantic telegrams. The *Zust* and the *De Dion* were shipped from San Francisco to Seattle. The *Protos*, still well short of San Francisco, accepted a 15-day penalty and was taken to Seattle by rail. The *Thomas* returned to join them, and all four were shipped to Vladivostok in Siberia to resume the race.

At Vladivostok, St Chaffray withdrew, deciding that his *De Dion* was too worn to risk what lay ahead. But on May 22 the remaining three were off again. The *Protos* was now in luck and forged steadily ahead while the *Thomas*, lost in a wild mountain maze, spent two days finding its way back to the route by stars and compass. Then it began to gain, overtaking the *Protos* 1900 miles from Vladivostok. Meanwhile, the *Zust* was steadily losing ground.

The Germans and the Americans exchanged the lead half a dozen times on the plains of Siberia. But on July 18 the *Protos* rolled into Moscow four days ahead of the *Thomas*. It was inspected by the Tsar, and awarded a $1000 prize for winning the race across Russia.

The 2587 miles from St Petersburg to Paris offered the best roads of the entire race, and the *Protos* covered the distance in eight days. But because of its 15-day penalty it was not to be the winner. Four days later the *Thomas* roared to a halt outside the offices of *Le Matin*. It had won by 11 days' driving time.

The stand-in was the hero

George Schuster, the young mechanic who had set out five months earlier to deliver the car to the starting line, was the hero of the day. He had become co-driver with George Miller, when the other starting driver dropped out during the gruelling crossing of America.

The *Thomas* had covered 12,116 miles at a rate of 108 miles a day. The *Zust* reached Paris two weeks later. Three of the six starters finished. They had demonstrated what the motor industry hoped to prove: the car had come to stay.

THE ATLANTIC CHALLENGE

Pioneer fliers had to do running repairs on the way

It was to have been a world fit for heroes. The heroes had won the war, but now thousands of them could not even get a job.

One of the army of demobilised fighting men trudging Britain's streets in January 1919 was 33-year-old Glasgow-born Lieutenant Arthur Whitten Brown, who had been shot down and suffered a shattered leg while serving as a navigator in the Royal Flying Corps. Using a stick, he limped from office to office, always drawing a blank, until a lucky chance took him to the Vickers aircraft works at Weybridge, in Surrey.

A job—and a prize

For the umpteenth time he repeated his qualifications. Then . . . could he navigate an aeroplane across the Atlantic? 'Yes,' replied Brown without hesitation. 'Right,' said Maxwell Muller, the superintendent, 'I have a job for you.' The job was to win a £10,000 prize offered by the *Daily Mail* to the first crew to fly a plane from North America to Europe.

The Vickers entry was a converted 'Vimy' bomber, a canvas-covered framework of wood and steel tubing, not quite 43 ft long, with a wing-span of 68 ft. She had a cruising speed of 90 mph and, fitted with extra tanks, it was estimated that she could fly 2440 miles in normal con-

FLIGHT RECORDER
This statue, at London's Heathrow Airport, commemorates the historic flight of Alcock and Brown.

ditions—a range which would give a perilously low margin even without allowing for unfavourable winds. The pilot was Captain John Alcock, just 26 years old, but a war ace with a Distinguished Service Cross to his credit.

For three months, designers and mechanics worked day and night on the Vimy. Alcock tested and retested the two Rolls-Royce 360 hp engines, while Brown pored over charts and such weather maps as there were. Finally, the plane was dismantled, crated and shipped to St John's, Newfoundland, where she was reassembled and the crew waited for favourable weather to take off.

Two rival teams had already come to grief when at noon on June 14 Alcock and Brown decided the time had come. They sat side by side in the open cockpit and stowed their provisions for the flight—sandwiches, coffee and beer. On the seat beside him Brown perched Twinkletoes, a toy black cat given to him by his fiancée.

To the spectators who came to wave her off, the plane, loaded with 870 gal. of fuel and 40 gal. of oil, looked as if she would never be able to get off the ground. Soon, however, Brown was tapping out his first Morse signal on the wireless set he had rigged up: 'All well and started.' Things did not remain well for long. Thick fog closed in, forcing the pilot to use a torch to read his instruments. Then the wind-powered generator mounted on a wing to work the wireless sheared off. Brown reported the setback on a notepad—for conversation was impossible above the noise. Alcock pencilled back: 'How about opening a bottle of ale?'

Exhaust pipe melts

After about five hours' flying, the fog lifted—but then the starboard engine started to rattle like a machine-gun. A section of an exhaust pipe melted away, and a stream of flame trailed from the damaged engine. Miraculously, the flimsy fabric of the fuselage was untouched—and the fliers pressed on. There was little choice: a short sight of the stars through a break in the clouds showed Brown that they had just about reached the halfway mark—the point beyond which they could not turn back.

END OF AN ADVENTURE *After battling through snowstorms and beating hazards like iced-up wings, the Vimy ended its Atlantic flight in an Irish peat bog that Alcock mistook for a field.*

For three more hours the Vimy flew on into the night, until a sudden storm, with hail and lightning, caught the plane broadside, tossing it about like a kite. The Vimy was forced into an almost vertical dive. From 5000 ft they fell to 2000 . . . 1000 . . . 500.

In minutes the wingtips were almost brushing the white caps of the waves. A glance at the compass showed that the plane had been spun right round and was heading back west at full speed.

Sinister sound

It took every bit of Alcock's flying skill to get the plane back under control, climbing again and on course. But once more the craft began to lose height, and the engines were emitting a new and still more sinister warning sound: the carburettor air intakes were becoming choked with freezing snow.

Brown knew there was only one thing to be done. Unhitching his seat belt and dragging his aching wounded leg behind him, he clutched the struts for support against the screaming wind, and clambered out on to the wing. Alcock, at the controls, struggled to hold the plane level: a pitch or roll would catapult his navigator into the Atlantic.

Laboriously, Brown opened his penknife with his teeth and chipped away at the frozen snow that was choking the life out of the engines. Before the air intakes were freed, he had to make six trips from wing to wing, returning to the cockpit each time for a rest, then clambering over Alcock and crawling out on the other side.

Finally, the engines throbbed with new life and Alcock was able to coax the plane to its absolute ceiling, 11,000 ft, above the snowstorm. But at that height they had to cope with another deadly enemy— ice. Vapour was freezing on the wings, and the flaps were becoming stiff.

They were now, however, on the last lap, only 80 miles from the Irish coast. Surely they were not going to be beaten now? With one final effort Alcock cut his engines back and eased the nose down. At 5000 ft the warmer air started to thaw the ice from the wings, and at 500 ft the pilot opened the throttles again. Minutes later the Vimy landed in an Irish peat bog which Alcock had mistaken for a field.

Victory—then death

The plane cartwheeled and came to rest on her nose. But the fliers were unhurt. They collected the £10,000 prize, and both were knighted within the week. In 16 hours 27 minutes they had blazed a trail which millions would follow.

But for them it was not a happy-ever-after story. Six months later Alcock was killed in an air crash in France. Brown was so shaken by the news that he never flew again.

SURVIVAL WITH SHACKLETON

Six men battled against the Antarctic Ocean

In March 1916, 28 desperate Britons stood shivering on the beach of an ice-covered, barren island in the Antarctic Ocean. For the past two years they had been members of a trans-Antarctic expedition, and had grown weak and sick in an 1800 mile battle against a wilderness of snow and limitless ice floes— great glacial monsters that had crushed and sunk their ship, the *Endurance*, five months before. Only a few days before they had cast off in their three remaining small boats from the drifting floe which had been their home; their leader had laid his course for Elephant Island, southeast of Cape Horn. Now even that dreary refuge had to be abandoned.

Gales that swept the unsheltered shore were whipping their tents to shreds; the food supply of penguin meat and seaweed was dangerously low. Freezing, hungry, the men turned again—as they had repeatedly through this whole nightmarish ordeal—to the man whose courage and calmness had thus far preserved them.

Tall, broad-shouldered, with an angular face overhung by dark brows, Sir Ernest Shackleton looked like a great brooding rock; the sort of rock men cling to when hope has almost gone.

'We have got to reach a point where we can get a ship,' he said quietly. It was a forlorn hope to make a long journey in a small boat, but he asked for volunteers. Every man offered to go.

Five men were chosen to accompany Shackleton on the 800 mile journey to South Georgia, the worst ocean in the world, in a boat only 22 ft long. They were Worsley, captain of their crushed ship, Tom Crean, Timothy McCarthy, McNeish, the carpenter, and Vincent, the boatswain. They caulked and ballasted the *James Caird*, a light, buoyant, double-ended craft, and stiffened her keel with the mast from another boat. Then they got ready to push off.

Two men fell overboard in the launching, then a rock drove a hole in the hull, which they plugged with a marlinespike. Finally they took on stores and set sail.

It was bitter going. A gale sprang up that drove the craft back nearly to the ice-pack. It was a grave set-back, and

UNENDURABLE *The inexorable power of the Antarctic ice grips Sir Ernest Shackleton's research ship* Endurance. *Pressure from the countless million tons of ice cracked her beams like matchsticks.*

Shackleton said: 'Skipper, if anything happens to me while those fellows are waiting, I shall feel like a murderer.'

But the boat ploughed on. Under the canvas deck was a cramped space reached only by a struggle over provisions and ballast, and at the end the only solace was a wet sleeping bag into which a man crawled wearily. Going to bed was as unhappy as getting up.

'Every swell coming toward us towered like an over-arching wall,' Shackleton wrote later. 'We were getting soaked every three or four minutes. A great sea would break over us, making us feel that we were under a waterfall. Then, before the next wave broke, we would get several minor seas that would just cover the boat and wet us again. This went on day and night. The cold was intense.'

Shackleton, suffering terribly from sciatica, remained cheerful. Worsley had to be held up on each side by a man while trying to get a sight, so that he would not go overboard with his sextant. Late one afternoon, through the constant mist which blurred the sun, he got a landfall—South Georgia!

That night a terrific gale, catapulted them toward the coast. They were so thirsty they could hardly swallow, their

lips were split, the spray shot from the boat high into the air, and the wind howled remorselessly. They bore down on a tiny island, and it was a question whether they would hit it, or round it into calmer water. 'She'll do it,' said Worsley. 'Of course she will,' Shackleton replied. 'She's damned well got to.'

Next day he proposed to land and cross the island to the whaling station on the other side. No human being knew what lay behind those glaciers and ice-covered mountains of South Georgia. But Shackleton was determined to try the route; if his boat were crushed against the rocks going around by water the men back on Elephant Island would die.

They went ashore in King Haakon's Sound and found a cave. Baby albatrosses were caught and killed for food, and the men were so hungry they ate the bones. Near by was a stream of water that tasted like nectar. Leaves and moss made a bed on the stones. For the first time in two weeks they could relax and sleep.

On May 19, 1916, the weather cleared, the moon shone, and Shackleton, Crean and Worsley started across the island, leaving behind three men unfit for travel. Worsley steered the group by his compass, and they roped themselves together. They found themselves in blind passes, made their way almost down to the sea and had to turn back, and once teetered on the brink of a gigantic chasm, 200 ft deep and 200 ft broad.

Finally they reached a ridge so steep they could sit on it and dangle their legs over each side. Fog and darkness had cut off retreat. If they did not move they would freeze to death. Cutting steps down the icy mountainside was so slow as to be useless. After a moment, Shackleton said: 'It's a devil of a risk, but we've got to take it. We'll slide.'

'We each coiled our share of rope into a pad on which to make our glissade,' Worsley later recalled. 'Shackleton sat on a step he had carved and I clasped him around the neck from behind. Crean did the same with me, so that we were locked together as one man. Then Shackleton kicked off.

'We seemed to shoot off into space. For a moment my hair fairly stood on end. Then suddenly I felt a glow, and knew that I was grinning! I was actually enjoying it. We were shooting down the side of a precipitous mountain at nearly a mile

LAST REST *Shackleton died of a heart attack in the Antarctic. He was buried in South Georgia.*

a minute. I yelled with excitement and found Shackleton and Crean were yelling too. It seemed ridiculously safe. To hell with the rocks!

'Little by little our speed slackened, and we finished up at the bottom in a snowbank. We picked ourselves up and solemnly shook hands all round.'

When the trio finally reached the whaling station, having crossed South Georgia in 36 hours, they were so wild looking that the commander, who had entertained them two years before, did not recognise them. Shackleton's hair had turned silver. When Worsley went back to King Haakon Sound to rescue the three men left there, they too did not know him. A bath, a shave and some decent clothes made that

much difference to his former appearance.

All the men on Elephant Island were found well—with the exception of one lad whose toes had been amputated. They had lived for four and a half months under two overturned boats, beaten by hurricanes, and pelted with ice from the mountains. Thus ended the last long expedition of Ernest Shackleton.

The record of his odyssey on sea and land—still the greatest Antarctic adventure of all—is best reflected in the words of a fellow-explorer: 'For scientific leadership give me Scott; for swift and efficient travel, Amundsen; but when you are in a hopeless position, when there seems no way out, get down on your knees and pray for Shackleton.'

THE SAILOR WHO DARED AND DIED

His epitaph was a centuries-old letter

As the men who sailed in the Arctic convoys of World War II had bitter cause to know, there is no crueller sea in the world than the ocean that reaches north from Norway.

Spray freezes in the air, crystallising all over a ship and capable of capsizing her with the weight. Shards of ice, razor sharp, cut through clothing and draw blood. Any man who incautiously grasps a rail with an ungloved hand is liable to strip the skin from his palm. Anyone falling overboard would die from the piercing cold in minutes.

This is the Barents Sea, named after the Dutchman Willem Barents who challenged it, and was killed by it, nearly 400 years ago. He wrote his own epitaph in a letter dated June 13, 1597, which he stuffed up the chimney of the wooden shack he built on a frozen island.

The letter was found there almost three centuries later, in 1871, when a party of Norwegian whalers rowed ashore from their ship to the barren island of Novaya Zemlya. It recalled an almost forgotten saga of man's struggles against the savagery of the northern sea.

SHELTER FROM THE ARCTIC WINTER *The hut which Barents and his crew built for themselves and stocked from their ice-locked ship. The structure was still intact when it was found by a party of whale-hunters nearly three centuries later.*

Barents, commissioned by Dutch merchants to discover the fabled North East Passage to the Indies, set out with two ships in 1596. After rounding the coast of Spitsbergen he found pack ice blocking his way north and decided to turn east and round the northern tip of Novaya Zemlya, as he had done once before. The captain of his other ship, Jan Rijp, refused to follow, preferring a better-known route to the south.

Locked in the ice

As Barents's lone vessel rounded the tip of the island it became terrifyingly obvious that Rijp had been right. The pack ice closed in and finally choked the ship. Now, as Barents's letter made starkly apparent, he and his crew faced the problems of how to survive the Arctic winter and get home without their ship.

They tackled the first problem by building a hut of driftwood on the island. They stocked it with food from the ice-locked ship, and killed Arctic foxes for fresh meat. For fresh water they burnt wood in a stove to melt snow.

Cold was a nightmare. Even though they huddled close to the stove, which they kept burning day and night, their backs were always coated with frost. They warmed their beds with heated stones. Somehow, all but two of them survived the winter.

Then came the spring, bringing sunshine that lengthened into an hour or two a day. The ship by then had been throttled into a near-wreck by the ice. Their only hope was escape in the two open boats.

Barents himself was by now weak from his privations and almost certainly had a premonition of his fate. With failing strength he wrote three letters so that, as he explained, the world should know the story if he never returned. One letter was carried in each of the two boats. The third he left in the chimney of the hut where the Norwegians found it 274 years later.

The little boats struggled round the northern tip of the island and headed south. Almost immediately, a storm threatened to batter the little boats to pieces and they had to drag them on to a large ice floe. It was there, a few days later, that Barents, the only man who could navigate the way home, died.

Sanctuary at Kola

When the storm abated the others struggled blindly on, sometimes having to drag their boats across the ice when it blocked their way. Once, the ice melted under one of the boats: most of their stores tipped out and were lost. Scurvy added its torments to cold and hunger, but after weeks at sea they sighted some Russian fishermen from whom they were able to buy food.

After travelling 1600 miles across the Arctic in open boats and surviving appalling hardships, the little band eventually reached the refuge of Kola. There, with his ship, was Captain Jan Rijp, a more wary mariner, who had paid due respect to the ferocity of the Barents Sea—and lived to sail another day.

TRAPPED AMONG THE ICE FLOES *An artist's impression of the scene when Barents and his men abandoned their ship and struggled over the ice to Novaya Zemlya. Barents had realised too late the wisdom of Captain Jan Rijp's decision to turn back.*

RELAY RACE WITH DEATH

Children's lives were in the hands of the tough trappers

Dr Curtis Welch looked down at the small boy, twisting and turning on the bed in a delirium of fever. The doctor's face was serious—for there was no longer any doubt about what was wrong with 6-year-old Richard Stanley.

The boy had diphtheria, a disease that attacks the throat and blocks the respiratory passages. Dr Welch had no way of knowing how many of Richard's playmates might already have contracted the disease. All he knew was that an epidemic would sweep through the little town of Nome, Alaska.

It was January, 1925. Although an anti-diphtheria serum had been available for some time, it was still in the development stage, and stocks were low.

Within 24 hours, Richard Stanley was dead, and several new cases had been reported. Dr Welch immunised known contacts with his own tiny stock of serum, which was soon exhausted.

More serum was desperately needed. The lives of dozens, perhaps scores, of children in the town were at stake. Getting further supplies to Alaska from the United States was a relatively simple matter. A shipment was on its way within hours. But it was when the serum reached Alaska that the trouble started.

The nearest railhead to Nome was at Nenana, more than 1000 miles away. Between the two towns lay a wilderness of snow, ice and forest, through which the fastest transport was sledge and dog-team. Normally, the trip took two weeks at the least.

Plea for help

But the stricken town could not afford a two-week delay. On January 27, two days after the outbreak was first reported, newspapers all over the United States carried the story and a plea for help from Nome's mayor, George Maynard.

At noon that same day, a tall, bearded trapper, 'Wild Bill' Shannon, walked into the sheriff's office at Nenana. He suggested that the trip to Nome could be made in one week instead of two by making it in relays. For between the two towns there were 15 small trading posts, and at each there was an experienced trapper.

Shannon volunteered to take the serum to the first post, where he would hand it over—and so it would go on, with a relay of trappers driving themselves and their teams to the limit, day and night.

That afternoon, a metal case containing 30,000 units of serum arrived at Nenana. Shannon secured it to his sleigh and set out on the first leg of the journey—to Tolovana, 50 miles away.

He drove his seven huskies mercilessly, hour after hour. Darkness fell, bringing bitter cold and a razor-edged wind, but Shannon refused to take shelter. Ice rimmed his face and eyes, half blinding him.

He reached Tolovana shortly before midnight and his dogs collapsed exhausted in the snow, as he handed over the container to trapper Dan Green. Green at once set out with his own team towards Manley Hot Springs, another 50 miles up the trail.

Gold prospector

Meanwhile, another dog team had set out from Nome, in the opposite direction. Its driver was 30-year-old Leonhard Seppala, who had come to Alaska to prospect for gold, and who was reputedly the fastest teamster in the country.

Unaware that help was already on its way, he had decided to make a dash for Nenana, pick up the serum and try to make the 1000 mile return trip non-stop, relying on fresh dog teams picked up at the trading posts.

Dan Green arrived in Manley Hot Springs on the morning of January 28 and handed over the serum to trapper Johnny Folger. Folger covered the 30 miles to the next post, at Fish Lake, in only three hours.

So it went on, mile after mile, station after station. Meanwhile, day and night, Leonhard Seppala battled eastwards through icy winds and snowstorms, from the other end of the trail.

By daybreak on January 31, Seppala had covered 200 miles. Suddenly, through eyes bleary with fatigue, he saw another team approaching. It belonged to Henry Ivanoff, who had set out from the post at Shaktolik the previous day and who was suffering badly from frost-bitten feet.

THE LONG TRAVERSE *Using sledges like these, relays of trappers covered 1000 miles in 144 hours (inset map), carrying the serum that saved the children of the Alaskan town of Nome.*

Seppala took the serum and turned back.

It was an agonising journey for his stalwart dogs. When the team was half-way across Norton Sound, a blizzard swept down. The swirling whiteness blotted out everything, forcing Seppala to rely on instinct alone as he pushed on.

Early on February 1 Seppala reached Golovino, a tiny settlement on the far side of the Sound. He was now only 100 miles from Nome, but the snow, ice and sub-zero temperatures had taken their toll of both man and dogs. Reluctantly, Seppala handed over the serum to prospector Charlie Olson.

At eight o'clock that evening Olson arrived in Bluff, 30 miles along the trail, and passed over the serum to another prospector, Gunnar Kaasen. Kaasen—who had taken part in one of Roald Amundsen's polar expeditions a few years earlier—was well known throughout the territory. So too was his lead dog, Balto,

a Siberian half-wolf, renowned for his skill and his ability to out-fight any other dog unlucky enough to cross his path.

Kaasen set out into the darkness at a fast pace as Balto followed the snow-covered trail unerringly. Kaasen was to have made rendezvous with a relief team, standing by in a trapper's cabin, but with no sure knowledge of his where-abouts he by-passed it.

At 5.30 on the morning of February 2, with a snow-storm raging, Kaasen reached the outskirts of Nome. The dogs col-lapsed, and Kaasen—his face torn by ice particles, temporarily blinded and almost unconscious—had to be chipped from the sleigh. The serum was a frozen block.

The epic race—1000 miles of mountain, forest and valley, through storm and gale-force winds in temperatures of 50° below zero—had taken 144 hours. Apart from little Richard Stanley, the epidemic claimed only one other victim.

241

TRAPPED IN A WHITE HELL

A bumper catch, then the trawler itself was caught

The announcement which appeared in several local newspapers one grey morning in February 1923 was brief and final. 'The steam trawler *Sargon*,' it said, 'is now much overdue and must be presumed lost with all hands. She was last sighted off North Cape on February 2 by another Standard Fishing Company vessel, and appeared to be homeward bound.'

A few weeks earlier, the crew of the Grimsby trawler *Sargon* had been hailed as heroes. Off the Norwegian coast, in darkness and fearful weather, they had spotted a faint distress rocket. Skipper John Patton ordered full speed ahead and, battered by mountainous seas, the *Sargon* turned in the direction of the signals.

Hours later, the wintry dawn revealed a ship in distress, rolling helplessly in the heaving sea. She was the Scottish trawler *Ethel Nutton*, and her drenched, exhausted crew were clinging to the icy rigging. Patton saw that she would not last another half hour—and cursed in frustration. For the *Sargon*'s lifeboat had been carried away by crashing waves during the rescue dash—and there seemed to be no way of saving the doomed men.

Across the raging water that separated the two vessels, he yelled: 'My boats have gone! I'll come as close as I can. Fasten lines to yourselves and throw the ends to my men as we come past!'

Leap to safety

Patton allowed the *Sargon* to drift broadside on towards the crippled *Ethel Nutton*, knowing that if the hulls of the two ships touched for even a moment, they would be wrecked. But, using all his skill, he manoeuvred the *Sargon* until she was just a few yards astern of the *Ethel Nutton*. With a strength born of desperation, the men on the listing trawler hurled their lines. On that first attempt, three were dragged to safety through the sea.

Five times John Patton repeated the manoeuvre and, on the last attempt, the two ships were so close that men were able to jump from the *Ethel Nutton* on to the *Sargon*'s slippery deck. All the *Ethel Nutton*'s eight men were safely aboard.

When the *Sargon* landed the survivors at their home port of Granton in Scot-

land, Patton brushed aside all attempts to make him a hero, and 24 hours later the *Sargon* put to sea once more, following a course that would take her round Norway's North Cape to the fishing grounds of the White Sea.

After one brief sighting by another trawler on February 2, 1923, the ship vanished. In April, she was officially written off—and the dependants of her gallant crew of 12 filed claims for insurance and compensation.

But even as their loss was being mourned, the men of the *Sargon* were still very much alive—fighting for survival in one of the sea's most gripping dramas.

The epic began on January 28, a week after the trawler had reached her destination in the White Sea. The fishing was poor, and Skipper Patton had just made up his mind to head for home when he ran into an unexpected shoal of fish. He was running short of fuel, but he could easily re-fill his bunkers in the Norwegian port of Tromso.

It turned out to be the biggest catch Patton had ever made. The following

BLUE FOR DANGER *The fierce beauty of the Arctic conceals a terrible power which can grind a ship to nothing between mountains of ice.*

evening, low in the water with the weight of fish in her hold, the *Sargon* at last turned her bow southwards, bound for Tromso, then the Humber—and home. But floating ice and fierce winds held her back; coal in the bunkers dwindled and at last ran out.

With the darkness came another menace: violent squalls of snow that reduced visibility to nil. For ten days they raged, pushing the *Sargon* steadily north-westwards, out of the shipping lanes.

There was no coal to feed even the galley fire. Huddled in one small cabin, the men tried to keep themselves warm by burning anything that would catch alight; tarry fishing-nets, panelling, wood from their bunks. But still the temperature dropped as the trawler went on drifting northwards, at the mercy of wind and sea.

Fit of depression

Late in February the weather cleared —and the sea around the *Sargon* froze solid. Food supplies ran out, and the men were forced to live on a monotonous diet of fish. For days they lay motionless in the cramped cabin, seldom speaking.

Patton spent most of his time calculating the *Sargon*'s position by taking bearings on the stars—until one day in a fit of depression he threw away his sextant, certain that death was imminent. After

that, there was no way of telling where they were.

On April 1, Patton came up on deck and his despair deepened. Across the western horizon marched what appeared to be a line of snow-capped mountains— monstrous, towering icebergs that were grinding their way towards them.

Hour after hour, the crew could only watch helplessly as the mountain range of ice loomed closer and closer, accompanied by a noise like approaching thunder. With a sudden roar the ice field that gripped the *Sargon* shattered under the enormous pressure. The trawler lurched, throwing the men off their feet, and she wallowed in the water.

For hours, on all sides, giant slabs of ice reared up into the air and collapsed again with a fearful crash. Like a cork, the *Sargon* bobbed helplessly around amid the white masses.

Then the miracle happened. One moment the *Sargon* was scraping past a wall of ice. The next, she was in the open sea. The danger was behind her.

The *Sargon* drifted for four days, but on the fifth a ship was sighted—the German trawler *Schleswig Holstein*. The *Sargon* was towed to Reykjavik and from there, battered but proud, sailed back to Grimsby under her own steam. After four months, John Patton and his crew had come back from the dead.

Detectives with spades and aqualungs

The quest for the past

THEY FELL INTO THE FUTURE

Monster skeletons were found in a coalmine

Fragments of bones of a prehistoric monster known as the iguanodon had been found in different parts of Europe during the 19th century, but never a complete skeleton. Then, astoundingly, in 1877, the skeletons of an entire herd of the giant reptiles were found . . . down a Belgian coalmine.

The discovery—at Bernissart, near the French border—was the biggest-ever find of the 16 ft tall monsters which roamed the countryside 120 million years ago. And their eventual reconstruction showed that scientists' previous conceptions of the iguanodon had been wrong.

The 20 or so iguanodon skeletons—many of them complete—were the remains of a herd that had probably been swept by a raging flood into what was then a deep ravine. Mud poured into the ravine with them, covered the bodies and preserved them in the excellent condition in which they were found.

In 1822 the first evidence of the creature that became known as the iguanodon was found in the form of teeth. They were discovered by Mrs Mary Ann Mantell, in a pile of stones beside a lane in the English county of Sussex.

Reconstructing the past

The name iguanodon—it simply means iguana-tooth—was first given to the creature by Mrs Mantell's husband in 1825. He found that the teeth were similar to those of the iguana lizard, but larger.

Many remains have since been found—particularly in the Weald area of Kent and the Isle of Wight, both once fertile delta areas where the tall, cumbersome

---

THE EARLIEST MAMMAL

A FRAGMENT of bone, smaller than a fingernail, helped scientists to establish that mammals—man's earliest ancestors—existed at least as long ago as dinosaurs. Until 1966 it was believed that the earliest mammals were cat-sized creatures that lived when the reign of the dinosaur was almost over—about 90 million years ago.

But the bone particle—found by Ione Rudner, a researcher from the South African Museum in Cape Town—proved otherwise.

Mrs Rudner was helping to unearth dinosaur remains on a hillside in the Orange River Valley of Lesotho when she noticed a tiny white 'blob' on a cliff face. Thinking it was unimportant, one of her team flicked it on to the ground and it broke. But Mrs Rudner was curious; she looked at the fragment under a magnifying glass and found that it had teeth.

More of the skeleton was found and after months of intricate reconstruction, it was restored. The bones were found to be those of a tiny shrew-like creature that lived 200 million years ago, about the time when dinosaurs were beginning to emerge to roam the great plains of the continent.

FOUR-LEGGED FALLACY *These reconstructions were based upon teeth found in England in 1822. But later evidence showed that the iguanodon walked on two feet and were not horned.*

beasts are believed to have died after being trapped in mud.

Tidal action in these areas during the following centuries broke up the skeletons and moved parts of them considerable distances. This may account for the fact that not one complete skeleton has been found in England.

A mock-up of the iguanodon, based on several remains that had been found, was built in the grounds of Crystal Palace in south London between 1853 and 1854, and still stands there today. It was then imagined to be a creature that went on all fours, with a spiked horn on the tip of its nose. But the finds in the Belgian coalmine proved this concept to be incorrect.

Today, there are two enormous glass cases in the great hall of the Royal Museum of Natural History in Brussels in which there are more than 20 iguanodon skeletons, some mounted in a standing position and others in the tumbled poses in which death had left them. These are

correctly restored as two-footed creatures. The spiked bone is not a nose horn but the last joint of two enlarged and spiky 'thumbs' that helped the creatures to defend themselves and tear down the plants on which they lived.

WHAT IT REALLY LOOKED LIKE *From skeletons found in a Belgian coalmine in 1878, palaeontologists were able to construct this more accurate concept of the 120-million-year-old reptile.*

BIRDS AS TALL AS ELEPHANTS

Powerful, but flightless—and now extinct

An old carthorse that collapsed and died while hauling a load of wood led to one of the world's great palaeontological discoveries.

When New Zealand farmer Joseph Hogden and his son, Rob, began to dig a hole in which to bury the animal, they found a mass of strange-looking bones. The find—in Pyramid Valley, North Canterbury, in 1936—turned out to be the remains of several birds of the extinct moa type—huge, flightless creatures unique to New Zealand.

When palaeontologists—geologists who study animal remains and fossils—excavated the site, they found about 800 skeletons to the acre over the three-acre swamp. Never before had so many complete sets of the birds' bones been found.

It enabled experts to determine structural details and classify the birds.

Flight power lost

Some 25 species have now been identified, ranging from a bush bird about the size of a turkey, to the giant *Dinornis maximus* which, reaching a height of 13 ft, was taller than any other land-dweller, except the African elephant and the giraffe.

At some crossroads of evolution, the ancestors of moas began to rely for their survival on strength and then running speed. It was at this point that they lost the power of flight.

During the first year of excavations, palaeontologists who flocked to the valley collected 50 skeletons—minus the necks and skulls. It is believed that some of the birds in Pyramid Valley became stuck in the mud of the swampy area and sank. Giant eagles may have attacked the birds' heads and necks as they were sucked down by the mud. Specimens found deeper in the mud still had their necks and skulls.

Also found were the fragments of an unlaid egg, which fell from the remains of a decomposing moa, and broke into 200 pieces. Reconstruction work, which took months, showed that the egg was 7 in. long by 5 in. in diameter.

It is known that two species of moa were alive when the first Polynesian settlers arrived in New Zealand around AD 1000, for their bones have been ex-

NEW ZEALAND'S 'DODO' *The giant moa,* Dinornis maximus, *stood up to 13 ft tall. It could not fly, but relied on its strength and speed.*

cavated from ancient Maori camp sites.

Smaller bush moas, living in remote parts of the South Island, were also recorded by European settlers in the early 19th century. But they were easy prey for hunters and wild animals, and soon became extinct.

MAN EXISTED 2,800,000 YEARS AGO

Theories upset by recent finds in southern Africa

In the 1970s three discoveries were made in Africa that sent shock waves through the anthropological world, for they challenged long-cherished theories concerning the origin and evolution of the human race.

One was the finding in Kenya of a human skull and bones below a layer dated about 2·8 million years ago. The second was the discovery that a cave in southern Africa, on the border between Swaziland and Natal, had been inhabited by men of modern type—possibly as long ago as 100,000 BC. The third was the finding of human teeth and jaw bones in Tanzania. They were reported to be 3.75 million years old.

According to previous evolutionary doctrine, the first primate that could be called man, *Homo erectus*, did not evolve until about a million years ago. Yet the bones dug out of deposits in the East Rudolph Basin in Kenya were more than twice as old, and were far more modern in shape than those of man's presumed, less-developed ancestor.

Biology textbooks said that probably the only humans in existence 100,000 years ago were beetlebrowed, bandy-legged Neanderthalers. But the remains unearthed in Border Cave in southern Africa were undoubtedly those of man's own species, *Homo sapiens sapiens*, who is supposed not to have appeared until about 35,000 BC, some 65,000 years later.

Art of mining

Equally disconcerting were the artifacts found with the fossils. They indicated that men had developed intellects and had embarked on the road to civilisation many thousands of years earlier than had been believed possible. The Border Cave dwellers had already learnt the art of mining. They manufactured a variety of sophisticated tools, including beautifully worked agate knives with edges still sharp enough to slice paper.

They also held religious convictions and believed in the afterlife. The body of an infant had been given ceremonial burial. Obviously they spoke a well-developed·language, for such abstract ideas as immortality cannot be conveyed by grunts and gestures.

Inspired detective work by two young South African prehistorians, Adrian Boshier and Peter Beaumont, led to the discoveries at Border Cave. In December 1970 they unearthed some 300,000 man-made objects and animal bones, many of creatures long extinct.

Charcoal from an overlying ash level, more recent than the stratum in which the child's skeleton was discovered, proved to be more than 50,000 years old. Stone implements and ground ochre appear right down to bedrock, suggesting that the cavern had been occupied for the past 100,000 years.

Bedding survived

The atmosphere of the cave had remained ideal for preservation during the ages. Even twigs, leaves, grass and feathers brought in for bedding had survived. 'Practically everything we found was three times older than the books said it should have been,' Boshier observed. The discovery of stone arrowheads places the invention of the bow more than 50,000 years ago, whereas its appearance in Europe had been dated at 15,000 BC.

Carefully notched bones, from a 35,000-year-old level, indicated that man had learnt to count.

On the evidence of 500,000-year-old skulls found in Java and near Peking, many scientists had been convinced that man originated in Asia and drifted westward. Africa, it was thought, played no part in this evolutionary scheme.

African genesis

Despite Professor Raymond Dart's discovery in 1924 of a far more ancient creature in Africa—more than half-way between man and the ape—the hypothesis held sway until it crumbled under discoveries made by the British anthropologists Louis and Mary Leakey in Tanzania's Olduvai Gorge. In 1959 they astonished the world by finding the nearly 2-million-year-old skull of a cousin of Dart's creature. In 1960 they found part of the brain case and lower jaw of a similar pre-human, together with chipped stone tools he had undoubtedly used for making weapons. They called this one *Homo habilis* ('handy-man').

247

Later that year they found fragments of a more advanced being, *Homo erectus*, the first man definitely known to have used fire. He was of the same species as Java and Peking Man, but more than half a million years older.

Today Africa, not Asia, is favoured as the most likely birthplace of the human race. It may be possible to trace the origins of *Homo erectus* back to the 2.8-million-year-old bones discovered in Kenya by Richard Leakey. Although the brain case of Leakey's Kenya creature is small, its whole shape is remarkably reminiscent of modern man's.

It may be years before prehistorians can fully evaluate the significance of these discoveries. But from the evidence it seems clear that modern man evolved far earlier than has been realised, and that most probably it was in an African cave that the miracle of human development had its genesis.

UNEXPLAINED SCENE FROM TASSILI *A warrior, exhausted from battle or hunting, kneels before a woman, while two people hasten to his aid.*

WHY NEANDERTHAL?

CROSSING A WIDE green valley in West Germany's Rhineland, a motorist could be excused for expecting to see heavy-browed cavemen stalking mammoths, or dragging women about by the hair. For a road sign reads: 'Neanderthal.'

The Neander valley is where bones of 'Neanderthal Man' were found in 1856—a missing link between man and the apes.

Workmen quarrying for limestone dug up the bones and, thinking that they belonged to a bear, presented them to a local secondary-school teacher, Johann Fuhlrott. When he started to assemble them, he realised that they had belonged to a creature that normally walked upright. Yet they seemed to come from something much more advanced than the then recently discovered giant gorilla of Africa.

He believed the bones represented a stage between the apes and man and belonged to a creature that lived from 85,000 to 65,000 years ago. But in the mid-19th century it was blasphemous to suggest that man's ancestors swung in trees. The Bible said that Adam and the animals had been created separately, and the fundamentalists insisted that every word of Genesis should be taken literally.

Fuhlrott showed his findings to the noted German anthropologist Professor Hermann Schaaffhausen, of Bonn. He was astounded and introduced the skeleton to an 1857 meeting of natural scientists at Kassel.

Fuhlrott presented a paper at the meeting and was greeted with outrage and derision. His main opponent was an anthropologist and physician, Rudolf Virchow, who denounced Fuhlrott and declared that the Neanderthal bones, although of an unusually heavy structure, had belonged to some wretch deformed by rickets.

In 1859 came a scientific bombshell in the form of Charles Darwin's *Origin of Species*, putting forward the powerful argument that man had evolved from the ape, and to some extent justifying Fuhlrott's idea of a missing link.

Virchow and his supporters were among the thousands throughout the world whose ideals were shaken by Darwin's theories, and skeletal remains similar to Fuhlrott's Neanderthal Man were soon being dis-covered in Gibraltar, France, Bohemia and Moravia.

It was proved that all these finds belonged to the last Interglacial period which ended about 65,000 years ago.

Fuhlrott was vindicated . . . but by then he was dead. Yet in his memory the missing link he helped to identify retains the name Neanderthal, after the valley near his grave.

Missing link comes to dinner. A 19th-century jibe at Darwin's theory of evolution.

WHEN THE SAHARA WAS GREEN

Civilisation that flourished long before the pharaohs

Outside the caves, troopers sat astride their camels, yawning and sweating beneath the scorching Sahara sun. Within, the young commander of the patrol, Lt Charles Brenans of the French Army, gazed in wonder at hundreds upon hundreds of paintings, vividly sprawled across the warm, dry sandstone walls of the caves.

What he had discovered, that day in 1933, was an art gallery 8000 years old: the record of people, long-forgotten, who inhabited the central Sahara when it was a green and fertile plain.

The caves lie in the now-desolate plateau of Tassili-n-Ajjer, 800 miles south of Algiers. For nearly 7000 years they were inhabited by a succession of tribes who left behind them pictures of simple family life, of hunting parties, of strange gods, elephants, herds of cattle and religious rites. Painted warriors carrying round shields and lances race across the walls in chariots.

Preserved in the dry desert air were records of several ages: naked hunters with bows and arrows; spear-hurling, round-headed soldiers; peaceful herdsmen wearing aprons and Egyptian-style headgear and driving cattle with long, curved horns.

Some of the animals depicted are long extinct. Others—the hippo, the rhino, the giraffe and the ostrich—can now only be found in the grassy plains 1000 or more miles to the south.

Deeply stirred by what he saw, Lt Brenans spent most of his tour of duty making sketches of the paintings.

Expedition organised

The French explorer and ethnologist Henri Lhote was among those who were inspired by the sketches, and he organised an expedition of his own.

Lhote, with the backing of French scientific and government agencies, assembled a team of artists and photographers to return to the plateau. By 1957, Lhote's team had taken back to Paris 16,000 sq. ft of copies and photographs of the paintings.

249

The stories the paintings tell are still being unravelled. The oldest scenes show a dark race, possibly negroid, hunting giraffes, rhinos and elephants with bows and arrows and lances. There are enormous white, half-human figures, possibly gods of the unknown tribes.

One, 19 ft high, is half man, half beast, with a head like a turtle and strangely positioned eyes, remarkably like those in paintings by Picasso.

The later pictures show far more life-like figures. Rounded, well-muscled legs, decorative tribal scars, belts, anklets and rings are clearly depicted.

Banquet scenes

There are banquet scenes, wedding ceremonies, a woman pounding grain for flour, a hut being built, a family with a pet dog, children asleep under an animal-skin blanket and other domestic scenes.

Between 5000 and 4000 BC it seems this people were gradually supplanted by a paler, copper-skinned race. These invaders added their own portraits to the gallery, in hunting scenes showing mountain sheep, giraffes and antelopes.

Still later paintings—from the third millennium BC—depict soldiers wearing bell-shaped tunics and riding in chariots. It is thought these may be the 'People of the sea' mentioned in ancient Egyptian records, who tried to invade Egypt from Crete or Asia Minor.

It is possible that, having been defeated by the pharaoh, the invaders retreated to set up homes in the labyrinthine caves of the Tassili plateau.

A dying land

As the watercourses dried up, the population of Tassili dwindled and little was added to the cave art. But that little speaks volumes.

The camel replaces the horse on the walls; horses could no longer live in the dying land.

Then silence. The desert dust blows through the abandoned caves, and for thousands of years, as empires rise and fall in other parts of the world, the brilliant portraits of vanished races stare emptily from the sun-blasted rocks of Tassili-n-Ajjer.

Until one day, a young soldier from a distant land stumbles across them and is moved to tears by what he sees.

ART GALLERY OF 30,000 YEARS AGO

How a little girl's find shed fresh light on prehistoric man

Nine-year-old Maria de Sautuola wandered deeper into the cave at Altamira in northern Spain, while her father, an amateur archaeologist, was digging near the entrance. Suddenly, from a side chamber, came the young girl's muffled screams: 'Bulls! Bulls! Papa—come quickly!'

Her father, Marcelino, dropped his pick and raced into the cavern. His daughter stood there pointing excitedly at the ceiling of the cave.

He raised his lantern and there, painted in browns, reds, yellows and black on the 60 ft by 30 ft ceiling were pictures of prehistoric bison; magnificent artwork dating back tens of thousands of years.

There were 17 of the bison on the ceiling in lifelike poses: pawing the ground, lying down, bellowing, dying of spear-wounds. Around them were pictures of wild boars, a horse, a doe and a wolf.

When Sautuola explored further into the network of caves, he found scores of other paintings of animals, many of which were extinct, or had disappeared from Western Europe centuries earlier.

The year was 1879. At first, Sautuola's finds were dismissed by archaeologists as forgeries: a plot to discredit Darwin's theory of evolution. The archaeologists could not believe that such sensitive work could have been done by a primitive people thought of as savages and hardly better than the apes.

But the paintings turned out to be among the greatest discoveries of prehistoric art, dating back between 30,000 and 10,000 BC.

In 1902, some 14 years after Sautuola had died, the archaeologist Abbé Henri Breuil visited the caves and unearthed animal bones, bearing engravings almost identical to those on the ceilings. They appeared to be practice sketches.

The authenticity of the paintings was no longer in doubt and the caves were hailed as the 'Sistine chapel of prehistoric art'. What was also remarkable about the paintings was their state of preservation. Although more than 100 other grottoes, decorated with Old Stone Age paintings and engravings, have been found in northern Spain, the French Pyrenees, the Dordogne, southern Italy and the Urals, many had faded and deteriorated through the ravages of time and weather.

But the Altamira paintings had been made in pitch-black caves, discovered only shortly before Sautuola's visit, in which the temperature and humidity had remained constant. Ventilation was good, but not excessive, and the moisture content of the air was sufficient to keep the colours from drying out and scaling off.

They had been sealed off for centuries by rock falls. Similar paintings at Lascaux, in southern France, suffered more damage in the 15 years they were open to the public—through perspiration, body heat and micro-organisms introduced by visitors—than they had in the previous 15,000 years.

Children were also instrumental in discovering the other great prehistoric art gallery at Lascaux.

There, in 1940, 18-year-old Marcel Ravidat led three friends to a hole made by an uprooted tree that he had spotted a few days earlier while walking his dog. The youths enlarged the hole and Marcel climbed down through it to the floor of a cave, about 18 ft below.

Finest primitive art

By the light of a few matches, he saw glimpses of beautiful wall-paintings. Next day the boys returned with lanterns—and discovered a whole array of horses, bulls, bison, deer and other creatures.

The boys reported their find to the Abbé Breuil, and today the Lascaux caves take their place with those at Altamira as some of the finest examples of primitive art ever discovered.

They include a chamber known as the Hall of Bulls, with masterly drawings executed in vivid colours: ebony blacks, brick reds and chrome yellows. In other compartments are hordes of horses and antlered deer heads, all exceptionally lifelike.

Like those at Altamira, it is clear that these are not the work of primitive savages but of sensitive artists—a far cry from the popular concept of man 15,000 years ago. They were made by the Magdalen-ians, so-called because the first remains of these people were found near the ruins of La Madeleine, in the Dordogne district of France.

Food gatherers

Those at Altamira are believed to have been made by another Old Stone Age group, Cro-Magnons, so-called after a group of rocks in the Dordogne where skeletons were found.

Both peoples were believed to be food gatherers, subsisting mainly by hunting during the Palaeolithic era, or Old Stone Age, after Neanderthal Man.

The paintings were made first by engraving the outlines with a pointed piece of flint, then adding colour. The artists had no greens or blues, but may have got black and violet-blacks from charcoal or manganese oxide. Brown, red, yellow and orange hues came from iron ore which was ground to powder between stones, then mixed with animal blood, or fat, and plant juices.

The paint was applied in several ways—by finger, brushes made of fur, feathers, or the chewed ends of twigs. The artists also used pads of lichen and moss, or blew paint through hollow reeds.

At Altamira, ochre crayons made with tallow have been found.

The paintings were executed with infinite care in dim chambers where daylight could barely penetrate—pointing to the suggestion that the artists had some type of long-burning lights. The ceiling paintings also indicate that some form of scaffolding was used.

The latest of the paintings was probably completed around 10,000 BC, as the last of the Ice Age glaciers retreated and the Old Stone Age peoples moved further north with the vegetation.

Magic ritual

Many archaeologists think the cave paintings may have been a form of 'sympathetic' magical ritual; once a beast's likeness was captured on a wall, it could no longer resist the hunter. The early people may also have believed that something of the power and strength of their prey was passed on to them by copying the likenesses of the beasts.

But the paintings may also have been used for instructing young hunters in how to kill: many show spears thrust into an animal's most vulnerable spots.

KING TUTANKHAMUN'S GOLD

The long hunt that led to a treasure house of history

Howard Carter was growing desperate. For nearly 20 years he had searched for the tomb of the boy king, Tutankhamun. Now money to finance his quest was running out. He faced mounting scepticism, and even derision, from his colleagues.

What made the prospect of failure harder to bear was that the English scholar remained convinced that the tomb was somewhere in the Valley of the Kings, site of the ancient capital of Thebes, for there were inscriptions about Tutankhamun in the nearby temple of Luxor. He believed too that the tomb had never been looted, for no relics had ever been reported.

But all he had found—15 years before—were jars of clothes bearing the king's name. Since then Carter had explored nearly the whole floor of the valley and found no trace of the pharaoh, who had died at the age of 18.

As Carter trudged through the dawn-cool sand to his diggings, he thought again of his patron, the amateur archaeologist

PORTRAIT IN GOLD *Covering the head of the boy king was a stylised mask, executed in gold and jewels.*

Lord Carnarvon, and remembered their last meeting at the peer's home, at Highclere in Hampshire, England.

Carnarvon had wanted to call off the search. 'It has cost me a fortune,' he told Carter. 'I can't afford it.'

But Carter pleaded with him to finance one last try. 'All right, Howard,' Carnarvon laughed. 'I'm a gambler. I'll back you for one more toss. If it is a loss then I am through. Where do we begin?' Carter showed him a map of the valley, indicating a small triangular area not yet explored as it was on the approach to the tomb of Ramses VI. 'There,' he told his patron. 'It's the last place left.'

Now, as he approached the diggings, Carter reflected that this looked like the dismal end to his dream. He and his workmen had found nothing but the rubble of huts that had been used by the labourers building the tomb of Rameses. For three days they had hacked at the rubble and found nothing.

When Carter reached the site his foreman, Ali, ran over. 'We have uncovered a step cut into the ground,' he said. Within two days they had cleared a steep staircase that led down to a sealed door. Carter immediately cabled Carnarvon:

AT LAST HAVE MADE WONDERFUL
DISCOVERY IN VALLEY STOP A
MAGNIFICENT TOMB WITH SEALS
INTACT STOP RECOVERED SAME
FOR YOUR ARRIVAL
CONGRATULATIONS

The date was November 6, 1922.

DOORWAY TO THE PAST *Beneath the sand of the Valley of the Kings lay a steep flight of steps untrodden for millenia.*

'WONDERFUL THINGS' *Treasures that Howard Carter saw by the light of a candle when he peered into the tomb through a hole chipped in the sealed door on November 26, 1922.*

THE SEAL *This closed door of the tomb beyond which lay a treasure store that human eyes had not looked on for over 3000 years.*

Once Carnarvon arrived, it took them several more days to break through the door and clear a rock-filled passage. Then the two men stood together in front of a second sealed door.

It was Carter's moment of truth. As Carnarvon peered over his shoulder, Carter chipped at the door until there was a hole big enough for him to push a light in and take a look. He wrote later:

'At first I could see nothing, the hot air from the chamber causing the flame to flicker. But as my eyes grew accustomed to the light, details of the room emerged slowly from the mist: strange animals, statues and gold—everywhere the glint of gold.

'For the moment—an eternity it must have seemed to others standing by—I was struck dumb with amazement; and when Lord Carnarvon, unable to stand the suspense any longer, inquired anxiously "Can you see anything?" it was all I could do to get out the words: "Yes— wonderful things." '

The sepulchre consisted of four rooms containing caskets, vases, a gold throne inlaid with precious stones, gems, furniture, clothing and weapons. In the burial chamber itself, flanked by two black statues, were four gold shrines, one inside the other, and a sarcophagus containing a nest of three coffins.

Tinge of colour

The inner one, of solid gold, held the mummified body of Tutankhamun, wrapped in a jewel-studded shroud. Over his face was a gold mask inlaid with quartz and lapis lazuli. Across his neck and breast was a garland of cornflowers, lilies and lotuses—probably a last offering from the pharaoh's young queen, Ankhesnamun. After 3300 years in the impenetrable blackness of the sepulchre, they still had a tinge of colour.

The tomb's contents were invaluable. Together they made up a complete capsule of the life of the legendary pharaohs in Egypt 1350 years before Christ. For Carter and his long-suffering patron Carnarvon it had been a long and frustrating hunt. But the final rewards made it all worth while: the most splendid of archaeological discoveries.

BODY-SNATCHERS OF 1500 BC

Priests exhumed kings to foil the tomb-robbers

By dead of night the priests slipped through the shadows of the valley where the kings of ancient Egypt lay buried. Silently they broke into the rock-hewn sepulchres and lifted the bodies from their coffins.

One by one they carried their macabre burdens along a path over the cliffs and out of the valley to a new, secret resting place.

It was the priests' last attempt to beat the robbers who for centuries had been looting the treasure-stocked tombs of Egypt's greatest emperors.

Even the most cunningly designed pyramids had been stripped. That is why the Egyptians stopped building them about 1500 BC. Instead, they tunnelled galleries into the cliffs of the Valley of Kings at Thebes—now known as Luxor —and concealed the entrances.

The architect Ineni, who designed the first of these sepulchres, boasted in his own epitaph: 'It was a great work . . . I shall be remembered for it.'

But the robbers went on winning, even penetrating tombs with mazes of passages and dead-ends, and chambers left unfinished to make it appear that the work had been abandoned.

THE CURSE OF THE PHARAOHS

WHEN HOWARD CARTER and Lord Carnarvon opened the tomb of Tutankhamun they set off a chain of mystery. Several of those connected with the discovery died violent or unusual deaths—victims, according to the legend, of the pharaoh's curse.

The sinister superstition is based on unconfirmed reports of a chilling series of happenings on the very day when the two archaeologists and their party had first penetrated the entrance to the tomb in November 1922. As the last man climbed back into the sunshine a sandstorm is said to have sprung up and swirled over the mouth of the cave. As it died away a hawk, the royal emblem of ancient Egypt, was allegedly seen soaring over the tomb to the west—towards the mysterious 'Other World' of Egyptian belief.

The spirit of the dead pharaoh, said superstitious people, had left his curse on those who had violated his tomb.

Five months later Lord Carnarvon, then 57, was bitten by a mosquito on the left cheek. The bite became infected, and weakened by blood poisoning, he contracted pneumonia. As he died in a Cairo hotel at 1.55 a.m., all the city lights went out. At the same time, back home in Hampshire, Carnarvon's dog howled—and died.

Strangest of all, doctors who later examined Tutankhamun's mummy reported finding a scab-like depression on a spot on the left cheek exactly corresponding to Carnarvon's mosquito bite.

In the following months of 1923 the curse was blamed for the deaths of several others who had visited the tomb.

Carnarvon's half-brother, Aubrey Herbert, died of peritonitis.

An Egyptian prince, Ali Farmy Bey, whose family claimed descent from the pharaohs, was murdered in a London hotel and his brother committed suicide.

George Jay Gould, an American railway tycoon, died of pneumonia after catching a cold in the tomb.

The Hon. Richard Bethell, who helped Carter to catalogue the treasures, was thought to have committed suicide at the age of 49. A few months later, in February 1930, his father, Lord Westbury, hurled himself to death from his London flat. An alabaster vase from the pharaoh's tomb was in his bedroom.

In the years after the discovery of the tomb in 1922 more than a dozen people who had been concerned with it in one way or another died unnatural deaths.

But one man continued to scoff at the legendary curse of the pharaohs—the one man who, it might have been thought, had most reason to fear it. Howard Carter died in March 1939—of natural causes.

Yet when the Egyptian government agreed to send the Tutankhamun treasures to Paris for an exhibition in 1966, its Director of Antiquities, Mohammed Ibraham, dreamt that he would face terrible danger if he allowed them to leave the country.

He fought the decision bitterly, right up to one last despairing meeting in Cairo with the authorities concerned. As he left the meeting he was knocked down by a car. He died two days later.

Finally the guardians of the 36 royal tombs realised that they could not hope to protect them while the sites were so well known—especially since the systematic looting was thought to be organised by court officials.

That was when the custodians of the royal burial places hit upon their secret plan: to take away the mummies and treasures still remaining in the tombs and hide them in a single sepulchre outside the valley.

The mummified pharaohs, with some of their queens, were removed furtively at night and carried up the clifftop path out of the valley. Then they were lowered into a cave at the bottom of a deep cleft in the rocks, the opening sealed and camouflaged.

For over 30 centuries the plan worked.

The cave might still be unknown to this day but for the fact that, in the 1880s, several ancient royal relics began appearing in Egyptian antique markets.

The suspicions of Sir Gaston Maspero, director of the Cairo Museum, were aroused. He was the modern 'successor' of the ancient priests as the man whose job it was to guard Egypt's treasures. He traced the 'leak' to a family who had found a tomb in 1871 and had since been selling their plunder in Luxor.

An informer led Maspero's assistant, Emil Brugsch, to the rifled tomb. Brugsch was lowered down a shaft deep into a cliff. Dazed with wonder, he saw before him, row upon row, the bodies of over 30 of the greatest pharaohs together with such treasure as had been left by the family of robbers.

255

SCROLLS FROM THE DAYS OF JESUS

A young Arab boy found the world's greatest manuscripts

Muhammad adh-Dhib, a 15-year-old Bedouin boy, was searching for a stray goat in a desert region at the north-western corner of the Dead Sea, when he saw a narrow opening in a rocky cliff. Idly, he threw in a few stones —and heard something breaking.

Thinking it might be hidden treasure, he brought a friend, Ahmed Muhammad, to the spot and, together, they squeezed through the opening into a cave 26 ft long and 6 ft wide. In it, among pieces of broken pottery, they found a number of clay cylinders, 2 ft high.

Excitedly, the boys wrenched off the lids, but instead of the gold or precious stones they expected, they found only some dark, musty-smelling lumps of material wrapped in linen. They consisted of 11 scrolls made of thin strips of sheepskin, sewn together, and coated in gummy, decomposed leather.

The scrolls—between 3 ft and 24 ft long —were marked on one side in an ancient form of Hebrew script. The boys were disappointed, but managed to sell the fragments to a dealer in Jerusalem for a few pounds. That was in 1947.

What the boys had discovered turned out to be one of the greatest of manuscript treasures—the Dead Sea Scrolls. Although an employee of the Department of Antiquities in Palestine at first described the scrolls as 'worthless', five of them were bought the following year by the Syrian Orthodox Monastery of St Mark for £90,000. The other six were bought by the Hebrew University in Jerusalem.

When the St Mark scrolls were examined by Dr John Trever, acting director of the American School of Oriental Research in Jerusalem, he found that one contained the Old Testament book of Isaiah. And the form of the lettering suggested that the scrolls dated back to before the time of Christ.

Unprecedented discovery

As there was no other extant book of the Old Testament in Hebrew known to be more than 1300 years old, it was truly an astounding discovery.

Dr William Albright, historian and archaeologist at Johns Hopkins University in the United States, examined photo-graphs of parts of the book and dated the scroll around 100 BC. It was, he declared, an 'absolutely incredible find—the greatest manuscript discovery of modern times'.

Other archaeologists and Bedouin tribesmen began combing the area round the Dead Sea and, by 1956, ten more caves were discovered, containing more scrolls and fragments.

Experts at the Chicago Institute of Nuclear Studies examined fragments of the linen in which the scrolls had been wrapped in the first cave, and dated it around 167 BC to AD 233.

As find after find was made, it became clear that the scrolls formed part of a large library that had, for some reason, been hidden in the wilderness.

Ruins of monastery

Excavations less than 600 yds from the original cave uncovered the ruins of a monastery, known as Khirbet Qumran, which once housed an obscure religious sect. In the writing room of the monastery's main building were found a pot of dried ink and a clay jar, identical to the cylindrical ones found in the first cave.

It appeared that the members of the Qumran community had hidden the documents at the approach of Rome's Tenth Legion, invading the area in AD 68 or AD 70.

Most of the documents and fragments found—some of them no larger than a postage stamp—are in Hebrew. Others are in Aramaic, believed to be the language spoken by Christ; and a few are in Greek. They represent more than 500 books, including all the books of the Old Testament. In addition, there are commentaries on the Old Testament and texts documenting the life, principles and disciplines of the community.

Mystic sect

Descriptions of the Qumran community's everyday life showed that it was similar to that of the Essenes, a Jewish mystic sect which existed between 125 BC and AD 68, and who were celibate and despised worldly possessions. They were said by the Roman historian Pliny the Elder to have made their headquarters west of the Dead Sea—in the region where the monastery was unearthed. The scrolls relating to the Old Testament have provided scholars with a mass of material that is another source of the stories of the first section of the Bible.

Christian beginnings

Some of the scrolls help to reconstruct the history of the Qumran community and contain references that some scholars consider to be important links with the beginnings of Christianity.

They mention a 'Teacher of Righteousness' who, although not named, appears to have been thought of as a preparer of the way for a Messiah.

This could be a reference to John the Baptist. For John roamed the wilderness of Judaea, preparing the way for Christ. Some scholars have even suggested that Jesus himself was an Essene.

But the writers of the scrolls themselves make no mention of Jesus by name, so there is no indication that Jesus was the Messiah they had been waiting for. All the scholars know for certain is that fragments of the texts closely match parts of the Gospels and Epistles in the New Testament.

But there is a possibility that the faith which grew into one of the most widespread religions in the world began—as did its founder, the son of a carpenter—in humble circumstances, and was linked with an obscure sect that lived and died in the time-worn desert of Galilee.

TREASURE CAVES *Hidden from the advancing Roman legions, the scrolls lay in the dark depths of these caves for more than 2000 years.*

MASADA : JEWISH ROCK OF DEFIANCE

The Zealots chose mass suicide rather than surrender to Rome

As the Roman Tenth Legion prepared a final assault on the rock pleateau fortress of Masada in the year AD 73, the band of Jewish Zealots trapped inside came to a terrible decision.

Rather than surrender and submit to the cruelty of Roman retribution and slavery, they chose to die by their own hands.

The martyrdom of the Zealots was recorded by the Jewish historian Flavius Josephus. According to Josephus, their leader, Eleazar ben Ya'ir, made a heroic speech: 'We must now expect thraldom and tormenting punishments if the enemy take us alive, since we first departed from their dominion and have been the last to resist them. We may deem it a favour if we are permitted to choose the death we would die . . . Let us die free, gloriously surrounded by our wives and children . . . Eternal renown shall be ours by snatching the prize from the hands of the enemy, and leaving him nothing to triumph over but the bodies of those who dared to be their own executioners . . .'

Ben Ya'ir ordered the entire fortress to be burnt (except for the ample food stores, for the Zealots wanted to show that they were acting from pride and religious belief, not out of desperation).

Then the married men slew their families. The survivors cast lots to choose ten men who would kill the rest of the garrison. The ten cast lots again, to choose one who would kill the others. Then he killed himself.

The Romans surged over the walls—and found a garrison of corpses.

Josephus wrote: 'When they came upon the rows of dead bodies, they did not exult over their enemies, but admired the nobility of their resolve, and the way in which so many had shown, in carrying it out without a tremor, an utter contempt for death.'

Of 967 Jews, only seven—two women

MASADA FROM THE AIR *Perched on top of a high rock, Herod's fortress dominated the plain of Judaea on the southern approaches to Jerusalem near the Dead Sea.*

and five children—survived to tell the story. They had hidden in a cistern and the Romans who found them were so moved that their lives were spared.

Masada is therefore one of the great stories of a people's struggle for independence. Yet the story had long been regarded as suspect as the only account came from a Jew, Josephus, who had been nowhere near the battle scene.

The evidence was found in 1963, in one of the most difficult excavations ever carried out. Five thousand volunteers from all over the world began to work under the direction of Professor Yigael Yadin, Israel's foremost archaeologist.

Masada is an enormous flat-topped outcrop of rock, 23 acres in extent, on the Judaean plain near the Dead Sea.

About 30 years before the birth of Christ, it was fortified as a citadel by Herod the Great, King of the Jews. A man who lived in constant fear of treachery, Herod built great walls and towers round the summit and excavated ten huge cisterns, each one capable of holding 9 million gallons of water, in case of siege.

On the slopes, Herod created palaces and pleasure villas on terraces all cut into the bare face of the rock. It was a retreat that was both safe and luxurious. Long after Herod's death, the Zealots under Menahem rebelled against Roman rule. Four years later, when the rebellion was all but crushed, Masada alone held out.

Vengeance of Rome

The Roman procurator of Judaea, Silvius Flavius, marched against Masada in the year 72 at the head of the formidable Tenth Legion. By early 73 he had built a containing wall around the citadel so that no man, woman or child should escape the vengeance of Rome.

Then he set about his campaign of attack. The only possible approach was by a spur on the western flank and he started to build a great 90 ft high ramp up towards it. By the spring the ramp was ready and was keyed into the spur with a massive bridge which the Romans could cross to storm the walls. It was only a matter of time. Masada was doomed.

Nineteen centuries later, the excavators uncovered evidence of the Zealots' desperate last day—food stores that had not been set on fire and a heap of bronze coins that had been used like ration coupons.

Under the floor of a small, smoke-blackened room, carefully hidden, they found 14 scrolls, each of which could be dated with some certainty to the years preceding AD 73. They contained excerpts from the Biblical books of Deuteronomy, Ezekiel, Psalms and parts of the Apocrypha. One scrap of leather bore a text similar to that of the Dead Sea Scrolls.

At a strategic point overlooking the direction of the expected Roman assault, the archaeologists found a senior officer's suit of armour. Beside it lay 11 pieces of pottery, each with a name inscribed on it. On one was the name Ben Ya'ir.

Was it possible that, along with the ten lots there had been an 11th—that of the heroic leader Eleazar ben Ya'ir? And that he was the last man left alive, to die by his own sword? A man of his calibre would hardly have shrunk from the terrible task he had asked his followers to perform.

Today, Masada is preserved by the Israelis as a sacred place. And every recruit to Israel's armed forces now makes this vow: 'Masada Shall Not Fall Again.'

THE PRINCESS AND THE CRONE

The ancient tomb's secret of a suicide pact

About 50 miles north-west of the Chinese city of Sian a cluster of 17 flat-topped pyramids rises boldly from the surrounding fields. This is the great burial field of T'ang royalty and here, nearly 1300 years ago, a young princess was buried.

She was Princess Yung-T'ai—meaning Eternal Peace—who lived during the T'ang dynasty of AD 618–907, often described as China's golden age.

The story of her life and death rings a tragic note, even after the passage of so many centuries.

In the year AD 700, the 16-year-old Princess Yung-T'ai was married to a high-born member of the T'ang court, a commander of the second rank of Imperial carriages. Soon after her marriage she became pregnant and her future in a brilliant world of pomp, extravagance and exquisite works of art, seemed secure.

THE PRINCESS'S OLD CLOTHES

Entombed in rock almost 2000 years ago, the bodies of prince Liu Sheng and his consort Tou Wan were removed from two chambers cut into the side of a low hill 150 kilometres from Peking. The excavation also brought to light 2800 funeral offerings to ease their passage in the next world.

THE CHINESE Princess Tou Wan died about 104 BC and, because she was buried in this jade suit, it was thought she would achieve immortality. Her husband, who died nine years earlier, was given a similar shroud and the pair were laid to rest in vast tombs hollowed out of a rocky hillside. When their remains were discovered in 1968 they created a sensation because of the staggering wealth of the 2800 funeral offerings that surrounded them. But most spectacular of all were the jade suits, each made up of more than 2000 tiny plates of thin jade, sewn together with gold thread. Nobles of the period believed gold and jade would, because they stand the ravages of time, confer immortality. But while they were right about the precious stone and metal, the mortal body of the princess herself had crumbled to dust.

But it was also a world that was dominated by Yung-T'ai's grandmother, the Empress Wu, who had clawed her way to The Dragon Throne of China by murdering the former empress and pickling her limbs in wine as a warning to any would-be rivals. Not without cause, she distrusted the entire court and imagined plots on every side.

One day, in the year 701, one of the palace's many informers overheard the young Princess Yung-T'ai laughing with her husband and brother at some aspect of court life they found absurd. The informer took the story to the empress, who saw in it the birth of a palace intrigue. At once, she ordered that the three young people must die.

Imperial decrees of this nature were backed by a strict protocol. All three knew what they must do, and on October 8, 701, they committed suicide.

The princess and her story faded from human memory until, one day in 1968, the Chinese authorities decided to excavate at least one of the pyramid tombs in the T'ang burial ground near Sian. They did not know the names of any of the occupants, only that they were members of the T'ang dynasty. One tomb was picked at random, and with their choice the long-forgotten princess took her place once more on the world's stage.

When the archaeologists made their first soil survey around the pyramid to determine where the entrance shaft lay, they discovered another shaft running vertically through the right hand side of the pyramid. It was obvious that tomb robbers had dug their way in to plunder the tombs that lay below.

Death of a thief

One of the robbers was still there. The Chinese archaeologists found his skeleton lying on top of debris that filled an underground passageway 50 ft down. His skull had been smashed by an iron axe that lay near by, and his share of the gold, jade and silver treasures were scattered around his bones.

The tomb chamber had been ransacked —it is thought, within 20 years of the burial—and the great stone sarcophagus had been scarred by crowbars, its heavy lid split, its contents rifled. Only the bones

of the dead had been left. But they had also left untouched the niches that lined the passage to the chamber. These were crammed with T'ang pottery—items that to the robbers were without value, but to modern eyes are priceless.

Their entry had also left undisturbed wall-paintings depicting many aspects of life in the T'ang court.

The archaeologists still did not know who the occupants of the robbed tomb had been, until they came across a great stone slab lying in the passageway. This slab was inscribed with the epitaph of the Princess Yung-T'ai.

After the Empress Wu was forced to abdicate in 705, her son, the father of Yung-T'ai, ascended the throne. Still sorrowing at the injustice of the sentences passed against his children and son-in-law he ordered that their bodies should be exhumed from the humble graves in which they had been placed, and be given instead a royal burial in the heart of the T'ang cemetery.

The emperor also tried to rewrite history. The T'ang history books had all recorded the name of Yung-T'ai and the traitor's death she had suffered. Perhaps in an effort to obliterate this memory, the inscription placed on the tomb by her father simply records that the former Princess Yung-T'ai of the great T'ang dynasty had died in childbirth.

LADY OF THE LAND OF SILK
She died 2000 years ago after eating melons

She was no great beauty. She was about 50 and stout—probably through over-eating. She had a deformed back and hobbled with a stick. But when the Lady Tai died around 150 BC she was buried in a style which gave her exhumation in 1971 something of the excitement surrounding the discovery of the legendary tomb of Tutankhamun.

The Marchioness of Tai was the wife of the Prime Minister to the Prince of Ch'ang-sha in the Hunan district of central China. A post-mortem examination 2000 years later revealed that she was prone to hardening of the arteries and died of heart failure brought on by colic —not surprisingly, since her stomach contained 138 melon seeds.

Not a romantic end; but as befitted the wife of a very important personage she was given a funeral which rivalled those of the ancient pharaohs.

Her tomb came to light when workmen were digging the foundations for a new hospital. In the grave-pit they discovered a hexagonal wooden coffin. It was insulated by a thick charcoal jacket and hermetically sealed so efficiently with china clay that after 20 centuries the body was still well preserved.

She was swathed in 20 silken cloaks and wraps and the tomb was lavishly supplied with everything that so rich and important a lady might require on a long journey. There were plates of meat, fish and fruit; jars of wine and even beef soup. There were bowls, boxes and jars, superbly

261

decorated specimens demonstrating the fine work of Chinese lacquer craftsmen.

The Lady Tai's wardrobe for the afterlife included a patterned silk gown, skirts as light as gossamer, socks, slippers, coats, combs, all carefully wrapped in perfumed sachets. Every item was checked and noted down on an inventory recorded on 312 slips of bamboo.

But the objects that most interested the archaeologists were the silks. The Lady Tai had lived in the period when China's reputation as the land of silk had spread to the furthest outposts of the known world, when long camel trains plodded the famous silk route across the Hindu Kush and through Samarkand to the markets of the Roman Empire.

The tomb, at Ma-wang-tui near Hunan, yielded by far the best specimens of these matchless silks ever found—more than 50 rolls stored in basket-weave boxes and still preserved by the dry atmosphere. One of the most exciting of these relics was a painted silk banner which had headed the funeral cortège, the pictures depicting heaven and hell as imagined by the artists. In the centre was a painting of the marchioness herself.

Brutally oppressed

No servants had been slaughtered so their spirits might accompany their mistress to the next world—as often happened in Asian kingdoms. Instead she was attended in death by 162 wooden figurines of maids and other members of her household, including musicians—all provided with a plentiful supply of bamboo instruments.

The Government of the People's Democratic Republic of China did not share the delight of its own archaeologists in this treasure trove. An official solemnly declared: 'The fact that the Lady's husband used so much labour and wealth on the burial of his wife shows how brutally the feudal ruling class oppressed and exploited the working people.'

THE SEARCH FOR TROY

A boyhood dream with a golden ending

Heinrich Schliemann was only seven years old when his father gave him the Christmas present that changed his life and fashioned an important chapter in the history of archaeology. The present was an illustrated book containing a picture of Troy in flames, after it had been captured by the armies of the ancient Greeks.

From the moment he saw that picture, one passionate, devouring obsession filled Heinrich's young mind: to find the remains of Troy and prove to a sceptical world that Homer's account of the siege of Troy was really true and not just a poetic fancy. An almost impossible goal for a grocer's messenger boy. Yet to equip himself for his task he taught himself Greek so that he could read Homer in the original. He also had to acquire a fortune; within a few years he had built up a career as a merchant from which he was able to retire in his early forties.

Athenian schoolgirl

Then, romantic as ever, he persuaded the Archbishop of Athens to find him an ideal wife, a Greek bride who would fill his four conditions of perfection: she must be poor; she must be beautiful; she must have a devoted nature; and she must be familiar with the works of Homer. Surprisingly, he found such a paragon— Sophia Engastromenos, a 16-year-old Athenian schoolgirl.

Buried cities

With the names of Hector, Achilles and Ajax still resounding in his mind, Schliemann and his wife set off in 1871 for the Dardanelles, to track down Homer's 'windy plain of Troy'.

He flung himself into the search with characteristic energy and recruited an army of 80 workmen.

Schliemann believed a local tradition that the site of Troy was on Hissarlik, a 162 ft mount opposite the Gallipoli peninsula, mainly because it fitted with his knowledge of Homer. Archaeology was not then the exact science it is today; nor had Schliemann tried his hand at excavation before.

His workmen simply drove a deep gash into the steep northern face of Hissarlik to see what lay beneath. At once Schliemann was faced with a bewildering mass of ruins, which were later identified as no fewer than nine different strata, one above the other.

Still Schliemann went on digging until eventually he lay bare what he was sure were the 20 ft ramparts of the lost city—the very walls from which Paris watched the advance of the Greek armies come to avenge the kidnapping of Helen.

Helen of Troy's treasure

On June 14, 1873, after two years' work, a dazzling prize spread before him—an astonishing hoard of 8700 golden objects, cups, vases, bracelets—and most glorious of all, a diadem of 16,000 pieces of solid gold, which hung from brow to shoulders.

With tears of joy in his eyes, he crowned his lovely wife with the diadem, hugged her and cried: 'Darling, this is the most beautiful moment of our lives. You are wearing the treasure of Helen of Troy.'

An ecstatic and romantic rainbow's end. But Schliemann was wrong. The buried city he had found was not Troy,

but one even older. And the diadem, dating from around 2300 BC, had been worn by another princess more than 1000 years before Helen was born.

It is thought today that Homer's Troy was destroyed about 1250 BC. Schliemann had worked right through its ruins as his army of workmen burrowed down through the nine strata.

Chasing a star

The treasure he had found belonged to another city, buried at the bottom of the great, layered mound, known as Hissarlik. Before he died, Schliemann sorrowfully acknowledged his mistake.

Nevertheless, later explorers have given him the credit for finding the site of the Homeric city and for discovering a more ancient city of a Bronze Age culture as well. They are worthy epitaphs for the grocer's boy, son of a poor pastor, who dedicated his life to chasing a star—and almost found it.

FOUNDATIONS OF A LEGEND *The ruins of a Roman theatre, or senate house, on the site of the ancient city of Troy, romanticised by the poet Homer and discovered by a former grocer's boy with a dream.*

263

IN THE SHADOW OF VESUVIUS

Pompeii—a city embalmed in lava

The man lay in the cobbled street, his hand still closed round a fistful of gold coins. Perhaps he was a thief. Perhaps he had saved the money carefully over the years. No one will ever know. Whatever his claim to the gold, it was his fate to hold it in his palm for more than 1500 years—buried by layers of ash and lava until his body was uncovered in the 18th century.

He was a citizen of Pompeii, the summer resort for wealthy Romans near the Bay of Naples, which was wiped out in one horrifying day, when Mount Vesuvius erupted on August 24, AD 79. But in destroying the city, the volcano also preserved it for all time.

Shopkeepers were closing their wooden shutters for lunch. Girls were gossiping at a corner fountain. A baker had just slid 81 loaves into his oven. In a wine shop, a customer laid his money on the counter for a drink. Then, suddenly, the first earthquake struck.

The barmaid did not stop to pick up the money. The loaves were left in the oven—they can still be seen, burnt to cinders, in a Naples museum.

Many fled at once, for the earthquake was only the first flexing of the volcano's muscles. But others were bound to the city by ties too strong to snap.

The hopeless flight

One group was uncovered sitting reverently at the funeral feast of a friend. Others dug to bury their valuables—and were buried themselves. Some hid in their houses, trying pitifully to barricade themselves against the volcano's remorseless power. Yet more loaded their belongings into carts—only to be trapped in the bottlenecks of Pompeii's narrow gates.

By the time Vesuvius fell quiet, 28 hours later, Pompeii was buried 20 ft deep, and 2000 of its 20,000 people were dead.

The city and its tragedy were for centuries largely forgotten. Then in 1748 the

ROW OF DEATH *All over Pompeii men, women and children like these were trapped by choking ash as they fought to escape the doomed city—and lie frozen for ever in their last moment of agony.*

King of Naples' engineer, Alcubierre, set about inspecting a 150-year-old tunnel that had been bored under the site to bring water from the nearby Sarno River.

By luck, he sank his first shaft into Pompeii's business quarter and unearthed a brilliant wall-painting. Another of his discoveries was the body of the Pompeiian with the fistful of gold. Alcubierre went on vigorously, if somewhat haphazardly excavating the site.

Then in 1763 a German cobbler's son, Johann Winckelmann, became fascinated by the secrets of Pompeii. He became an expert on its history. But the snobbish officials who controlled the site would not let him visit it. Winckelmann went on all the same, studying the finds and bribing

a foreman to let him look at the site. By hard-won scholarship, he turned a miscellaneous jumble of relics into a record of six centuries of life in the ancient Roman seaside resort.

But Winckelmann was murdered by a chance acquaintance in Trieste in 1768, before he could develop his work.

It was another century before an Italian archaeologist, Giuseppe Fiorelli, founded the present scientific policy of moving forward slowly—house by house and street by street—to make sure that nothing was lost in the excavation of the city.

For, amazingly, two-fifths of Pompeii is still to be uncovered. The unknown that still lies in its lava shroud may be yet more breathtaking than the known.

THE TRIBE THAT INVENTED ZERO
Rise and fall of the Mayas' jungle empire

They began as a Stone Age people who never grasped the principle of the wheel. Yet they rose to artistic and intellectual heights that no other race in the ancient Americas could match.

They could calculate the movements of the planets and predict eclipses with an accuracy not repeated until the 20th century. Yet they could not build a simple arch.

Their writing was still in a crude picture form when other peoples had a sophisticated literature. But their system of mathematics was unrivalled even in ancient Egypt. They could count in millions and used the concept of zero 1000 years before the rest of the world.

The Mayas of Central America built up a civilisation that was both splendid and barbaric; a culture whose sudden disappearance remains the most puzzling in history.

Human sacrifice

How they developed from simple village communities of farmers and fishermen around 1500 BC into a mighty race whose cities remain dotted about Honduras, Guatemala and the northern states of Mexico, is not clear. But they did. And they did it alone.

As they grew, the Mayas developed a distinctive class system of hereditary nobles under a priest-king; free, working

commoners; and slaves—usually prisoners taken in battle. High-ranking captives, however, became human sacrifices to the Mayan god Hunabku.

Their mathematics used only three symbols: a dot for one, a bar for five, and a shell shape for zero. Yet it enabled them to calculate in hundreds of millions.

The Mayan calendar took as its starting

STAIRS TO SLAUGHTER *Humans were sacrificed on this temple-topped Mayan pyramid at Tikal.*

point a day in the year 3113 BC, counting the number of days that had passed since then, although why that particular year was chosen is not known. Instead of weeks, months and years, the Maya used the *kin* (one day), the *uinal* (20 days), the *tun* (360 days), the *katun* (7200 days) and the *baktun* (144,000 days).

Their cities had populations numbering up to 40,000 and were supported by an elaborate trading system.

But suddenly, inexplicably, around the beginning of the 10th century AD, Mayan civilisation disintegrated. Their cities were left abandoned. There have been plenty of theories to explain the downfall, but all of them are just guesswork.

One suggests that their agricultural system collapsed as the soil became exhausted and retreated before the jungle that choked their fields.

Others suggest earthquake, disease, or invasion from Mexico. Or there might have been a revolution by the commoners and slaves against the unproductive, religious overlords who, it seems, were obsessed with the contemplation of time and its mysteries.

Perhaps the most fascinating theory is that the Mayans simply gave up the struggle for life against the heat and the ever-present jungle. Modern anthropologists have discovered that the Mayans had small families because they suffered from a lack of protein in their diet, which reduced sexuality.

Some experts believe that the Mayans had a much slower heartbeat than modern man. One theory put their pulse a full 20 beats slower at 52 beats a minute.

This, they argue, shows that the Mayans, secure and isolated in their jungle empire, became lazy—and tired of life itself.

Modern man's pulse rate, of 75–80 beats a minute, may sometimes lead to ulcers. But the alternative to dynamism may be death.

LOST FORTRESS OF THE INCAS

Where the beautiful Chosen Women hid from the conquistadores

For more than 300 years tales of a lost Inca city, perched in the Peruvian Andes, were considered little more than folklore. It was said, but not really believed, that the survivors of the Inca dynasty fled to these forbidding peaks in 1530, to escape slaughter at the hands of the Spanish conquistadores.

High in a saddle between two peaks, the Incas were said to have built their last refuge, an impregnable fortress city.

Explorers searched for the city in vain. They criss-crossed the wild jungles and hills near the mountain Machu Picchu, but found nothing of any interest. Disappointed, they abandoned the search convinced that no such city could exist.

But Hiram Bingham, a young assistant professor in Latin-American history at Yale University, was determined to prove them all wrong. He had made several attempts but, like his predecessors, his ventures into the mountains succeeded only in running into a series of dead ends.

In July 1911 he mounted yet another expedition. Accompanied by two friends and some Indian helpers, he set off by mule train along the Urubamba Canyon, following up yet another lead.

One rainy morning Bingham's party sat disconsolately in their camp, debating whether to go on with an expedition that seemed doomed to failure, when a local planter appeared. He told them the old, old story of a ruined city said to be on the mountain top across the river.

Only the ever-optimistic Bingham was inclined to take him seriously. His colleagues refused to go and so he set out with only the planter for company.

The two men and their mules scrambled across the river and up the 2000 ft slope. Still there was nothing in sight to indicate a ruined city. And then they met two Indians who gave them water . . . and casually told them that there were some old houses and walls 'just around the corner'.

After so many disappointments, Bingham was still dubious. But not for long. He rounded the hill and there the lost city stood, far more beautiful and breathtaking than he had ever imagined.

There was a flight of 100 perfectly built terraces, hundreds of feet long, each covered with soil carried laboriously up from the valleys. It was a huge hanging garden in the hills, like a New World

LANDSCAPE GARDENING *So that the fortress city could grow its own food, the Incas hewed terraces from the rock and filled them with topsoil carried up from the valleys by an army of labourers.*

Babylon. The city was a complex of white granite buildings, large enough to hold 2000 people and impregnable to attack from below. The Incas had looked for security from the Spanish armies, and they had created it here, with their own hands.

The city was a masterpiece of construction. Centuries ago, the Incas had moved granite blocks uphill without the aid of wheels. No two blocks were alike. Each was cut in irregular shapes, and each dovetailed exactly with its neighbours, as in an immense jigsaw puzzle.

The ultimate fate of the city's inhabitants remains a mystery. There are no writings to explain it.

Strangely, in its last days Machu Picchu seems to have been a city of women. A later party, again led by Bingham, discovered 174 skeletons in the burial caves,

and 150 of them were female. Bingham offered this explanation:

At the height of the autocratic rule of the Incas, special schools were maintained all over the empire in which the most beautiful girls were trained to serve the nobility and assist in religious rites.

Bingham believed that as the Spanish advanced, these girls, called the Chosen Women, were taken to the new city so that they could continue to worship the sun, moon and the stars and pray for the hated invaders to be driven from the land.

The city is believed to have continued for 40 years. As the years passed, so the women grew old and died. The men guarding them drifted away, and in time the jungle again crept over Machu Picchu, leaving no one to tell of its short and baffling history.

CITY IN THE CLOUDS

Did ancient Egyptians inspire pyramids in the Andes?

Long before the Spanish conquistadores overran Peru—in fact, long before the Incas built their empire—the mysterious city of Tiahuanaco lay in ruins. Its people had vanished into the mists of the Andes. Only their tumbled monuments remained to tell of the skill of Tiahuanaco's master builders, the men who built pyramids in the sky.

The Tiahuanacans had no beasts of burden, no wheels and tools made only of stone. Their city in the clouds stands above the Andes timberline, 3 miles high on the border of Peru and Bolivia. Yet somehow they were able to transport

blocks of stone weighing more than 100 tons from a quarry 25 miles away across a rugged plateau and the grey expanse of Titicaca, the world's highest lake.

Once on site, the blocks—far bigger than anything used in ancient Egypt— were ground to accuracies of less than 1/50 in. and fitted on to huge, flat-topped pyramids.

Three of these monuments remain at Tiahuanaco: the Akapana or fortress; the Kalasaya or temple, and the Palace of the Ten Doors. Early accounts by visiting Spaniards suggest that in the 16th century there were many more.

Biggest of the pyramids is the Akapana, a natural mound which has been shaped and faced with stone into a man-made mountain 500 ft wide and 700 ft long, towering 50 ft over the plain. The biggest stone block is the largest piece of cut rock in the world: an intricately carved 200 ton monolith that stands at the entrance to the Kalasaya (temple).

On its side is the first of the two surviving archaeological clues to the identity of Tiahuanaco's founders. It is a figure, carved into the rock, of the city's weeping god—known in Indian legends as Con-Tici Viracocha.

Long ears and beards

According to the legends handed down through the Andean tribes, Viracocha was a tall white man, with a squarish face, blue eyes and fair hair cut into a monk's tonsure. In the carving his hair is concealed under an elaborate headdress. From his staring eyes fall round tears. He is said to have arrived in the 5th century AD, to have taught the people agriculture and irrigation, and to have put up statues of a people who had long ears and beards.

Less than 100 years later, say the legends, he went to the western coast, where he spread his mantle upon the water, sat on it and sailed away for ever.

The second clue is a twice life-sized statue of a man which stands near the temple. It is known as The Bishop and it appears to be carrying a book, yet it was carved hundreds of years before writing is known to have evolved in South America.

From these clues and others buried in the patterns of the buildings, archaeologists now believe that two sets of outsiders helped to build Tiahuanaco and its empire. The first moved on to the plateau some time before AD 450, subduing an earlier primitive culture near Lake Titicaca. They abandoned the city when the second group arrived in the 8th century. Then the second group disappeared.

By AD 1000 the Tiahuanacan empire had unified for the first time the patchwork cultures of the Peruvian Andes. But its power was now spent, its capital city already crumbling into ruin. The empire was to lie in fragments for 200 years before it was reassembled by the Incas as the nub of their continent-spanning empire.

That much is known. What no one knows is who the outsiders were, where they came from or where they disappeared

to. All the historians have are theories.

One such theory suggests that a Greek or Phoenician explorer could have crossed the Atlantic by chance or design long before Columbus sailed in 1492. As early as 380 BC, the Greek writer Theopompus referred to an island of 'immense extent' beyond Gibraltar.

Chinese annals record a journey by Buddhist monks before AD 500 to a land 5000 miles across the Pacific.

Could these monks have been the models for the weeping god? Or could Viracocha have been an Irish monk? There is a legend that Ireland's St Brendan sailed west across the Atlantic in a small animal-skin curragh in the 6th century. Although it seems unlikely that he himself made the journey, Irish monks certainly sailed thousands of miles from their homes looking for a refuge from the barbarians who were driving west.

The second group of Tiahuanacans could have been Portuguese priests. A group led by an archbishop is known to have sailed west in AD 734, and discovered an island which they called Antillia. This island might have been one of the West Indies or even part of Brazil. Some of them could have reached Tiahuanaco.

The most fascinating theory of all is the one argued by Norwegian Thor Heyerdahl. His view offers an explanation not only of where the gods came from, but where they may have gone.

In 1947 he proved, by making the voyage himself with a hand-picked crew, that pre-Incan explorers from Peru could have reached Polynesia on balsawood rafts. And he showed that the square-headed long-eared statues of Easter Island are uncannily like the statues Viracocha is said to have carved. Heyerdahl's raft was called *Kon-Tiki*, a variation of Viracocha's other name: Con-Tici.

Men of the old world

In 1970 Heyerdahl pursued his experiment even further. He built a papyrus reed boat called *Ra II*, and sailed it from Africa to Barbados to prove the other half of his theory—that the pyramid style of building in Tiahuanaco and other ancient South American cultures could have been taken across the Atlantic by Egyptians.

If he is right, then the bearded gods who built the city in the clouds were men of the old world, brave enough to sail the oceans on bundles of reeds and spongy wood.

EL DORADO

The name that deluded treasure hunters for centuries

For centuries the hearts and minds of men have been held enthralled by El Dorado, the legendary city of gold, a treasure-house hidden somewhere in the Andes.

Hundreds of fortune-hunters have trekked through the jungle and the high sierras—and died in the quest.

However, recent evidence suggests that their search was hopeless from the beginning, for El Dorado was probably not a city at all . . . but a man.

The legend of El Dorado first reached the world through the Spanish conquistadores, who invaded Central America under Balboa in the early 16th century.

As they plundered their way across the continent, the Spaniards heard tales of the sun-worshipping Chibcha Indians who lived in the high, cold plains near where Bogotá, the capital of Colombia, stands today. The tribe, it was said, venerated gold as the sun god's metal. They wore golden ornaments, and for more than 2000 years had covered their buildings with sheets of the precious metal.

Luis Daca, a Spanish officer, reported in 1535 that an Indian had told him of a holy mountain lake that was full of gold. Others told of meeting a golden chieftain in a city called Omagua.

On ancient maps

As the tales spread, El Dorado came to be thought of as a city of gold; it is even shown on ancient maps of Brazil and the Guianas, though its exact position was vague.

In the 16th century, Bartolomeus Welser, a banker, sent several expeditions into what is now Colombia to seek El

GLORIOUS CHIEF *The exquisitely wrought golden model of the raft that carried El Dorado. The rowing figures have their backs to the chief, so that their eyes may not see his glory.*

Dorado. His men tortured any unfortunate Indian they came across to extract information, but with little result. All the expeditions came to grief.

But the legend of the fabulous city seems to have blinded the hunters to a clue that lay in the very words constantly on their lips. El Dorado in Spanish has two meanings—the Golden Place and the Golden Man.

It was the latter meaning that fitted perfectly with another Chibcha legend that had been largely ignored by the fortune-hunters.

The Golden Man

The Chibchas worshipped gold, their chief and a god who lived in the lake. The chief was so sacred that normally no tribesman was allowed to look at him. But once a year he became the centre of an elaborate ceremony. Keeping their eyes closed, the tribesmen would smear the chief with sticky resin and blow gold dust over him until he glistened from head to foot—literally an El Dorado.

Then they loaded a raft with a huge pile of golden animal images and ornaments. The raft was rowed into the middle of the sacred Lake Guatavita, where the chief tossed the tribe's priceless offerings overboard.

Lake Guatavita is a real lake. But supporting evidence for the Golden Man remained as elusive as that for the city —until, in 1969, two farm workers, searching for a lost dog in the hills a few hours drive from Bogotá, peered into a small cave. There, they found an exquisite model raft made of solid gold. On board were eight tiny oarsmen—rowing with their backs to the regal golden figure of their sacred chief.

Yet Guatavita still refuses to yield its golden treasures. The Spaniard Gonzalo de Quesada, who conquered the region in 1537-8, forced 8000 Indians to dig a breach in the side of the lake to lower its level. But the walls of the channel collapsed and the Indians stopped work, fearing that the Sun God was angry with them for stealing his treasure.

In 1823 and again in 1900 efforts were made to drain Guatavita, but although valuable relics were found, the funnel-shaped depths of the lake were never plumbed. And it is there that El Dorado— the Golden Man—is reputed to have submerged the most valuable offerings to appease the angry gods.

SIGNPOSTS ON THE FACE OF THE DESERT

ONLY FROM THE AIR is it possible to get a proper view of the strange patterns that were etched on the face of the Nazca Desert in Peru more than 1000 years ago.

On a 40 mile long plateau above the irrigated settlements where they lived, the Nazca Indians scratched out on the sun-baked, barren ground shapes of giant lizards, birds, animals and flowers.

The figure on the left resembles an eight-legged spider 150 ft long. The arrow-like shape on the right, equally mysterious, has been compared with the appearance of a long-billed humming bird. Only slightly less puzzling are the geometrical figures— angles and triangles, lines running dead straight for up to 5 miles—which scar the face of the desert. Some scholars think these may have served as astronomical calendars to help calculate dates for planting crops or for digging ditches to catch seasonal rivers. But because their signs and symbols can only be viewed in true perspective from the air, other theorists have suggested that they were guide paths for visitors from another planet.

THE FIRST AMERICANS

The migrants from Asia 40,000 years ago

José Cortés was digging a drainage ditch when he struck something hard with his spade. Scooping some earth away he uncovered a huge curved tusk. Near by was another, and both were attached to the enormous skull of a long-extinct mammoth.

José's farm was at Tepexpan 20 miles north-east of Mexico City, and the year was 1950. Two years later, when Mexican palaeontologists investigated the fossil, they were dumbfounded to find the point of a weapon in its rib cage. In the next few days tools—scrapers—were found.

Apparently the mammoth had become bogged down in a marsh, making it an easy victim for a band of hunters armed with stones and spears. But had men existed in America as long ago as the mammoth? Work stopped, and the announcement of the find went out to the archaeological world.

The discovery supported earlier work of anthropologist Helmut de Terra. Digging in the same area in 1947, he had found the skeleton of a man. Because its bones were alongside those of a mammoth, De Terra decided that the Tepexpan Man, as he called him, had lived possibly 11,000 years ago. But De Terra's claim had been dismissed by others with a charge of sloppy excavation work.

Men from Asia

The 1950 discovery linking man and mammoth as contemporaries proved him right, and spurred new research into the peopling of America. It is now thought that the first men arrived on the continent from Asia up to 40,000 years ago, walking to Alaska across the Bering Strait, then a land bridge.

This theory is based on recent discoveries of simple tools made of stone or animal bone in the Yukon Territory, Alaska and Mexico. Scientists believe that many of these tools—weapon points, cleavers and scrapers (used to dress hides for clothing)—date back to 35,000 years ago.

Astonishingly, men did exist in America at a time when mammoths, mastodons, 20 ft sloths, gigantic sabre-toothed cats, camels, a species of horse, and lions larger than the African lions all roamed the countryside.

After the melting of the North American ice sheet about 12,000 years ago, these first Americans gradually spread across the north of the continent. And hunting animals and seeking a pleasant environment, they wandered southwards and probably reached southernmost South America more than 8000 years ago.

The earliest farmers

In the Old World, the first farmers seem to have emerged in Asia about 10,000 BC, and over the next few thousand years men began to live settled lives in many parts of the eastern hemisphere.

Just when the early Americans turned to agriculture and began to live in communities is not known. But there is some evidence that by 5000 BC pumpkins and squash and other crops were grown in Central America and Peru. And in some other areas a reliable supply of fish or meat enabled people to adopt a semi-settled way of life.

By then the mammoth and other huge animals had become extinct. Able to adjust to his changing ecology, man outlived them all.

THE STONEHENGE OF THE USA

MYSTERY HILL has been called the Stonehenge of America. It is a jumble of 22 stone beehive-shaped structures and rough walls covering about 12 acres in Salem, New Hampshire. At the site, one slab, weighing nearly 5 tons, is called the Sacrificial Table—for it is thought that it may have been the centre-piece of some ancient rite. Stone columns around the perimeter seem to relate to the seasons. Charcoal discovered around assorted old tools was scientifically dated back to 2000 BC. About 150 similar sites have been found in New England. One theory links them with Europe's Bronze Age culture.

THE SEA GIVES UP A GHOST

How a worm signposted the way to a ship's grave

August 10, 1628, was a great day for Stockholm. The city filled with patriotic, excited crowds as news spread that *Vasa*, the mighty man-o'-war named after the Swedish royal family, was to sail at last.

King Gustavus Adolphus himself had masterminded her design. Intended to carry 300 fighting men as well as a working crew of 133, she displaced about 1400 tons. Forty acres of timber had gone into her construction.

Her topgallant soared to 164 ft, and 64 bronze cannon were mounted on her three decks.

Now the great warship was ready for the sea. It was 4 o'clock in the afternoon: to the cheers of the crowds on shore and the thunder of the fleet's guns fired in salute, *Vasa* weighed anchor and slid gracefully away.

Then came disaster, sudden, startling and total. A squall blew up in the bay and the ship listed to port. Before the crew could haul the guns to redistribute the weight, water was pouring in through the square, open gunports of the lowest deck. In minutes, the sea closed over *Vasa*. There were few survivors.

Discovery under the sea

It was not until almost 300 years after the loss of the ship that two clues, which at first seemed insignificant, led a determined young man to pull off one of the most spectacular coups in the history of underwater exploration.

The first clue was *teredo navalis*, or shipworm, a destructive 1 ft long mollusc, which has plagued wooden ships since man first ventured to sea.

Cruising off the west coast of Sweden in the late 1930s, Anders Franzen, who was then just 20, came across some flotsam riddled with teredo worm. This seemed odd to Franzen who, accustomed to sailing in the Baltic, had never before seen timber so badly worm-eaten.

He investigated, and learnt that the Baltic is not sufficiently salty for the teredo worm to flourish. So he reasoned that the *Vasa*, which had sunk in Baltic waters, might still be intact.

After the war, Franzen, who had dreamt of salvaging an old ship, gleaned every scrap of information available about the *Vasa* and the place where she had sunk. He swept the harbour floor with grapnels and drag-wires—bringing up nothing but old bedsteads and all manner of junk. For four years his prize eluded him. But all the time he was getting closer.

Oak turned black

Then the second clue that was to guide him to his goal fell into his hands. Sounding the harbour floor one day in 1956, his core-sampler—a device for picking up samples of the sea-bed—struck something solid. He raised the line and brought up a piece of ancient, black oak. Franzen knew that in these waters it took at least 100 years for the oak to turn black, so he must have stumbled upon an old ship. Could it be *Vasa*?

Franzen's hunch was confirmed by naval divers, who found *Vasa* 110 ft down, wedged up to her original waterline in 16 ft of mud.

The first stage in the salvage operation

NAVAL GLORY *More than 1000 gilded carvings —of heroes and saints, surmounted by the Swedish royal arms—graced the ship that never sailed.*

RAISING THE WRECK *After divers had passed steel cables under the* Vasa, *she had to be 'bounced' into shallower water, then raised by two inflatable pontoons and a system of hydraulic jacks.*

was to pass steel cables under the ship, suspended from pontoons, and then, by raising and lowering the pontoons, 'bounce' the hulk free and into shallower water. This took two years.

Next, divers closed all the gunports, plugged every possible leak, and finally brought her up on April 24, 1961, with cables, inflatable pontoons and a system of hydraulic jacks.

Today, the *Vasa* rests in a specially built museum in Stockholm. She is continuously sprayed with steam and special chemicals to stop her timbers warping and shrinking to destruction.

Her resurrection was a triumph of underwater discovery and salvage; an achievement for which history will award some part of the credit to a destructive little creature called the shipworm.

THE WRECK OF THE 'MARY ROSE'

'The more cooks, the worst potage'

The crew's last terrible cries of despair echoed across the waters of Portsmouth Harbour. Thousands of spectators stood, rooted in anguish, as the gaily bannered *Mary Rose*, pride of Henry VIII's navy, rolled over and sank before their eyes.

One of the onlookers, the young wife of Admiral Sir George Carew, fainted into the arms of a nobleman of the court; she had just watched her husband die.

It was July 19, 1545. France and England were once more at war, and a 200 strong French invasion fleet stood in line of battle off the Isle of Wight. Becalmed, the English fleet lay along the coast from Portsmouth to Gosport, praying for wind. Their plight was desperate, for the French oared galleys were able to close in and fire on the English more or less as they chose. But suddenly wind and tide changed together, and the English streamed out to meet the French. The formidable flagship, the *Great Harry*, led the van, closely followed by the *Mary Rose*.

Henry VIII and his court crowded the battlements of Southsea Castle, eagerly awaiting the result of the action. Below

THE SCENE OF DISASTER *This engraving helped McKee in his search for the wreck of the* Mary Rose. *In the centre are the masts of the sinking ship; in the foreground, Henry VIII on horseback.*

them on the coastal plain was the militia of the southern counties, ready to repel any invader who got ashore.

Before these thousands of spectators the *Mary Rose* came round before the wind, gallantly heeling as her sails filled. Her lower gunports, just 16 in. above the water, were already open for action. With the helm hard over, the ports dipped under and in an instant the ship was on her beam ends and sinking rapidly.

Handful of survivors

Within minutes, only her topmasts stood above the surface; 700 men, hopelessly trapped, had gone to their deaths. There was only a handful of survivors.

The cause of the disaster is still disputed. Her 91 heavy guns were run out, which may have affected her stability. It seems likely too that some of the guns were badly secured. As the ship heeled, they may have broken loose and careered down the sloping deck, increasing the list still further. But witnesses testified later that the vessel had been grossly mishandled. One account said that it was a matter of 'the more cooks, the worst potage'—each of the mariners on board considered himself fit to be a shipmaster in his own right, and none would take orders from another.

Certainly this view is borne out by Sir George's last words, shouted to his uncle,

who was commanding a nearby ship: 'I have the sort of knaves I cannot rule.'

The great sea battle dwindled to a skirmish, neither side being prepared to commit itself. Almost immediately a massive salvage operation was set up, and there was every confidence that the *Mary Rose* would be quickly hauled up and restored to the fleet.

Her recovery was especially important to Henry for he had ordered her building in 1509 when he first came to the throne at the age of 18. She had been named after the king's sister, Mary Tudor, and his family emblem—the rose—and she was still considered one of the most formidable warships afloat.

However, her 700 tons proved too much for the primitive salvage equipment of the day, despite the assistance of a team of divers from Venice. She was forgotten until one day in 1840 when a diving team, led by John Deane, working on the 18th-century wreck of the *Royal George*, were asked by some fishermen to free their nets which had become snagged underwater close by. Deane dived and found the net hooked round some ancient timbers. His curiosity aroused, Deane explored the site and discovered five brass cannon dated 1535 and 20 iron guns which he had hauled to the surface. Once more, the *Mary Rose* was in the public eye.

But somehow she was forgotten again until 1965, when naval historian and keen amateur diver, Alexander McKee, set out to find her. He suspected that the ship's hull, buried in mud for the last four centuries, might still be intact, and that it might be possible to bring her up.

Such an operation had been accomplished only once before when, in 1961, Swedish marine archaeologists lifted the 17th-century *Vasa* from the bottom of Stockholm's harbour.

With a small team of divers McKee managed to locate the *Royal George*, but after scouring the area was forced to conclude that the *Mary Rose* lay somewhat further away than the records suggested. So he turned to contemporary accounts of the actual sinking and particularly to an engraving, taken from a 16th-century painting. But the original painting had long vanished and there was a danger that the engraving, made in 1773, was not an accurate copy.

Marked on an ancient chart

McKee had already formed a clear idea of the general area in which the wreck lay, when unexpectedly he came across a chart of 1841—the year following Deane's discovery. There, right in the middle of McKee's search area, was a mark pinpointing the *Mary Rose*.

McKee and his associates, exploring the site with the very latest sonar equipment, found a wreck 200 ft long and 75 ft wide, although it lay 20 ft beneath the sea bed.

It was larger than McKee had expected for an Elizabethan warship, but in 1970 a single timber and an iron gun were dug out of the mud. The gun was proof that this was the *Mary Rose*.

Bones under the sea

On the first dive of the 1971 season, McKee found that during the winter the mud had shifted so much that a considerable amount of planking had been revealed. As more of the hull was exposed, bones were found and pieces of leather which might have been clothing.

McKee is now keen to have the wreck moved to an underwater dock, so that excavation can continue without the problems caused by sea and weather.

His dream is that one day the old ship will be raised and exhibited in a specially built hall alongside Nelson's *Victory* in Portsmouth dockyard. Such an operation he thinks, might take 20 years and £5 million to complete.

This might be a small price to pay in exchange for the answers to ancient mysteries. No one knows how 16th-century warships were constructed or how they were armed. *Mary Rose* may tell us. Once again, thousands of people will come to see her—a not unfitting memorial to the 700 men who died in the public's gaze so long ago.

PIECES OF EIGHT!

Treasure fleet of the Spanish Main

On any morning after a storm on Florida's Atlantic coast, treasure-seekers can be found studying the wet sand in the hope of uncovering something washed up from the Spanish wrecks that litter the offshore reefs and shallows.

It is estimated that along the state's coastline there are between 1200 and 2000 wrecks. Many date from the time when galleons laden with treasure sailed the Spanish Main.

From the middle of the 16th century until well into the 18th, convoys would assemble in Havana, sail through the Straits of Florida and ride the Gulf Stream north. Then off the Carolinas they could pick up the westerlies which would blow them back home to Europe.

In May 1715 two small fleets under the command of Generals Ubilla and Echeverz joined forces at Havana.

In its heyday the Spanish navy had mustered as many as 100 ships for its annual transatlantic convoy. But by the 18th century, against British, Dutch and French competition, it was past its prime.

The combined fleets at Havana in 1715 comprised a niggardly 11 ships, and not one of them was really seaworthy. The best of Ubilla's five vessels was a former English warship, the *Hampton Court*, which had been captured by the French and presented to Spain.

Nevertheless, there was much treasure for the ships to carry—including a cargo of precious works of Chinese craftsmen shipped across the Pacific and then carried over Mexico on mule-back.

Seams leaking

By the time they were loaded at Havana, all 11 ships were so low in the water that their seams leaked. And when they sailed on July 24, it was dangerously close to the hurricane season.

For two days they sailed through calm seas under a clear sky north towards the Bahamas. But on the third day thick cloud filled the sky and visibility was almost nil. That night the wind rose, the ships began to roll and passengers and cargo were thrown about. In the morning the sky was black, the heat unbearable and purplish squalls could be seen on the horizon.

As the fleet entered the straits of Florida, the wind doubled its force. The ships were caught between the sharp coral reefs of the flat Florida coast and the dangerous Bahamas Bank.

No more than three days out from

TREASURE ROUTE *The treasure fleets sailed from Cuba through the Florida Straits to Spain.*

SPANISH GOLD *Doubloons of 1714 are slightly bigger than a British 10 pence piece— about 3 cm across.*

Havana, the hurricane broke in full force. With their heavy hulls and short rudders the ships could not manoeuvre before the storm, which blew them rapidly towards the Florida coast. Masts snapped and the decks became a mass of splintered wood and sodden rigging.

Sole survivor

Those who were not swept overboard knelt and prayed. Ubilla's flagship hit a reef first, and the rest quickly followed. The only survivor was the French *Grifon*, whose captain had disobeyed orders and sailed further out to the north-east and was thus able to flee before the storm.

Over 1000 men were lost, together with silver, gold and other goods valued then at nearly £4 million. Some of the survivors lucky enough to be swept up on the shore, took what they could of the small amount of washed-up treasure, and vanished with it into the interior. Others made rafts and floated to St Augustine, about 300 miles up the Florida coast.

The Spaniards quickly sent eight ships from Havana and St Augustine to set up a large-scale salvage operation. They established a camp and a storehouse to hold the salvaged valuables.

Using divers who simply held their breath and carried heavy stones to speed their descent, the Spaniards brought up millions of pieces of eight.

Pirates rob the camp

Then news of the disaster reached Jamaica, the haven of English pirates. Two of these, Captain Edward Teach, better known as Blackbeard, and Captain Henry Jennings, attacked the Spanish camp and Jennings alone got away with 350,000 pieces of eight. Despite this the Spaniards eventually returned to Havana with about a third of their treasure.

The rest lay undisturbed for almost 250 years, when the wrecks became the site of one of the longest and most lucrative of all the Florida treasure hunts.

The searches, still continuing, brought worldwide fame to an amateur Florida treasure-seeker called Kip Wagner.

Wagner moved to the Florida coast in 1949, and became interested in Spanish wrecks after hearing stories from friends who had looked for coins on the beaches. After buying himself an army surplus metal detector for $15, he found a large number of coins on an 8 mile stretch of

beach between Sebastian and Wabasso, about 25 miles south of Cape Canaveral. From where the coins lay, he began to formulate theories about the positions of the wrecks themselves. The coins were concentrated in small water-courses at various points along the shore. Wagner wondered whether a different wreck lay off each point.

Rare-book discovery

Wagner and a colleague, Dr Kip Kelso, conducted extensive research in libraries and institutes in America, and eventually Kelso located a vital volume in the rare-books section of the Library of Congress. It was called *A Concise Natural History of East and West Florida* and was published in 1775. It described the wreck of the Spanish fleet in 1715, and mentioned 'pistareens and double pistareens, which kinds of money probably yet remaining in the wrecks are sometimes washed up by the tide'.

The pair got in touch with the curator of the Spanish naval records in Seville, who provided 3000 microfilmed pages of ancient documents. When deciphered, these revealed the entire history of the 1715 disaster, the salvage work and the rough locations of many of the wrecks.

It seemed that Wagner was on the track of the sunken Spanish convoy, but there were many years of work ahead. The operations were made more difficult by the weather on the Florida coast, which permitted salvage work for only a few months each year.

Wagner began by searching for the Spanish salvage team's base camp and store near Cape Canaveral, and after many days combing the higher ground behind the beach with his metal detector he located a ship's spike and a cannon ball. He excavated and charted what turned out to be a half-acre site, finding more cannon balls, fragments of Chinese pottery and a gold ring richly encrusted with seven diamonds.

Wagner knew from the records that a wreck lay off the camp. He spent many days floating on a motor-car inner-tube with a home-made face mask, peering through the silt and seaweed before he detected a cluster of cannons. Diving down, he found a large anchor. This was his first wreck, and now that he knew what these ancient relics looked like from above, he lost no time in chartering a plane from which to scan the reefs and shallows for others. His aerial search was a success and he charted the locations of a number of wrecks.

In 1959 Wagner assembled eight men, mostly experienced divers, and formed what he called the Real Eight Company— eight men in search of pieces of eight. He tested the group on a wreck that was mostly covered with rocks. Using an old launch and a home-made sand dredge, they worked hard for six months without finding anything.

The team was losing enthusiasm and was on the point of breaking up when at last one member surfaced clutching six wedges of silver. Overjoyed, the others dived over the side to see what they could find on the ocean bed.

Carpet of gold coins

Over the next few weeks 15 wedges were found before Wagner decided to move the group to a different wreck. From then on his dreams of treasure moved rapidly towards fulfilment.

The first day's work on the second wreck yielded a staggering haul of silver coins estimated to be worth $80,000. Then, one day after a storm, Wagner took his young nephew beachcombing. Wagner was picking up coins when his nephew ran towards him with a gold chain wrapped round his arm.

It was 11½ ft long and made up of 2176 links. Attached to it was an exquisite gold dragon whose open mouth was a whistle. A gold toothpick was hinged to its back and the tip of the tail was a tiny earpick. This was later identified as General Ubilla's badge of office and was sold for a handsome $50,000.

Finds continued over the years, and the group expanded. Perhaps its most amazing underwater feat was the salvage of 30 pieces of Chinese porcelain in near-perfect condition. The Spaniards had packed them in a special clay called petuntze.

One of the best years was 1965. On May 31 the group were using a machine they had developed themselves. By directing a powerful jet of water downwards from their boat's propeller, the treasure-seekers blasted a crater in the sand without disturbing the precious objects which the treasure-seekers were now confident were resting on the sea-bed.

As the water cleared, Wagner and his colleagues were spellbound to find themselves looking down at a carpet of gold which spread as far as they could see. The salvage that day was 1127 gold coins, worth more than $1 million.

THE MOST VALUABLE FIND EVER

WHEN EDWARD TUCKER and his brother-in-law Robert Canton, salvage men working in Bermuda, spotted some cannons in a deep sand pocket between two reefs, they thought little of it. They lifted the cannons and some other objects which had come from an old Spanish wreck, and sold them to the Bermuda Monuments Trust.

It was not until four years later in 1954, when they returned with better equipment, that they began to find more interesting treasure, hidden for centuries.

Painstaking research identified the wreck as the Spanish ship *San Pedro*, which had sunk in 1595. In and around her Tucker and Canton found 2000 silver coins, some assorted jewellery and gold bars, and a number of guns which threw some light on the ship that had carried them.

But the most exciting find by far was a golden crucifix, 3 in. long by 2 in. wide, set with seven perfectly matched emeralds.

The crucifix was identified as a pectoral cross, symbol of a bishop's authority. It is thought to be the most valuable single item ever recovered from the sea; estimates of its worth range from about £10,000 to £30,000—it is hard to put a price on it.

Bishop's pectoral cross: thought to be the most valuable single item ever recovered from the sea.

part
3

Contents

Ancient defences to counter perils of the unknown

Strange customs and superstitions

NEVER ON A FRIDAY

Man has done many strange things for the sake of luck

Not only was the ship called the *Friday*, but its keel was laid on a Friday and, for good measure, it was commanded by a Captain Friday. The British Admiralty had decided to expose the absurdity of one of the Royal Navy's most cherished superstitions—that Friday is an unlucky day. Their plans might well have worked. But on its maiden voyage—on a Friday—the ship disappeared with all hands. No trace was ever found.

The Admiralty has consistently denied that this story is true, but their denials are unimportant; generations of British seamen have accepted every word of it. For superstition cannot be overcome by logic. In many cases it is a survival from those primitive religions in which man worshipped the wild elements in the pious hope that they might help him in his struggle for survival.

For instance, touching wood for luck reflects early man's belief that every natural object—a tree, for example—was inhabited by a particular god. The significance once attached to fire and iron lingers on today with the carrying of a piece of coal or a small replica horseshoe as a good-luck charm.

To spill salt meant misfortune, because for centuries it was the only means of preserving meat in the winter.

To primitive peoples it was essential that the home was blessed with kindly spirits. The focal point was the hearth, the part of the house where, according to the Romans, household gods lived. In Western Europe, the fireplace, or inglenook, was thought to be the home of the 'brownies' and other fairies who brought good luck to the household. Some even thought they helped with the chores.

It was unwise to offend the fairies. In their attempts to appease the spirits, housewives in the Western Isles of Scotland would leave part of the fire burning in the hearth to keep the fairies warm through the night.

When a family moves to a new home, it is still traditional in some parts of Britain to take the embers from the old fireplace and burn them in a new one. Housewarming parties are a development of this old custom.

Kitchen folklore

Superstition also dominated a woman's work in the kitchen. Some housewives believe a meal will be spoilt if the food is stirred 'widdershins'—that is, against the sun's course. In order not to offend hens and so stop them laying, no egg shells were thrown on the fire.

No implement has more superstitious connections than the knife. Made of iron, it was thought to be a protection against evil of many kinds. This may stem from a time long ago when people armed with weapons of stone or bronze were easily overcome by sharp-edged—and apparently magical—swords of iron.

Another belief is that if two knives are crossed on a table, a quarrel is indicated

On the unlucky 13th of every month, an Eccentrics Club would meet at a London club and deliberately defy popular superstitions. Umbrellas were opened indoors, salt was spilt, ladders were walked under and waiters poured drinks into cracked or broken glasses.

unless a second person uncrosses them.

There are many superstitions about bread. It was thought disastrous if bread did not rise in the oven, for it was believed the Devil lurked inside unrisen bread. For this reason a cross was cut in the top to help the bread rise and also let the Devil out. But when cutting bread, it was considered foolish to slice off both ends of a loaf, as the Devil would be able to fly all over the house.

Even the table has superstitious significance. If a white cloth is left on a table during the night the household will soon be in need of a shroud.

Above all, never allow 13 people to sit down to eat at the same table. This superstition is generally associated with the Last Supper, when 13 were present, including Judas Iscariot, Christ's betrayer.

But the belief is older than Christianity. In Norse mythology, 12 gods were feasting when the Spirit of Strife—Loki—appeared and provoked a quarrel which ended in the death of Baldur, the favourite of the gods.

Outside the house further dangers lurk. One of the most widely known superstitions is the one about not walking under a ladder in case a tool or a pot of paint falls from above. But the reasoning is far older than that. Anyone walking between the ladder and the wall was breaking the triangle—the early Christian symbol for the Trinity.

Another theory on the origin of the ladder superstition suggests that it was once associated with the gallows. One method of hanging was to turn the victim off a ladder so that he dropped 'under' the ladder to the rope's end.

Chickens and fowl generally have long been regarded as reliable guides to what fortune holds. The Romans were frequently consulting their entrails, but self-confidence seems to have a lot to do with consulting a fowl. On one occasion, an ancient Greek admiral was told by his soothsayers that the holy fowl refused to eat, which was a bad omen. He replied tartly: 'Well, let us see if they will drink.' He tossed the lot overboard, engaged the enemy and won a resounding victory.

Some superstitions transcend national boundaries; others are peculiar to one country or race.

Scotland: Three swans flying together mean a national disaster. Red and green should not be worn together. It is unlucky to stand with your back to the edge of the door or to throw vegetables on to the fire. Love letters should not be posted on Christmas Day. Carrying a spade through the house means a grave will soon be dug.

Ireland: It is unlucky to use broken tombstones for the walls of a cottage; but wise

CONFOUNDING THE DEVIL *The clocks on the church at Mosta, in Malta, were set at different times to confuse the Devil.*

to take care of the 'fairy fort'—a tree in the centre of a field. And it is lucky to spill a drink on the ground—a relic of the ancient custom of pouring a libation to the gods.

Malta: It was the custom for churches to have two clock faces, one showing the correct time and the other a false one, to confuse the Devil about the time of the service.

Ibiza: Priests are not allowed to board fishing boats, probably because of a vestigial respect for the pre-Christian sea gods.

Iceland: It is unlucky to shoot a sea bird that follows a boat. An unmarried person who sits at the corner of a table will not marry for seven years. A pregnant woman who drinks from a cracked cup is risking her baby having a hare lip.

Holland: When touching wood, it is necessary to touch the unpainted underside of, say, a table. People with red hair bring misfortune (a belief common to lands once invaded by the Danes).

China: Any death by accident or foul play is to be feared, as the ghost may seek revenge on the seventh night. Sweeping out a house expels all good fortune—especially done on the Chinese New Year.

Nigeria: Sweeping a house at night brings bad luck—but a good sweeping first thing in the morning gets rid of evil spirits. If a male is hit with a broom he becomes impotent unless he retaliates seven times with the same broom. Sweeping after a person leaves the house gets rid of all bad spirits.

Japan: A comb picked up with the teeth facing the body is unlucky. Killing a spider in the morning is destroying a human soul. Most cats bring bad luck.

But as well as national superstitions there are also racial superstitions. For instance, a Jewish child must not be watched while it sleeps (because of the similarity to the death vigil). Nor must it be shown its reflection until it has grown its first tooth.

Gypsies believe that it is dangerous to eat food that has been stepped over, or drink from a stream that a woman has walked over. And all caravans must be burnt after their owners die.

It is easy to dismiss superstition as absurd, but only those who can break a mirror without a second thought are fully entitled to do so.

THE MAN WHO BOUGHT THE BLACK SEA

PRINCE URUSSOFF, a Russian nobleman, had a family superstition initially very expensive but ultimately very profitable as well. While he and his beautiful young bride were honeymooning on the Black Sea, the wedding ring slipped off her finger and disappeared beneath the waves. The prince, remembering the family belief that the loss of a wedding ring caused the loss of the bride herself, did the only thing he could. He bought both shores of the Black Sea from hundreds of owners for more than $40 million. He reasoned that if he owned both shores he owned the sea itself and everything that lay at its bottom.

When the prince died his heirs no longer needed to own the ring. So they sold the Black Sea for $80 million.

THE FIRST REAL CHRISTMAS CARD *It was designed by J. C. Horsley in 1843. The Christmas-card vogue caught on when the new postal services made it possible to send greetings this way.*

THE HOLY TIDES

The ancients had their own celebrations long before Christ

Christmas and Easter, although the greatest festivals in the Christian calendar, are celebrated with customs which originated in superstition and heathen rites hundreds of years before Christ was born.

Even the dates owe more to pagan practices than to the birth and resurrection of Jesus. It was not until the 4th century that December 25 was fixed arbitrarily as the anniversary of the Nativity —because the pagan festivals from which so many Christmas customs spring were held around that time.

And Easter, still a movable feast despite much pressure to allot it a specific date, falls according to the phase of the moon which the pagans long ago observed in deciding the appropriate time to venerate their gods.

Although Christianity has swept the world in a relatively short time, as the history of great religions go, the early missionaries faced an uphill task. The pagans were reluctant to give up their false gods and ancient practices.

So the missionaries, unable to convert them easily to an entirely new code of worship, did the next best thing. They took the pagan festivals as they were, and gradually grafted the observances of the new faith on to these festivals and the rites and customs surrounding them.

December 25 was not called Christmas until the 9th century. Until then it had been the Midwinter Feast, a combination of the Norse Yule Festival and the Roman Saturnalia, both of which took place in late December.

Week-long junket

The seven days of Roman junketing were an occasion for exchanging presents— one of the pagan customs that was gladly incorporated into Christmas. Even the sternest advocates of the new faith could not eradicate the notion that Saturnalia was a time for merrymaking. The Romans used to switch roles with their slaves, who were encouraged to elect their own 'king' for the holiday. He would preside over a great banquet, at which the master would wait on him and his fellow servants.

A similar idea survives in the armed forces in Britain, where it is still an honoured tradition for the officers and senior NCOs to serve the Christmas dinner in the lower ranks' mess. The reason Christian practice could never go the

EASTER IN HUNGARY *Village boys call on eligible girls and sprinkle them with water 'to make them good wives'.*

whole way with the Roman custom is that the unfortunate slave 'kings', after their brief exaltation, were taken to the amphitheatre and put to death.

When the Normans invaded England in 1066, they introduced into the Christmas festivities a mock king, called the Lord of Misrule, whose job was to ensure that the celebrations were conducted in the old pagan style.

Wearing paper hats and pulling crackers are throwbacks to the wilder excesses of ancient Rome. Yule logs and candles belong to the Norse tradition: they were symbols of fire and light bringing welcome relief in the cold and darkness of the northern mid-winter.

In the centuries that followed the Norman Conquest, as Christianity gained a firmer hold, carols and the nativity play were added. And Father Christmas evolved as a mixture of the red-robed Lord of Misrule and St Nicholas (Santa Claus), the patron saint of children.

The guilty mistletoe

Mistletoe, a plant sacred to the Druids, was hung outside Viking homes as a sign of peace and welcome to strangers. But the early Christians believed that Christ was crucified on a mistletoe-wood cross, and that the plant's shame had shrivelled it. So mistletoe was not used as a church decoration. Apart from that, the plant's 'guilt' never seriously affected its popularity as an emblem of Christmastide.

The custom of kissing under the mistletoe seems to be confined to the English-speaking world: no trace of it can be found in other countries.

Even in relatively modern times, Christmas has not always been celebrated with unmixed enthusiasm. Under the 17th-century Puritan regime it was attacked because of its heathen associations, and Cromwell's soldiers were ordered to tear down seasonal decorations.

The prohibition spread to America, where it remained in force until 1836 when the strait-laced descendants of the Pilgrim Fathers finally overcame their distaste, and December 25 was proclaimed a national public holiday.

Easter, like Christmas, was made by the early Christians to fit smoothly into the pagan timetable. In this case they chose the spring festival of Eostre, the Goddess of Dawn, held around the vernal equinox—the date when day and night are of equal length.

'One a penny, two a penny . . .'

Hot cross buns, eaten nowadays by many millions every Good Friday, are a survival from this pagan festival. All over Europe at this time women used to bake little 'magic' wheat cakes. Two such buns, each with a cross on it, were found in the ruins of Herculaneum, destroyed when Vesuvius erupted in AD 79.

The origins of the Easter egg go back even further in history. Most of the ancient civilisations regarded the egg as the seed of life and fertility, or a symbol of reincarnation. So it is not surprising that it was adopted along with the spring festival as a reminder of Christ's resurrection.

The egg-rollings of today are leftovers from the days when farmers hopefully rolled eggs across their fields to ensure good crops.

In Washington, in the 1870s, so many children used the Capitol grounds for this pastime that the turf suffered and the game was banned. Mrs Rutherford Hayes, the president's wife, took pity on the disappointed children and put the White House lawn at their disposal.

From this beginning, Easter Monday egg-rolling at the White House has become a national institution—a good example of a modern holiday custom that has its roots way back in pagan history.

EVEN IN WARTIME *American forces serving in Britain during the Second World War celebrated Hallowe'en with the traditional hollowed-out pumpkins in which they lit candles.*

ALL HALLOWS' EVE

When ghosts, demons and witches are abroad

Like Christmas and Easter, the festival of Hallowe'en originated in a pagan celebration, even though its name derives from the Christian festival of All Hallows' or All Saints' day.

It was introduced in the 7th century to commemorate all those saints and martyrs who had no special day to themselves, and was held on May 13. But in the 8th century All Hallows' day was moved to November 1, to counteract the pagan celebrations held on that date.

October 31, the eve of November 1, was the last night of the year in the ancient Celtic calendar, and was celebrated as the end of summer and its fruitfulness. It was a festival which the Celts of Northern Europe marked with bonfires to help the sun through the winter.

Winter also called to mind the chill and blackness of the grave and so it was a time when ghosts would walk, and supernatural spirits, warlocks and witches would hold their revels.

Only since the late 18th and early 19th centuries has Hallowe'en developed as a jolly time for children, with costumes, lanterns and games. Before then it was regarded as a night of fear, and wise men, respectful of hobgoblins and wandering demons, stayed indoors.

In the 17th and 18th centuries, however, it was customary for 'guisers'—people in weird masks and costumes—to go from house to house, singing and dancing to keep evil at bay, or as representations of the ghosts and goblins of the night.

Trick or treat

This custom has survived today in many parts of the world, as a children's masquerade. In North America, children go from door to door in costume on a ritual known as Trick or Treat.

They usually carry a sack or pillowcase and threaten to play a trick on householders if they are not given a 'treat' in the form of sweets or biscuits.

The Hallowe'en lantern, made from a hollowed-out pumpkin or turnip with a candle inside it, is a relic from the days when food offerings were made to the spirits of the dead.

THE BECKONING BELLS

Witches feared them; ghosts fled from them

Church bells that call people to prayer were once believed to have supernatural powers. In many Roman Catholic lands in the Middle Ages, when a new bell was consecrated and installed, gifts were presented to it and the event was celebrated with much eating and drinking.

When England was ravaged by the Black Death in the 14th century, ringing the church bells was widely believed to help to disperse the plague. Almost three centuries later Dr Francis Hering, in *Certaine Rules, Directions, or Advertisements for the Time of Pestilential Contagion*, advised: 'Let the bells of cities be rung often: thereby the aire is purified.'

The ringing of bells at a funeral was once supposed to drive away the dead person's ghost. When the ancient Romans held their feast in honour of the family dead in the month of May, it was customary to ring bronze bells and intone: 'Ghosts of my fathers, go forth.' In the *Roman Pontifical*, the ringing of bells is recommended for expelling 'the gibbering spectres of the dead'.

Many legends have told of bells being rung without human aid. Alexandre Dumas, in his *Pictures of Travels in the South of France*, said that in 1407 unearthly noises, including the chiming of a bell, were heard just before the collapse of the ancient bridge over the River Rhône.

Until the middle of the 18th century it was believed in Breslau, Poland, that if the cathedral bell rang by supernatural agency one of the canons would die.

Witches' rôle

Witches, who were said to fear church bells, were often credited with removing them from their belfries at night. At Canewdon in Essex, a bell which had been dropped in the river by seven witches is said to have been heard tolling from under the water during great storms.

As recently as 1852 all the church bells were rung—unsuccessfully—in Malta to disperse a severe storm; and in the same century the bells were rung at the parish church of Dawlish in Devon in the hope that their spirit would overcome 'the spirit of the lightning'.

THE FOOD OF LOVE

It has taken some strange forms—and still does

If an ancient Greek went for a walk with the udder of a hyena tied round his left arm, he was confident that no girl would be able to resist him. Even if this should fail, he could work a still more powerful love magic with calf's brains, hair from a wolf's tail, snake bones, the feathers of a screech owl—or even bits of human corpses.

Through the ages both sexes, of all races, have sought some kind of love potion. Women of ancient Rome brewed concoctions so strong that they were ruled dangerous and made illegal.

The poet Lucretius was popularly thought to have been driven mad by one such potion; and according to the historian Suetonius, Emperor Caligula suffered a similar misfortune. According to gossips of the day, he was thrown into a fit by potions administered by his wife in an effort to retain his affection. There is no record of the ingredients used.

In the harems of Constantinople, around 400 BC, cakes made from asses' milk and honey were used on the recommendation of Hippocrates, the Greek 'father of medicine'. Honey is still highly esteemed by some as an aphrodisiac, though without any scientific support.

Many of the oldest love potions were made from flowers and herbs. Usually, to achieve the best results, they had to be gathered on Midsummer's Eve.

The herb briony, known in its male and female forms as mandrake and womandrake, was reputed in the Bible to have the qualities both of an aphrodisiac and a fertility drug. The Book of Genesis records that the childless Rachel bargained with Leah for some mandrake which Leah's children had picked while playing in a field.

In Merrie England of the 16th century,

marigolds—sometimes known as summer brides—were regarded as a symbol of constancy and lasting love. They are still popular with some brides today when they choose their wedding posies.

Worried women in south-east Europe in the Middle Ages employed a more complex means of correcting a husband or boy friend with a wandering eye. They dug up earth from around his footprints and sowed marigold seeds in it. If this did not bring him back to fidelity, nothing would be effective.

About the same period, cyclamen and fern seeds put into cakes were recommended as 'a good amorous medicine'. But a girl had to be very careful not only to gather these seeds at the critical time—Midsummer's Eve—but also to collect them in exactly the right way.

This meant that a Bible had to be placed under the plant and the seeds shaken into a pewter dish with a hazel-wood fork. On no account must she touch the plant itself. Otherwise, instead of winning romance, she was likely to be tormented by demons.

The amorous tomato

Many items of ordinary diet have been prized more for their qualities of stimulating the mating instinct than for their health-giving properties—and many still are.

The ancient Greeks used to bake their bread in phallic forms, believing that this would give them prowess in love. People ate eggs in the past for the same reason, because the egg was regarded—and still is—as a symbol of procreation and new life.

When the potato was introduced into Spain in 1534 it is said to have fetched up to £250 a pound, not as a gastronomic novelty but as a love food.

The tomato was for centuries similarly esteemed, possibly because one of its many early names, *pomo d'ore*—golden apple—became corrupted into *pomme d'amour*—apple of love. In England, love apples were frowned upon as being conducive to excessive passion. Rumours were circulated by the Puritans that they were poisonous, with the result that they went out of fashion for 200 years. It was not until around 1830 that the tomato returned to favour as an item of food.

Lovers through the ages are recorded as having eaten spices, because they are hot and said to arouse amorous passion. Many sea foods—for example oysters, octopus and red mullet—have been, and to some extent still are, favoured, possibly because Aphrodite, the goddess of love, emerged from the sea.

Magic of the rhino

One of the most long-cherished beliefs in the realm of love lore, and one that remains relatively unshaken in the East, centres on the magical qualities of powdered rhinoceros horn.

Because of the insatiable demand for it, the Indian rhino was hunted almost to extinction, and about 60 years ago the authorities had to establish a government sanctuary to preserve the species. But the superstition lingers on, and rhino horn is still prized as an aphrodisiac in India and the Far East.

Another delicacy highly esteemed in the Orient as a love stimulant is bird's-nest soup, made from the unique substance which sea-swallows exude from their mouths in order to make nests.

There is not a shred of scientific evidence that any of these love charms, potions and philtres—ancient or modern—has the slightest use in producing the desired result.

THE SACRED RATS OF KARAI MA

MORE THAN 100,000 rats swarm over the marble courtyard of a temple near the city of Bikaner in the Indian state of Rajasthan. Karai Ma, the goddess to whom the temple is dedicated, is also the goddess of a caste of professional poets, called Charans. Whenever a Charan dies, according to the legend he returns to the temple as a rat; and every rat that dies in the temple returns to earth as a Charan poet. If one of the temple rats crawls over the bowed head of a believer it is taken as a good omen for his versifying in the future. But if anyone should accidentally step on a rat and kill it, the penalty is a fine of silver equal in weight to that of the dead poet he has gone to revere.

LOVE AND MARRIAGE

How different peoples love, honour and cherish

When two women of the Choroti and Chaco tribes of Paraguay want to marry the same man, they don tapir-skin boxing gloves and fight it out between them.

Girls from the Trobriand Islands, near Papua, begin their love overtures in a different way—by going up to the man of their choice and biting him. In fact, courting habits, both ancient and modern, involve the most complicated rituals and taboos.

A cold-climate courting custom known as 'bundling' was popular in Holland, Switzerland, New England, Scotland and Wales. It allowed couples to lie in bed provided they were clothed and wrapped separately in blankets.

In 19th-century rural Scotland, pregnancy was almost the rule for brides. A Royal Commission of 1868 established that nine out of ten women were pregnant on their wedding day in Scotland, a situation hardly in accord with the highest Victorian precepts.

In other societies, however, betrothal sometimes involved complete separation of the intended couple. A girl betrothed to a chieftain or other dignitary in the Solomon Islands in the Pacific was kept imprisoned in a cage, sometimes for years, under the watchful eye of her father, until her wedding day.

On the German island of Borkum in the mouth of the River Ems, an ordeal by smoke and water was once the punishment meted out to a man who had been courting a girl but was dilatory in naming the day. Young men of the village would surround his house and block the chimney, filling the place with smoke. Then they would remove the roof tiles, climb inside through the loft and challenge the lover: 'Are you engaged?' If he said he was, the whole village celebrated, but if his answer was 'No,' he would be dragged at the end of a rope three times through a pond.

Many of the present-day wedding customs that we take for granted are really born of age-old traditions. For example, the wedding veil was introduced by ancient Greeks and Romans to protect the bride from the evil eye of a jealous rival suitor.

The wedding ring, in general use in Christian marriages by the 9th century, dates back to the ancient Egyptians. The ring is placed on the third finger of the bride's hand because it was thought that this finger carried a vein leading directly to the heart. Made from gold, the most enduring of metals, the wedding band is supposed to confer upon its wearers a perfect and lifelong union; hence the superstition that a broken wedding ring is a portent of disaster.

Home-made underwear

The trousseau derived from the old French *trousse*, or small bundle of valuables which was originally paid to the husband. Until a century ago in most parts of the Balkans, the bride was expected to provide her groom with sets of underwear which she had made herself.

The practice of throwing rice and confetti at weddings has its origins in an old Greek fertility rite of showering sweetmeats over the couple. The act was also

LOVE SPOONS *These 18th-century wooden spoons were carved by youths in Wales as love tokens. A young man calling on his sweetheart was made to carve wooden spoons for her parents—to make sure his hands were kept occupied!*

meant to confer prosperity on the pair.

In the Celebes, or Sulawesi Islands of Indonesia, the belief is that unless the groom's soul is bribed with a shower of rice, it will fly away after the wedding and never return.

Feasting has always been a way of cementing kinship. At Malay weddings, the bride and groom feed each other continuously during the ceremony with uncooked rice. And in marriages in New Guinea the bride and groom share a newly killed pig, or at least as much of it as they can eat. Similarly, bushmen of South Africa gorge themselves with eland, a type of antelope, and leave nothing but the bare bones.

The Western idea of giving out pieces of wedding cake to guests originated in a Roman custom of breaking bread over the head of the bride to ensure prosperity. Each guest would then take away a portion of the broken bread.

Among the Lambodis, a semi-nomadic tribe of parts of central and north-east India, marriage is an occasion for lament. The morning after the wedding, the bride traditionally stands on the back of a bullock and wails her regret at leaving her father, mother and family.

Aphrodisiac drink

In many societies the consummation of the marriage is more important than the ceremony itself—to the family, as well as to the bride and groom. The term honeymoon, when the consummation takes place, derives from an old Northern European custom of drinking honeyed wine or mead as an aphrodisiac during the first month of marriage.

An old Greek-Cypriot custom is to roll a chubby baby boy up and down on the bridal bed before the consummation to ensure the couple will be blessed with healthy male children.

It was once customary among the peasants of Languedoc in France, for friends to burst into the bridal chamber and offer the groom and bride soup from a chamber pot. The soup was meant to endow the couple with vigour, so ensuring that their marriage would be quickly blessed with children.

Newly married couples of 17th-century Brittany were expected to wait three nights before consummating their marriage. The first night was dedicated to God, the second to St Joseph and the third to the groom's personal patron saint.

The Yezidi sect of Northern Iraq are considerably less restrained. They lock the couple in a room, and after consummation the bridegroom knocks three times on the door which is opened by the priest, who fires a gun as a signal for general acclaim and the commencement of the festivities.

Conjugal claims

When a young man of the Todras tribe of Nilgiris, a district of Madras, marries, his brothers have conjugal claims on the bride because she is considered married into the family.

If the bride becomes pregnant a ceremony known as *Pursutpimi* is performed to fix paternity. After a discussion among the potential fathers, the man chosen presents the bride with a symbolic bow and arrow under a kiaz tree, in the presence of an elder.

Any further children are also considered to be those of the man first selected in *Pursutpimi*—including those born after his death—until some other man performs the ceremony.

GETTING TO KNOW YOU *This water-pouring ceremony is aimed at helping a Hindu bride and groom to become better acquainted.*

BELIEFS OF ANCIENT MARINERS
The legends of men before the mast

In the 18th century it was no un-common punishment for a sailor to be given 24 lashes or more for being drunk on duty. Old hands at the game of cheating authority had a word of advice for newcomers: 'Get a crucifix tattooed on your back.' Not only would the bosun's mate flinch from laying his cat into the face of Christ, but the lash itself, it was believed, would cringe away.

Yet in other legends of the sea, Christian symbols, and parsons too, are feared because they bring bad luck.

Faced with the perils and mysteries of the sea, sailors have adopted beliefs from anywhere and in anything that seems to work. Animals, birds, names, even an action as apparently harmless as whistling, can be dire omens at sea.

The beliefs are taken so seriously that the British Admiralty still takes enormous care over the names of ships in the fleet. Reptile names for instance are almost completely banned nowadays. For the Navy has in the past lost four *Vipers*, four *Serpents*, a *Cobra*, an *Adder*, an *Alligator* and a *Crocodile*—as well as a pair of *Snakes*, two *Dragons* and a trio of *Lizards*.

Sailormen have their own religious observances. The salute to the quarter-deck which the sailor makes on coming

DETERRENT TO FLOGGING *Sailors hoped that tattoos of a crucifix would avert the lash.*

aboard has its origin in the time when a crucifix hung there.

But some fishermen will stay ashore for the day if they meet a priest or a nun on the way to harbour. In the Faeroe islands between Norway and Iceland, whale-hunters believe that their huge prey will get away if a boat with a minister aboard sails between them and the shore.

Even reading aloud or quoting phrases from the Bible at sea carries a terrible risk, except during a burial.

As he was marched up to stand beneath the yard-arm gallows in 1707, a con-demned sailor shouted the words of the 109th psalm: 'Let his days be few and let another take his office; let his children be fatherless and his wife a widow; let there be none to extend mercy unto him.'

The ship was the *Association*, the flag-ship of Admiral Sir Cloudesley Shovell. Later the same year the *Association* and two other ships sank off the Scilly Isles with the loss of 2000 men.

According to legend, Sir Cloudesley, the man who had passed sentence on the sailor, was washed ashore unconscious—and buried alive. The woman who found him on the beach of St Mary's Island con-fessed on her deathbed that she had murdered the admiral and hacked off his fingers in order to obtain the ruby and emerald rings he wore.

In the days of sail, dead mariners were believed to be reincarnated in the bodies of petrels and seagulls. If one of these birds appeared over the ship in mid-ocean, it was a sign of storms to come.

The bird that was regarded with the most awe was the huge albatross of the southern seas. To see one meant that a storm was certainly coming.

To kill one brought an eternity of bad luck, as Coleridge recounts in his poem 'The Rime of the Ancient Mariner'.

In 1959 the cargo ship *Calpean Star* had to carry an albatross on its way from the Antarctic to a German zoo. When the ship docked at Liverpool with engine trouble, the crew walked off, claiming that the bird was responsible for a cata-logue of misfortunes on the voyage. Only after the bird died in its cage a day later was the captain able to find another crew to take the *Calpean Star* out of port.

Mentioning rabbits and pigs at sea is also unaccountably taboo. Sailors instead refer to pigs as Grecians or Jacks. Perhaps most curious of all, whistling is banned. The logs of modern liners show that even during the past 50 years, seamen have been disciplined for breaking the taboo.

Whistling was thought to encourage high winds, and was allowed only when the ship was becalmed or shrouded in mist.

Another way to get rid of mist or buy a calm is to throw a coin overboard. When a storm blows up near the Bishop Rock lighthouse off the Scilly Isles, the keepers 'blame' one of their number who has to hurl a coin into the sea.

It has long been believed that a drum owned by Sir Francis Drake possesses strange powers. When he was dying—off the West Indies in 1596—Drake ordered his drum to be sent back to his home, Buckland Abbey near Plymouth, where it hangs still.

Drake vowed on his deathbed that if anyone beat upon it when England was in danger, he would return to defend his country. But the legend has changed down the years. Now, the drum rolls out ghostly warnings on its own.

It is said that the drum gave a growl when Napoleon was brought as a prisoner to Plymouth following the Battle of Waterloo. And it has been heard three times this century: once in 1914 when the First World War started, four years later

DRAKE'S DRUM *The drum is thought to sound by itself when England is in danger.*

aboard the flagship *Royal Oak*, and once in the Second World War, during the retreat from Dunkirk.

In 1918, as the German fleet steamed into Scapa Flow to surrender, a drum began an echoing tattoo somewhere within the *Royal Oak*. Twice messengers were sent from the bridge to discover the source of the noise. The commander himself made a search of the ship. But every man was at his battle station, and no sign of the drummer was ever found.

When *Royal Oak* dropped anchor, the drum's victory roll stopped—as suddenly and mysteriously as it had begun. Drake was at rest once more.

LOOK BACK IN ANGER

The power of the evil eye

People who use the expression 'if looks could kill' are unwittingly reviving the once almost universal belief that the human eye had the power to injure or destroy an enemy. This fear is believed to have arisen from a primitive terror of being watched by wild animals, hostile tribesmen, evil spirits or jealous gods who resented human success.

Before the development of medical science disease and death were often attributed to the evil eye. Young children and animals were particularly vulnerable.

The evil eye was held responsible for male impotence and female frigidity. It was also thought that someone with the evil eye could blight crops.

Men and women with a physical de-

formity who might be suspected of envying their neighbours were considered the most likely possessors of the evil eye. This particularly applied to hunchbacks and dwarfs. Those with a squint, or eyes set at

PROTECTING THE DEAD *Ancient Egyptian coffins bore painted eyes to protect the dead.*

uneven levels, or those whose eyebrows met, were also suspected.

In Africa the Congolese Lugbara tribesmen believe an evil-eyed man can be identified from his squinty eyes and bad-tempered disposition. He should quickly be placated with presents of beer and tobacco.

During the 16th and 17th centuries, when witches were said to destroy their victims by the power of the evil eye, hundreds of women were executed solely on the evidence that someone had died after receiving an angry look. The judges were so fearful of being bewitched when passing sentence that it was not uncommon for the accused to be led into court backwards. Methods of protection against the evil eye—or 'overlooking' as it was called in Britain—took a variety of bizarre forms.

In the Near East and Turkey, passages from the Koran were painted on the outside walls of houses to provide a sacred barrier against the eye's influence. The symbol of the eye, which even today can be seen painted on the bows of fishing boats in some ports of the Mediterranean, was also supposed to counteract the effects.

Bunches of sage were used for protection in Portugal, and garlic was used throughout south-eastern Europe, particularly among the Slavs and Greeks.

The Rwala Bedouins of Northern Arabia carry two marbles wherever they go— one black, for protection by night, one white for daytime insurance.

PROTECTING THE LIVING *Maltese fishing boats have an evil eye painted on their bows— to shield the ship from other evil eyes.*

Throughout 18th-century Europe, red —the symbol of blood and good health— was believed to protect the wearer against the evil eye.

Italian brides covered their heads with a large red veil. In Rumania oxen had red rags tied to their horns. And Scottish crofters tied red ribbons to the tails of their livestock, or bound crosses of wood from the sacred rowan tree with strands of red thread.

Antidote—a hangman's rope

In the days of public executions it was common for a spectator who believed himself to be bewitched to buy a used rope from the hangman and burn it to ashes. These were mixed with cold water and swallowed to offset the dangers of the evil eye.

People who were convinced that their misfortunes were caused by the evil eye often attempted to return the curse to its source by throwing water upon the footprints of the person they suspected.

No one, it seems, was immune from possessing the power of the evil eye. Pope Pius IX (1792–1878) was said to be involuntarily endowed with the ability to kill those upon whom his glance rested.

King Alfonso of Spain was also reputed to have the evil eye. In 1923 he paid an official visit to Italy. Several sailors of the fleet sent to greet him were washed overboard, there was an explosion in one of the submarines, an ancient cannon fired in his honour blew up, killing its crew, and a naval officer with whom the king shook hands collapsed and died shortly afterwards.

During the king's tour of Lake Gleno a dam burst, drowning 50 people and making 500 homeless.

The Italian dictator Benito Mussolini, who was terrified of the evil eye, refused to meet Alfonso personally, and conducted all negotiations through an intermediary.

Similar fears persist today, for at the United Nations some delegates still turn away when they see eye-like designs. Their anxiety has given rise to a story that the peacocks which once roamed the lawns of the UN headquarters in New York were removed to allay the peril of the evil eye. The truth is more prosaic. The climate did not suit the imported peacocks: they died and were never replaced.

WHISTLING UP TROUBLE

The hidden charms—and taboos—in show business

First-night telegrams, congratulating actors on their performances, are usually stuck on dressing-room mirrors. If they turn yellow quickly, it is considered a sign that a production will enjoy a long run.

But on the closure of a show they must be taken down after each actor's last entrance on the final night. Some are torn up, especially if the show has not been a success. Others are kept in the hope that the 'good luck' will carry on.

To many actors, the phrasing of the first-night message is very important. In America, it is considered acceptable to wish an actor a 'great opening' or that he 'knocks the audience for a loop'. But to hope he has 'a good run' is a jinx.

Most actors have a great belief in luck, crediting it with an ability to store itself in an object and re-emerge when required. For instance, if an actor uses soap belonging to a 'lucky' colleague, it is thought that some of the luck may rub off on him. To abandon something lucky, on the other hand, is risky. An actor who leaves soap behind in a dressing room may never be employed again.

Hats and cats for luck

Many actors cherish good-luck charms; talismen or dolls, often associated with a previous good run. The British actor John Mills has a lucky black cat, given to him by the late Sir Noël Coward, which he always keeps in his dressing room at the theatre or film studio.

If something continually brings good luck, its use can turn into a habit. Hollywood star John Wayne, for example, likes to appear with the six-gun he used in his first western, *The Big Trail* (1930). And James Stewart wore the same hat all through his career, even when it began to fall to pieces. He even refused to continue with a film when a director suggested that he should change it.

In the theatre, actions, as well as 'good luck' tokens, are considered important. For instance, though theatre cats are pampered as lucky mascots, it is a very bad sign if one happens to run across the stage during a performance.

While umbrellas and combs are not in themselves unlucky, to open an umbrella or drop a comb on stage is asking for trouble. And if someone is knitting anywhere near the stage or in the wings, the actors must beware.

Some of the most ominous actions take place offstage, often in the dressing room. For example, an actor will rarely look over the shoulder of a colleague into a dressing-room mirror. And to spill the contents of a make-up box is unlucky.

But perhaps the worst omen of all is someone whistling in the dressing room, for this means that one of the cast will soon be out of work.

An actor who inadvertently whistles must either curse loudly and vehemently, or leave the room and knock before re-entering. And anyone who fails to do this spontaneously must be sent out and made to turn round three times before returning.

Actors are not only superstitious on the stage or film set. It is a portent of failure even to try the wrong door of an agent or manager when embarking on a new venture. And because it is considered very bad luck, the last line of a play is not delivered at rehearsals. A smooth-running dress rehearsal is considered unlucky, while one fraught with problems portends a good opening.

As the barrier between the actor and

TRUSTY SIX-SHOOTER *Actor John Wayne prefers always to use the six-gun he had in his first western film.*

his audience, the curtain is highly symbolic, and there are a number of taboos surrounding it. To look out through the curtains is always unlucky.

Unlucky yellow

Curtains which are part of the set must never be yellow. In fact theatrical designers have to avoid yellow whenever they can, because it is an unlucky colour for many actors. Peter Sellers, though, dislikes anyone wearing purple on stage, while English actor Wilfred Hyde White is worried by an actor who wears green.

The fact that peacocks are especially abhorred by actors may be due to their vivid colours, or to an association of the many 'eyes' of a peacock's tail with the 'evil eye'. Whatever the reason, their feathers, and any representation of them or reference to them, are completely taboo on stage.

Anouilh's *Cry of a Peacock* and O'Casey's *Juno and the Paycock* are plays that are said to have had unfortunate histories.

As recently as 1974 bad luck plagued a 'peacock' production which millions of viewers had been following on British television. Union trouble interfered with some BBC productions, and *The Pallisers* series, which had a peacock as its opening screen symbol, had to be taken off with the last two episodes still to run.

THE TRUTH ACCORDING TO MARX

COMEDIAN Groucho Marx has his own, highly individual, interpretations of the many popular superstitions that still survive, both inside and outside show business:

'When a person's nose itches, it's a sign that it should be scratched.

A black cat crossing your path signifies that the animal is going somewhere.

Thirteen at a table is unlucky when the hostess has only twelve chops.

Shaking hands across the table means that two parties are lazy.

Singing before breakfast is a forewarning of a fight with a neighbour—if the neighbour is trying to sleep late.

Throwing salt over the shoulder is likely to give the impression that the man who throws the salt has dandruff.

Recognising the number 13 is a sign that you have been to school.

Finding a four-leaf clover is a sign that you have been down on your hands and knees.

To get out of bed on the wrong side probably means that you have had too much the night before.

To carry a rabbit's foot is a sign that you are a good shot with a gun—or have a friend who is.

When three men get a light off one match it is indicative of the fact that they have only one match or are Scotsmen.'

TAPPING HIS WAY TO VICTORY
Even the greatest sportsmen rely on rites and rituals

The world's tennis crowds had never seen a player quite like the American Art Larsen. As he stood to serve, the gangling, nervous left-hander, perhaps the most superstitious sportsman of all time, would tap the court several times with his foot and his racket. Then he would bounce the ball . . . then tap-tap . . . bounce the ball again . . . tap-tap, tap again—and finally serve.

As he walked about the court between points, Larsen would tap baselines, tramlines, the umpire's chair, the net—almost anything that there was to tap. The crowds of the early 1950s called him 'Tappy' Larsen, and loved every minute of his performances at major tournaments.

Did his superstitions work? In 1950 Larsen became the American singles champion at Forest Hills.

Slow, slow . . .

A South African cricketer, Hugh Tayfield, just before running up to bowl, would repeatedly tap the turf with the toe of each boot. Inexperienced batsmen were driven to distraction by this mannerism and there is little doubt that it helped Tayfield to become his country's most successful slow bowler.

Footballers are notoriously superstitious, not just as individuals, but as entire teams. The Tottenham Hotspur team of London puts great faith in three 'angels'. Three is the club's lucky number and the angels are supporters in fancy dress.

Once on the field, many soccer teams believe that if the captain or centre-forward bounces the ball three times, it will bring luck.

Two caps

Russian international goalkeeper Lev Yashin always took two caps to a match. He wore one and placed the other behind him in the net for luck. He was convinced that this tactic worked and, in fact, in the early 1960s he was the world's foremost goalkeeper.

For sheer pre-match tension, few sports can beat the build-up to a boxing title fight. Possibly to calm their minds, many fighters therefore follow extravagant and eccentric rituals.

Former World Heavyweight Champion Joe Louis always insisted on having his left glove put on and tied before the right one.

Henry Cooper, former British, Commonwealth and European Heavyweight Champion, never polished his boxing boots, following a bout early in his career when he did so and lost. The World Light-Heavyweight Champion of the mid-1960s, Willy Pastrano, used to tie his wedding ring to his left bootlace before each fight as a lucky mascot.

Baseball players have been known to be superstitious about their superstitions: they will not even talk about them. But Joe Dugan's pet eccentricity was there for all to see when he played for the New York Yankees. Dugan, one of the greatest third basemen of all time, would *never* throw the ball directly to the pitcher unless there was a chance of actually putting an opponent out.

Joe DiMaggio began a hitting streak the day after he dated a Broadway chorus girl. The girl became a symbol as DiMaggio's hitting streak continued and he dated her every night. Then one day he went hitless, and a New York newspaper reported: 'Miss X and DiMaggio have come to the parting of the ways.'

Fishy yarn

Azam Khan, the Pakistani who was World Squash Champion four times from 1958 to 1961, believed it was unlucky to wear or use anything new for a championship game. Days beforehand he would start preparing by wearing-in shorts, shirts and shoes, and practising with an ample supply of rackets.

Anglers, too, have long-standing customs. Many will throw back the first catch of the season if it is female, probably in the belief that females are the weaker sex and a bad omen for the rest of the season.

In professional sports, it is sometimes hard to distinguish superstition from a touch of showbusiness. A classic example of this is that for years South African golfer Gary Player wore all-black outfits, even in the hottest of climes. Player insisted that black brought him luck—but there is little doubt that it also made him instantly recognisable to the legions of spectators who followed him.

HANDS OF FATE

The giveaway signs of a seasoned gambler

If a man at a card table sits bolt upright, picking up his cards in a strange way and breathing on them, the chances are that he is a seasoned gambler. For gamblers, with their unswerving belief in Lady Luck, are the most superstitious people of all.

The obsessive gambler who allies superstition to expertise breathes on his cards because, though he may not consciously realise it, he shares the primitive belief that the breath contains the essence of the soul. So by breathing on his cards he is projecting all his powers into them.

Ritual blessings

A true gambler will never cross anything—not even his legs. He will always pick up his cards in the same way. He will give his dice a precautionary rub, performing much the same symbolistic ritual as when he breathed on his cards.

The folklore of gambling is colourful and comprehensive, and enshrined in rules such as these:

He who wins the first game will win the third.
To play cards on a table without a tablecloth is unlucky.
Never play before 6 p.m. on Fridays.
To make a man win, stick a pin in his coat.
If playing for money, walk straight from the table, then make a round turn.

Many gamblers have their own private superstitions and, like those above, they probably owe their origin to someone's experience. But most gamblers' superstitions seem to be merely the result of man's desire to formulate laws—even to govern the one factor that obeys no law: chance.

However, consider the following.

If a gambler plays cards with a cross-eyed man, whether his partner or his opponent, he will lose.
A man who lends money at play will lose, but if he borrows, he will win.

Do cross-eyed men make people nervous? Lending money certainly does. And a nervous gambler is likely to lose. He may also show his nerves, thereby giving substance to some other superstitions.

To drop a card on the floor is a bad omen.
To sing while playing cards is a sign of losing.

People who are worried sometimes relieve their tension by singing. They frequently drop things. Perhaps the superstition that says it all is: to get into a passion or bad temper when playing cards will mean more bad luck, for the demon of bad luck always follows a passionate, evil-tempered player.

The gruesome superstition at Monte Carlo that after a suicide all those playing against the bank will win perhaps reflects a loss of concentration by the croupiers. Whether there is a psychological explanation or not, there is always a headlong rush to exploit the tragic news.

SMOKE SIGNALS OVER ROME

The puff that means 'Long live the Pope'

When a new pope is elected, the eyes of the world are focused on Rome. Millions of people, Catholics and non-Catholics alike, anxiously await the cardinals' decision which is formulated in a ceremony wrapped in secrecy and age-old custom.

No television cameras scan the ballot chamber, no reporters canvass the opinions of the voters. No one outside knows who the successful candidate is until the tell-tale plume of white smoke, signifying a decisive result, puffs from an iron chimney in the Vatican. Then a cardinal proclaims the name of the new pope from a balcony to the waiting crowd in the square below.

A period of from 15 to 18 days after the death of the old pope is devoted to the obsequies in the Basilica of St Peter's. During this time the cardinals—the senior prelates of the Roman Catholic hierarchy —will have been assembling in Rome from all over the world.

Then begins their solemn conclave, the series of secret discussions and votes which will eventually determine which of them is to wear the Fisherman's Ring, symbol of authority of the man to whom 683 million Roman Catholics owe obedience.

SECRET BALLOT *Cardinals have traditionally met and talked for days behind sealed doors before voting for a new pope.*

BURNING QUESTION *Smoke from this chimney relays the news. A separate alarm system informs the Vatican Press Corps of the decision.*

The ring is usually made of gold, and set with a precious stone—a new ring for each new pope. The tradition of the Fisherman's Ring is many centuries old, though it is not known who was the first pope to wear it.

To preserve the security of the conclave, the doors of the meeting place are walled up, and any necessary communication with the outside is by means of closely guarded turntable boxes in the walls which enable messages, food and so forth to be passed in or out without the people involved seeing one another. As the voting goes on, the ballot papers are counted by three scrutineers, chosen from the cardinals and changed for each vote.

A ballot is indecisive unless it gives a candidate a clear majority of two-thirds plus one vote. Otherwise the ballot papers are mixed with wet straw and burnt, producing the black smoke which signals: no result.

Finally, often after many days, the cardinals will give the necessary decisive majority to one of their number. Only then are the papers mixed with dry straw and burnt. Then the excited cry will be raised in St Peter's Square: 'White smoke! Long live the Pope!'

The traditional account is that wet and dry straw is still used for the ceremony. However, there were complaints in 1958 when the election of Pope John XXIII was greeted with a tiny, greyish puff of smoke. During the election of Pope Paul VI in 1963, it is said that the cardinals bowed to the demands of Press and television and used black and white smoke bombs supplied by the Italian army.

Although the smoke tradition goes back for centuries, it is only recently that any significance has been given to the colour. In the past it was the volume of smoke that counted. A thick cloud meant no decision. But when the people of Rome spotted a faint wisp, they knew they had a new Vicar of Christ.

HOMAGE TO A DEAD QUEEN

IN THE Portuguese city of Coimbra, a macabre ceremony took place in the late summer of 1360. On the king's orders, the highest dignitaries of the land came forward one by one and kissed the hand of a corpse seated upon a throne.

It was the body of the Castilian Princess Inês de Castro, beloved mistress of the newly crowned King Pedro of Arragon (right). Inês had gone to Portugal in 1342 as lady-in-waiting to Pedro's wife. Pedro was then heir to the throne, and when he fell in love with her, his father, King Alfonso, feared intrigue and had her beheaded.

For the time being Pedro was obliged to suppress his grief and rage. But on becoming king five years later, he had the hearts torn out of her assassins. And he made the court do obeisance to her corpse as Queen of Portugal.

EXIT LINES

Rituals that were designed to stop the dead returning

Man has always been of two minds about death. On one side is the bright figure of St Peter at the gates of heaven; on the other the dark spectre of the Grim Reaper.

Funeral ceremonies have always reflected both images. Some people have laid offerings in the graves of their loved ones to make their life in the next world easier—others have put stakes through their hearts to make sure that they never came back.

In the East, one of the earliest ways of satisfying both requirements was cremation. The soul or spirit was helped on its way up to heaven by the flames, while the body was destroyed so that it could not haunt the earth.

Soul destroying

But in Christian countries, cremation was outlawed for centuries because it ran counter to the doctrine of bodily resurrection. That was why medieval witches were burnt at the stake—to destroy their bodies *and* their souls.

In Britain, cremation began to gain acceptance less than 100 years ago, when

PIONEER OF CREMATION *Dr William Price, an eccentric Welshman, paved the way for modern crematoria.*

Dr William Price, an eccentric Welshman who believed himself to be an arch-Druid, cremated his own son. Price was prosecuted in Cardiff in 1884, and his acquittal —because the judge ruled that cremation was legal, provided it caused no nuisance to others—paved the way for modern crematoria.

Burial, on the other hand, was designed to preserve the body, either because of the Christian belief in the Day of Judgment or because the physical body was thought to be needed in the after-life.

The internal organs of Egyptian pharaohs were carefully removed and embalmed separately from their bodies. Then, before the tomb was finally sealed, they were placed in the coffin beside the mummy; this was to ensure that the dead king would be physically complete in the next world.

It has been common for centuries to lay possessions to rest along with the dead. And archaeologists have been able to tell from the gifts that were chosen what sort of after-life was expected.

The Egyptians expected a rich and luxurious life after death, so they buried ornaments and household objects with their dead. The Vikings could not imagine a heaven in which there was no fighting, so they buried their heroes with weapons for use in Valhalla.

The gifts also had the purpose of making the dead person so content with his new world that he would not be tempted to return to the old one. Wreaths of flowers were meant originally not only to honour the dead with beauty, but to act as a magic circle to contain the departed soul and stop it wandering.

For similar reasons, ancient Greeks laid a coin in the grave to pay the fare for the ferry across the Styx to Hades. In Scandinavia, shoes were bound to the feet of a corpse to ease the long tramp to the next world. And America's Zuni Indians bury bread so that the dead warrior will not go hungry and come back looking for food.

In extreme cases, the custom has been extraordinarily expensive—for example, the fabulous treasure buried with the Egyptian boy-king Tutankhamun—while others were positive holocausts. At the funerals of ancient Scythian kings like

Darius and Arianthus (*c*. 550 BC), scores of wives, slaves and horses were buried alive to serve them in the after-life. Only 100 years ago, many Hindu wives accepted the custom of *suttee*—throwing themselves on to the funeral pyres of their husbands so that death did not part them. The British in India were still trying to stamp the custom out early this century, although in some states it has been banned by law since 1829.

The Chinese have a much cheaper way of sending possessions and valuables through the vale of death. They burn paper replicas of them at the funeral.

The Tibetans, who believe in reincarnation, put as much stress on the 'art' of dying as on that of living. When a person dies, an elaborate ritual is performed that involves reading the *Bardo Thödol*, the Tibetan Book of the Dead, to the corpse. The idea is to instruct the dead person in the mysteries that lie ahead before his return to earth in a new life.

Safely below ground

Tombstones also had originally the dual purpose of consigning the dead to the care of a god, and of keeping them safely below ground. The cross has been used since the earliest times to mark graves, as an alternative to the ring cross of the ancient sun-worshippers. Later, when the cross became the central symbol of Christianity, the ring cross was adopted as the symbol of the early Celtic Church. The marking of graves at all, however, was mostly confined to the rich people

until the latter years of the 16th century.

Even the alignment of the grave has been important in speeding the departed soul on its way. Some old Welsh tribes used to bury their dead upright so that their souls could more easily ascend to heaven.

Often, Christian graves are laid east to west, so that they point towards Jerusalem. In Japan, however, the dead are laid with their heads towards the north— and the superstition has persisted so strongly that even now Japanese travellers sometimes use a compass to avoid the unlucky position at bedtime.

Death has not always been seen as the great leveller of men. In some churches in Scotland and northern England the northern part of the cemetery was reserved for criminals because it was considered unlucky, and the east was set aside for the saintly because it was closest to the Holy Land. The gentry got the southern end, and the common people huddled in the west.

Suicides have been particularly harshly treated. As self-murderers, they were banned from being buried in consecrated ground, and until 1824 in England— when the law was changed—a suicide was buried at a crossroads with a stake through his heart. This was because it was believed that people buried outside a churchyard would come back as malign ghosts to torment the living, unless they were tethered to one spot by a stake. Even if the spirit did get free, it would be confused by the choice of roads.

THE COLOURS OF DEATH

DEATH IS associated with different colours in different societies. In the West, mourners traditionally wear black. In China, white has always been acceptable, because it represents happiness and prosperity in the next world. Gypsies used to wear red at funerals to symbolise physical life and energy. Red was also the colour representing death in the Celtic world and foretelling disaster. Moslems believe that the souls of the just assume the form of white birds. This idea spread to Europe in the Middle Ages, and mourners in England wore white for centuries before black became the fashion.

To the Chinese, the hereafter is thought of as a new life of happiness and prosperity, so at funerals, white has always been an acceptable colour to wear.

THE SCREAMING SKULLS

Strange beliefs in the power of the death's head

Among primitive people of many races the human skull was regarded with superstitious awe. They believed that the skull housed the soul.

Head-hunters preserved the skulls of their fallen enemies as trophies of war. Scandinavian warriors drank from skulls, hoping to acquire the martial valour of their foes. The ancient Celts decorated their shrines with skulls.

Widows in the Trobriand Islands of Papua impaled their dead husbands' skulls on poles as a kind of keep-out sign, or sometimes used them as pots.

Skulls have always had an important role in witchcraft and black magic. They figured prominently in an English trial in 1612 in which Anne Chattox, head of a Lancashire family of witches, was accused of digging up three skulls from a churchyard to use in some ritual or demoniac recipe. She was hanged.

But skulls have not always been just the passive instruments of the sorcerer's craft. At Wardley Hall in Lancashire, the skull of a 16th-century Catholic martyr, Father Ambrose Barlow, is on view at the head of the staircase, and an old legend warns that should it be disturbed in any way it will emit blood-curdling screams.

In the 17th century, a girl named Anne Griffiths, who lived at Burton Agnes Hall in Yorkshire, was attacked and savagely beaten by robbers. As she lay dying from her injuries, she expressed the curious wish that her head should be buried in the home she had loved so well. She was, nevertheless, buried in the village churchyard.

After the funeral, terrifying groans and the sound of mysterious crashes and slamming doors were heard in the house. The dead girl's skull was exhumed and bricked up in a wall off the staircase. Since then, Burton Agnes Hall has been at peace.

Broken promise

The most curious of all skull legends in Britain is that of the screaming skull of Bettiscombe Manor, in Dorset, ancestral home of the Pinney family. The story goes that during the 18th century, a Pinney who had been living in the West Indies returned home with a negro slave. Shortly afterwards the slave died, after making his master vow that he would be buried in his homeland, the Caribbean island of Nevis. But the squire apparently broke his promise and the negro was buried in the local churchyard. Soon, passers-by were terrified by blood-curdling screams from the grave. The present owners of the manor, however, Mr and Mrs Michael Pinney, believe that the slave's dying wish was fulfilled—and that the legend was largely the invention of Judge J. S. Udal, a 19th-century antiquarian.

Mrs Pinney says: 'We believe the skull was found in a Celtic shrine behind the manor and brought into the house as a good-luck charm around 1690 to 1694. Judge Udal visited the island of Nevis in 1897, where he heard the tale of the slave who had gone to England. On his return, he assumed the skull belonged to the negro and read a paper about it to the local antiquarian society.'

In fact, when the skull was examined by an expert it was said to be that of a girl and was 2000 years old.

Yet the legend remains that if it is ever removed from the house, the skull will scream, and the person who moves it will die within the year.

UNHAPPY SKULL *Although forensic evidence refutes the original legend, respect for the skull's power lingers on at Bettiscombe.*

THE MOUSE THAT DREW A MAP

Divine guidance via the animal kingdom

A group of generals gathered round a map spread on a table in their headquarters, anxiously following the progress of a mouse. Its feet had been daubed with ink so that every movement traced out a trail on the map. It was not some impish soldiers' game, but a desperately serious conference on military strategy.

The year was 1796, and the Austrian campaign against Napoleon was going badly. The generals were worried and at a loss to know what to do. In desperation they decided to resort to a weapon as old as war itself—the use of a living creature to obtain guidance or knowledge of the future. But the mouse failed to indicate a way to victory, and Napoleon annihilated the Austrian forces.

Mice, cats, cockerels, animal bones, vegetables, even parts of the human body —all have been used in methods of divination throughout the world. Superstitious people who see a black cat as a good-luck omen if it crosses their path at the start of a journey are using a simple version, dating back thousands of years.

The ancient Greeks, always careful to ensure that the gods were on their side in any important venture, would draw a circle and divide it into 24 sections, each containing a letter of the alphabet and a grain of corn. A cockerel was put in the centre of the circle. The order in which he pecked up the corn spelt out the message of the gods.

People who sometimes say 'I'm certain of such-and-such a thing; I feel it in my bones', might be surprised to know that, probably quite unconsciously, they are claiming similar powers to those of primitive seers. For this is a saying that has survived the custom of strewing animal bones on the ground and studying what is revealed by the way they fall.

It is also reminiscent of a divination method still practised by the tribal medicine man in Guatemala, who addresses his question to a spirit supposed to live in the calf of his right leg. The spirit residing within signals 'yes' to a question by causing the calf to twitch. If nothing happens, the spirit is saying 'no'.

Not only have nature's products been used to search for the secrets of the future, but as a key to present truth as well.

Hence the use of a few peas to decide whether a person accused of theft was guilty or innocent. In parts of Europe in the Middle Ages the peas would be spread on a table under an upside-down basin, and all the suspects made to walk up to the table in turn. The peas were the key witnesses in this identity parade. They would, so it was held, bounce up and down when the guilty person stood near.

Handmaiden of justice

This curious belief in pea-power is no great surprise, for magic was the handmaiden of justice for hundreds of years, even in the western world. Britain and most European countries were much preoccupied with witches in the 16th and 17th centuries, and the methods by which suspects were 'tried' often savoured of witchcraft.

One favourite means of settling whether a suspected witch was guilty was to tie her up and throw her into a river or pond. If she sank, she was quickly rescued and declared innocent. But if she floated, she was condemned, for it was held that water would reject a child of Satan. Records do not show how many 'Innocents' drowned.

Fire and water have always been held in special veneration as instruments for reading the future. In ancient Rome, poppy seeds were thrown into a fire and secrets disclosed by the way they burnt. In the modern world there are still homes where a coffin-shaped cinder shooting from an open coal fire is seen as a warning of an impending death in the family.

The water method of foretelling the future has usually been based on the simple principle underlying the witches' ordeal: sink or swim. A custom among the Populuca Indians of Mexico, for instance, is to throw tiny balls of incense into jars of water. If the balls float, the answer to a particular question is 'yes'.

Until fairly recently, it was a widespread practice in the New England states of America for a girl to read her romantic future by writing her boyfriends' names on separate slips of paper and ducking them in bathtubs. The first slip to rise and float would be the one bearing the name of the young man she would marry.

301

SECRETS OF THE TAROT

The future revealed at the turn of a card

The tarot is a pack of 78 elaborately decorated cards that can be used, like modern playing cards, for games or for fortune-telling and divining. They were probably introduced to Europe by gypsies in the 14th century and are believed to be the forerunners of modern packs, although their true origin is unknown.

The 78 cards are divided into two arcanas (from arcanum, meaning 'mystery'): the major arcana of 22 trump cards and the minor, of 56 cards, itself consisting of four suits of 14—Cups, Coins, Swords and Wands. These suits may represent four classes of medieval society: cups or chalices for the clergy, coins for merchants, swords for the nobility and wands or staffs for the peasantry.

As in modern packs, there are ten numbered cards in each suit, but there are four face cards—Knave, Knight, Queen and King. The major arcana consists of ornate picture cards—although designs vary from country to country—depicting a series of symbols. The meanings of the ones pictured above are:

Top row, left to right: folly and extravagance; subtlety; mystery; fruitfulness; power; marriage; love and beauty; providence; courage; prudence, but also treason; destiny or success.

Bottom row: rightness; wisdom or sacrifice; destruction; moderation; violence; calamity; loss or privation; hidden enemies and terror; happiness; outcome or renewal; assured success.

Some believers in the supernatural think that the whole pack represents a system of philosophy that embraces the

THE LOVERS. THE CHARIOT. STRENGTH. THE HERMIT. WHEEL of FORTUNE.

THE STAR. THE MOON. THE SUN. JUDGEMENT. THE WORLD.

true nature of man, the universe and God. They believe they can gain insights into these mysteries by setting out the cards and meditating on them; that the fall of the cards is not random but guided by unseen forces.

More popularly, however, the cards are used for fortune-telling, and there are several established ways of setting them out. One of the most widely used is to shuffle the cards, then lay them out in a pattern known as the Tree of Life, based on an ancient Hebrew symbol.

The cards are placed in ten piles of seven, face downwards, and the rest are put aside. Each of the ten piles represents a different aspect of the inquirer's life, and each card has a meaning relating to that particular aspect. As each card is upturned, its symbolism is interpreted in relation to its position in the pile in which it falls—Health, Knowledge and so on.

KEY TO THE TAROT *In the Tree of Life pattern, the ten piles refer to: 1. Intelligence, 2. Creativity, 3. Knowledge, 4. Virtue, 5. Physical and mental strength, 6. Imagination, 7. Love, 8. The arts, 9. Health, 10. Home life.*

These are, however, general categories and other interpretations are applied by tarot users.

303

ANIMALS THAT BROKE THE LAW

They had to answer for their crimes in court

Punishing animals that break the law is a practice as old as the Bible. According to the Book of Exodus: 'If an ox gore a man or a woman that they die, then the ox shall surely be stoned.'

It was not only four-footed beasts that fell foul of the law. Offenders have included horseflies, moles, caterpillars, locusts, snails—and a Russian goat which was banished to Siberia at the end of the 17th century.

The first recorded 'animal' trial was in AD 864, when the Diet of Worms decreed that a hive of bees which had stung a man to death should be suffocated.

St Bernard was preaching in a French church in the 11th century when a swarm of flies irritated him with their buzzing. He excommunicated them on the spot.

Next day the flies had to be shovelled out of the church in heaps—killed, it is suspected, by a severe overnight frost.

More often it was the larger animals that were brought to justice. In 1639 a horse was sentenced to die at Dijon in France for throwing its rider and causing his death.

Birds, too, were not immune from the law. In 1471 a cockerel of Basle, in Switzerland, was found guilty of laying an egg 'in defiance of natural law'. It was condemned to death and burnt at the stake as 'a devil in disguise'.

Murderous swine

Pigs roamed the village streets in France in the Middle Ages—a freedom which the law sometimes held them to have abused. One was hanged in 1394, in Normandy, for eating a child. A sow and her six piglets were accused of a similar crime in 1547. The sow was executed, but her family were spared because of their youth and the bad example set by their mother.

One of the most merciful sentences was that pronounced on some moles which were the subject of criminal proceedings at Stelvio, in northern Italy, in 1519. The moles were accused of damaging crops 'by burrowing, so that neither grass nor green thing could grow'. They were required 'to show cause for their conduct by pleading their exigencies and distress'.

They did not turn up at court in answer to the summons and were sentenced in their absence to exile. But the court, in its mercy, promised them safe conduct 'and an additional respite of 14 days to all those which are with young, and to such as are yet in their infancy'.

Animal trials were normally conducted according to established legal procedure, and some lawyers made a reputation as defence counsel. The trial of a bear which had ravaged some German villages in 1499 was delayed for over a week for legal arguments, on a submission that it had a right to be tried by its peers—in this case a jury of fellow-bears.

Counsel for the rats

Bartholomew Chassenée, a French lawyer, made a reputation with his skilful defence of some rats which had destroyed a barley crop in 1521. When his clients failed to appear, he successfully argued that the summons was invalid: it should have been served on *all* the rats in the district.

When the new summons too was ignored, Chassenée pleaded that 'evilly disposed cats' belonging to the prosecutors were intimidating them, and demanded a cash guarantee that the cats would not molest the rats on their way to court. The prosecution refused to give this undertaking, and the case was dismissed.

Animals have appeared in court not only as felons in the dock but also as witnesses in murder trials. In Savoy in the 17th century it was believed that God would given an animal or bird the power of speech, rather than allow a murderer to escape justice. So, if a man accused of committing a murder in his own house swore his innocence in front of his own domestic animals and they made no protest, then he was acquitted.

One of the strangest 'animal' cases was that of the Italian caterpillars which were asked to appear in court in 1659 on charges of trespassing and wilful damage to property. A copy of the summons was nailed to a tree in each of the five districts where the damage had occurred.

The accused were asked to return to the woodlands and refrain from destroying the crops. The court in fairness conceded the caterpillars' right to enjoy life, liberty and the pursuit of happiness, provided that their behaviour did not

CRIME AND PUNISHMENT *A pig, dressed in human clothes and tied to a wheel, is publicly flogged. This was a scene not uncommon in medieval France, where free-roaming pigs sometimes broke the law.*

'destroy or impair the happiness of man'.

Some 50 years later, a community of Franciscan monks in the Brazilian province of Maranhão complained that termites were eating their food and gnawing their furniture. The termites, summoned to explain their conduct, were allocated a lawyer who made an eloquent speech on their behalf. He pointed out that the termites were the original owners of the land, and pleaded that their industry put the monks to shame.

After a long trial the judge arrived at a compromise verdict, which was read aloud to the termite hills. The judgment was, in effect, that both parties were bound over to be of good behaviour: the termites should stop worrying the monks, and the monks on their part, should not harass the resident termites.

As recently as the 19th century, in the same spirit of live and let live, American families plagued by rats would send them a polite letter asking them to leave. All proper courtesy was observed by coating the letter with butter and treacle and 'posting' it in the rats' warren.

Trials of animals survived in Europe into the present century. The most recent was in Switzerland in 1906, when two brothers and their dog were tried for murder. The men were sentenced to life imprisonment. The dog was condemned to death.

And as recently as 1974 in Libya, a dog was tried for the crime of biting a human, and sentenced to a month's imprisonment on a diet of bread and water. It served its sentence and was released: justice was seen to have been done.

AFFLUENT SOCIETY IN THE DESERT

If leisure has a value, the Bushmen are well off

In today's world, unlimited leisure is a luxury which most people attain only after a lifetime's hard work. Yet there are communities which provide ample leisure for people of all ages.

The people who have time on their hands are those who are in many ways still living in the Stone Age—the Hadza of Tanzania, the pygmies of Central Africa, some of the more inaccessible tribes of South American Indians, the

Nuniamut eskimos, and a few other remote pockets of hunter-gatherers.

All told, they number only about 0·001 per cent of the world's 4000 million population. Yet if affluence is measured by the amount of leisure a society affords its ordinary people, they are the most affluent on earth.

According to the 'leisure' theory, the bulk of the human race took a wrong turning about 12,000 years ago, when

305

agriculture was invented, somewhere between northern Greece and Iran.

Once leisurely hunter-gatherers, they became farmers, obliged to accept the discipline of working to a timetable imposed by the seasons and the needs of their animals. The Bible makes the point, when it records Adam's banishment from Eden for eating the forbidden fruit:

And you shall eat the plants of the field.
In the sweat of your face you shall eat bread
till you return to the ground . . .

Food was there for the picking in Eden —as it usually is for the world's most primitive peoples. The Bushmen of Africa's Kalahari Desert, for example, can gather all they need in an average 'working week' of 12-19 hours. Research has shown that one group lives mainly on mongono nuts, which give them a daily protein diet equal to 14 oz. of steak. Other edible plants and animals are abundant.

They even run their own form of welfare state. The young and the old are not expected to work, but are supported by the 20-60 age group.

In Tanzania, the Hadza tribe have an even easier time. It has been calculated that the average Hadza spends less than two hours a day finding food. The men spend most of their time gambling.

It may be argued that the hunter-gatherer way of life is precarious, and that a primitive community can be wiped out by a few lean years. But the facts suggest that in all except the very worst droughts, primitive peoples are better equipped to survive than their more advanced and harder-working neighbours.

Famine relief

In Botswana, on the fringes of the Kalahari, a quarter of a million cattle died in 1966, in one of the worst droughts ever to afflict southern Africa. Starvation faced remote farming tribes which were beyond the reach of a United Nations relief programme. Then the Bushmen, who plant no crops and raise no cattle, came to their aid. Their womenfolk showed the farmers' wives where to find the wild plants and nuts on which the Bushmen lived. Faced with a crisis, the agriculturalists survived by returning to mankind's oldest way of life.

DEATH—OR HONOUR?

FROM A rickety tower of bamboo and vines more than 90 ft tall, men of the Pentecost Islands in the South Pacific dive into the air, with liana creepers tied around their ankles. It is a semi-religious ceremony called the Gol, and is intended to demonstrate the divers' courage.

The nearer to the ground a man can swing, the greater his courage. The lianas are cut so that the diver will swing only inches from the ground.

Early in 1974 the Queen, the Duke of Edinburgh and other members of the British royal family were present at a Gol ceremony when one of the divers' vines snapped. The man broke his back and died later.

All that saves a native from certain death are liana vines tied to his ankles. Sometimes the vines stretch and the diver crashes to the ground.

TOP HAT, WHITE FACE — AND SKULL

The dread ritual of voodoo

For hours on end the ritual chants are repeated to the incessant beat of the wood and skin drums. The rhythms become faster and faster. Perspiring dancers, visible in the night by a glowing fire and candles in the forest clearing, are exhausted. But still they whirl around, arms flailing, eyes glazed with excitement, mouths contorted with exertion and ecstasy.

Suddenly, all activity ceases. Only the flames from the fire and candles flicker. A figure in black clothes and wearing a top hat emerges from the shadows of the trees. His face is painted white, and in his hands are a rod and a skull.

He lifts his head up and screams a name into the night: 'Baron Samedi, Baron Samedi.' The drums end their silence. The dancers spark into action. The chants continue their weird message.

Lord of the underworld

This is how a tourist would see a voodoo ritual on one of a dozen islands in the Caribbean, in some parts of Brazil or in certain areas of the Deep South in the United States.

The contortions of the dancers are caused by the voodoo gods possessing their subjects. The man in the hat is the high priest, and the name he has screamed is that of the lord of the underworld, king of the voodoo cemetery spirits.

The word voodoo comes from the African word *vodun*, which means sacred object, spirit or god. It was taken to Haiti by African slaves from Guinea and Dahomey in West Africa.

Voodoo is a blend of beliefs derived from the West African religious cults, Catholicism and the debased ceremonial magic of the grimoires, or textbooks, of ritual magic in France of the 18th century.

The wood and skin used in the drums during the rite, in which Baron Samedi's name is shrieked, are primarily symbolic of resurrection. Such is the hypnotic effect of this frenzied worship that participants have later been genuinely unable to remember what happened.

One of the more gruesome facets of voodooism is belief in zombies, or the walking dead. Such 'beings' are very real to many of Haiti's superstitious population. They believe that a magician can restore the dead to life—as slaves. The zombie belief made many converts during the great labour shortage in Haiti's sugar plantations in 1918. To cash in, sorcerers were alleged to have exhumed corpses, revived them and sold them as slaves.

But some authorities believe that these 'slaves' were people who had been drugged into a coma, taken for dead, buried, then dug up again and revived with other drugs. Before selling their victims, the sorcerers first cut out their tongues, so that they could not reveal their origins. The practice was so widespread that a law was introduced treating the administration of soporific drugs as murder. Several so-called sorcerers were allegedly tried and hanged.

A form of community 'devil dancing', still practised in some remote villages in southern India, seems akin to the dark rites of voodoo. But it has only one distinct purpose—to 'charm' away the dreaded disease of smallpox.

People infected by smallpox were believed to be transformed into devils, a superstition strengthened by the hideous pock marks and delirium—characteristic symptoms of the disease.

Professional devil dancers are hired by families to induce the 'devil' to switch to one of the dancers. These 'exorcists' are people who have developed immunity by contracting smallpox and surviving.

Mask with tusks

The dancers usually wear a costume of leaves and a brass mask with tusks, and features exaggerating the symptoms of smallpox. They drink large quantities of a locally brewed strong liquor called arrack, and dance with violent contortions to the beat of drums.

At the climax of the dance, the chief dancer severs the head of a goat with his sword—and drinks the blood gushing from the animal's neck. Other dancers will bite off the heads of cockerels, gyrating with the birds still dangling from their clenched jaws.

Once the dancers believe they are possessed by the 'devil', they run off into the countryside—taking the disease away with them.

FIREWALKERS OF THE WORLD

Is pain banished by religious ecstasy?

The mastery of man over flames has for many centuries been an essential part of many religious and magical rites. Holy men in Fiji and Sri Lanka and even in the Balkans traditionally have the power to walk unharmed and without flinching across red-hot stones or coals.

On the tiny Fijian island of Beqa, the gift of firewalking was, according to legend, granted to Tui-na-iviqalati, a prince and leader of the islanders, who caught an eel which transformed itself into the god Tuimolawai.

The god begged to be spared, and promised to make his captor into the greatest fisherman or warrior. The prince refused. He was already both these things.

The god then offered him immunity from fire. The pact was sealed. A pit was dug and lined with stones which were heated by a fire which burnt for four days and nights. Tuimolawai invited the prince to lie on the stones and cover himself in fire to achieve complete immunity. Tui-na-iviqalati, not trusting the god, replied that he would be content merely to walk on the glowing stones.

Firewalking at Beqa is performed by the priest, called an *mbete* and his novitiates. The *mbete* is said to be a direct descendant of Tui-na-iviqalati.

A 15–20 ft diameter pit is dug, usually 4–5 ft deep. A great pile of logs and stones is placed in it, and as the logs burn the stones sink into a compact layer. When all is complete, the *mbete* tests the stones by scattering dried leaves. They instantly explode in flame. The stones are ready.

The *mbete* then leads the firewalkers slowly over and around the glowing stones and they emerge unscathed.

A similar ceremony takes place annually at a small fishing village north of Colombo in Sri Lanka. There, beside an old Hindu temple, a pit is filled with coals so hot that the men tending the fire have to douse themselves with water.

The walkers are then led to the pit by a priest who is first to cross it. He does so with unhurried dignity. The procession follows—some of its members carrying children—and moves across the coals at a rather faster pace . . . without mishap.

Another similar ceremony is performed every year in some villages of southern India, notably at Udaipur. Once the fire-pit is prepared—usually 15 ft by 6 ft and 3 ft deep—the heat makes it impossible for spectators to approach closer than 30 ft.

In the Balkans, a Greek sect called the Anastenaria practises firewalking to honour the feast day—May 21—of St Constantine and St Helena.

Western science can offer no rational explanation as to why firewalkers should not be badly burnt. Doctors examined firewalkers in Fiji and Sri Lanka. The soles were not burnt, and they still had normal sensitivity.

It seems that the walkers are able, as a result of long religious training, to put themselves into a profound trance, in which they feel no pain and need fear no harm. In this case, the explanation could be the simplest and oldest of all—faith.

INTO THE FLAMES *Western science can offer no rational explanation why firewalkers should not be burnt. Perhaps faith is the answer.*

THE THROW-AWAY SOCIETY

To demonstrate their wealth, the Kwakiutl Indians destroyed it

In most societies the world has known, amassing wealth and worldly goods has been a sure passport to status. But less than 100 years ago, there existed in Canada a society in which a man's social standing was decided in exactly the opposite way—by how spectacularly he could ruin himself.

This extreme example of the throw-away society flourished down the North-west coast of Canada and America from the mid-19th century until well into the 20th, reaching its peak among the Kwakiutl Indians of Vancouver Island. Their chiefs publicly burnt food, blankets, canoes and ornaments in the ceremony of potlatch, a word which means 'giving'.

The Indians of the North-west lived in a society obsessed by rank, and would arrange elaborate potlatch feasts to mark any significant event.

The birth of a chief's heir, the marriage of an important man, a dispute about who should be a tribe's next chief—all of these were celebrated or settled at a potlatch, with feasting, speechmaking and gasps of astonishment at the more spectacular examples of conspicuous waste.

The American traveller and scholar Franz Boas described a potlatch among the Kwakiutls in the 1890s, which began with gallons of precious oil being poured liberally on to a fire. Then a chief called Nolis outdid his rival by throwing on to the fire seven canoes and 400 blankets. There was such a blaze, said Boas, that the great cedarwood feasting hall had all its roof boards singed, and was nearly burnt to the ground.

At some earlier potlatches, human lives were sacrificed. But even the beheading of a slave did not bring a man as much honour as breaking up a copper plaque.

These decorated plaques, beaten from lumps of ore, were for the Indians the highest and most desired forms of wealth. Individual plaques were given names, and a chief who destroyed one earned enough respect to last him for the rest of his life.

One famous Kwakiutl copper, which went by the appropriate name of 'Causing Destitution', was almost beyond price. To buy it would cost 20 canoes, 20 slaves, 10 smaller plaques, 20 lynx skins, 20 marmot skins, 20 mink blankets. The list was endless.

Chief Tlatilitla ensured his supremacy among the Kwakiutls by breaking up such a plaque and giving the pieces to two rivals. The first man collapsed and died on the spot, unable to live with the humiliation of not being able to return a gift of like value. The other lived on for six months in misery and seclusion until he, too, died of shame.

Wasteful though the potlatch ceremony may have seemed to outsiders, at least it was an improvement on the bloody inter-tribal wars of earlier years. The Kwakiutls, once known for their relentless ferocity and skill in battle, described themselves in the days of potlatch as 'fighting with wealth'.

The custom may well have developed as a kind of famine relief system, through which, in lean years, tribes who were not so hard hit would give food and blankets to those in distress. The 'haves' would gain prestige because of their generosity, and the 'have-nots' receiving the gifts would lose status. But at least no one would starve.

DIAMOND OF DOOM

A jewel that drove men mad

In the Smithsonian Institution in Washington lies the priceless Hope Diamond. Its blue rays flicker from an ice-cool heart. It seems harmless. Yet this cold and brilliant gem has a history of such blood and passion that more than 20 deaths have been blamed on its impassive beauty.

Across three centuries, kings and paupers, thieves and courtesans, have looked upon its opulence—and been driven mad.

Its first victim, according to legend, was a Hindu priest who fell under its spell 500 years ago, soon after it was mined on the Kistna River in south-west India. He stole it from the forehead of an Indian temple idol. But he was caught and put to death by torture.

The diamond turned up in Europe in 1642 in the hands of a French trader-smuggler named Jean Baptiste Tafernier. He made enough money from selling it to buy himself a title and an estate. Tafernier's son got so badly into debt through gambling that the trader was forced to sell all he had gained. Bankrupt, Tafernier headed back to India to remake his fortune—and was torn to death by a pack of wild dogs.

The gem reappeared in the possession of the French king, Louis XIV, who had it cut from its original 112·5 carats down to 67·5 carats. Nicolas Fouquet, a government official who borrowed it for a state ball, was convicted in 1665 of embezzlement, and imprisoned for the rest of his life. Louis himself, the Sun King, died a broken and detested man as his much vaunted empire crumbled in a series of military catastrophes.

Ignorant of the evil that they had added to their crown jewels, three more of the French royal family were to die.

The Princess de Lamballe, who wore it regularly, was beaten to death by a mob. Louis XVI and his queen, Marie Antoinette, who had inherited it, died on the guillotine.

Then, in 1792, while post-revolutionary Paris was still in turmoil, the diamond vanished again . . . for nearly 40 years. The gap left plenty of room for legends. A French jeweller, Jacques Celot, is said to have gloated over its beauty—until he went insane and killed himself. A Russian prince, Ivan Kanitovski, gave it to his Parisian mistress—then shot her dead, and was later murdered himself. Even Catherine the Great of Russia is believed to have worn the stone before she died of apoplexy.

It was only rediscovered for certain after a Dutch diamond cutter sheared it down to its present weight of 44·5 carats —and committed suicide when his son stole it from him.

The jewel bounced on from hand to bloody hand across Europe—and to Henry Thomas Hope, a very wealthy Irish banker who bought it for just £30,000, and gave it its modern name. His grandson later died penniless.

In 1908, the Turkish Sultan Abdul Hamid bought it for $400,000. He gave it to his wife Subaya, then stabbed her. A year later he lost his throne. The jinxed jewel moved back west to America, where it was bought for $154,000 by business tycoon Ned McLean in 1911.

Over the next 40 years, his young son, Vincent, was run down by a car; McLean was financially ruined and died in a mental hospital; his daughter died in 1946 of a drug overdose, and his wife, Evelyn, became a morphine addict.

Only American jeweller Harry Winston, who bought the blue stone from the heirs of the McLean family, has escaped the rays of doom. He gave it away—to the Smithsonian Institute.

MOUNTAIN OF LIGHT . . . OR DARKNESS?

The present Queen Mother's crown at the Tower of London; in the lower cross—Koh-i-Noor.

TWO legends enhance the lustre of the Koh-i-Noor diamond: that its owner will rule the world, and that it must never be worn by a man.

Koh-i-Noor means the Mountain of Light. But in its time the stone has sparkled over avalanches of destruction that have wiped out two mighty empires.

It flashed among the possessions of the Mogul Emperor Mohammed as he fell to Nadir, the Shah of Persia—and saw its new owner die in a palace revolt in 1747.

One hundred years later it was the brightest jewel in the turban of the Sikh empire when its male-dominated lands were taken over by the world-colonising British—and their queen, Victoria.

It has glittered since then over the heads of three queens of England. No British king has ever worn it.

O-KEE-PA, THE TORTURE TEST

The savage ordeal that a warrior had to survive

Before a young man of the Mandan tribe of Red Indians could become a fully fledged warrior, he had to undergo one of the world's most painful initiation rituals.

Early in the last century the Mandans lived in earthen, dome-shaped huts and roamed the Missouri plains, hunting buffalo. To become a warrior, a young brave had to survive the ordeal of O-Kee-Pa, a torture designed to test his endurance and his courage.

First, the young man had to go without food, drink and sleep for four days and nights. Then, wearing ornate clothes and with his body painted, he entered a ceremonial hut.

The chief medicine man carved slices from the chest and shoulders of the warrior-to-be with a jagged knife and thrust wooden skewers through the bleeding flesh behind the muscles.

Stout thongs, secured to the rafters of the hut, were then tied to both ends of the skewers, and the initiate was hoisted from the floor. To increase the agony, heavy weights were attached to his legs, and he was twirled round and round until he fell unconscious.

When—and if—he recovered from this treatment, the young brave was given a hatchet, with which he had to chop off the little finger of his left hand.

In the final stage, his stamina was tested by tying ropes to his wrists and making him run in a circle, like a horse being broken in, until he dropped unconscious from exhaustion.

If he survived all this, he was then able to return to his family in triumph

HANGING ON *Suspended by skewers through the flesh, two young Mandan Indians undergo the test of fitness to become warriors.*

as a fully fledged warrior of the tribe.

No one knows how many braves died under O-Kee-Pa. Indeed, the ritual might never have been recorded at all but for an American artist called George Catlin, who went to live among the Indians in 1831, and preserved its brutal details on canvas.

In the end, however, bravery alone was not enough to save the Mandans. In the 1840s they were almost wiped out by an enemy too small to see—the terrible scourge of smallpox. And the few survivors were assimilated into other tribes.

WHEN THE COBRAS CALL A TRUCE

SNAKE WORSHIP still forms an important part of popular religion in many regions of India. One day in the year—around the beginning of August—is devoted to a 'festival of the serpents' when, it is believed, cobras will not bite anyone. The festival, which is called Naga Panchami (the words mean 'snake' and 'fifth'), falls on the fifth day of the Hindu month of Shravan, which runs from early July to early August.

On that day, live cobras, or their images, are worshipped. Sometimes the snakes are handled by devotees of the cult. Snake worshippers also ritually feed sacred cobras reared in special shrines, and even leave out milk as offerings to wild cobras in places frequented by them.

THE MAGIC OF MAKE-BELIEVE

What lies behind nursery characters like Humpty Dumpty?

In Anholt, the Danish island in the Kattegat, children sing what is, to them, a nonsense rhyme. But most English-speaking children would see some sense in it:

Jeck og Jill
Vent op de hill
Og Jell kom tombling efter.

The rhyme demonstrates the powerful oral tradition that lies behind the survival of nursery rhymes, or Mother Goose songs as they are known in the United States.

For 'Jack and Jill' was taken to the Danish island by British soldiers during the Napoleonic wars and, although meaningless to children there, still survives as an amusing jumble of sounds.

Rhymes and superstitions

The origin of many nursery rhymes is obscure, but the majority can be traced at least as far back as the 17th century. Some are rooted in old superstitions. For example:

Jack be nimble,
Jack be quick,
Jack jump over
The candlestick.

Jumping over a lighted candle was an ancient method of telling fortunes in medieval England. If the candle stayed lit, good luck was forecast. If it went out, bad luck would follow.

Other popular verses are said to have been penned as virtuous advice. 'Rock-a-bye baby,' probably the best-known lullaby in America and Britain, with its story of the child falling when the bough breaks, is an example. When it first appeared in a nursery-rhyme book in 1765, a footnote said: 'This may serve as a warning to the Proud and Ambitious, who climb so high that they generally fall at last.'

Cromwell's goose-steppers

Other verses stem from such diverse sources as snatches from the poems of strolling players, old proverbs and seemingly lighthearted references to unpleasant events of the past.

'Goosey, goosey, gander,' for instance, refers to Cromwell's goose-stepping soldiers hunting for Royalist fugitives after the English Civil War. Any suspect who would not accept the Puritan ways was

thrown into jail. As the rhyme puts it:

There I met an old man
Who would not say his prayers,
So I took him by the left leg
And threw him down the stairs.

'Ring-a-ring o' roses' is thought to date back to the Great Plague. A rosy rash was a symptom of the plague. Similarly the popular saying, used today in Britain and America, 'Cross my heart and hope to die; drop down dead if I tell a lie', has a sinister origin dating back to when perjury was a capital offence, particularly when committed under the sign of the Cross.

Many rhymes have parallels in different countries—even though in translation they do not readily appear to have any relationship.

Thus, 'Humpty Dumpty' appears in France as 'Boule, boule', in Denmark as 'Lille, trille', in Switzerland as 'Annebadadeli', as 'Hillerin-Lillerin' in Finland, and in Germany as various forms including 'Hümpelken-Pümpelken'.

'Humpty,' who may be thousands of years old, originated as a riddle. Once, the rhyme ended with the question, 'Who was Humpty Dumpty?' The answer, of course, was 'An egg'. But since every child now knows he was an egg, the question has long since been dropped.

Counting the 'little piggies'

Some nursery rhymes, as well as being a way of keeping children amused, were also an elementary means of teaching them. Such rhymes as 'This little piggy went to market', recited while taking hold of a child's fingers or toes, one by one, are still used as early aids to counting.

Still others—'Eeny, meeny, miny, mo' and 'Hickory, dickory, dock'—may have had somewhat sinister beginnings. Some scholars believe that both were part of the ancient Druids' method of seeking the will of the gods in choosing a victim for human sacrifice.

Another, simpler explanation is that 'Eeny, meeny, miny, mo' is a corruption of the prehistoric Celts' way of counting out 'one, two, three, four'. 'Hickory, dickory, dock,' similarly, may be derived from 'Hocera, cocera, dik', the old Celtic form of 'eight, nine, ten'.

Hickory Dickory Dock.

THE MOUSE RAN UP THE CLOCK *Once, the rhyme may have chosen sacrificial victims.*

the counting rhyme, but it became slightly corrupted to: 'Ena, mena, mona, mite,' and in New York, 150 years ago, children would chant: 'Ene, tene, mone, mei.' Similarly, an American rhyme known as Indian counting, went 'Een, teen, tether, fether, fip'.

Another elementary educational aid, for remembering the number of days in the months through the rhyme 'Thirty days hath September', dates back to 13th-century France.

Back to the knights

Many children's rhymes and chants use words that have long since passed from everyday use, but still survive in playtime vocabulary. 'Truce' words used in children's games can be traced back for centuries to medieval times.

The term 'barley', widely used in Wales, the Scottish borders and northwest England, dates back to the 14th century. It was used by knights, offering their jousting opponents a few moments' rest between charges. In southern England, truce words include 'fains' or 'fainites'—survivals of the medieval English expression 'Fain I', or 'I decline'.

In the 18th century, nursery rhymes began to appear in books for children, and eventually a host of writers concentrated on original verses for youngsters.

Many of them, in addition to being amusing verses, contained veiled references to political events and figures. 'Wee Willie Winkie,' for example, was said to be a Jacobite nickname for William III.

The fact that the Celts were involved in Druidical practices—stamped out by the Romans in their British territories during the 1st century AD—may mean that both explanations hold good.

Forms of these counting rhymes were used by Cumbrian and Westmorland shepherds, totting up their flocks, well into the 20th century.

In Wisconsin, settlers' children kept up

GRANDFATHER'S PRIVILEGE—GETTING DRUNK

THE CODEX MENDOZA is a collection of ancient Mexican manuscripts and drawings describing life in the 14th century. One of these drawings, reproduced here, depicts the drinking of what was known as the 'white wine of the earth', made from the sap of a plant found growing on a mountain—called the 'frothy mountain' because the wine was effervescent. The potency of the brew apparently gave rise to a general ban on over-indulgence, for the Mexican script explains that the man drinking was allowed to get merry 'on account of his age and his having grandchildren'.

A second look at long-cherished notions

Popular facts and fallacies

THIS SAUCER EARTH

Did moonwalkers march across a studio floor?

When astronaut Neil Armstrong set foot on the moon for the first time, on July 21, 1969, it represented one of the most inspiring achievements in man's history to millions of people throughout the world. But to a small organisation called the International Flat Earth Society, it was nothing more than a piece of cleverly stage-managed science-fiction trickery.

And Armstrong's historic words when stepping down from the *Eagle* module on to the dusty lunar surface 240,000 miles from Earth—'one small step for a man, one giant leap for mankind'—was a phrase that could have come only from the pen of a scriptwriter.

The evils of science

As for the pictures reputedly taken in space showing the earth to be a rotating sphere—well, they were just too ludicrous for words. The sun, say the Flat Earthers, circuits the earth instead of the earth revolving around the sun, a notion that most people take for granted.

The society, whose membership is variously estimated but is believed to be fewer than 100, dismisses much of accepted modern thinking about the shape of the earth as sheer nonsense, and is convinced that the entire human race is being subjected to the greatest hoax in history.

From its headquarters at Lancaster, California, the society wages a war of words through newsletters and pamphlets against the evils of science.

The society was founded around 1800 in Britain and America and, says its American president Charles Johnson, was descended from the Zetetic Society, which took its name from an ancient Greek philosophical school of sceptics. It survived under this name until 1956, when the new secretary, William Shenton, of Dover, in Kent, England, changed it to the present title.

The society's belief is this: that the earth is flat, with the land masses grouped around the central point of the North Pole.

The Antarctic region is not the compact island mass it is commonly believed to be, but an impenetrable ice-cold girdle around the earth. The Flat Earthers argue that trans-Antarctic expeditions have never happened. Explorers, misled by instrument faults, merely travelled an icy arc within the girdle.

Mr Shenton, who died in 1971, also argued about the nature of space itself.

The moon, he said, is a mere 32 miles in diameter, against the official 2160 miles, and only about 2550 miles away from the earth. The sun, slightly larger than the moon, is really only 3240 miles from the earth and not 93 million miles, as people had been led to believe.

'Can you imagine what sort of summers we would have if the sun were as far away as scientists believe?' he scoffed.

And as for stars, they were very small bodies a 'few thousand miles apart!'

But if the earth is flat, as the society maintains, the tricky question remains as

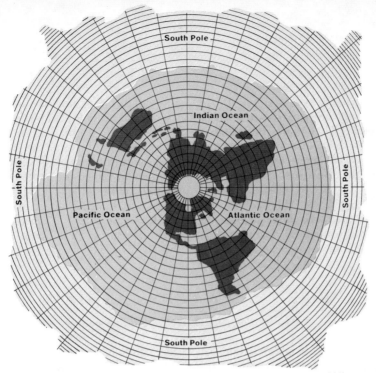

WORLD PLAN *According to Flat Earthers, the North Pole is the hub of the world, whose oceans are girdled by the South Polar regions. What lies beyond this icy barrier is somewhat vague.*

to what lies on the other side. Mr Shenton said that water is on the other side. But as to what lay beneath the waters, he confessed himself perplexed.

The society claims biblical support for its beliefs, pointing out that Moses, author of the first five books of the Old Testament, wrote of the heaven above and the earth beneath, and the water under the earth. Mr Shenton first became convinced of the immobility and flatness of the earth in 1918, at the end of the First World War.

He had the idea of setting up an international haulage firm using balloons, and it occurred to him that if the earth were revolving, as he had been told, all he needed to do was send up a balloon and, barring winds, it would stay still until the destination reached the balloon.

But this could happen only if the earth really was spinning—a belief which Mr Shenton could not bring himself to share. Since the earth was in fact stationary, he reasoned, the launching site would stay just where it was, underneath the balloon.

WORLD INSIDE THE WORLD

The new land where a man wanted to plant the American flag

If John Symmes's theory had been correct, the first men to reach the North Pole would have dropped into the earth through an opening in its crust and discovered a vast new country inside, rich in minerals and peopled by a strange race of men.

So strong was his conviction, and so many were persuaded by him, that his proposals for an expedition to the world within the earth got as far as the US Congress. But the sceptical American legislators would have nothing to do with them.

John Cleves Symmes, born in New Jersey in 1780, had a distinguished army career behind him, rising to the rank of captain, before he became passionately interested in astronomy. The more he studied, the firmer grew his conviction that the earth was hollow.

This theory was not entirely new. It had been put forward in the past by such notable men as the English astronomer Edmond Halley—after whom Halley's Comet is named—Leonhard Euler, the German mathematician, and Sir John Leslie, the Scottish scientist. Halley and Leslie suggested that there might be separate planets within our own.

Symmes agreed, but his 'worlds within worlds' were concentric spheres, one inside the other but all open at the Poles. No one could prove that his theory was wrong, for at that time the Polar regions were still unexplored.

Symmes cited as evidence of his theory the then unexplained northward migration of birds. They were, he believed, attracted to the source of warm ocean currents and an inner-earth sunshine—of which the Northern Lights are a reflection.

If birds could visit this inner world, Symmes declared, so could men. He wrote to scientific institutions all over the world: 'I declare that the earth is hollow, habit-able within, one within the other, and that it is open at the Pole . . . I pledge my life in support of this truth, and am ready to explore the hollow if the world will support me in the undertaking.'

When he failed to get US backing, Symmes tried to join a Russian Polar expedition, but could not raise the fare to the departure port, St Petersburg.

He died in 1829, still convinced that the earth was hollow.

MORE THAN A BODY CAN STAND
Myths about the human mind and body

People falling from a great height are dead before they hit the ground Rather than be burnt to death in his blazing shell-torn Lancaster on a bombing raid over Germany in 1944, RAF gunner Sergeant Nicholas Alkemade jumped from 18,000 ft without a parachute, calculating that this would be a quicker and less agonising death.

He landed uninjured and still conscious. The last few feet of his 120 mph fall were broken by the branches of young pine trees, thick, springy undergrowth, and finally deep snow. 'It was rather like bouncing on a trampoline,' he recalled.

Sergeant Alkemade's experience is a dramatic rebuttal of the idea that people falling from great heights are dead before they hit the ground. Asphyxia, brought about by the speed of the fall, or heart failure through shock were thought to occur long before the final impact.

The fallacy of this belief has been amply demonstrated by free-fall parachutists who regularly drop several miles before opening their parachutes. In 1960 Captain Joseph Kittinger jumped from a balloon in the USA and fell 16 miles before opening his parachute. He landed conscious and unhurt.

Cold causes cold The common cold is the world's most widespread illness—which is probably why there are more myths about it than any of the other plagues that flesh is heir to.

The most widespread fallacy of all is that colds are caused by cold. They are not. The causes are viruses which are passed on from person to person. You catch a cold through coming into contact with someone who already has one. If cold causes colds, it would be reasonable to expect the Eskimos to suffer from them permanently. But they do not.

In the germ-free atmosphere of the Poles, explorers have reported being completely free from colds until coming into contact again with infected people.

During the First World War, soldiers who spent long periods in the trenches, cold, wet and miserable, showed no increased tendency to catch colds.

In the Second World War, prisoners at the notorious Auschwitz concentration camp, naked and starving, were astonished to find that they seldom had colds.

At the Common Cold Research Unit at Salisbury, Wiltshire, volunteers took part in experiments in which they took hot baths, then stood without drying in draughty corridors. After half an hour of wearing only bathing costumes they were allowed to dress, but had to put on wet socks. Others were sent for walks in the rain, and on their return they were confined to rooms with no heating without being allowed to dry themselves. The volunteers were split into two main groups, only one of which were exposed to cold viruses. Neither group showed any increased susceptibility to colds. Similar groups in Chicago met with the same results.

If, then, cold and wet have nothing to do with catching colds, why are they more prevalent in the winter? Despite the most painstaking research in Britain and America, no one has yet found a satisfactory answer. The nearest the scientists have got to a solution is a theory that people tend to stay together indoors more in cold weather than at other times, and thus make it easier for the virus to be passed on.

Nor has anyone yet found a cure for the cold. There are drugs and pain-suppressors such as aspirin, but all they do is relieve the symptoms.

Hair and nails continue to grow after death Seven years after her death in 1862, the body of Elizabeth Siddal, wife of the painter-poet Dante Gabriel Rossetti, was exhumed from its grave in Highgate Cemetery, London. Charles Augustus Howell, who was a witness, described the awesome sight of the undecayed body with luxuriant red-gold hair practically filling the coffin.

If the hair was as remarkable as Howell described, it must have been as it was when she died. Alternatively, Howell was exaggerating. For hair does not grow after death. A certain amount of drying and shrinking of the skin takes place after death, and might reveal a small extra amount, maybe $\frac{1}{16}$ in., of hair on the chin, but not enough to fill a coffin.

Hair and nails grow from the root by cell multiplication, and are fed by the bloodstream. When death occurs, the heart stops and the blood ceases to circulate. The supply of nutriments to the cells ends and they can grow no more.

Hair can turn white overnight It is sometimes said of a person who has suffered a terrible shock' that 'his hair turned white overnight'. But although bad health or nervous disorders can cause hair to begin turning white, no natural agency could suddenly complete the process. Hair grows only about $\frac{1}{2}$ in. a month, so it would take weeks for a normal head of hair to change colour.

Hair grows from the roots, and what emerges above the surface is actually dead. So if it all began to turn white, the white roots would begin to show quite soon, especially if the hair was kept cut short. But turning white overnight? Never, without the aid of bleach.

A scratch from a rusty nail causes tetanus Lockjaw, or tetanus, is an acute infectious disease caused by the toxin produced by a bacterium called *Clostridium tetani*. A scratch from a sterile piece of rusty metal cannot cause tetanus, because neither the rust nor the metal are poisonous.

On the other hand, a scratch from a *dirty* nail would be dangerous if there was

LUXURIANT HAIR *Elizabeth Siddal's hair was said to have grown profusely after she died. But the claim is highly doubtful.*

any tetanus-producing organism present in the dirt. This would be especially true of a cut from a gardening implement which could have picked up such infections from the soil.

Some people are double-jointed Stage contortionists, practitioners of advanced yoga and others may appear to have unusual joints. The truth is that heredity and constant exercise have given the fibrous tissue binding their bones together more elasticity than most people's.

But no one has yet been born possessing truly double joints.

A drowning man surfaces three times A drowning man, so it is said, comes up three times before sinking to his death. It is not necessarily true.

A person who panics in the water tends to sink and draw water into his lungs each time his head goes under. This may occur any number of times—or not at all—before he dies from asphyxia.

A dying man sees all his life flash before him Poets and novelists are largely to blame for the notion that a person's past life flashes through his mind in the moments before death. Nobody has come back from the grave to confirm it. But there are many cases of people being saved from what they believed to be certain death, and disproving the idea.

An Englishman, A. R. Bayley, who was saved from drowning, wrote in 1916: 'I remember thinking it was all up with me, but the events of my past life did not pass before me.'

A pilot shot down in 1918 said after the crash: 'I was sure I was going to be killed. I was just shaking my head, thinking of my girl friend in England.'

Only a sudden shock will cure hiccups
Thousands of remedies have been proposed for hiccups, each with its enthusiastic backers. Some seem to work, others do not. Research into known cases indicated that if a sufferer firmly believes a particular treatment will succeed, more often than not it does. So doctors have been led to the conclusion that the cure is at least partly psychological.

One widely held belief is that a sharp fright will end a troublesome bout of hiccups, but doctors have pointed out that far more people die from fright than from hiccups. So the 'cure' could be worse than the disease.

Between 1948 and 1956 Jack O'Leary, an American, reckoned he hiccuped 160 million times. He tried 60,000 remedies, all in vain. Finally, in desperation, he prayed to St Jude, patron of hopeless causes. His hiccuping stopped.

Another victim was Heinz Isecke, a 55-year-old Hanover plumber, who hiccuped for eight months after an operation in November 1973. Suggestions poured in from all over the world. He tried them all, without success. Doctors, alarmed by his failing strength, operated again. Still the hiccups went on.

Eventually, in despair, Heinz drank a 'secret' herbal mixture sent by an anonymous donor. By the evening of that day his hiccups had gone. Was it the mixture, or his faith in it, that cured him? As yet, no one can say.

People who survived execution were automatically reprieved Although there have been reprieves in cases where equipment failed or the victim recovered, there was never any law that made this obligatory, either in England or America.

Nevertheless, when the death sentence was lawful in many countries, there was a sense of humanity which sometimes resulted in mercy for criminals who survived execution attempts.

The most famous of all English cases was that of the murderer John Lee, still remembered as 'the man they couldn't hang'. Three times, as he stood on the scaffold at Exeter Gaol in 1885, the trapdoor under his feet failed to open, although each time it had functioned perfectly under tests.

It was later thought that a warped board was responsible and that the weight of the prison chaplain—who was present only at executions and not the tests—caused it to bend and jam the trap.

After the third unsuccessful attempt to hang him, Lee's sentence was commuted to life imprisonment on humanitarian grounds. He was later released and emigrated to the USA, where he died in 1933.

One of the earliest authenticated cases of a person being completely freed after 'execution' is that of Ann Greene, sentenced to be hanged for infanticide at Oxford in 1650. After hanging for half an hour, she revived as a surgeon was about to dissect her 'body'. She recovered completely, married and had three children.

In New South Wales in 1803, Joseph Samuels, still protesting his innocence on the scaffold, accused another man of the crime for which he was about to be hanged. Twice the rope broke, and once it stretched so that Samuel's feet touched the floor. The governor reprieved him, and the man he had named was later hanged in his stead.

John Smith, sentenced for 'scandal' in 1705, had been hanging at Tyburn in London for 15 minutes when a reprieve arrived. It was later found to be a hoax, but in the meantime Smith had been cut down and revived. He was pardoned, and spent the rest of his life celebrated as 'Half-hanged Smith'.

Thirty-five years later William Duell, an English murderer, was hanged but, like Ann Greene, recovered on the dissecting table. The death sentence was commuted, and he was transported to Australia.

No such mercy was shown to an American murderer named Bullen, who was sent to the electric chair at Sing Sing in 1932. He recovered on the way to the cemetery and leapt out of his coffin. But he was caught and electrocuted again.

Among the most curious of all cases of condemned people surviving their 'executions' is that of Margaret Dickson, of Musselburgh, Scotland. Customers at an inn, it is recorded, were 'greatly scared' when they saw her climb out of her coffin on the way to be buried after her hanging in 1728. Under Scottish law at that time, as she had been officially executed, her husband was a widower. So, to legitimise their union, she was required to marry him again.

The Russian republic of Georgia has the world's oldest people Centenarians, according to a United Nations estimate in 1972, numbered 25,000 throughout the world. According to the Soviet Union at that time, no fewer than 21,000 of them lived in Russia. If the Russians had not put their figure so high, it might have been accepted without too close examination. But statisticians were suspicious.

Georgia, birthplace of Stalin, was particularly famed for the longevity of its inhabitants: 39 in every 100,000 of the population were said to be aged 100 or more. But in 1961 the Russians had claimed that, in the republic of Azerbaijan, the figure was 63 per 100,000. The same survey on which this claim was based discovered 592 people who had passed the age of 120. Occasional reports from the Caucasus region have spoken of inhabitants aged 150. One man who died in 1973 had given his age as 168.

All these claims have been subjected to close scrutiny, and the result is a good deal of scepticism.

Firstly, although Russia claims to have several hundred citizens well over the age of 114, that is the top limit of any *confirmed* case of long life anywhere.

Secondly, wherever these self-styled centenarians exist in exceptionally large numbers, there are anomalies which the statisticians regard as suspicious—such as the fact that there are no correspondingly large numbers of people in their eighties and nineties. Why, they ask, the gap? If people born more than 100 years ago are living so long, why are those born only 70 or 80 years ago dying so young?

Doctors have strengthened these suspicions. Medical examination of the 'grand old men' of 100 or more has suggested that

WEAK CHINS—STRONG CHARACTERS

FOOLISH ARISTOCRATS are sometimes mocked as 'chinless wonders', the idea being that strength or weakness of character is shown by the shape of a person's chin.

The notion has no basis in fact. Frederick the Great, Queen Victoria, General Wolfe, the conqueror of Quebec, the Brontë sisters —all these had what might be called 'weak' chins, but they were all strong characters.

The fallacy seems to have been fostered by the fondness of early fiction writers for type-casting their characters. A boxer, for instance, or a ruthless business tycoon, would have 'a forceful, thrusting chin'. A villain was branded by his low forehead and close-set eyes.

Criminologists say that there is no such thing as 'criminal features'. The study of faces as reflectors of character is not a science at all, simply a superstition.

Frederick the Great, a king who earned his title without the aid of a 'strong' chin.

Queen Victoria, a woman whose forceful personality did not show in her face.

General James Wolfe, a war hero, but who would guess from his picture?

SAMSON AND THE LION *According to the Old Testament, Samson's strength lay in his hair.*

many of them really are probably only in their seventies.

Many of these ancients are illiterate. They have no idea of dates, and there are no records of their births. In the areas where they live, old men are venerated, so there is great prestige in being regarded as a patriarch. It has even been suggested that some of the less naïve added years to their age in 1914 to avoid military service in the armies of the tsar, and have had to keep up the deception ever since.

Whatever the truth of the matter, the statisticians suspect that there are parts of the world where a man is not, as they say in the West, as old as he feels, but as old as he says he is.

Hairy men are stronger Samson lost his strength when Delilah cut off his hair. It made a good story, and the belief has persisted that a man's power and virility reside in his hair. But it is merely legend. Hair is already dead once it has emerged from the skin: it has nothing to contribute to the owner's strength.

It was not until well into this century that research dispelled many of the old fallacies connected with hair and baldness. These are now known to depend on inheritance, the presence of hormones, and to some extent age.

About one man in 20 notices that his hairline is receding before his 21st birthday. One in six will sooner or later go bald

NO HAIR ON THEIR CHESTS *But these Japanese wrestlers, at 36 st. each, are no weaklings.*

on top. The pattern tends to run in families: it has nothing to do with strength.

People who can be hypnotised are weak minded In fact weak-minded, submissive people are the least susceptible to hypnosis. The best subjects are those who can channel their thoughts in a specific direction—an attribute of high intelligence.

Another mistaken belief is that a person can be hypnotised unawares or against his will. It cannot be done without the subject's co-operation. Nor is it possible to persuade a person under hypnosis to do anything normally repugnant to him or foreign to his everyday character.

Men have one rib fewer than women In fact men and women have precisely the same number of ribs—12. The fallacy probably arose from the account of the Creation given in Genesis ii, 21 and 22. God was said to have taken a rib from Adam while he was asleep and from that Eve was fashioned.

Although male and female bones are different in size in most cases, there is only one instance where there is sometimes a numerical difference—the coccygeal or tail vertebrae. Women often have one fewer than men.

A woman's brain is smaller than a man's Taking into account the proportionate sizes of the bodies, the weight of the brain in both sexes is about equal. Brain size varies only in proportion to body weight, stature, age and race.

There is little evidence, moreover, that the size of the brain is related to the intelligence of its owner.

HARD TO SWALLOW

Beliefs about food that are completely unfounded

Brown eggs are more nutritious British mothers tell their children that brown eggs have more goodness than white eggs, but in America, the opposite is believed—that white eggs are purer. Naturally, farmers in both countries strive to produce more of whatever is in demand.

Both beliefs are myths. Eggs are not designed to be eaten by humans. They are to provide nourishment for the developing chick. The colour of the shell, which is a late stage in the development of the egg, depends merely on the breed of the hen, and by the time the shell is formed the nutritional value is already established.

Brown bread is better than white Nutritionally, there is no difference between brown bread and white. White bread is simply made from flour from which the bran and outer coating of the wheat have been removed. Wholewheat contains the bran and wheat. Both contain the necessary vitamins, nutrients, minerals and carbohydrates for adults and children.

There is one school of thought, however, that considers the 'roughage' in wholewheat bread beneficial to people with intestinal problems.

While all white flour sold in the United Kingdom must, by law, be enriched by nutrients, the standards vary from country to country. In the US, where standards are higher, 92 per cent of white bread is enriched, while the content of riboflavin nutrient in Scandinavian countries is twice the required level in the US.

Eating seeds causes appendicitis Few medical reports have ever recorded the presence of seeds in appendices that have been removed. But among the objects that have been found are gold tooth fillings, toothbrush bristles and the end of a thermometer.

Never eat oysters unless there is an R in the month It is sheer coincidence that the first four and last four months of the year contain Rs, and it has long been said that only during these months it is safe to eat oysters. Before refrigeration, the eating of oysters in the warmer summer months may have been risky. The chemical com-

THE OYSTERFEST *Each year, the mayor of Colchester, England, marks the opening of the local fishermen's oyster season—in September.*

position of the oyster alters from season to season, especially during its spawning period in May and June. After spawning it contains less glycogen and is paler and more watery. But it tastes much the same and is certainly not poisonous.

Eating fish is good for the brain No particular food contributes specifically to the brain or any other part of the body. The tissues take what they require from the materials absorbed into the bloodstream during digestion. A balanced diet will satisfy all the requirements of the cells, although a lack of some types of food may result in deficiencies.

The belief that fish, in particular, is good for the brain, grew up in the 19th century. The German philosopher and physician Friedrich Büchner (1824-99), on learning that the brain contained phosphorus, declared that 'without phos-

321

phorus, there is no thought'. The French chemist Jean Dumas (1800–84) confirmed that fish are a rich source of phosphorus. The Swiss naturalist Jean Louis Agassiz (1807–73) connected the two ideas and suggested that fish is good for the brain.

In fact, because of its abundance in the rocks and minerals of the earth, varying amounts of phosphorus are present in most foods.

It is easy to tell a mushroom from a poisonous fungus There is no simple method of distinguishing between the two, because neither edible mushrooms nor poisonous fungi such as toadstools have any one common feature that is not found in the other.

The idea that mushrooms are edible if they are white, or have a ring at the foot of the stalk, for example, is a fallacy. The fungus *amanita virosa* has both these characteristics, but is inedible. Nor is a mushroom that has turned a bluish colour necessarily poisonous. The edible *boletus edulis*, when bruised, can turn dirty brown, light or deep blue, green, red, purple, violet or even inky black. But it is still edible. The colour changes simply mean that a fermentation process is taking place.

Smell is not a guideline, either. Some deadly poisonous fungi, such as the *amanita phalloides*, may smell quite pleasant. On the other hand, some unpleasant-looking fungi can be eaten with no ill effect.

Several 'kitchen hints' about discovering whether fungi are safe to eat are also erroneous. One is the fallacy that edible mushrooms, unlike toadstools, can be peeled. The idea that soaking or cooking poisonous fungi in vinegar will make them edible is also false. It may neutralise poisonous or indigestible species slightly, but dangerous and deadly fungi are never truly safe to eat.

The best way to identify mushrooms and other fungi is by use of one of the many illustrated guides available. But the ultimate rule should be: if in doubt, do not eat the fungus.

Drinking seawater causes madness There is nothing in seawater that specifically causes insanity, although it may contain harmful chemicals. But if seawater is drunk without any fresh water to dilute it, the concentration of salt will poison the kidneys and eventually cause death. Drinking small amounts to supplement fresh water is not harmful.

Canned foods become poisonous after opening Whatever container food is in, it may become infected with germs and cause food poisoning if it is not in sterile conditions. But food in opened tins is no more susceptible than fresh, and there is nothing about the tins themselves which could cause poisoning.

Food in damaged tins, however, may have become contaminated by germs entering through cracks or splits.

MAN-MADE MYTHS ABOUT NATURE

Can flying fish fly and are gorillas really ferocious?

Flying fish fly There are about 100 species of fish that fall within the general category popularly called flying fish. But none of them is capable of genuine flight.

These fish, which have enlarged pectoral fins that look like wings, can, however, glide just above the surface of the water at about 10 mph for up to 200 yds. They have even been known to land accidentally on the decks of passing boats. Their gliding is usually an effort to escape predators, particularly dolphins.

Moths eat clothes The six species of moth which are responsible for damage to clothes and other materials, do not eat at all. But they lay prodigious numbers of eggs from which larvae hatch, and it is these which are voracious devourers of wool, carpets and upholstery.

There is no method of assessing just how much cloth an average moth larva might eat, since it depends on how long it spends in the larval stage. This in turn depends on such factors as the temperature and the availability of food.

Octopuses are extremely dangerous The idea of octopuses holding divers in a vice-like grip is largely fiction. Occasionally, swimmers are held by the suckers of an octopus's tentacles, but few cases have been reported of anyone coming to harm as a result. E. G. Boulenger, former

IMPOSSIBLE DREAM *The idea of an octopus holding a man, let alone a ship, in a vice-like grip is largely fiction. The largest Alaskan species has a radial span of 32 ft. Most are smaller.*

director of the aquarium at London Zoo, says that a firm grip on an octopus's head and body is sufficient to induce the creature to relax its hold.

While the deep-sea octopus found off the Alaskan coast can grow up to 32 ft from the tip of one tentacle to another, most species are much smaller. One, found off the coast of Sri Lanka, is less than 2 in. across.

On the rare occasions that swimmers have been bitten by an octopus's beak-like mouth, which can inject venom, the usual result has been only a slight, temporary swelling.

Thunder turns milk sour Thunder is a vibration of the air that cannot affect milk in any way. What does cause milk to turn sour during stormy weather, however, is the formation of bacteria that converts the sugar in milk into lactic acid. These bacteria thrive best in the humid weather that often accompanies thunderstorms in the summer. Milk is therefore far less likely to turn sour during winter thunderstorms.

Thrashing about in the water will frighten sharks away Running down each side of a shark's body, from head to tail, are sensory systems by which it can detect vibrations in water over long distances. To a shark, any creature thrashing around in the water is either wounded or crippled in some way and is therefore likely to provide an easy meal.

Jacques-Yves Cousteau, the French underwater expert, says that wild splashing does not frighten away sharks. He says the best protection lies in easy movement, swimming slowly and avoiding any abrupt change of position.

Sharks can also detect blood in the water a quarter of a mile or more away. While most fish have a keen sense of smell, the shark's is exceptional because a large proportion of its brain is concerned with this faculty. On either side of its snout it has two organs that are so sensitive the shark can steer itself along a scent trail, making corrections in its course as it picks up weaker or stronger scents to the left or right, rather like an aeroplane following a radio signal. In this way the shark can 'zero in' on wounded prey.

Catgut comes from cats Catgut is made from the intestines of sheep, horses and several other animals—but never cats. Nor is there any record of the material ever having been made from the entrails of cats.

The origin of the word is uncertain. It could be a contraction of 'cattlegut' or may have arisen over confusion between

DEAF TO MUSIC *Snakes are charmed by the tap of the foot, the sway of the body and pipe—but not by the music that the snake charmer makes.*

'kit' and kitten—a kit was a small violin that would have had catgut strings. The *Oxford English Dictionary* includes the story that it may originate from the 'caterwauling' sound of a violin—though it does not guarantee the authenticity of the tale.

Snakes hypnotise their prey and can be charmed by music While some animals may become curious or even freeze with fear when confronted by a snake, no zoologists seriously entertain the idea that the reptiles have any hypnotic powers. The courtship 'dance', consisting of rhythmic swaying, of some snakes may have given rise to ideas of mesmerism.

Snake charming, on the other hand, is a form of hypnotism—of the snake. Snakes have extremely limited hearing and can only detect low-frequency sounds; so it is unlikely that they can respond to the music of a charmer's pipe. Cobras used by Hindu snake-charmers respond to the tap of the charmer's foot, the beat of his stick on their basket, or the swaying of his body and pipe. Burmese snake charmers use rhythmic swaying movements to fascinate snakes which will sway in a similar way, looking for a place to strike. In other parts of the world, charmers 'talk' to their snakes and the snakes respond to the vibrations they pick up through the ground.

But the swaying from side to side of a charmed snake is a physical necessity to keep the upper part of its body off the ground. When it stops swaying, it is forced to slide back to the ground.

Rats desert sinking ships Rats do not instinctively leave ships that are fated to sink, but probably leave the bilges where they usually live if a ship springs a leak and starts to take in water.

Droves of rats scurrying out of a ship's hold in this way might well have made sailors suspicious of a vessel's seaworthiness. It is also possible that rats may be more sensitive than men to minor earth tremors or falls of plaster. For this reason, an ancient belief that rats leave houses that are about to collapse might have some substance. Rats were once believed to be useful in sensing impending cave-ins in coal mines.

Ostriches bury their heads in the sand The most popular belief about ostriches is that they bury their heads in sand in the hope that their enemies will not notice them. But this, say naturalists, is almost certainly a myth.

Allan Pocock, a resident of the Oudsthoorn region of South Africa, where 200,000 ostriches were once reared for their feathers, noted that during the 80-odd years when records were kept, no one had reported a single case of an ostrich burying its head, or even apparently attempting to do so.

Ostriches may well listen intently for sound with their heads near the ground, and sometimes they even lower their heads to rest their neck muscles. They also poke their heads into bushes inquisitively —but never bury them in sand. If they did, they would probably suffocate.

Gorillas are ferocious by nature Belief in the ferocity of gorillas, probably engendered by their appearance, was universally established by the late 19th century, and was perpetuated in drawings, paintings and novels.

But in their natural habitat both the lowland and mountain species of gorilla are relatively peaceable, despite their terrifying looks. The mountain type can grow to a height of 6 ft 6 in.—more than 7 in. taller than the lowland variety. Other

MOVIE MYTH *The 1933 film* King Kong *helped to perpetuate the idea that gorillas are aggressive by nature. Zoologists say that in the wild they are shy, despite their appearance.*

vital statistics include a chest measurement of 67 in., 25 in. biceps, arms that can span 9 ft and a weight of 700 lb.

The American naturalist George Schaller, who spent months observing gorillas in the wild, reported that they were extremely shy, and that if a human encountered one and stood his ground the gorilla would usually go away.

In defence of their young, gorillas have been known to inflict terrible bites on humans; but there are no authenticated cases of their crushing people to death.

The 1933 film *King Kong*, based on a novel by Edgar Wallace, in which a gigantic gorilla runs amok in New York, has contributed to the myth of the creature's aggressiveness.

Swans sing before dying The belief that the usually voiceless swan sings beautifully before dying is an ancient piece of folklore beloved of poets and philosophers. The ancient Greeks thought that swans were creatures of Apollo, the god of music. According to Socrates in Plato's *Phaedo*, swans sing 'not out of sorrow or distress, but because they are inspired of Apollo'. Shakespeare refers to the 'swan song' in his plays and poems, and the image is also used by Lord Byron in 'Don Juan' and by Tennyson in 'The Passing of Arthur'.

A vaguely musical sound is produced by the whistling swan of Iceland, an accomplishment beyond the ability of all other species, whether on the point of death or not. The most common species in the Northern Hemisphere, for instance, is capable of no more than a violent hiss-

ing when it is angry or protecting its young—usually as a prelude to attack. The absence of voice is reflected in its name—the mute swan.

SWAN SONG? *As a tribute to Apollo, swans are said to sing before dying. But the most common species in the Northern Hemisphere is mute.*

Mice love cheese above all other food Experiments by rodent controllers show that to guarantee catching a mouse, cheese is not the best bait.

Edward Batzner, an American exterminator, uses lemon-flavoured sweets. These, he says, have the dual advantage of stickiness, which holds the mouse for the second it takes for the trap to spring, and sweetness, which attracts the mouse more readily than cheese. It is equally

325

SWEET TOOTH *An American expert exterminator advocates sweets, not cheese, as mouse bait.*

Porcupines and hedgehogs can shoot their quills As a defence mechanism, the quills of the porcupine and hedgehog are highly effective. Apart from their obvious deterrent effect, they are frequently impregnated with dirt and bacteria and can cause serious infection. Also, the fact the quills are barbed makes it difficult for the victim to dislodge them.

But neither the hedgehog nor the porcupine possesses the necessary muscular mechanism to 'shoot' their quills—although the porcupine's 18,000 or more quills can become easily detachable when they are raised in defence.

fallacious to make similar presumptions about other animals—that all dogs prefer meat, for instance, or that all cats prefer fish. A creature's 'preference' for a particular food is usually dictated by 'conditioning'—what it has become used to eating. Thus, some cats prefer milk to water, some dogs will eat only raw meat in preference to cooked offal.

Camels carry water in their humps The hump of the camel contains fat on which the animal can live for perhaps a week or ten days if no other food is available. Undoubtedly, in digesting the fat the animal does produce a certain amount of water, but it has no reservoir in its hump.

NATURAL ARCHER? *Neither the porcupine nor the hedgehog can shoot their quills.*

GALLANTS, FIDDLERS AND FAIRY TALES

The stories behind some long-loved fables

Nero fiddled while Rome burned One of the most cherished legends of ancient Rome tells how the megalomaniac Emperor Nero was obsessed with the idea of building a magnificent new city as a permanent memorial to himself. Thwarted by the owners of family shrines that blocked the streets, the tyrant himself put Rome to the torch.

But there is no historical evidence that Nero had any part in the starting of the fire. Even more doubtful is the story's most famous detail—that Nero stood on top of a tower in the city and fiddled. The violin was not invented until the 16th century. However, other versions of the legend claim he played a lyre or a lute.

The historian Tacitus (about AD 56–120) wrote, only a few years after the fire, that Nero had been 50 miles away at his villa at Antium when the blaze started. Far from gloating over the inferno, Nero

raced to the city and made frantic efforts to stop the blaze.

Whatever his motives, it was the only praiseworthy act of an otherwise deplorable life. Brought to power by his mother, Aggrippina, as a boy of 17, he was hated by the people for having usurped the position of his half-brother.

His private life was a scandal, even by Roman standards. What must have been even more painful was his insistence that everyone should attend performances of his plays and operas. Apparently, his lack of talent was equalled only by the awfulness of his voice.

His cruelty towards the Christians is legendary. They were an unpopular sect, suspected of witchcraft, and they provided both Nero and Rome with a useful scapegoat for the fire. Hundreds were executed —though there is no record of them having been thrown to the lions.

RUINS OF ROME *Emperor Nero was blamed for the fire that devastated Rome in AD 64, but according to the historian Tacitus, he was 50 miles away, at Antium, when the blaze started.*

Finally, his cruelties and debaucheries sickened even his closest adherents. The Praetorian Guard—the emperor's private bodyguard—deserted him. Faced with inevitable deposition and execution, he committed suicide in AD 68.

Sir Walter Raleigh laid down his cloak for Elizabeth I The handsome young gentleman stood amid the crowds as the Queen of England passed by with her retinue. When she was almost at his side, she paused. A mud puddle was in her path. The quick-witted gallant, a seaman named Walter Raleigh, immediately threw his cloak over the puddle. The queen, impressed by his courtesy, stepped on it, smiling her gratitude for this expensive protection of the royal feet.

A romantic and fateful meeting of two great figures of history—but untrue.

The story is believed to have been the invention of the historian Thomas Fuller (1608–61), who frequently added fictitious anecdotes to enliven dull facts. The tale was perpetuated by Sir Walter Scott in his novel *Kenilworth* (1821). Here, Raleigh swears he will never brush the cloak 'as long as it is in my possession'. The queen, who appreciated a compliment, tells Raleigh to go to her wardrobe-keeper with an order to give him 'a suit, and that of the newest cut'.

Raleigh is also said to have been the first man to bring potatoes to England, in 1586. However, there is no contemporary account of this. John Gerard, in his book *Herball* (1597), refers to a C. Clusius who had cultivated potatoes in Italy in 1585. The vegetable gained immediate popularity and was cultivated in most European countries during the following decade.

Similarly, Raleigh is usually credited,

SUPREME GALLANTRY *Sir Walter Raleigh's famous gesture was merely a romantic invention.*

or blamed, for introducing tobacco into England, on his return from the British colony of Virginia in 1586. But a Frenchman had introduced tobacco to France as early as 1559 or 1560. He was Jean Nicot, from whom *nicotine* is derived.

George Washington and the cherry tree
At the age of six, the future first President of the United States stood accused of chopping down his father's favourite cherry tree. 'I can't tell a lie,' he admitted to his father, 'I did cut it with my hatchet.'

This irresistible mixture of boyish mischief and honesty has made the young Washington's confession one of the most famous 'events' in American history. Here, surely, were the honest, forthright qualities of a great leader in the making.

Yet very little is known about the childhood of Washington. In one of the first biographies written about him—by a clergyman, Mason Locke Weems—Washington's entire early life occupies only a single page.

In the first edition of this *Life of George Washington*, published in 1800, the year after the president's death, no mention is made of the cherry-tree incident. It was later revised to include a number of new anecdotes, including young George's exploits with the hatchet.

Weems claimed that he heard the story from an anonymous 'aged lady' who was once associated with the Washington household. But the author was known to have spent a great deal of time inventing 'biographical anecdotes' for his books, lifting some of his stories from works

about completely different people.

He even admitted as much later, although he did not say that the cherry-tree story was one of these. In his *Life of William Penn*, the founder of Pennsylvania, Weems made up the story of a treaty between the Indians and the settlers, complete with suitable quotations. But no such treaty existed.

Weems's biography of Washington ran to more than 70 editions during the 19th century, firmly establishing the cherry-tree story in American folklore. But no modern biographer accepts it as true, and some omit it altogether.

However, on a German stoneware mug, stamped with the date 1776—the year of the Declaration of Independence, when Washington was 44—there is an illustration of a story very similar to that of young Washington and the cherry tree.

A youth in costume of the period is shown with a hatchet and a felled tree, and the initials 'C. W.' or 'G. W.' appear in two places.

King Harold was shot in the eye by a Norman arrow As the Battle of Hastings drew to a climax in 1066, the tall and powerful English King Harold stood his ground, surrounded by his bodyguard of housecarls. Although his army had dwindled, the remainder continued to beat off one Norman assault after another. His adversary, William, Duke of Normandy, ordered his archers to fire up into the air so that their arrows would fall into the densely packed knot of men around the king. A stray arrow pierced Harold's eye

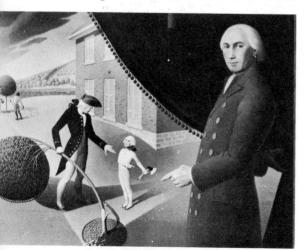

DID HE OR DIDN'T HE? *American Grant Wood's version of the Washington myth, with biographer Mason Weems (right).*

DEATH OF A KING *Was Harold mortally wounded by an arrow (left)—or hacked down and killed by the Norman cavalryman (right)?*

Umbrellas began as parasols and were carried only by fashionable women at first.

In this illustration from an 1862 edition of Defoe's novel, Crusoe sports a parasol.

In 1750 Jonas Hanway was the first to adopt the umbrella, amid public mockery.

UMBRELLAS began, not as protection against rain, but instead as sun shades. They are depicted being used in this way in ancient Egyptian, Greek and Byzantine art. It was in 16th-century Europe that they were first made with leather and oiled, rainproof materials, rather than delicate silks.

At first, umbrellas were carried only by women and it took the courage of a philanthropist, Jonas Hanway in 1750, to suffer jeers and catcalls in the streets of London before they became acceptable to men. The 19th-century Dickensian character Sarah Gamp, perpetually carrying a large umbrella in the novel *Martin Chuzzlewit*, popularised the nickname 'gamp'.

and, as apparently depicted in the famous Bayeux Tapestry, he fell, and in the next charge was slain by the Normans.

But according to the historian Lewis Thorpe, this account of Harold's death is not true. In his book, *The Bayeux Tapestry and the Norman Invasion*, Thorpe says that Harold was hacked to death by a Norman soldier, possibly one of four who attacked the king simultaneously.

The story of Harold's death may have become confused because at the place where the tapestry says, in Latin, *Harold rex interfectus est* (Harold the king is killed) there are two figures, either of which could be taken as Harold. One, on the left of a Norman horse, is standing, holding a shield and apparently trying to pluck an arrow from his eye. The other, falling, to the right of the horse, is being attacked by a Norman with a sword.

The arrow-in-the-eye story appears in 12th-century accounts of the battle by such historians as William of Malmesbury, Henry of Huntingdon and Robert Wace. But Thorpe takes as a more acceptable account that of a Norman historian, Guy of Amiens, written in 1068, only two years after the battle, in a book called *Carmen de Hastingae proelio* (The Song of the Battle of Hastings).

According to this account, William

'called Eustace of Boulogne to his side and moved up to give all the relief that he possibly could to those who were being slaughtered by Harold'.

In the attack, Eustace was joined by Hugh de Montfort, Ivo, heir to Ponthieu, and Walter Gifford the younger. 'By the use which they made of their weapons,' the Amiens version goes, 'these four between them encompassed the king's death. With the point of his lance the first pierced Harold's shield and then penetrated his chest, drenching the ground with his blood. With his sword the second cut off his head. The third disembowelled him with his javelin. The fourth hacked at his leg and hurled it far away. Struck down in this way, his dead body lay on the ground.'

Eve gave Adam an apple in the Garden of Eden Though the apple has become the symbol of man's fall from grace, nowhere in the story of the Temptation—recounted in Genesis 3—is there any mention of an apple. It is simply described as 'the fruit of the tree which is in the midst of the garden', and it has been suggested that since Adam and Eve dressed themselves in figleaves after eating the fruit, the tree may well have been a fig.

The apple probably entered the story

via Greek and Celtic mythology, in both of which the fruit belongs to love goddesses, and symbolises desire. When Aquila of Pontus translated the Song of Solomon from Hebrew into Greek in the 2nd century AD, he rendered 'I raised thee up under the apple tree; there my mother brought thee forth' as 'I raised thee up under the apple tree; there wast thou corrupted'—evidently taking the verse as a reference to the forbidden tree. St Jerome, translating the Old Testament into Latin, followed suit, and the idea that the fruit was an apple has persisted ever since.

Thumbs-down was the signal for death in the Roman arena A painting by the French artist Jean Léon Gérôme (1824–1904), that was first exhibited in 1873 and became extremely popular in the form of engravings, showed a Roman emperor giving the 'thumbs-down' sign to a gladiator to kill his fallen opponent. Perhaps it was from this painting that the legend of the gesture arose, for so far as is known, the signal for death in the arena was apparently never indicated by the turning down of a thumb.

A 1693 translation of the *Satires* of Juvenal (AD 60–*c.* 128), referred to 'where with thumbs bent back they popularly kill'. The classical scholar John Mayor, in his 1853 edition of Juvenal's work, explained: 'Those who wished the death of the conquered gladiator turned their thumbs toward their breasts, as a signal to his opponent to stab him; those who wished him to be spared turned their thumbs downwards, as a signal for dropping the sword.'

Roman emperors would seek the guidance of spectators before giving the life-or-death signal to a victorious gladiator.

The *Latin Dictionary* of Lewis and Short (1880) gives, under the entry for *pollex* (thumb): 'To close down the thumb (*premere*) was a sign of approbation; to extend it (*vertere, convertere, pollex infestus*) a sign of disapprobation.'

Cinderella wore glass slippers In the early French version of the popular children's fairy story, Cinderella wore *pantoufles en vair*—slippers of fur or white ermine. But by the 14th century the word *vair* had gone out of use, and when the French author Charles Perrault (1628–1703) rewrote the story in 1697, he was unfamiliar with the word, and took it to be *verre*, meaning glass.

The popular western version of the story is derived from Perrault's story, and so the glass slipper has passed into common retelling of the tale.

The story of Cinderella is rooted in obscure folk-tales and in the more than 500 versions that exist, the slipper invariably appears made of some rare or expensive material—of gold or silver, encrusted with jewels or pearls.

It is a folk-tale that occurs all over the world, not just in Europe. One of the earliest known versions is a Chinese story of the 9th century AD.

CANUTE ORDERED BACK THE SEA

IT IS NOT absolutely certain that the story of King Canute (about AD 994–1035) ordering back the waves and being soaked, ever occurred. And if it did, it seems, the

According to one historian, Canute's seaside escapade was a demonstration of his great humility.

tale may be misunderstood. The earliest version, contrary to popular supposition, does not make out the king to be stupid, but as a man of great humility.

A century or so after Canute's death, Henry of Huntingdon wrote, in his *Historia Anglorum*, that the king, angered by the flattery of his courtiers, who constantly told him he was capable of any achievement, arranged the sea-shore experiment. After ordering back the sea and getting his feet wet, Canute then said: 'Let all men know how empty and worthless is the power of kings, for there is none worthy of the name, but He whom heaven, earth and sea obey by eternal laws.'

Afterwards, according to Henry, Canute never again wore his crown. He hung it instead in Winchester Cathedral.

THEY NEVER SAID IT

Memorable, but misremembered phrases

Alas, poor Yorick, I knew him well— *attributed to Hamlet*
This line is a distortion of the one in Shakespeare's *Hamlet*, Act V, Scene 1, which reads: 'Alas! poor Yorick. I knew him, Horatio.'

Hamlet says the words to his friend Horatio after being handed the skull of Yorick, former court jester.

Tomorrow to fresh fields and pastures new— *attributed to Milton*
The saying, often used when embarking on some new venture, or taking final leave of friends, is a misquotation of a line by the poet John Milton, with one word altered.

In 'Lycidas', first published in 1638, Milton wrote:
At last he rose, and twitch'd his mantle blue; Tomorrow to fresh woods, and pastures new.
In common usage, 'fields' replaces 'woods' probably because alliteration with the word 'fresh' helps it to roll more easily off the tongue.

The English are a nation of shopkeepers *—attributed to Napoleon*
The phrase is commonly attributed to Napoleon as a reflection of his contempt for the English as a race of *petit bourgeois* —small businessmen.

But the phrase 'nation of shopkeepers', or merchants, was already in print when Napoleon was a boy, and was hardly his own creation. It was used in a political tract by the Welsh economist Josiah Tucker in 1766, later by the Scottish economist Adam Smith in his *Wealth of Nations* (1775) and the following year in Philadelphia by Samuel Adams.

Later, when Napoleon was in exile, the phrase was attributed to him by two biographers. Napoleon's doctor, Barry O'Meara, in *Napoleon in Exile, or A Voice from St Helena*, reported a conversation with the emperor on February 17, 1817, in which he said of the English, 'They are a nation of merchants'.

It is clear from O'Meara's text that, while Napoleon agrees with the assessment, he is himself quoting the Corsican patriot Pasquale de Paoli (1725–1807).

The journal of Gaspard Gougaud, who was also with Napoleon during his exile,

certainly shows that the emperor regarded the English as profit-oriented.

But it was Adam Smith's book—well known to Napoleon—which said: 'To found a great empire for the sole purpose of raising up a people of customers, may at first sight appear a project fit only for a nation of shopkeepers.'

Money is the root of all evil— *attributed to St Paul*
What St Paul actually said was: 'The *love* of money is the root of all evil'—he did not mean that money was evil in itself.

Let them eat cake — *attributed to Marie Antoinette*
In October 1789 the poor women of Paris marched on the royal palace of Versailles in an attempt to force Louis XVI to create a new, fairer government.

According to tradition, when his queen, Marie Antoinette, heard the women outside and was told they were hungry and had no bread, she said: 'Qu'ils mangent de la brioche.' This became popularly translated as 'Let them eat cake'.

The story was widely circulated at the time, and after the queen's execution. It was held to typify either her stupidity or her callous indifference to the sufferings of the poor. But there is no evidence that she ever made the remark.

The first reference to the phrase was in the 1760s—in Jean-Jacques Rousseau's *Confessions*—when Marie Antoinette was still a young girl.

Rousseau relates an anecdote about a 'great princess' who, when told that the peasants had no bread, replied: 'Qu'ils mangent de la brioche.' 'Brioche', a superior type of bread, was the only kind the princess knew—so in fact, the remark was kindly meant. It is possible that one of France's revolutionaries, who had read Rousseau, deliberately ascribed the remark to Marie Antoinette.

The Battle of Waterloo was won on the playing fields of Eton— *attributed to the Duke of Wellington*
When the first Duke of Wellington was a boy at Eton there were no playing fields and no organised team games, and as one of his descendants remarked, the first

EARLY CRICKET AT ETON *The school had neither playing fields nor team games when Wellington was a pupil there, so he is unlikely to have referred to them after his victory at Waterloo.*

duke's career at the school was 'short and inglorious'. It is therefore highly improbable that he ever made this famous remark.

It was first attributed to him in print by a Frenchman, Count Charles de Montalembert in his *De l'avenir politique de l'Angleterre* (England's political future), which was published in 1855, three years after Wellington's death.

But there is no contemporary evidence that the duke made the statement, or even that he is likely to have done so, for he had no great affection either for his school or for the public-school spirit. It was only later in the 19th century that these were emphasised as the chief causes of England's military and colonial successes.

Up Guards and at 'em— *attributed to the Duke of Wellington at Waterloo*
It is doubtful whether Wellington ever used this phrase. One of his contemporaries, J. W. Croker, reported in 1884 that he had written to the duke asking if he really did give this command at the Battle of Waterloo. In an undated letter, the duke replied: 'What I must have said and possibly did say was "Stand up, Guards", and then gave the commanding officers the order to attack'—so repulsing the last attack of the French Imperial Guard.

Elementary, my dear Watson!—*attributed to Sherlock Holmes*
The very phrase brings to mind Sir

Arthur Conan Doyle's creation, Sherlock Holmes—most famous detective of all time. Yet nowhere in any of Conan Doyle's books does Holmes ever utter the oft-quoted words.

The closest Holmes comes to saying it is in the story *The Crooked Man*, published in the *Strand Magazine* in 1893 and later included in *The Memoirs of Sherlock Holmes*, published in 1894.

In the story, Dr Watson, Holmes's former assistant, has got married and no longer lives at Holmes's flat at 221B Baker Street, London. When Holmes calls on Watson to ask for his help in solving a mystery, he makes a few deductions about his old friend. He observes, for example, that Watson still smokes the same pipe tobacco—from the ash on his coat—and that he is very busy.

Watson asks how he knows this. Holmes says that Watson takes a Hansom cab when he is busy and walks when he is not. Watson's boots are dusty enough to have been outdoors, but not enough to have been walking; therefore, Holmes says, he must have taken a Hansom. Therefore, he must be busy.

'Excellent!' Watson says.
'Elementary,' says Holmes.

Play it again, Sam—*attributed to Humphrey Bogart*
Although this is one of the best known catch-phrases associated with the tough-guy screen image of Humphrey Bogart,

MELODY FOR SCREEN ROMANCE *Humphrey Bogart and Ingrid Bergman in the film* Casablanca, *with Dooley Wilson as the club pianist who was asked to 'Play it, Sam'—but not by Bogart.*

he never made the remark at all. The association arose from Bogart's 1942 film *Casablanca*. He played a nightclub owner who was haunted by the song 'As Time Goes By', because it reminded him of his love for the film's heroine, played by Ingrid Bergman.

In fact, it was Miss Bergman who said 'Play it, Sam' to the club's pianist, overcoming his boss's injunction against the song. Bogart heard the tune and realised that his lost love had returned. His wrath for Sam was forgotten.

THE GREAT LOVER *Charles Boyer charms Hedy Lamarr in* Algiers . . . *without inviting her to the Casbah.*

Come with me to the Casbah—*attributed to Charles Boyer*
Charles Boyer built up a screen image that was to talkies what Rudolph Valentino had been to silent films. He was suave, handsome and had a thrilling French accent. In his 1938 film *Algiers*, Boyer spent a lot of time in the Casbah of Algiers—but although his Gallic tones

might well have been admirably suited to saying 'Come with me to the Casbah', he never used the phrase.

By the time Boyer made the film he was a famous actor much parodied and imitated as the archetypal French lover. It was probably through these imitations that the phrase became attributed to him.

You dirty rat—*attributed to James Cagney*
Throughout three decades the name James Cagney personified gangster films in the same way that Boris Karloff was a master of the horrific genre. Cagney was the craggy-jawed, rasping hoodlum in the snap-brimmed trilby hat. Yet he claims that he never said, in any of his countless films, 'You dirty rat'—although the line is the one all impersonators use when they imitate the Cagney style.

TOUGH GUY *James Cagney epitomised the screen gangster—but in none of his films did he use his impersonators' expression, 'You dirty rat'.*

333

Theories abound, but the questions remain

Intriguing
and unsolved mysteries

---•---

NO ROOM IN THE ARK?

End of the dinosaur's 140 million year dynasty

Dinosaurs had the run of the world for 140 million years. They dominated the plains of the earth, the jungles, the swamps and the rivers. Then, 65 million years ago—as far as modern man can make out—these reptiles suddenly died out and no new dinosaurs evolved to replace them. No one yet can be certain why.

It is one of the great unsolved mysteries of science. What makes it so baffling is that there was not just one kind of dinosaur, but many genera and hundreds of species.

Some were the sluggish monsters so often depicted by film-makers, but others were quick-moving hunters.

Palaeontologists—scientists who study extinct animal forms—used to suggest that dinosaurs were 'stupid'. But more recent study suggests they were no more so than reptiles of our own day.

Hunters from space

Dinosaur remains have been found in many different parts of the world. Yet, until recently, scientists could see no reason why these animals should have disappeared completely. All that emerged was a mass of theories, some rather absurd . . .

Raids by hunters in flying saucers;

Lack of room in Noah's Ark;

Annihilation by cavemen (dinosaurs died out millions of years before the emergence of man);

Extraction of the moon from the Pacific Ocean, with cataclysmic consequences (if this ever did happen, which most astronomers doubt, it would have been millions of years before the appearance of any advanced life forms on earth);

Lemming-like mass-suicide by all the species in all those places at more or less the same time! And even, as one researcher put it . . .

Paleoweltschmerz, a superb term which suggests that the dinosaurs became so disillusioned with their ancient world that they died of sheer boredom.

Other theories seem more plausible—but only at first glance . . .

Disease and parasites: again, it is unlikely that so many species in so many places could be affected by an epidemic;

Cosmic radiation: the theory is that, with the explosion of a supernova star in the galaxy, radiation on earth greatly increased, causing fatal mutations. But, if so, since primitive mammals were also present, why should only a few groups of creatures be affected while many others survived?

Starvation: carnivorous dinosaurs may have become so efficient that they killed off all the plant-eating dinosaurs and then died of hunger. The converse, however, may be more likely—that as the plant eaters died out for other reasons, the flesh-eaters would then also be doomed for lack of prey.

Inadequate construction: the idea that dinosaurs became too large for their environment gains some credence from the fact that in the fossil casts of some species it has been found that the pituitary gland, which controls an animal's growth, was excessively large. It may have become overactive through mutation and destroyed the dinosaurs by interfering with their metabolism. But some were no more than $2\frac{1}{2}$ ft long.

A dwindling brain: many dinosaurs had tiny brains for their size. One of the earliest species to die out, *Stegosaurus*, for example, was 30 ft long, weighed $1\frac{3}{4}$ tons yet had a brain little larger than the size of a walnut.

Egg-eating mammals: it is highly probable that other animals ate dinosaur

STARK RELIEF *A dinosaur skeleton emerges as a palaeontologist, working with great care, chisels sandstone away from a fossil at a site in Utah. This creature, a* Camarasaurus, *was 25 ft long.*

eggs—but hardly to the extent that the creature should become extinct. Several creatures eat crocodile eggs, but crocodiles still exist.

Senility: the idea that dinosaurs suffered from a form of racial old age is hard to reconcile with the known fact that they were so profuse and so active.

In the last decade, more sophisticated theories have evolved. Most of these are interlinked, and although the mystery may never be completely solved, bits of information begin to fit together like a huge biological jigsaw.

In 1972 a team from Bonn University discovered eight dinosaur eggs—two of them intact—in a rock wall near Corvières in the French Pyrenees.

These showed signs of a phenomenon known as 'egg-shell thinning'—which threatens many birds and reptiles today —and is known to be the result of hormone disturbances triggered by environmental stresses.

When this state occurs, the shells become so fragile that they break prematurely, or else cannot provide sufficient calcium to feed the embryo creatures within. Overcrowding is one of the environmental stresses known to produce this condition.

But the dinosaurs were probably already doomed, for overcrowding into a few places implies that enormous danger already threatened their environment.

Their extinction coincided with the end of the warm Cretaceous period. During this time, large mountain ranges were formed; this would have had a great influence on the climate, which would have become cooler.

The cold winters would have become particularly hazardous if, as some scientists now believe, the dinosaurs were warm-blooded. Lacking the external insulation of feathers and hair that protect birds and mammals, they would be unable to endure low temperatures.

The colder weather undoubtedly killed off many dinosaurs and possibly caused overcrowding in warmer areas. But the great dinosaur-killer—the single factor that wiped out the largest land animals that ever existed—may have been the innocent flowering of a few wild plants.

This theory, propounded in 1974 by Tony Swain of the Kew Botanical Gardens, London, hinges on the fact that dinosaurs, like most reptiles, probably had poor taste buds.

When the first flowering plants appeared about 120 million years ago, some gradually produced greater and greater amounts of bitter-tasting alkaloids. The dinosaurs, unable to taste the alkaloids, might easily have poisoned themselves.

With the dying out of the herbivorous dinosaurs, the days of the species that preyed and lived on them were also numbered. New players dominated the stage—mammals, some of whom eventually became man's far-off ancestors.

THE DINOSAUR LIVES?

Dinosaurs, generally regarded as extinct for 65 million years, may still be with us. According to one theory, it may be possible to see them by glancing out of almost any window. For two scientists claim that birds are really dinosaurs. Robert T. Bakker, an American, of Harvard University, and Peter Galton, an Englishman, of Bridgeport University in the United States, partly base their claim on the theory that, unlike other reptiles, dinosaurs were warm-blooded—as are birds. That theory is accepted by some palaeontologists, rejected by others, and many regard the evidence as inconclusive either way. Bakker and Galton cited the work of a leading American palaeontologist, John Ostrom, who in 1973 pointed out what he claimed were similarities between the skeleton of the earliest-known bird, *Archaeopteryx*, and that of a certain type of dinosaur. Palaeontologists had previously believed that birds and dinosaurs evolved separately from thecodontians —primitive reptiles which lived 200 million years ago. The birds would have to be descended from early dinosaurs because they were already living as contemporaries of the later dinosaurs some 140 million years ago. That is to say, although none of the dinosaurs from the latter half of their long reign has survived, that a lower branch of the family tree may have survived as birds.

REMAINS OF A MAMMOTH *The body of this beast was found on the Beresovka River in 1902 after a big thaw, but more carcasses have been found in northern Siberia and Alaska.*

TEN-THOUSAND-YEAR-OLD STEAKS
The riddle of the mammoths who ate buttercups

A mammoth discovered half kneeling, half standing in a bank of the Beresovka River in Siberia perplexed scientists for many years; for the strangest thing of all about the frozen, well-preserved monster was that it had buttercups in its mouth. This odd fact, at first overlooked, was to provide a clue to a terrible moment in earth's history.

Mammoths were long-tusked, hairy members of the elephant family, which roamed the world for half a million years and became extinct about 20,000 years ago. In the permanently frozen territories of northern Siberia, Alaska and Canada many of these ancient beasts can still be found, for ever preserved like sides of beef in a deep-freeze.

In spite of the thousands of years which have passed, the meat is still good enough to eat—according to those who have tried. Other long-extinct animals have also been found in the same deep-frozen condition, their bodies often tumbled together in heaps of bones and mangled flesh.

Scientists had no difficulty in explaining this ancient tragedy. Huge herds of mammoths used to roam the tundras—the great Arctic plains—feeding off the grass, reeds and other plants that still cover the land in summer. Every now and then one of them would get trapped in ice, or would fall to its death down a crevasse in a glacier; there the carcass would freeze and be preserved, almost unchanged, through the ages.

The explanation was obvious; unfortunately, it was totally wrong.

To begin with, the carcasses were found in the wrong places. Vast areas of the Arctic are covered with ice, but most of the tundra is composed of soil—sand, river-silt and loam—bound together by frozen water. And the frozen mammoths were discovered not in the ice, but in the silt layers.

Moreover, during the relevant period, there were no glaciers in Siberia except

337

in the upper reaches of the mountains where the mammoths did not graze.

A new theory was put forward: the mammoths had fallen into rivers and had been carried downstream to the estuaries, where they were buried in silt. But this did not fit either; the monsters were being found in the tundra where rivers had never been. And they could not all have drowned, because many of the animals were still standing up.

Experts in the deep-freeze butchery trade were consulted. But instead of clearing up the mystery they made it far more puzzling. It was not possible, they said, to deep-freeze a creature as large as a mammoth at the relatively moderate temperatures of Arctic ice.

If meat is frozen slowly at ice temperature, crystals form in the cells of the flesh, bursting the cells and dehydrating the meat. This makes the meat unfit for consumption; and no such process, the butchers added, could have produced the deep-frozen mammoth meat.

To satisfactorily freeze a side of beef takes 30 minutes at $-40°C$ ($-40°F$). To deep-freeze a huge living mammoth, insulated in thick fur, they estimated that stupendously cold temperatures of below $-101°C$ ($-150°F$) would be required. Such temperatures have never been recorded—not even in the Arctic.

The evidence seems to show the absurdity of such a theory, particularly the evidence of the Beresovka mammoth. At the time of its death this beast had been eating sedges, grasses and buttercups.

Suddenly frozen stiff

As many gardeners know to their cost, buttercups enjoy temperate conditions with alternating sun and rain.

Yet, apparently, at one moment the mammoth was munching away peacefully at the grass and buttercups growing lush in the sunshine of a temperate plain. The next—so the deep-freeze men insisted —it was subjected to cold so bitter that it was deep-frozen where it stood.

These were unalterable facts. The scientists had to explain how it could have happened, not only on the Beresovka, but at many places all over northern Siberia and Alaska where mammoths were suddenly frozen stiff.

No known variation in climate can explain the sudden deep-freezing of so many great beasts so many thousands of miles apart. Only a sudden cataclysm of hitherto undreamt proportions could have been responsible.

The evidence suggests an earthquake and volcanic eruption more violent than any ever recorded in history.

The crust of the earth, which floats 20 to 60 miles thick over the molten interior of our planet, is known to be composed of several plates, pressed one against the other. Where two plates meet, under titanic thrusts from every side, volcanic eruptions and earthquakes may occur.

It is thought that the eruption, which caused the death of the mammoths, was the result of two plates grinding together and bursting open a vast seam deep within the earth's crust.

Cold unimaginable

In so violent an eruption, not only would fiery lava be spewed out from the interior of the earth, but there would be a great discharge of volcanic gases.

If these gases were shot high enough into the upper atmosphere, they would be chilled to incredibly low temperatures. Then, in the upheaval, they would spiral towards the poles, eventually descending on the warm blanket of air beneath. Through this they would penetrate as violent gusts, cutting through the blanket at its thinnest spots and hurtling at incredible speeds down upon the earth.

The result in the localities where the gases struck would be unimaginably cold, sufficient to produce the $-101°C$ ($-150°F$) temperatures postulated by the deep-freeze experts.

In Siberia, the unsuspecting mammoth would have been grazing on the tundra when a cold so fierce descended on him that it immediately froze his lungs, and literally turned his blood to ice. In a few seconds he would have died; in a few hours he would be a solid statue, ready to sink into the earth over the years and be buried in the dusts of time.

Or perhaps the cold was accompanied by a wind so violent that every living creature—mammoths, tigers, lions, woolly rhinoceroses, bison and beavers—would be hurled along in a maelstrom to the side of a hill, where they would be deposited in a frozen mass, to lie forever in a tangle of trees, boulders and soil.

The picture is a terrible one, the more so as mankind has no guarantee that it will not happen again.

THE GIANTS OF EASTER ISLAND

Who carved the great stone heads—and why?

Dutch admiral Jakob Roggeveen had never seen anything like it in his life before—an uncharted island in the mid-South Pacific inhabited by what appeared to be 30 ft tall giants. The giants seemed to be standing on huge walls which resembled the battlements of a gargantuan fortress.

As Roggeveen sailed his three ships closer, he was relieved to find that the giants were only statues and the men he could see walking among them were of normal size.

With a small landing party, Roggeveen went ashore next day to find that the 'battlements' were only platforms for the statues. On each stood the bust of a man with long ears and a red headpiece.

The date was Easter Day 1722, and so Roggeveen named his discovery Easter Island. He then sailed away.

It was almost 50 years before Europeans landed again on Easter Island, and another 100 years before serious explorations began.

By then, the statues were no longer erect as Roggeveen had seen them. During tribal wars, most had been toppled from their platforms to the ground, as they remain to this day.

The giant statues proved to be carved from volcanic rock found in the dormant crater of Rano Raraku. More than 300 of them had been carved from the crater walls and then lowered down its slope. They had somehow been manoeuvred into an upright position on the platforms.

Inside the crater were some 400 uncompleted statues. Some had only a few chisel marks on them while others were almost ready for transportation.

Obsidian hatchets and chisels, abandoned by the ancient sculptors of the giant statues, were also found in the crater.

They had been left as though the craftsmen had intended to return some day, but never did. Down the road leading from the crater were dozens of completed statues. They lay scattered every 50 yds for as far as the eye could see.

Several weighed up to 30 tons and stood 12 ft tall. One unfinished giant was 66 ft tall and weighed about 50 tons.

Long-eared people

Some of the statues were 10 miles from the crater, and to this day experts have still not worked out how the island's inhabitants transported the monuments or erected them on their bases.

Theories that logs were used as rollers were discounted, after tests showed that the Easter Island soil could not support

THE ANCIENT GIANTS *Scientists have asked for centuries how and why the huge stone sculptures came to be erected on the island in mid-ocean.*

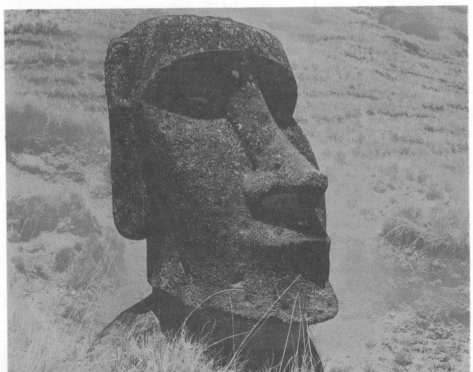

trees of the size required for such an exercise. Another possibility considered was that vines woven into ropes were used to haul them. But this, too, was ruled out when it was proved that vine ropes could not stand the strain of pulling 30 tons.

Traces of ancient settlements indicated that Easter Island once supported from 2000 to 5000 people. Drawings which have been found show that they were probably divided into two classes. The 'long-eared' people portrayed in the statues were probably the rulers—who used weights to stretch their ear lobes— while the 'short-eared' people were most likely their subordinates.

Similar ear weights were used by the Incas of pre-Conquest Peru. But the present inhabitants seem more closely akin to the Polynesians than to the people of South America.

The vital key to Easter Island's mysteries could have been removed by a late-19th-century Peruvian slave trader who captured 1000 natives, including the last king and 'wise man' of the island.

No one knows exactly what happened to all the men who were carried off into bondage. Some may have returned, bringing disease with them that killed off the remainder of the population. With their disappearance may have gone the answers to questions of how a stone-age people created an army of monoliths.

THE GREY-EYED INDIANS
How Raleigh's 'lost colony' may have survived

Explorers driving inland along the Lumber River of North Carolina, early in the 18th century, were astonished to find a tribe of grey-eyed Indians whose native language was a kind of English!

They claimed that their ancestors could 'talk in a book', which, the explorers understood, meant that they could read.

Today, the descendants of these mysterious people still live in Robeson County where they were discovered. Known as the 'Lumbee Indians', they have complexions ranging from dark to very fair. To this day, blonde hair and blue eyes are not uncommon.

No one knows the tribe's true heritage, but an intriguing theory has been pieced together over the years.

It is now thought that they may be the remnants of Sir Walter Raleigh's 'lost colony' of Roanoke Island, from which all the English settlers disappeared without trace in 1590. The Lumber River is about 200 miles from Roanoke.

When Elizabeth I granted a charter to Raleigh, two attempts were made at colonisation. The first was abandoned in 1586 because of recurring Indian attacks and shortage of supplies.

The party of more than 100 men and women, led by Governor John White, who arrived in 1587, fared little better. Eventually White decided to sail back to England with a skeleton crew of 15 to seek help and supplies. He left instruc-

tions that if the remaining colonists were forced to leave in his absence, they should inscribe their destination 'in a conspicuous place'.

Fortress ransacked

Because of the war between England and Spain, it was not until 1590 that White was able to return. A fortress had been built at Roanoke, but it had been ransacked and then abandoned; the settlers had vanished without trace. Only one clue remained—the word CROATOAN, carved into a post.

Historians still argue over its meaning. Some believed it was the name of an Indian tribe that attacked the settlement and massacred the colonists.

But Croatoan was an island south of Roanoke, which the colonists knew was inhabited by the friendly Hatteras tribe. If the colonists had managed to reach that island and then had intermarried with the Hatteras, their descendants could be today's Lumbee Indians.

Governor White assumed that the settlers had moved to Croatoan voluntarily, but because he was unable to search for them, he returned to England.

Yet there is now strong evidence to suggest that he was right. About 1650, many Hatteras Indians migrated to the mainland and settled in the Lumber Valley. Moreover, of the 95 surnames of the 'lost' colonists of Roanoke, only 41 can be found today among the Lumbees.

'BEE IT KNOWNE VNTO ALL MEN' *This brass plaque, apparently declaring Drake's annexation of 'New Albion' in 1579, was found on a beach in California in 1936.*

BRITISH CALIFORNIA

The plaque that establishes England's claim

One summer's day in 1936, Mr Beryle Shinn, a San Francisco shop assistant, was picnicking on the shore north of the Golden Gate bridge. Picking up a rock, he was mildly surprised to find a dirty old brass plate beneath it.

Mr Shinn took it home, thinking that it might come in useful for car repairs.

In the name of Her Majesty

He left the plate in his garage and forgot about it for eight months. Then coming across it again early in 1937, he cleaned it up with soap and water. It measured 5 in. by 8 in. It had a jagged hole at the bottom and there was writing scratched on it. The word 'Drake' could be faintly deciphered.

The discovery of that piece of brass was to start an international argument that involved American historians, metallurgists, scholars of old English and antiquarians. For on the plate were written the words of the formal annexation of California by Sir Francis Drake in 1579.

Shinn had the plate sent to Dr Herbert Bolton of the University of California,

who carefully cleaned it and deciphered the inscription:

BEE IT KNOWNE VNTO ALL MEN
BY THESE PRESENTS
IVNE 17 1579
BY THE GRACE OF GOD AND IN THE NAME
OF HERR MAIESTY QVEEN ELIZABETH OF
ENGLAND AND HERR SVCCESSORS FOREVER
I TAKE POSSESSION OF THIS KINGDOME
WHOSE KING AND PEOPLE FREELY RESIGNE
THEIR RIGHT AND TITLE IN THE WHOLE
LAND VNTO HERR MAIESTIES KEEPEING NOW
NAMED BY ME AN TO BEE KNOWNE VNTO
ALL MEN AS NOVA ALBION
FRANCIS DRAKE

Triumphantly, Dr Bolton announced to a surprised California Historical Society: 'Here it is. Recovered at last after a lapse of 357 years. Behold, Drake's plate —the plate of brass. California's choicest archaeological treasure!'

Gods in California

But it was not as simple as that. The great argument was just beginning. It is known that Sir Francis Drake visited California in 1579 during his round-the-world voyage. He was being hunted by the Spaniards after sailing round the southern tip of South America and into the Pacific.

Trying to escape pursuit by reaching the fabled North-West Passage, which early navigators imagined would connect the Pacific with the Atlantic to the north of Canada, he landed in California near what is now San Francisco. He and his crew were warmly received by the Indians. They thought the Englishmen were gods and offered them their entire country along the Californian seaboard.

According to reports of the voyage, Drake graciously accepted the offer, ordered a plate to be nailed to a post and set up on shore, announcing that the territory had now become a domain of Queen Elizabeth and would henceforth be known as New Albion.

Until Mr Shinn's picnic, nothing more had been seen or heard of the plaque.

But now the whole academic world of the United States was agog. Experts denounced the plaque as a forgery.

They pointed out that contemporary reports said that Drake had landed at a spot marked by 'white bancks and cliffes'. There was none at the picnic spot.

Then the date on the plaque was hard to accept. The reports said that although Drake had landed on June 17, the Indians had not ceded the territory until June 26.

Science raises doubts

Analysis of the metal showed that the brass had a higher zinc content than was usual in the 16th century. And tests on the exterior of the metal showed it to have a high carbon content—as if fire had been used to hasten the ageing process.

But the main attack came over the lettering and the words used. The letters were all Roman, used only by scholars in Elizabethan days in preference to the more common ornamental Tudor lettering. Besides, the words had a suspicious conformity in a day when spelling varied from page to page. And the engraver had used the modern forms for words which in the 16th century were more often spelt 'Yngland', 'Kyng', 'Quene' and 'yt' (it).

As a final objection they said the spelling 'herr' (for 'her') did not exist in the 16th century.

However, Dr Bolton was able to answer his critics point by point.

The Indians might well not have formally ceded the territory until June 26,

but accounts of the voyage stated clearly that the plate was engraved on 'the day and yeare of our arrival'.

Moreover, the brass was now found by scientific analysis to be ancient and covered with a naturally acquired coating 'formed over many years'. Plant cells in the jagged hole were 'undoubtedly mineralised', which could only have occurred if the plaque had lain in the open for a considerable period.

Grooves examined

The report concluded: 'Each individual groove of the lettering was examined under the microscope at magnifications of 50 to 200 diameters because, in the case of fraud, there is always the chance of finding a hidden area which would disclose a fresh, corrosion-free surface. . . . No indication or clue of artificial patination of any kind was found.'

As for the lettering and the spelling, Dr Bolton's supporters had answers to rebut the sceptics. Were there not scholars on board with Sir Francis, or at least books from which Roman script could be copied? Was it not reasonable for spelling to be uniform over so short a text? And were the 'modern' spellings not current among Elizabethan variations?

Soon it was discovered that Drake himself had used the spelling 'herr' in a prospectus for lands. The only criticism he was unable to refute was that Drake had landed near white banks and cliffs —until a surprising thing happened.

When the news of Mr Shinn's find was published, a chauffeur named William Caldeira came forward. Four years previously, he stated, he had been waiting for his employer on the shore at Laguna Beach, when he had turned over a clod of earth with his foot. Under it was a brass plate bearing what he thought was a Chinese inscription, although he had recognised the word 'Drake' in English.

He too had kept the plaque for possible car repairs, but a few months later had thrown it away not far from where Beryle Shinn found it. Mr Caldeira had found the plate at Drake's Bay—the spot traditionally accepted as the landing-place— and whose most outstanding features are tall, white cliffs. The plate was vindicated, and Britain's title deed to the state now rests in the University of California. So far, the British have generously refused to take up their option.

SLOW TRAIN TO IZMIR

The girl who vanished with the treasures of Dorak

Archaeologist James Mellaart took little notice of the dark-haired girl sitting opposite him on the train from Istanbul—until a glance at the bracelet she was wearing told him it was thousands of years old, and made of solid gold. That glance was to lead him to a hoard of priceless treasure—and a year-long battle to defend himself against a campaign of suspicion and calumny.

Was it all a hoax? Or was Mellaart the victim of a sinister plot to undermine his reputation? At the time he simply could not believe his luck.

No archaeologist could have ignored the bracelet. As the train trundled across Turkey he introduced himself. The girl told him the bracelet came from a collection at her home, and agreed to let him examine the remainder.

By the time the train drew into Izmir, on Turkey's Aegean coast, that evening in 1958, Mellaart was burning with eagerness. So he paid little attention to the ferry-and-taxi route they took to the girl's home, where the collection was lifted piece by piece from its hiding place in a chest of drawers.

Mellaart was astounded. Here was a find comparable to the discovery of Tutankhamun's tomb. He asked if he could photograph it. The girl refused, but said he could stay in the house while he made sketches.

Mellaart jumped at the chance. For days he worked without a break on the fabulous pieces, copying their intricate designs, taking rubbings of their hieroglyphs, noting every detail.

The girl, who said she was Greek, told him that the collection had been found during the Greek occupation after the First World War. It came from a secret excavation at a small lakeside village called Dorak.

To Mellaart the implications were staggering. For he knew that the pieces were 4500-year-old Bronze Age relics, and that he had stumbled on the first evidence that a great seafaring city had flourished near Homer's Troy, ruled by a warrior caste and rivalling Troy itself in wealth and influence. It was an archaeologist's dream. All the theories would now have to be re-examined.

Finally, late one night, he finished his work and left. It was the last time he saw the girl, or the treasure. Mellaart realised only much later just how little he had discovered about the girl who was the key to his find. He could remember only that she spoke English with an American accent; she had given her address as 217 Kazim Direk Street; and her name was Anna Papastrati.

Mellaart's acceptance of this without checking up was his first dangerous mistake. Later, suspicious Turkish investigators said they could find no trace of anyone of that name; moreover, Kazim Direk Street simply did not exist.

His second mistake came when he reported to his chief at the British Institute of Archaeology in Ankara, Professor Seton Lloyd. Mellaart, who was the assistant director, told Lloyd that he had found the treasure six years earlier and had only just received permission to publish his findings. It was a lie, invented for an entirely innocent reason. Mellaart had been married for four years, and he did not want his wife to be embarrassed by gossip that he had spent several days in another girl's home.

The lost letter

Mellaart was to regret both mistakes during his long and bitter fight to vindicate himself against the accusations flung at him following the publication of his findings in the *Illustrated London News* in November 1959. He had written to the Turkish Department of Antiquities to warn them of the planned publication, but the letter had been mislaid.

When the article appeared, with Mellaart's drawings, Turkish officials were furious. They demanded to know where the treasure was, where it had been found, and why they had not been told. Thinking that a precious national treasure had been spirited away, they blamed Mellaart. Mellaart helped them all he could, but Anna—and the treasure—had vanished totally without trace.

There was no evidence to implicate Mellaart in any way with the disappearance of the treasure. Nevertheless, two and a half years later a smear campaign was launched, instigated by the Turkish newspaper *Milliyet*. The newspaper claimed that the date of the Dorak excavation was false; the finds, it said, had been made in the 1950s, when Mellaart and a mysterious woman had been seen near the site.

This was proved false. But the campaign of smears and cold-shoulder treatment went on. Though police inquiries had been dropped, Mellaart was banned from further work on a Turkish archaeological site where he had already made several important discoveries.

Secret and influential enemies were busy in the background. But why should they try to discredit him by suggesting that his story was just an invention to further his career? Mellaart had already achieved a world reputation: he needed no publicity stunts.

And who was Anna? Was it sheer coincidence that she met Mellaart on the train that day? Or was she 'planted' there by someone who knew that her bracelet could hardly fail to catch the archaeologist's eye?

Art gang's dupe

One theory is that Mellaart was the bait in a cunning trap set by a smuggling gang who already had the Dorak treasure hidden away and ready for sale. Such a gang would know that the value of their loot on the world black market would be enormously enhanced once it was pronounced genuine by an unsuspecting expert of Mellaart's repute. The authoritative article in the *Illustrated London News* provided this stamp of authenticity: were the pieces then quietly shipped away to secret buyers all over the world?

If that is what really happened, then the truth about Anna and the vanishing fortune may have been locked away for ever—behind the doors of some of the world's wealthiest and most unscrupulous art-collectors.

THE PITCHFORK MURDER

Was the harmless old villager a witch?

His two-pronged pitchfork was thrust through his neck, pinning him to the ground. His hedger's slash-hook was embedded in his chest. The dead face of the old man was frozen in an expression of terror. This was how they found Charles Walton in 1945, victim of possibly the last ritualistic 'witchcraft' murder in Britain. Detective Superintendent Fabian—the famous 'Fabian of Scotland Yard'—spent many months leading the investigation of the crime. But the mystery of who did it, and why, was never solved. It remains an enigma, horrific in its savagery and wrapped in an atmosphere of mystic fear.

Odd-job man

To all appearances Charles Walton was a harmless, endearing old man, such as one might meet in any English village that has not been caught up in the pace of modern life. He lived with his niece in a thatched cottage in Lower Quinton, Warwickshire, earning enough to keep body and soul together by doing odd jobs about the farms at 18 pence an hour.

He was not seen much in the local pubs, preferring to buy cider by the gallon and drink alone by his kitchen fireside. He was a man, as they say in the country, who 'kept himself to himself'.

But Old Walton, though not over-fond of human companionship, was at home in the countryside, alone with nature. He would spend hours talking to the wild birds—and he believed there was an understanding between them.

He did not much care for dogs, but in his back garden he bred toads—big natterjacks. There was a local legend that he used to harness them in a miniature plough and follow them across the fields.

Whispering of witchcraft

It was a winter's day in February when Charles failed to return from his work in the fields, and searchers found his mutilated body under a willow tree. Donald McCormick, who wrote a book on the crime, claimed that he could make a good guess at who the killer was. So too could Fabian.

But no evidence could be produced to justify a prosecution. Only tales of Old Walton's communion with the birds, of his toad plough-teams . . . and sinister whisperings that he was killed because he was a witch.

MARTYR OR MURDERER?

The hero who confessed to witchcraft

To the people of Brittany, that September day in 1440 must have seemed like the ending of the world. The magnificent, prodigiously wealthy Baron Gilles de Rais had been arrested and charged with sorcery, sacrilege and the ritual murder of little children.

Even in the brilliant and extravagant court of 15th-century France, few careers had been so meteoric as that of Gilles. Heir to the greatest barony of Brittany, he had fought with Joan of Arc against England and was Marshal of France at the age of 24. So rich did he become, that the number and splendour of his castles were second only to those of the king.

Then the blow fell. The prosecutors alleged that he maintained an Italian magician, Francesco Prelati, with whose assistance he had kidnapped and murdered large numbers of children. Their blood was alleged to have been used by Gilles, in fearsome potions, to gain magical power over his enemies.

On October 21, the marshal confessed to all the crimes with which he had been charged, and explained that his motives were simply to gratify his passions. 'I tell you that there was no other motive. Have I not already told you enough to put ten thousand men to death?'

Gilles was hanged with his associates at Nantes, before the end of October. Few people doubted his guilt; after all, surely no man, not even Gilles, could have achieved so much without some assistance from the Devil?

But the trial was held behind closed doors and there were some disquieting doubts. Gilles' henchmen were certainly tortured, and the baron may have been subjected to the same treatment himself. Was he the victim of a conspiracy? If so, suspicion falls on John, Duke of Brittany, who stood to gain de Rais' lands.

Gilles was an easy target for accusations of sorcery, for he paid scant regard to conventional morality and interested himself in alchemy and astrology. Also, his gluttony, extravagance and sexual activities were notorious. Regrettable, perhaps, but no evidence that he was a murderer of children.

Why, then, if he was innocent, did he confess to such foul crimes? Perhaps he did so under torture. But there is a more likely explanation.

Gilles knew that once under the power of his enemies he was doomed, and since his life was forfeit in any case, his only concern would be for the safety and welfare of his family.

If Gilles denied the charges and was found guilty, his lands and wealth would be confiscated. But, if he confessed and died repentant, then the law provided that at least part of his estate would pass to his children.

And so it happened. Although Gilles' castles were granted to the Duke of Brittany, most of his wealth remained with his family who suffered no great disgrace. Some of them rose to high office in royal service—but none became so dangerously rich and powerful as Gilles himself.

ST JOAN'S LIEUTENANT *Gilles de Rais' supposed excesses earned him the title of 'Bluebeard' and a shameful death.*

345

RICHARD III ON TRIAL

Was he really the 'wickedest uncle in history'?

When the bones of two small boys were found beneath a staircase in the Tower of London in the late 17th century, it seemed to confirm the old story that Richard III, cruel, hunchbacked and the wickedest uncle in history, had in fact murdered his nephews. Not that most people needed convincing: Shakespeare's portrayal of Richard, crippled and twisted in body and mind, and his re-creation of the crime in the Tower had already established the king's niche in the pantheon of villainy.

Yet some historians believe that if Richard were brought to trial today, the prosecution would fail for lack of evidence: indeed, what proof there was might point in another direction entirely.

When Edward IV died in 1483, his brother, Richard, was appointed Protector of the Realm and guardian of Edward's sons, the boy king Edward V and his young brother Richard, Duke of York.

While preparations began in London for Edward's coronation, Richard rode to Stony Stratford, near Northampton and escorted the boy king back to the Tower of London.

The younger nephew, Richard, had been taken by his mother for sanctuary in Westminster Abbey, but soon joined his brother at the Tower.

On one or two occasions the boys were seen playing together in the Tower gardens. Then they disappeared for ever from the public gaze. Sir Thomas More, in his biography of King Richard III, wrote that the king had the boys suffocated with a pillow. But More was writing from hearsay more than 30 years later.

There is not even any firm evidence that Richard stood to gain by the princes' murder. Only two months after their father's death it was being claimed by Robert Stillington, Dean of St Martin's, that the boys were illegitimate.

When Edward IV had married their mother, Elizabeth Woodville, in 1464, he had been betrothed to the daughter of the Earl of Shrewsbury. At the time such a formal betrothal was as binding as marriage itself, so technically the wedding was invalid—and Richard was the legitimate heir.

But if Richard did not murder the boys, who did, or who at least had sufficient motive? Many scholars believe the most likely suspect is Henry Tudor, who defeated Richard at the Battle of Bosworth Field in 1485 and became Henry VII.

Henry was the great-grandson of an illegitimate son of Edward III and had thus been excluded from the succession. He based his claim to the throne only on the right of conquest, and to make his position more secure, married Elizabeth, sister of the princes in the Tower.

He had Elizabeth declared legitimate, but in so doing, restored the legitimacy of her brothers. If they were still alive, and Henry was to be king, he would have to dispose of them.

Nevertheless, there is no proof of Henry's guilt, any more than there is of Richard's. But Henry did not announce that the boys had been murdered by their uncle until July 16, 1486—nearly a year after Richard's death. As Henry had accused Richard of cruelty and tyranny immediately he gained the throne, why did he not announce the murder then?

SLAUGHTER OF INNOCENTS *A Victorian artist re-creates the popular notion of how the princes died in the Tower.*

THE MAN IN THE VELVET MASK

The prisoner the Sun King dared not kill

During the 60th year of Louis XIV's reign, a mysterious man died in the Bastille. He had spent 34 years in prison, his face forever concealed from the world by a velvet mask.

A letter written by a French princess to a friend at the English court tells of the 'ancient prisoner':

'For many years a man has lived, masked, in the Bastille and masked he has died. Two musketeers were always at his side to kill him if he unmasked. There must, no doubt, have been some reason for this, as otherwise he was very well treated, well lodged and given all he wanted. No one has ever been able to find out who he was.'

The romantic novelist Alexandre Dumas changed the nature of the mask in his book *The Man In The Iron Mask*, and popularised the idea that the unidentified prisoner was either King Louis himself or a twin brother. But the known facts point to an even stranger explanation of the mystery.

Extraordinary precautions

From the moment he was arrested in the port city of Dunkirk in 1669, the prisoner was subjected to the most extraordinary security precautions. When he was sent to the prison of Pignerol, near Turin, then part of France, Monsieur St Mars, the governor, was given these instructions: 'You are to threaten him with death if he ever opens his mouth to you on any subject other than his day-to-day needs.'

Whenever St Mars was transferred to another gaol, his prisoner went with him, transported in a sedan chair sealed from curious eyes with wax paper. It is said he almost died of the heat.

In 1698 St Mars took over as governor of the Bastille and even then, nearly 30 years after the arrest, he was instructed to take all precautions to prevent the man being recognised.

It appears that the mask was a precaution and not a punishment. Yet no one in the public eye was unaccounted for during the period, so why should such a precaution be necessary? The key to the riddle may well be that the prisoner bore a startling resemblance to a very important person—and that this close resemblance could be very embarrassing.

One suggestion, put forward by the statesman and scholar, Lord Quickswood, and one that fits all the known facts, is that the prisoner was none other than the true father of Louis XIV.

For 13 of their 22 years' marriage, Louis XIII and Anne of Austria had no children. Cardinal Richelieu was at that time the effective ruler of France, and it was in his interests that the king should have an heir, who could also be controlled by the Richelieu faction.

For years the king and queen had lived apart. But Richelieu now managed to stage a formal reconciliation. And to the utter surprise of all France, the queen gave birth to a son in 1638.

Since the royal couple had never had a child before, and cordially detested one another, it is not beyond the bounds of possibility that Richelieu persuaded the queen to allow some handsome young nobleman to sire the child in her husband's stead. In Paris at the time there were many illegitimate sons of the promiscuous

ROMANTIC VERSION *Such concepts of the mysterious prisoner were wrong. His mask was made of velvet and he lived in style and comfort.*

347

Henry of Navarre—all half-brothers of Louis XIII—so there would be no necessity to search outside the royal Bourbon blood. Richelieu might easily have found a personable and willing young Bourbon, and persuaded the queen there was no other way out of their dilemma.

Certainly, during the boy's childhood, it was said at court that the young Louis, strong and active, was as unlike his father as it was possible to be.

If the suggestion is true, the real father would probably have been sent abroad—possibly to the French colony of Canada. Eventually he may have returned to France, imagining that the affair had been forgotten—or possibly hoping for a pension or other favours from his son, now the all-powerful Sun King.

The theory is that he resembled the king too closely, that his appearance would have been an embarrassment at court and threatened the throne itself.

The obvious solution, to have had him quietly murdered, would be out of the question. Louis was not over-scrupulous, but even he would have balked at killing his own father. The alternative was total obscurity—a life that was comfortable yet utterly cut off from any human contact except that of his gaolers.

He died as he lived, faceless and unknown, his anonymity preserved even to the grave. Like all who ended their lives in the Bastille, he was buried under a false name. The man who may have been the Sun King's father was listed on the records as Eustache Dauger, valet.

RIDDLE OF THE MONEY PIT

Fortune hunters swamped by ingenious engineering

For nearly 200 years, singly and in syndicates, men have been boring and tunnelling on a small island off Nova Scotia in search of a fabulous treasure.

Vastly more treasure—nearly $1·5 millions—has been poured into the search than has ever come out of it; for whoever dug the Money Pit on Oak Island was a brilliant engineer, who harnessed the sea to keep out trespassers.

The pit consists of a deep shaft, furnished with an ingenious series of side-tunnels which allow the sea to flood in whenever diggers plumb its depths. Party after party of hopefuls have retired, soaked and baffled.

The only finds so far have been: three links of a chain that may have been gold or copper (accounts vary); a tiny scrap of parchment showing two letters, V and I, written with a quill pen; and, found 90 ft down the shaft, a cipher stone with odd symbols, which were optimistically taken to mean '10 ft below £2 millions are buried'.

The hunt began in 1795, when 16-year-old Daniel McGinnis paddled over from the little Nova Scotian town of Chester to hunt game on uninhabited Oak Island. In a clearing at one end of the island, an old ship's tackle block hung from a tree over the centre of a 12 ft wide depression.

Undeterred by tales of hauntings and fired by legends of pirate treasure, he and two other boys started digging. They found a 13 ft wide circular shaft dug through flinty clay, with thick oak platforms at 10, 20 and 30 ft. The work became harder, and for various reasons —including the difficulty of getting help from superstitious townsfolk—was abandoned until 1804.

In that year, a wealthy Nova Scotian named Simeon Lynds formed the first treasure company—and found the first and greatest obstacle to all further 'open' explorations of the pit: water.

The diggers had broken through eight oak platforms, three of which were sealed with ship's putty and coconut fibre. The cipher stone was found at 90 ft, and when the hole had been dug only another 3 ft deeper, a crowbar hit something solid. Lynds was sure it was a treasure chest.

Next day he was mortified to discover that the pit was filled with 60 ft of water. Weeks of bailing with buckets and crude pumps failed to lower the level.

In 1805 Lynds's miners sank another shaft, close to and parallel with the pit, and at 110 ft started burrowing towards the 'treasure'. They had to scramble for their lives when water suddenly burst into their shaft—and filled it to the same level as the water in the pit. Once-wealthy Simeon Lynds was now nearly penniless.

TRAIL OF MYSTERY *For two centuries Oak Island (above) has tantalised fortune seekers. Beneath the shaft (inset), a deep pit (below left) is reputed to contain a legendary hoard.*

**Diagram labels (left column, top to bottom):**

- stones
- oak platforms
- tide level
- airlock
- oak platform sealed with putty
- oak platform
- airlock
- oak platform with putty and coconut fibre
- oak platform
- oak platform sealed with coconut fibre
- cipher stone
- airlock
- oak platform sealed with putty
- chests?
- spruce platform
- High Tunnel to shore (Smith's Cove)
- 180ft
- Low Tunnel to shore (Smith's Cove)
- underground stream?

The original discoverer of the Money Pit, Daniel McGinnis, died. But in 1849 the two boys who had helped him with the first dig in 1795, John Smith and Anthony Vaughan, now in their seventies, tried again with the help of a syndicate from Truro, Nova Scotia.

Two or more chests

Their shafts, drillings and pumpings seemed to confirm the existence of two or more chests that might contain treasure in some form; but their work weakened and undermined the pit itself and caused the bottom to collapse into what was thought to be a vast cavern—carrying down the chests and possibly breaking them up and dispersing the contents. But the Truro syndicate did discover why the pit flooded to a level which rose and fell with the tide.

A man-made tunnel, 111 ft down, connected with the sea. The tunnel was dynamited and blocked in 1893, but still the pit filled uncontrollably. A second tunnel, at 150 ft, was discovered in 1942.

There may be others. Nearly 200 years of drilling, digging and pumping have so confused the area that the exact location of the original pit is not known.

There, for the moment, the matter rests. But the burning questions remain:

who buried what, and why? Early legends of Captain Kidd, perennial favourite of treasure seekers, may be safely dismissed. Whatever Kidd's skills as a seaman, he was quite incapable of executing so remarkable a piece of engineering. Obviously, the work had been carried out by a professional, backed by a team of skilled miners.

Rupert Furneaux, author of *The Money Pit Mystery*, has advanced the most plausible theory. Considering the state of the block and rope discovered in 1795, the pit could not have been dug much earlier than 1780, placing the operation in the middle of the American War of Independence. In 1778, the British garrison in New York was threatened by Washington's army, and capitulation loomed. The governor held the pay chests of all British

forces in America and it seems likely that, anxious for their safety, he ordered their concealment in a secret place. The unit entrusted with the task may well have been a detachment of the Royal Engineers stationed in Halifax, Nova Scotia. Mr Furneaux argues that only a treasure of immense value—such as the pay chests —would call for so complex a hiding place as the Money Pit. And the only group in the area with sufficient expertise for the task were the British Royal Engineers.

The big problem is that there is no record of the British Army losing any great sums of money at the time—a scandal which would have led to the court-martial of the general concerned. This may mean that, when the danger was past, the chests were recovered and the Money Pit is, in fact . . . empty.

WHAT HAPPENED TO THE ROMANOVS?

Someone died in the cellar . . . but was it the Tsar?

The revolutionary Bolshevik government announced in Moscow at the end of July 1918 that Nicholas Romanov, once the Tsar of all the Russias, had been executed for 'innumerable foul crimes'. The official statement said that the tsarina and her children had been moved to a secret place.

More than once the Bolsheviks changed their account of the execution, leaving a question mark hanging over the whole affair. Historians have no clear evidence to show if the tsar was put to death alone; if his entire family was shot with him; or if all the royal family—including Nicholas —was sent into secret exile.

Nicholas II was swept from power by the Russian Revolution in the early months of 1917. With the tsarina, Alexandra, and his five children—Alexei, Olga, Maria, Tatiana and Anastasia— he was imprisoned by the Bolsheviks in the Tsarkoe Selo Palace outside St Petersburg (now Leningrad).

No chance of rescue

In August of that year they were moved to the small Siberian town of Tobolsk, a place so remote that there would be small chance of rescue by royalist sympathisers. Then, in 1918, they were moved again, this time to a house in the Urals town of Ekaterinburg.

The people of Ekaterinburg were Bolsheviks to a man, and were bitterly hostile towards the Imperial family. Even so, tsarists made several unsuccessful attempts to storm the house.

It was perhaps because of the ever-present threat that the tsar might be liberated to lead the opposition forces, that the Bolshevik government in Moscow may have decided to have him executed. Alternatively, they may have decided only to announce that he had been killed and then hide him.

Orders from Moscow

The announcement of July 1918 shocked the world, particularly Western Europe, where the Romanovs had royal relatives.

But a few months later there was even more appalling news. The Bolsheviks said that the entire Romanov family had been executed by a firing squad on the night of July 19, 1918. According to this report, the orders came from Moscow and the sentence was carried out under the command of a man named Yurovski, who fired the first shot in the massacre.

The Romanovs were given no warning. They were marched downstairs into the cellar, where they were invited to sit on a row of chairs. Yurovski's opening shot was followed by a volley from the Bolshevik guards, who were using new revolvers

IN CAPTIVITY IN SIBERIA *One of the last photographs of the tsar, sitting on the roof of the prison in the remote town of Tobolsk with members of his family. At this time he had already abdicated.*

drawn from the local armoury especially for their grim task.

With the Romanovs was the Imperial physician, Dr Botkin, and three servants, who had all been ordered to stand alongside the royal family. When the shooting stopped, 11 bodies lay on the floor. The guards made doubly sure with bayonets and rifle butts.

In the early hours of the morning, the bodies were heaped on to a waiting lorry and driven to the Four Brothers Mine, 14 miles from Ekaterinburg.

There they were doused in petrol and burnt. The charred remains and personal effects were then soaked in acid and thrown down the mine-shaft.

Four days later, on July 23, Ekaterinburg fell to the counter-revolutionary White Army. They found the cellars splashed with blood but the walls had been partly washed and there was no evidence to prove whether it had been royal blood or not.

The tsarists' revenge

All the same, 28 local revolutionaries were later charged with having participated in the massacre of the royal family, and five of them were executed.

But the evidence was by no means conclusive, and to this day the Romanovs' fate remains shrouded in doubt. The only remains ever recovered from the mine-shaft were teeth and glasses, later identified as belonging to Dr Botkin, and shreds of clothing which might have been worn by the servants.

The Bolsheviks had one very good reason to keep the tsar alive. They had already made a treaty with Germany to allow him to leave Russia, unharmed, and the release of an irrelevant ex-emperor would have gained sympathy for their cause in the West.

Unanswered question

The question still unanswered is: who died in the cellar? Some people believe that the blood found by the White Army was that of Dr Botkin and the servants only—who could have been executed to simulate the deaths of the Romanovs and remove all witnesses to their secret exile.

Rumours persist that Britain and America could have concluded an agreement with the revolutionaries. In 1919 an American secret agent published a book *Rescuing the Tsar*, in which he claimed to be the person responsible for taking the family through a secret tunnel into the British Consulate in Ekaterinburg before they were 'spirited' out of Bolshevik Russia and eventually exiled to Tibet.

The book has never been accepted by any serious researcher or historian as a true account of what really happened to the Romanovs, for it presented little evidence to substantiate its claims.

But down through the years odd incidents occurred which seemed to suggest that the family might have survived.

When a memorial service was held for the tsar in London, George V refused to attend or send a royal representative. Could it be that the king knew the tsar was still alive? Even today the US State Department is said to keep an open file on the Romanov family.

Polish spy's claim

In 1961 a Polish spy, Michal Goleniewski, defected and claimed that he was the tsar's son, Alexei. Three years later, two women signed themselves by the names of two of the tsar's daughters—Olga and Tatiana—when they witnessed Goleniewski's marriage in New York. Long afterwards Goleniewski continued to maintain that he was heir to the Russian throne. He said he had exposed some 200 Russian agents to the Americans because of his hatred for the Communist cause.

No 'royal' disease

However, not even Michal Goleniewski could explain how he could be the haemophiliac son of the last Russian tsar, when he did not suffer from the 'royal' disease.

Witnesses who really know what happened at Ekaterinburg—if any have survived—must now be growing old. It may well be that the secret of the Romanovs will go with them to their graves.

'I AM ANASTASIA'

Was the bedraggled near-suicide a Grand Duchess?

Out of the mists that enshrouded the ultimate fate of the Romanovs, there emerged a whole host of pretenders. Some were cranks, genuinely believing themselves to be members of the Russian royal family; others, impostors hoping to establish some claim on the vast wealth of the tsar.

But the story of a teenage girl, dragged semi-conscious from a canal in Berlin on February 17, 1920, had such a ring of truth about it that she was accepted by many leading Russian aristocrats in exile. She claimed to be the Grand Duchess Anastasia, youngest daughter of Tsar Nicholas.

There was much at stake. A great deal of the immense Romanov fortune was reputed to have been smuggled out of Russia just before the Revolution and deposited in Western banks. Some estimates put the family's wealth in cash alone at £800 million. Estates in Germany would add a great deal more.

Were the children spared?

According to the Bolshevik government's statement in July 1918, the tsar himself was executed, but the family was spared and sent to a secret place. If so, it was always possible that one or more of the children might turn up.

The girl dragged from the Berlin canal carried papers in the name of Anna Tschaikovski. But as soon as she regained her strength in hospital, she claimed to be Anastasia, and gave a detailed account of how she had escaped execution.

She said that she had been taken with the rest of the royal family for execution in the cellar at Ekaterinburg. She had been wounded in the shooting and had passed out. But she claimed that she regained consciousness to find herself hidden in a peasant cart with two men and two women.

Smuggled to safety

The men were two of the Bolshevik guards, brothers named Tschaikovski, who had wanted no part in the killing. They told her that she had been left for dead on the cellar floor, but while they were carrying the bodies out of the cellar, they found that she was still breathing. So they had decided to smuggle her out of Russia to safety.

With money obtained by selling a pearl necklace and uncut emeralds sewn into her dress, Anastasia and her companions managed to reach the Rumanian capital of Bucharest, where all three lived with relatives of the Tschaikovskis.

Anastasia, still too frightened of the Bolsheviks to emerge from hiding, married one of the brothers and had his child. But soon afterwards her husband was seen on the streets by Bolshevik agents, recognised as a deserter, and assassinated. Anastasia suffered a breakdown and the child was taken away to be adopted.

Her brother-in-law, Sergei Tschaikovski, decided to take her to Berlin, where she would be safer from the Bolsheviks. But on the day of their arrival after a fearful journey, Sergei disappeared. Anastasia was so exhausted and in such despair that she decided to end her life by jumping into the canal.

For the next ten years she lodged claims for the return of her title and family fortune and made contacts with tsarist sympathisers.

No trace was ever found of the Tschaikovski brothers or of her child. But Anastasia's knowledge of even the smallest details of the royal family life won her many supporters in the West.

Denounced as an impostor

The Russian community in Berlin was divided. Many believed she was the Grand Duchess, while others denounced her as an impostor. Most of those who could have positively identified her were dead. Others stood to lose their shares of the Romanov fortune if her claim was proved to be true.

Pierre Gilliard, former French tutor of the family, was convinced that she was an impostor. He claimed that she did not understand Russian and crossed herself in the manner of a Roman Catholic, rather than in the fashion of the Russian Orthodox Church.

Grand Duke Cyril, the tsar's cousin, and surviving head of the Romanovs, refused her an audience or any further discussion on the subject.

Princess Irene of Prussia, the tsarina's sister, was sure that her forehead and eyes were those of Anastasia, but she had not seen the girl for more than ten years. Grand Duke Andrew, a cousin of the tsar, accepted her completely and said: 'She is indeed the Grand Duchess.'

Anastasia later claimed that her 'uncle', Grand Duke Ernest of Hesse, had made a visit to Russia from Germany in 1916— while the two countries were at war. Cyril denied it and accused Anna of being a 'blatant liar'—but in 1949, a former commander of a Russian Guards regiment, Colonel Larski, swore on oath that Ernest was on a visit to Russia at the time Anastasia had claimed.

In 1933, the Berlin Court granted a

ANASTASIA *A portrait of the Grand Duchess taken before the Russian Revolution in 1917.*

document of inheritance for the tsar's property in Germany to six surviving relatives—assuming Anastasia's death. The fight for Anastasia's recognition was renewed once more.

Anastasia underwent searching medical examination in hospital and X-rays revealed serious head injuries which could have been caused by the butt of a gun. Bunions on her feet were in exactly the same place as those of the tsar's daughter. And a scar on her right shoulder blade, where a mole was once cauterised, was similar to one shown in Anastasia's medical records.

Hand crushed

Another small scar on the middle finger of her left hand was claimed to be the damage caused by a careless footman, who slammed the coach door on her hand as a child. Her opponents denied that this had ever happened, but a former lady-in-waiting corroborated her story.

In 1938 her lawyers brought an action to have the 1933 document cancelled. The Second World War prevented it being heard in court.

In May 1968 a court in Hamburg ruled against her—but speculation continues. Many people still believe that the Romanov story did not end in the cellar at Ekaterinburg.

'THE JEWELS ARE GONE!'

How Ireland's national treasure was stolen

The Star and Badge of the Order of St Patrick—the Irish Crown Jewels—disappeared in July 1907. Suspicion and tragedy surrounded the men responsible for their safety; distinguished careers were ruined and the jewels were never recovered.

The jewels—emeralds, rubies and diamonds presented to the Irish nation by William IV in the 19th century—were kept in a safe in Dublin Castle's Bedford Tower. They were in the care of Sir Arthur Vicars, the Ulster King of Arms, his nephew Pierce Mahoney, and two assistants—Francis Shackleton and Francis Bennett-Goldney.

On June 28, 1907, Vicars reported that his key to the tower's main door had vanished. Five days later a cleaner, Mrs Farrell, found the main door unlocked when she arrived for work. Then, on July 6, she noticed something even more strange—the door to the strongroom where the jewels were kept had been left open overnight.

That afternoon, a castle porter named Stivey entered Vicars' room while Vicars and Mahoney were examining the gold and enamel collar of the Order of St Patrick. Vicars gave the porter a safe key and ordered him to put the collar with the rest of the jewels. A few minutes later Stivey returned with the alarming news that the safe was already open. Vicars made a swift inspection and cried, 'My God, the jewels are gone!'

Police later found that the thief had spent at least 15 minutes carefully unscrewing the jewels from their seatings. Clearly, he must have been someone whose presence would not have aroused the castle staff's suspicions. Within a month a team of Scotland Yard detectives produced the name of their prime suspect but the report was suppressed, and the Chief Inspector recalled.

That autumn, Edward VII demanded that all four men responsible for guarding the jewels should resign. Vicars was outraged and refused; he also boycotted a commission of inquiry set up the following January. But the commission censured him for negligence, and ordered his dismissal as Ulster King of Arms.

Tragic ends

All the heralds met tragic ends. Bennett-Goldney later died in a car accident, and Mahoney was killed while out shooting alone. Shackleton was gaoled for defrauding an old woman; on his release from prison he vanished into obscurity.

Vicars too died mysteriously. On April 14, 1921, his body was found in the garden of his home in County Kerry. It was riddled with bullets and bore a label saying, 'IRA Never Forgets'—but the Irish Republican Army insisted that it was not involved. In any case, most people in Ireland believed Vicars to be an innocent man who had been badly treated by the British Government.

No trace has ever been found of the stolen treasure, and it seems that the identity of the thief will remain shrouded in mystery.

STOLEN TREASURE *The diamond St Patrick Star (above), a gem-studded collar (left) and the St Patrick Badge (right).*

PUZZLE OF THE 'DEAD' PRINCE

Who was inside the Dauphin's coffin?

The heirs to the wealth of France's Bourbon royal family may be living in obscurity somewhere in the world, unaware of their claim to fame and fortune. For they would be the descendants of the Dauphin Louis Charles, son of Louis XVI and Marie Antoinette and heir to the throne . . . who 'died' in 1795.

When his parents were executed in 1793, Louis Charles was put in prison to await the decision on his future. Seventeen months later it was announced that he had died at the age of ten.

Five people who inspected the body testified that it was the Dauphin—yet not one of them had ever seen the boy when alive. His sister, who was in the same prison, was not consulted.

When the funeral took place many people wondered why so large a coffin was used for such a young child. Then, as evidence was pieced together, suspicions grew that a switch had taken place.

The changeling

A married couple who had been appointed gaolers to the Dauphin gave up the job on January 19, 1794, when the boy was a robust, mischievous nine-year-old. About seven months later, General Paul Barras—soon to become dictator of France—visited the youngster and was confronted by a child who was obviously dangerously ill.

This astonishing change in the prisoner's health was explained 20 years later by the woman who had been his gaoler. She told nuns nursing her in hospital that she and her husband smuggled another boy into the gaol and substituted him for the Dauphin on the day they left. She would reveal nothing more to the nuns, apart from asserting: 'My little prince is not dead.'

The woman's story was borne out to some extent by events that followed General Barras's visit to the prison. A new gaoler was engaged, and he told the general that the child was an impostor. Barras immediately organised a nation-wide search for the Dauphin.

Meanwhile, other government officials visited the prison. One is said to have concluded that the child was a deaf mute; another described him as 'the most pitiable creature I have ever seen'.

A prominent banker named Petitival denounced the Dauphin's death certificate as a forgery. Less than a year later he and his whole family were murdered. When Barras reported to his government colleagues, he announced that everyone in the Petitival household had perished 'except the child you know'.

The doctors' verdict

From that it has been suggested that Barras's search for the Dauphin was successful, and that the general's fellow-ministers were aware that the boy was at Petitival's home.

Who, then, was the child who died in prison? When the body was exhumed in 1846 two doctors pronounced that it was a boy aged 15 or 16, rather than 10. In 1894 the bones were examined again. Once more it was agreed that the remains were those of a boy between 16 and 18. Whichever theory was correct, the child in the coffin could not be the Dauphin.

After Napoleon's fall in 1815 the Bourbon monarchy was restored . . . to be plagued by a procession of 'Dauphins'. Twenty-seven men laid claim to the title —which meant, in effect, that each was demanding to be king. Most, however, were obvious charlatans. Then, in 1833, Karl Wilhelm Naundorff appeared on the scene with strong evidence to support his claim that he was the missing heir.

He was recognised by the Dauphin's nurse and by Louis XVI's Minister of Justice. The Dauphin's sister steadfastly refused to see Naundorff, although she was told that he bore a strong resemblance to members of her family. His adherents took her refusal as confirmation of his claim. It was known that she supported her uncle, Charles, as the rightful king.

One remarkable aspect of Naundorff's story was that it did not conform to the generally accepted theory that the Dauphin's gaolers smuggled him to safety. He claimed instead that Barras had transferred him to another part of the prison and put the second boy in his place. Then, on the day the substitute died, the Dauphin was smuggled out and taken first to Italy, then to Prussia, where he took the name Naundorff. To push for-

A QUEEN AND HER CHILDREN *Marie Antoinette nurses her son, Louis Charles. On her left is the Dauphin, who died in 1789, and on her right Louis' sister, Madame Royale.*

ward his claim to the title, Naundorff began a civil court action—and was promptly arrested and expelled from France. He went to London, where an attempt was made on his life. Nine years later he died in Holland—and was described on the death certificate as 'Louis Charles de Bourbon, aged 60, son of Louis XVI and Marie Antoinette'.

To this day, Naundorff's descendants pursue their claim in the French courts. But if he, too, was really an impostor another possibility remains: Louis Charles may have lived the life of a commoner, unrecognised and perhaps unwilling to establish his identity. He may well have decided that being a royal heir was too dangerous in an era of revolution.

KASPAR HAUSER'S SECRET PAST

Was the boy who knew nothing heir to a dukedom?

On Whit Monday 1828, a strange boy of about 16 years of age suddenly appeared in Nürnberg. He was wearing rough peasant clothes, and all who met him thought him to be either drunk or an idiot. The newcomer carried a letter addressed to 'The captain of the 4th Squadron of the 6th Regiment of Cavalry in Nürnberg'.

A shoemaker took the boy to the captain's house where the lad repeatedly announced: 'I want to be a soldier as my father was.' When taken to the nearest police station, the boy answered every question put to him with, 'I don't know'.

The mysterious youth seemed to have the mental age of a boy of three or four, but when handed paper and pencil, he was able to write the name 'Kaspar Hauser'.

Kaspar was sent to a detention centre for vagabonds while the unsigned letter he had been carrying was studied. It read in part: 'Honoured Captain, I send you a boy who is anxious to serve his king in the army. He was left at my house on October 7, 1812, and I am only a poor day-labourer. I have ten children of my own and I have enough to do to bring them up. I have not let him out of the house since 1812 . . . If you do not want to keep him, you can kill him or hang him up the chimney.'

Kaspar was taken into the home of the gaoler who observed many things about the boy. His new charge was well built but had feet as soft as a baby's. He had the smile of an innocent child but no other means of facial expression, and he seemed to be incapable of using his fingers. When trying to walk, he stumbled about like a baby taking its first steps.

An amazing background

Kaspar quickly learnt to talk in broken sentences, but could eat only bread and water, anything else making him sick. He showed no embarrassment when the gaoler's wife bathed him, and did not seem to appreciate the difference between men and women. The gaoler concluded that the lad was no impostor and that some great mystery surrounded him.

Public interest in the mysterious foundling grew, and a young scholar, Dr Daumer, supervised his education. Eventually, Kaspar was able to offer glimpses into his amazing past.

Kaspar claimed that before arriving in Nürnberg he had seen only one other human being in his life. For as long as he could remember he had lived in a cell 6 ft long, 4 ft wide and only 5 ft high. He had always sat or lain down, having a straw bed to sleep on, and a shirt and leather trousers to wear.

Each morning he found a jug of water and a piece of bread at his side. Occasionally the water had a bitter taste and made him fall asleep, awaking to find that his clothes had been changed and his nails cut. There was never a light in his cell.

One day a man entered and showed him how to write Kaspar Hauser and to say 'I want to be a soldier as my father was'. The man later lifted Kaspar on to his back and carried him outside where the light and open air made him faint. The next thing he remembered was finding himself wandering in Nürnberg.

Interest in the boy spread across Europe. He was visited by lawyers, doctors and public officials who were convinced that he was somebody special. Because of Kaspar's remarkable resemblance to them, his name was freely linked with the grand ducal family of Baden. In 1830, about the time of Kaspar's birth, the family had suffered the sudden deaths of two baby princes in the direct line of succession.

Soon after the death of the reigning Grand Duke in March 1830, the English Earl of Stanhope, who seems to have been a friend of the Grand Duke's successor, applied to become Kaspar's guardian. That application was granted.

Stanhope publicly stated that Kaspar was of Hungarian origin and had no connection with the family of Baden. He also desperately tried to persuade others to change their stories to say they had always thought he was an impostor. But Anselm Ritter von Feuerbach concluded that 'the crime against Kaspar's liberty was not prompted by hatred or revenge, solely by selfish interest. Kaspar Hauser is the legitimate son of royal parents and was put out of the way to open the succession to other heirs'.

When von Feuerbach died suddenly in 1833 it was rumoured that he had been poisoned after finding proof of Kaspar's royal origin. But nothing of that proof was ever produced.

Stabbed in the heart

Like everything else in his short life, Kaspar's ending was tragic and mysterious. One afternoon in 1833, he was lured to a park in Ansbach with the promise of information about his royal parentage. There he met a man who stabbed him in the heart. He managed to stagger home, but he died three days later.

It was reported that the Grand Duchess Stephanie of Baden, Kaspar's reputed mother, wept bitterly when she learnt of his death. Her husband, Karl, had been the last of the direct ducal line, and failure to produce an heir would leave the succession open to the children of the Countess of Hochberg.

There is a story that when Stephanie gave birth to her first child, the Countess of Hochberg smuggled the dead child of a peasant woman into the palace, switching it with the baby prince—Kaspar Hauser. The countess handed Kaspar to Major Hennenhofer, who placed the child in the care of a former soldier. Some say that when questioned, Hennenhofer confessed.

All the evidence, repeated attempts on Kaspar's life, the involvement of Stanhope, and the Baden family's efforts to hush up the matter seem to confirm the story. But Kaspar Hauser's tale can never be proved for, when Hennenhofer died, all his private papers were destroyed.

SPRING-HEELED JACK
Superman with eyes of a devil

Out of the mists of the night he came, a leaping, bounding superman who held a nation in a grip of terror for more than 60 years.

At first, he was just a rumour. No one took much notice when people crossing Barnes Common in south-west London first reported seeing an alarming figure that flew through the air in great leaps across their path. But the reports persisted, until they were terrifyingly confirmed a year later, in February 1838.

Jane Alsop was young and pretty. She lived with her two sisters and their father in a little London back street in Bow called

LEAPING AWAY *The descriptions of Spring-heeled Jack varied little, although he was seen in many different areas.*

Bearhind Lane. She had heard of the bogeyman called Spring-heeled Jack. But she was too sensible to heed such tales.

One night there was a violent knocking at the door. Jane went to answer it. The man standing in the shadows near the front gate swung round. 'I'm a police officer,' he said. 'For God's sake bring me a light, for we have caught Spring-heeled Jack in the lane.'

'The stories were true after all,' thought Jane excitedly, as she ran to fetch a candle. 'I'll see him being arrested.' She rushed back outside with the candle.

But as she gave it to the man at the gate, he grabbed her by the neck and pinned her head under his arm. Then he

ripped at her dress and body. She screamed and tore herself away. He chased her, caught her by the hair and clawed her face and neck. A sister, hearing the screams, ran into the street and raised the alarm. But before anyone could stop him, Jack soared away into the darkness.

Jane later described her inhuman attacker to Lambeth magistrates. 'He was wearing a kind of helmet,' she told them, 'and a tight-fitting white costume like an oilskin. His face was hideous, his eyes were like balls of fire. His hands had great claws, and he vomited blue and white flames.'

It was a description that was to be repeated over and over again in the following years. Always the leaps, the flames and the eyes of hell.

Lucy Scales was 18 years old, the sister of a respected Limehouse butcher. She had just left her brother's house one evening on her way home with her sister. As they walked along lonely Green Dragon Alley, a tall cloaked figure jumped out of the shadows. He spat blue flames at Lucy's face, blinding her.

During the 1850s and 1860s, Spring-heeled Jack was sighted all over England, particularly in the Midlands.

In the 1870s, Army authorities set traps after scared sentries reported being terrified by a man who darted out of the darkness to slap their faces with an icy hand, or sprang on to the roof of their sentry boxes. Angry townsfolk in Lincoln shot at him when he appeared in the streets one night in 1877. Always, he laughed and melted away.

No one, even today, really has any idea who—or what—Spring-heeled Jack was. For a while, suspicion rested on the eccentric young Marquis of Waterford. But though the 'mad marquis', as he was known, was one of the wild ones of Victorian society, he was never vicious.

Jack's eyes of hell were last seen in 1904 at Everton, in Liverpool—67 years after the first sightings in Barnes. There he started a panic one night by bounding up and down the streets—leaping from cobbles to roof-tops and back. When some of the braver ones tried to corner him, he simply vanished into the darkness from where he came—this time for good?

JACK THE RIPPER

The killer whose name became a legend

Five times the unobtrusive little man stepped out into the swirling night of London's Whitechapel. Five times he talked to women of the streets. Each time the woman died, slashed in the style that was the bloody trademark of the man called Jack the Ripper.

Dozens of detectives—amateur and professional—have advanced theories as to who the little man was. No one has ever finally settled the question. His brutal crimes remain baffling, fascinating and unsolved, nearly a century after he committed them.

The East End of Victorian London was a festering sore on the face of England. Mean houses huddled along the sides of streets that stank of refuse.

At night, the alleys, yards and corners were black caverns beyond the candlelit windows. Indoors, an overcrowded population fought for elbow room in hovels.

Outside, men, women and children scratched a miserable and often criminal living in the streets. The only relief was oblivion, which could be found in a bottle of gin for a few pence. For many women, prostitution was the only means of making a living.

Jack the Ripper stepped into this cauldron in the autumn of 1888. Fear and panic came with him.

Mary Ann Nicholls was down on her luck. At 42 she was getting too old to attract men. She could not even raise the four pennies demanded by doss houses for a bed—the few coppers she possessed had already been spent on gin. When the little man approached her in the tiny street of Buck's Row, Mary saw only the chance to make enough to enjoy a good night's sleep. Even when he drew her back into the shadows she was not alarmed. There were people just a few yards away.

DON'T LOOK NOW *A suspect is followed by a band of vigilantes during the Jack the Ripper terror which seized the East End of London during the late 1880s. The killer struck five times.*

By the time she realised anything was wrong it was too late. The Ripper stepped behind her and put his hand over her mouth. Then he cut her throat. A carter found her mutilated body in the early hours of Friday morning, August 31, 1888. The Ripper's reign of terror had begun.

He waited exactly seven days before he struck again. The victim was, as all of them were to be, a prostitute: 47-year-old Annie Chapman. Dark Annie, as she was known, was dying of consumption—a wasting disease of the lung—when the Ripper cut her down. Her body was found by a Spitalfields market porter in a backyard at 29 Hanbury Street. Her rings and a few coins had been laid out neatly at her feet, below the sickening remains of her corpse. She had been completely disembowelled.

By now Whitechapel was aflame with rumours. One story had it that the killer carried his knives in a little black bag. Riots broke out as hysterical crowds chased anyone who carried such a bag. Vigilante groups were formed to patrol the streets. Police arrested dozens of innocent suspects.

But the Ripper had left no clues. All that police doctors could deduce was that he was left-handed and had some medical knowledge. The killings, said an inquest surgeon, had been 'deftly and fairly skilfully' performed.

Solitary clue

On the night of September 30, the Ripper butchered two more women, and left what may be the only direct clue of his grisly career. 'Long Liz' Stride was found with blood still pouring from her throat behind 40 Berner Street. The body of Kate Eddowes—the most terribly mutilated of all—lay a few minutes' walk away in Mitre Square.

From her hacked body a trail of blood led to a doorway, where someone had scrawled in chalk: 'THE JEWES ARE NOT THE MEN TO BE BLAMED FOR NOTHING.' Did it mean that the Ripper was a Jew out for revenge on a world that had persecuted him? Or was he a crazed judge who had become his own executioner? The message—whatever it meant—could have been vital.

But it was never properly studied. For mysteriously, inexplicably, the head of the Metropolitan police, Sir Charles Warren, ordered it to be rubbed out.

The whole of London was gripped by the horror of the double murder. Rumours flew. The Ripper was a mad doctor. A Polish wild man. A Russian tsarist secret agent trying to discredit the police. A Puritan obsessed by the city's vice. It was even suggested that Jack the Ripper was an insane midwife with a murderous hatred for prostitution. No one knew. The real Ripper remained at large. And on November 9 he struck again.

The last person—apart from the killer —to see 25-year-old Mary Kelly alive was a passer-by called George Hutchinson. She asked him for money to help pay the rent of her tiny room at 13 Miller's Court. Then he watched her move off to accost a small, well-dressed man with a fair moustache and a deerstalker hat. Her dismembered corpse was discovered next morning in her room.

Mary was the Ripper's last victim. He never went back to his gruesome business. Detectives have tried to follow his trail ever since, but with no conclusive results. Police files on the case have been locked away in Scotland Yard. They are not due to be released until 1992. And even then they may contain only more speculation.

For the Ripper left few tracks. Each time he killed, he simply vanished back into Whitechapel's seething crowds. How? If he was a poor man, how did he acquire the medical knowledge to carry out his fiendish surgery? If he was wealthy, why was he not noticed among the East End's abject poverty? And how could he have worked unnoticed when surgeons of the time estimate that his terrible operations would have taken up to an hour to perform? The questions are still unanswered. Police closed their file on the case a few months after Mary Kelly's death. And although others have raked over the trail ever since, their conclusions have always been guesswork.

The most likely theory of the Ripper's identity seems to be that put forward by author and broadcaster Daniel Farson. He based his research on the notes of Sir Melville Macnaghten, who joined Scotland Yard the year after the killings and became head of the CID in 1903. According to Macnaghten, police had concentrated on three suspects: a homicidal Russian doctor called Michael Ostrog; a woman-hating Polish Jew called Kosmanski; and a depraved lawyer called Montague John Druitt.

In the end, says Macnaghten, they decided Druitt was the killer.

Farson, after years of research into Druitt's family, agrees. He says that Druitt's family believed him to be the Ripper; and he points out that his cousin, Dr Lionel Druitt, had a surgery at the Whitechapel Minories—only a ten-minute walk from the furthest of the murder sites. Druitt's mother, Farson adds, was insane, and Druitt may have feared he was going mad as well.

Druitt was never arrested. He disappeared soon after the last murder. His body was found floating in the Thames seven weeks later—on December 31, 1888. Did he commit suicide? Or could he too have been a murder victim? If Druitt really was the Whitechapel butcher, it would have been poetic justice.

Only one man ever knew the truth of it all . . . Jack the Ripper himself. By now, whoever he was, his dreadful secret has been buried for ever.

LONG AT THE FAIR

Did the young English girl book in alone?

Paris in 1889, the year of the Great Exhibition, was packed with businessmen, buyers and tourists. Most hotels were fully booked.

In May, an English mother and her daughter arrived in the city from Marseilles, where they had disembarked from India. They had booked two single rooms at one of the most famous hotels in Paris.

They signed their names in the register and were taken up to their rooms. The mother was placed in room 342, a luxurious apartment with heavy curtains of plum-coloured velvet, rose-covered wallpaper, a high-backed sofa, oval satinwood table and an ormulu clock.

Almost immediately, however, the older woman fell ill and took to bed. The hotel doctor who was called examined her and put some questions to the daughter. He and the hotel manager then conferred excitedly in a corner of the room. Though the girl did not speak French, she was able to understand the instructions slowly spelt out to her by the doctor. Her mother was seriously ill and required a particular medicine available only at the doctor's surgery on the other side of Paris. As he himself could not leave the patient, he asked the girl to go in his carriage.

The girl set out at what proved to be an exasperatingly slow pace. After an agonising wait at the surgery and an equally slow journey back, she arrived with the medicine. Four hours had passed.

Jumping from the carriage, she rushed into the foyer. 'Comment va ma mère?' she asked the manager. He stared blankly at her. 'To whom do you refer, Mademoiselle?' he asked. Taken aback, she stammered an explanation of her delay.

'But, Mademoiselle, I know nothing of your mother. You arrived here alone.'

Distraught, the girl protested: 'But we registered here less than six hours ago. Look in the book.' The manager produced the register, and ran his finger down the page. Half-way down was the girl's signature, but immediately above it, where her mother had signed, was the name of a stranger. 'We both signed,' the girl insisted, 'and my mother was given room 342. She is there now. Please take me to her at once.'

'Plus ça change'

The manager assured her that the room was occupied by a French family, but they went upstairs. Room 342 was empty save for the personal belongings of strangers. There were no plum-coloured curtains, no rose-covered wallpaper, no high-backed sofa and no ormulu clock.

Downstairs again she encountered the hotel doctor and tackled him about her mother's fate. He too denied ever having met her before and swore he had never attended her mother.

The girl reported the story to the British Ambassador who would not believe her; nor would the police or newspapers. Eventually she returned to England, where she was lodged in an asylum.

One explanation of this strange story is that the mother had contracted plague in India. The doctor, having recognised the symptoms, had conspired with the hotel manager to conceal the news, which would certainly have wrecked the Great Exhibition. But could room 342 have been redecorated in four hours? What happened to the mother's body? The mysteries remain.

HMS NATAL IN 1910 *Although the cruiser's armour plates were blown from the inside out, the court of inquiry brushed aside evidence of an enemy incendiary device.*

WARSHIPS THAT JUST BLEW UP

Admiralty pooh-poohed suspicions of German sabotage

On the afternoon of December 30, 1915, a fleet of warships lay at anchor in Cromarty Firth. The war with Germany was at its height, but for these ships all was peace.

On board the cruiser *Natal*, Captain Back was entertaining officers and their families with a film show. Small boats were taking parties of sailors off for a few days' shore leave.

Then at 3.20 p.m. a deafening explosion shook the firth. From one of the boats a rating saw 'a sight to freeze the blood'. From the stern of HMS *Natal* a sheet of flame shot into the sky, the rear decks and gun-casements were disintegrating and the whole ship was heeling over to port.

Lieutenant Fildes, standing on the quarter-deck, was flung down by the blast. Lying half stunned against the teak boards, he saw with horror that the pitch in the deck seams was bubbling and boiling in the intense heat.

Within moments another explosion tore open the side of the ship and in three minutes it had sunk, carrying more than 350 to their deaths.

The *Natal* was one of the Royal Navy's most modern cruisers and in 1911 had been chosen to escort the king and queen to the great coronation durbar in India. Her crew came mainly from Chatham and the villages of North Kent. Some of those small communities lost half of their menfolk in the disaster.

It was suspected that the *Natal* had been torpedoed. But Cromarty Firth was well protected against submarines, and divers reported that the cruiser's sides had been blown out from the inside.

Magazines suspected

There was also the possibility of an accident in the magazines. But this seemed unlikely. They were in the lowest, well-ventilated part of the hull, and the explosive charges were kept at a controlled temperature. Ratings who worked there wore felt slippers to avoid sparks from their heels. The electric lights had specially thickened glass covers protected by stiff, wire cages.

Lieutenant Fildes, one of the few officers who survived to give evidence, told the commission of inquiry that, before the explosion occurred, he had heard a suspicious crackling noise in one of the ventilation shafts leading to the magazines. He had sent a rating down to investigate, though nothing had been discovered.

But his suspicions of an incendiary device were brushed aside. The commission concluded that there had been an accident in the magazines, 'the exact cause of which is impossible to ascertain'.

Had the *Natal* been the only warship to explode in home waters, such complacency might have been excusable. But on November 26, 1914, a few weeks after the outbreak of the war, HMS *Bulwark*, a 15,000 ton battleship, had exploded in the Medway.

'It is probable,' the Admiralty's official commission of inquiry said on that occasion, 'that the actual cause will never be discovered.'

Still there were strong doubts felt in some quarters, and on July 14, 1917, suspicions were confirmed. After a long and ominous silence, the Admiralty announced that five days earlier 'HMS *Vanguard* blew up while at anchor in Scapa Flow, as a result of an internal explosion'.

German saboteurs

By this time more had been learnt about German sabotage methods. It was known that German saboteurs in New York had succeeded in starting fires in British munitions ships docking there. They used a small, cigar-shaped incendiary bomb, containing sulphuric acid and potash separated by a copper membrane. When the acid had eaten through the membrane, the bomb glowed white hot, igniting everything around it.

One of these devices had destroyed the munitions ship *Phoebus* in mid-Atlantic in 1915. The German agent responsible had been later sentenced to four years' imprisonment by an American court.

At the inquiry into the *Vanguard* disaster disquieting facts emerged. Only hours before the explosion two civilian ordnance fitters from Chatham had left HMS *Vanguard*. One of them, a chargeman, seemed evasive to the commissioners. 'We are inclined to believe,' they said, 'that he knows more than he wishes to disclose.'

The chargeman's record was examined. It was found that he had left HMS *Natal* in precisely similar circumstances a few hours before she blew up.

A German Bible

Also before the commission was a selection of debris recovered from HMS *Vanguard*. Amongst it was a German Bible and several letters written in German.

The Admiralty pondered. Then to the general astonishment they announced that the explosion had been due to 'unavoidable causes of an uncertain nature'.

Rumour had it that a man had been secretly executed. But the Royal Navy said nothing—the 'silent service'.

CASE OF THE MURDEROUS AUTHOR?
Edgar Allan Poe based brutal fiction on brutal reality

The famous thriller writer draws a scarf or a stocking tightly around the throat of a beautiful young girl. Tighter and tighter . . .

It's all in his imagination, of course; the man is working on his next plot.

Or has it happened? Is it possible that an author, his name known to millions, did commit a brutal and sadistic killing? And not only got away with it, but had the audacity to write about it afterwards!

This is the eerie conclusion reached by modern-day investigators into a murder that has remained officially unsolved since the body of a pretty brunette was found in the Hudson River at New Jersey on a day in July 1841.

She was Mary Rogers, just 21. Her hands had been tied behind her back. She had been sexually assaulted and strangled with a piece of lace, which could have been torn from her dress.

As a teenager, Mary had been a 'cigar girl' at John Anderson's tobacconist shop on Broadway. She had been courted by actors, writers, gamblers and celebrities of all kinds.

First disappearance

She had disappeared once before, in October 1838, while working at Anderson's. The incident was headline news. Two weeks later she turned up with the terse explanation that she had 'felt tired' and had been resting with some old friends in Brooklyn.

Now, in July 1841, her murder was the sensation of a long, hot summer. John Anderson, who had often escorted her home until she quit her job in 1839, was the prime suspect. Mary had other suitors who were investigated—a man called Alfred Crommelin, and David Payne, a lodger at her mother's boarding house in Hoboken, New Jersey.

The New York and New Jersey police worked long and hard, came up with nothing of substance, and eventually closed the file.

Then, 18 months after Mary's death, the case took a strange turn. It became immortalised, literally, in a famous detective story, *The Mystery of Marie Roget*, first serialised in the magazine, *Snowden's Ladies' Companion*.

The facts of the case were followed closely by the author, Edgar Allan Poe—except that he transferred the action to Paris, merely changing the names and addresses of those involved.

But he also gave his work a guarded, frustratingly inconclusive ending.

Feeble ending

His brilliant, sardonic detective, Dupin, refers to a 'lonely assassin' and seems on the point of naming him, when the plot hastily winds up with a feeble device whereby the editor of the magazine supposedly 'censors' the ending for no good reason at all.

Unless it was that Poe knew the killer only too well.

With hindsight, it is astonishing that

AUTHOR OF DEATH *Edgar Allan Poe was fascinated by death, especially that of desirable young women.*

Poe himself was not among the police suspects. Everyone who has since investigated the crime agrees that he must have known Mary Rogers, possibly intimately, from the time she was a cigar girl.

Poe, habitually dressed in black with an old army cape slung across his shoulders, a reminder of his days at West Point military academy, was a poet with a cruel and devious streak.

He was court martialled and dismissed for his drunken, turbulent behaviour at West Point.

Numerous biographers have described his sexual aberrations and his many sexual adventures and intrigues.

His own sick self

In his books, his egocentric heroes project his own sick self—superior individuals who claim it as their right to indulge their passions and perversions, whether for incest, sadism . . . or murder.

Death held a peculiar fascination for him, especially in the case of desirable women. It gave him a poetic thrill, he told acquaintances.

It is believed that on October 3, 1838, Poe entered Anderson's shop and lingered to flirt with the vivacious cigar girl.

This was about the time Mary disappeared for the first time. Was she with him for those two weeks?

Then again, three days before her body was fished out of the Hudson, she was seen walking with a 'tall, dark man aged about 26' in woods near the river. With his shabby cape making him look a little taller than he was, the description could easily have fitted Poe. Was it him?

Poe, a drunk and a drug addict, died in 1849 at the age of 40, whispering: 'Lord help my poor soul.' And he died without once having been questioned about a savage murder of which he had written with such great passion and such extensive knowledge.

Today, there are people who believe that the truth about Mary Rogers' death could still be pieced together.

Oddly, however, the police file has remained closed and attempts by serious crime researchers to have it reopened have failed.

Is it possible that the authorities knew that the truth would shock the literary world, and simply did not care to be remembered as having been party to such infamy?

MINE OF SOLID GOLD NUGGETS

It protected its riches with violent death

Somewhere in the Superstition Mountains of Arizona there is reputed to be a gold mine so rich that if the walls are tapped with a hammer, nuggets of gold come tumbling down.

But the fabled mine has guarded its treasure well. Death and disaster have struck down many who sought to despoil it. And for the past 50 years it has been lost.

It is known locally as 'The Dutchmen's Mine' because two of the many 19th-century claimants were thought to be prospectors from Holland, although in fact they were Germans.

The discovery of the mine is lost in legend. It is thought that the Apache Indians showed it to Europeans when the first Spanish monks reached Arizona from the colonies in Mexico.

Tales were rife of a mine where gold could be shovelled out of the earth in spadefuls; and it is likely that expeditions travelled north to search for this Eldorado —but with what success is not known.

The mine is first mentioned in Spanish registers as included in a grant made in 1748 by Ferdinand VI of Spain. He gave 3750 square miles of what is now Arizona to Don Miguel Peralta.

The Peralta heirs are supposed to have made several trips to the mine from their homes in Mexico for the next 100 years. Then, according to later claimants, an Enrico Peralta took an expedition to Arizona in 1864.

Apaches on warpath

By this time the Apaches were no longer friendly. Enrico's party was ambushed, and all, save one man, were killed during a three-day running battle. The survivor reached Mexico with a map of the area showing the mine.

There was another European discoverer. He was a Dr Abraham Thorne, who lived in Arizona and was on friendly terms with the Indians. In 1870 the Apaches offered to show him a place where he could pick up gold. The only condition was that he should be blindfolded during the journey of 20 miles.

When the bandage was removed Dr Thorne saw he was in a canyon. A mile or so to the south was a sharp pinnacle of rock. There was no sign of a mine, but at the base of one of the canyon's walls was a pile of almost pure gold. He picked up as much as he could carry and was led to his home. He sold the gold for $6000.

A year later the 'Dutchmen' came on the scene. They were two German adventurers, Jacob Waltz and Jacob Weiser, who said they had rescued a man called Don Miguel Peralta from a brawl in the Mexican town of Arizpe.

Share of profits

Don Miguel was Enrico's son and he told his rescuers of the family mine. The two Jacobs agreed to go with him to Arizona for a share of the profits. According to stories later told independently by Waltz and Weiser, they found the mine with the aid of the Peralta family map and the three men picked up $60,000 worth of gold. Don Miguel sold the map and the title to the mine to the Germans for their half of the proceeds.

Soon afterwards Dr Thorne returned to the area with a group of friends. But this time the Apaches attacked and killed them all.

In 1879 the Germans, using Don Miguel's map, returned to the canyon alone, and shot dead a couple of Mexicans they found working the mine.

Before his death 12 years later, Waltz described the terrain. 'It was such rough country that you could be right in the mine without seeing it,' he said. The mine was a large pit, shaped like a funnel. Enrico had cut a tunnel into the hillside to the bottom of the pit.

The Germans continued to work the mine, but then disaster struck. Waltz came back to their camp one evening to find Weiser had disappeared. On the ground was a blood-stained shirt and Apache arrows.

Soldiers shot dead

During 1880 and 1881 the mine was twice found by chance. The first discoverers were two young soldiers who appeared in the town of Pinal with their saddlebags full of gold. They said that the ore came from a funnel-shaped mine in a canyon near a sharp pinnacle of rock. They set off to return to the mine. A search party found them shot dead. Then, in 1882, the Apaches decided that they must hide the mine. Through the white man's lust for gold it had brought only death and violence.

An Indian known as Apache Jack later told of the tribe's decision. The squaws were set to work filling in the pit. Then rocks were shifted around to disguise the area. Soon afterwards, Providence lent a hand. An earthquake further rearranged the landmarks.

Eight years later Jacob Waltz died, and with him the secret of the mine's location.

Documents forged

Prospectors continued to search for the Dutchmen's mine, but in 1895 an event occurred which further confused the whole issue. A man called James Addison Reavis was convicted by a court at Santa Fe, Arizona, of forging the ancient documents giving Don Miguel Peralta the land grant. The court case revealed that Reavis had travelled to Mexico and Spain to insert his forgeries into registers. He topped off his work by marrying a Mexican girl who was alleged to be the heir of the Peralta family.

It is likely that Reavis based his forgeries on fact. There is strong circumstantial evidence that a Mexican family did own a mine in Arizona and that members of the family made forays into Arizona to collect ore. It also seems likely that Weiser and Waltz were given, or stole, a map of the area.

And there have been two confirmations of the story this century.

Ingots in the grass

In 1912 prospectors found gold ingots in the long grass at the spot where Enrico Peralta is alleged to have fought the Indians in 1864. And, near by, there are the remains of camps and evidence that trees were cut down for pit-props. In this area is a sharp rock pinnacle now known as Weaver's Needle.

In 1931 a man called Adolph Ruth told his friends that he had acquired a map from someone called Peralta and went off into the mountains. A few weeks later his decapitated body was found. In his jacket was a piece of paper with 'About 200 feet across from cave' written on it. Underneath was the Latin tag 'Veni, Vidi, Vici' (I came, I saw, I conquered).

Since then, although the area has been carefully prospected many times, there has been no further sign of the fabulous Dutchmen's Mine.

THE BURNING OF THE REICHSTAG
An excuse for Hitler to destroy the Communists

Marius van der Lubbe, a 24-year-old Dutchman, was executed on January 10, 1934, for arson. His crime: starting a fire that gutted the Reichstag, the imposing German Parliament building in Berlin.

But was Van der Lubbe, a Nazi-hater and Communist, truly guilty? Or was he a scapegoat of Adolf Hitler and his Nazi henchmen? And were there any other conspirators involved?

The blaze was a turning point in German history, for it enabled Hitler to seize dictatorial power.

It was first spotted by a theological student, Hans Flotter, who was walking past the south-west corner of the building shortly after 9 p.m. on February 27, 1933.

Flotter, hearing the sound of glass breaking, looked up to see a man with something burning in his hand, on a first-floor balcony.

He ran off and alerted a police sergeant, who dashed to the front of the building. There the policeman fired his revolver at a man who appeared to be carrying a burning torch, rushing from window to window on the first floor.

By 9.40 p.m. some 60 fire pumps were on the scene. The building's Assembly Hall was a wall of flames and other parts of the building were ablaze.

In the Bismarck Hall, a policeman arrested at gunpoint a man, bathed in sweat and naked to the waist. His passport bore the name of Marius van der Lubbe. Asked why he did it, he told the arresting officers: 'As a protest.' He confessed to having tried unsuccessfully to set fire to three other public buildings.

The political effect of the fire was tremendous. It elevated Hitler, who had at the time been Chancellor of Germany for only 27 days, to Führer of the Third Reich. When told by Hermann Goering of the fire and the arrest of Van der Lubbe,

THE REICHSTAG BLAZES *The fire in Berlin on the night of February 27, 1933, was a landmark in Adolf Hitler's dramatic rise to power.*

MARIUS VAN DER LUBBE *He was executed for starting the fire, but was he just a scapegoat for the Nazis? Some historians think so.*

Hitler is reported to have said: 'It is a sign from Heaven. This is the beginning of the Communist rising. Every Communist official must be shot. All Communist Deputies must be hanged this very night. There must be no mercy.'

The Nazis needed to turn the German people against the Communists. For although the Nazis had the largest party in Parliament, the left wing blocked their way to absolute power.

Overnight 5000 Communists were rounded up, and within a few days four party leaders were charged with complicity in the act of arson.

In a General Election called for March 5, 1933, the Nazis still did not gain the two-thirds majority they needed to have overall rule. They had only 44 per cent of the vote.

'No single culprit'

But in the absence of the Communist Deputies, who were barred from attending, Hitler got Parliament to pass an Enabling Act, handing over all powers to his cabinet.

Experts from the Berlin fire brigade were of the opinion that the fire could not have been the work of a single arsonist, but must have needed about six or seven accomplices. Yet a trial in Leipzig acquit-

ted four of Van der Lubbe's supposed fellow-accomplices.

Although Hitler blamed the fire on the Communists, and the feeble-minded Van der Lubbe paid with his life, the rest of the world had little doubt that the Nazis themselves had planned the blaze.

The Communists, in a brilliant stroke of counter-propaganda, suggested that Goering and a group of accomplices went along an underground passage to the Reichstag, started the fire, and left by the way they had come. At the Nürnberg trials after the Second World War, General Halder, Chief of the German Staff, recalled that Goering had boasted in 1942: 'The only one who really knows about the Reichstag is me, because I set it on fire.'

The final twist

Goering denied having made the remark, but as everyone knew the Nazis were masters of the double-cross. The final twist came years after the war, when modern research pointed to the conclusion that there had been a triple-cross— and the Nazis were its victims.

Van der Lubbe, it seems, started the fire entirely on his own using four packets of fire-lighters and a box of matches, and Goering's men at worst exploited it by hampering the fire services.

367

MYSTERY OF THE *MARY CELESTE*

The ship that sailed herself

The *Dei Gratia*, a barque sailing from New York to Gibraltar, was fast overhauling the strange two-masted square-rigger. The ship's course was unsteady, as though she were being crewed by drunks. When the wind veered, she shifted aimlessly before it.

The captain of the *Dei Gratia* could see no one at the helm. He ran up a signal, but there was no answer.

As the barque closed in, a boat was lowered and the captain, the second mate and two men pulled toward the oddly silent ship. Then, as they rowed closer, they saw her name painted clearly across the stern—*Mary Celeste*.

The captain and the mate clambered aboard. It was 3 o'clock on the afternoon of December 5, 1872.

What the two men found sparked off a mystery that has bobbed tantalisingly beyond explanation for more than a century. For when they reached the deck no crew member came forward to meet them. They searched the ship from stem to stern, but the vessel was deserted. The *Mary Celeste* was sailing herself—alone across the wide Atlantic.

The ship was in first-class condition. Hull, masts and sails were all sound. The cargo—barrels of alcohol—was still lashed in place in the hold. There was plenty of food and water.

Captain's last breakfast

In the fo'c'sle the crew's sea-chests and clothing lay dry and undisturbed. Some razors lying about were still unrusted. In the galley, pots containing the remnants of a meal hung over a dead fire.

The table in the captain's cabin had been laid for breakfast though it looked as though the meal had been abandoned half-way through. There was porridge in one of the plates, and the top of a boiled egg had been sliced off. Next to one plate was an open bottle of cough medicine. The cork still lay beside it.

On the other side of the cabin was a smaller table with a sewing machine, and on it a child's nightgown. Near by were bottles of oil, cotton and a thimble, and against the wall a collection of books and a harmonium in a rosewood case.

Everything was undamaged and in its proper place, as though the entire crew had made a sudden and collective decision to hurl themselves overboard together. Whatever had occurred could not have been very long before, because the food would have rotted and metal tarnished in the sea air.

The mate's cabin was the same—perfectly in order. On the desk lay a piece of paper with an unfinished calculation written on it. He too, it seemed, had been interrupted. Gold lockets, jewellery and money were still locked in the ship's safe. All that was missing was her chronometer.

Was it mutiny?

The *Dei Gratia*'s captain suspected mutiny. But if there had been a mutiny how had the crew escaped? The *Mary Celeste*'s lifeboat still hung on its davits. So they must either have been taken off by a passing ship, or had jumped over the side.

The captain and mate of the *Dei Gratia* did find some clues—of a sort. In one cabin there was a cutlass, smeared with what seemed to be blood—though this was later derided at the official inquiry. They found similar stains on the starboard deck rail, near a cut that looked as though it had been made by an axe. On each side of the bows, a strip of wood 6 ft long by 1 in. wide had been recently cut from the outer planks. There was no obvious reason why this should have been done.

When he examined the ship's log, the captain of the *Dei Gratia* found that the last entry was on November 24, ten days earlier, when the *Mary Celeste* had been passing north of St Mary's Island in the Azores—more than 400 miles west of where she was found.

If she had been abandoned soon after that entry, she must have drifted unmanned and unsteered for a week and a half. Yet this could not have been. The *Mary Celeste* was found with her sails set to catch the wind coming over her starboard quarter: in other words, she was sailing on the starboard tack. The *Dei Gratia* had been following a similar course just behind her. But throughout the 400 miles from the Azores, the *Dei Gratia* had been obliged to sail on the port tack.

It seems impossible that the *Mary Celeste* could have reached the spot she did with her yards and sails set to starboard. Someone must have been working her for several days at least after the final log entry. But who? Or what?

The investigation by the British Admiralty's Gibraltar office did nothing to answer the questions. The inquiry discovered that the *Mary Celeste* was listed on the 1871 American Lloyd's Register as a New York-based brigantine of 206 tons, and that one of the barrels of alcohol had been tampered with. They found, too, that besides the chronometer, her sextant and cargo documents were missing.

They also found that ten people had sailed aboard the *Mary Celeste*—Captain Briggs, seven crewmen, and the captain's wife and young daughter. None of them was ever seen again.

Official explanation

The explanation that seemed most reasonable at the time was the official one put out by the British and American authorities. This suggested that the crew had got at the alcohol, murdered the captain and his family, and then somehow escaped to another vessel. But the story does not really stand up. There were no visible signs of a struggle on board, and if the crew had escaped, some of them would surely have turned up later.

Dozens of theories were, put forward. Had the vessel been attacked by an octopus, or some other monster which had somehow or other managed to extract the crew without damaging the ship itself? Or could the ship have encountered a mysterious island, newly risen from the deep? Might the crew have gone ashore, then, unable to regain their ship, drowned as the island descended once more into the Atlantic? Marginally less bizarre was the notion that every soul on board had been sucked off the decks by a whirlwind or waterspout.

The Fosdyk papers

A far more remarkable solution was advanced in 1913, 40 years after the event, in an article in the *Strand* magazine in London. It was written by a Hampstead schoolmaster named Howard Linford, who told the story of some papers left him by one of his employees, a well-educated and much-travelled man called Abel Fosdyk.

The dead man's papers contained notes which explained not only the fate of the crew but also the curious marks cut into the bows of the *Mary Celeste*.

Fosdyk claimed that he had been a secret passenger on the ship's last voyage —and the only survivor of the tragedy which overtook it. He was, the papers revealed, a close friend of Captain Briggs. Briggs had agreed to give him secret passage because Fosdyk—for some undisclosed reason—had to leave America in a hurry.

During the voyage, Briggs had the ship's carpenter build a special deck in the bows for his small daughter. It was the supporting struts for this deck that were slotted into the cuts in the bow planks.

One day Briggs had a lengthy argument with the mate about how well a man could swim with his clothes on. To prove his point, Briggs leapt into the water and started swimming round the ship. Two men followed while the rest of the crew watched from the deck.

Suddenly one of the sailors swimming round the bow gave a yell of agony. Everyone, including the captain's wife and child, crowded on to the newly built deck—which promptly collapsed under their combined weight. All were flung into the sea, where, according to Fosdyk, they were devoured by the sharks which had attacked the first seaman.

The one that got away

Only Fosdyk survived, and he, unable to regain the ship, clung to the shattered decking as the *Mary Celeste* drifted away. He floated for days until he was washed up half-dead on the north-west coast of Africa. The Fosdyk papers tell a neat tale. But they offer no solution to the mystery of how the ship got to where she was found. And they are wrong on details that should not have escaped an educated man. Fosdyk says the *Mary Celeste* weighed 600 tons. In fact she weighed a third of that. Fosdyk also says that the crew were English when in fact they were mostly Dutch. And most of all, it seems highly improbable that anyone would go swimming round a ship which, according to the *Dei Gratia* evidence, must have been making several knots at the time.

Bizarre as it is, no better explanation than Fosdyk's has so far emerged. And after more than 100 years, it is unlikely to do so. The enigma of the ship that sailed herself seems destined to puzzle forever.

369

THE VANISHING SPY-DIVER

What really happened to Buster Crabb?

Commander Lionel Crabb, Britain's foremost underwater expert in post-war years, booked into the Sally-port Hotel in Portsmouth on April 17, 1956, with Bernard Sydney Smith, an agent of the British Special Intelligence Service. On the following day, the Russian cruiser *Ordzhonikidze*, accompanied by two destroyers, anchored in Portsmouth Harbour. She was carrying Soviet Premier Nikolai Bulganin and the country's Communist Party First Secretary Nikita Kruschev on a state visit to Britain.

Downing Street had issued a directive that no attempts were to be made to spy on the Russian visitors. Yet, while Bulganin and Kruschev were in London, 'Buster' Crabb—on the instigation of the SIS man—secretly made a series of dives in the harbour to inspect the hull of the Russian warship.

Under the ship

He began the operation with test dives on the day the cruiser docked. Then, shortly after dawn on April 19, Crabb entered the harbour again and emerged to report that he had been under the ship, but was having trouble with the breathing apparatus of his frogman's suit. The equipment was Royal Naval issue, considered dangerous for use below 33 ft, and Crabb explained that he had had to surface to clear the system of poisonous excess carbon dioxide.

He then made another dive—and Smith never saw him again.

The cruiser and its two attendant destroyers sailed for home on April 29, and the following day the Admiralty issued a statement saying that Crabb was presumed dead 'as a result of trials with certain underwater apparatus'. According to the official announcement, Crabb was lost in the vicinity of the Russian ships on April 20.

Diplomatic Notes passed between the Soviet Embassy and the British Government, the British emphasising that Crabb had been operating without government permission having been granted.

When John Dugdale, MP for West Bromwich, asked in the House of Commons for more information, he was told by the Prime Minister, Sir Anthony Eden, that it would 'not be in the public interest' to disclose the circumstances in which Crabb was presumed to have died.

He added that because 'what was done was done without the authority or knowledge of Her Majesty's Ministers', disciplinary action was being taken.

This was all very well, but what had happened to Crabb?

Being a civilian, he was in death disowned by those in whose service he had died—if, indeed, he had died at all.

Had he been killed by some top-secret underwater protective device? Had Russian frogmen done it? Had the Russians captured him and taken him back to the Soviet Union?

To reach any conclusions it is necessary to look at Crabb's background and discover what sort of man he was. He started his career during the Second World War as a bomb and mine-disposal expert with the Royal Navy. Although an indifferent surface swimmer, he was a skilled and daring skin diver and an acknowledged expert at his craft.

Awards for bravery

During the war he dealt with Italian underwater saboteurs off Gibraltar. After this, he helped combat terrorists attempting to sabotage ships in the Mediterranean. He won the George Medal and was made an OBE.

He retired in 1955. The end of his service career seems to have taken much of the old spirit out of him, for he became bored and even talked to friends of suicide. Crabb was also an increasingly heavy drinker who tended to be talkative about his undercover exploits. It is known that he was drinking the night before he left the hotel for his last dive.

He was an eccentric, who enjoyed wearing his rubber wetsuits under his street clothes, and even in bed.

Why should the SIS hire such a man for their delicate mission?

An answer to that is that they needed a civilian, for a serving officer would be much more difficult to explain away in the event of failure. Crabb was an expert diver at a time when skin diving was not a popular pastime. He was experienced in what the SIS wanted—and he would be easy to persuade, for he needed the money desperately.

None of this could, of course, be verified, for Smith, the Intelligence agent, was spirited away from prying questioners immediately after the failure, along with the page in the hotel register which he and Crabb signed.

More than a year later, on June 9, 1957, the body of a man in a rubber suit was found by fishermen in Chichester Harbour, a few miles east of Portsmouth. Conveniently, it had no head or hands.

The body had a scar on one leg, similar

UNDERWATER spy 'Buster' Crabb vanished when he dived near the three Russian warships. Was he killed or captured on that ill-fated mission at Portsmouth?

to one on Crabb's leg, the wetsuit was of the Italian make that Crabb favoured, and the corpse had hammer-toes, like Crabb, although seemingly less distorted than his had been.

There were no positive identification factors—skull, teeth or fingerprints— but the Chichester coroner declared himself 'quite satisfied' that it was Crabb's body.

Far from ending the case, the inquest verdict fanned interest in it, and speculation once again became intense.

At this time, strange and disturbing stories began to reach Britain, allegedly from Russian sources. A West German newspaper carried a story claiming that a Russian naval officer had said Crabb was a Soviet prisoner.

Join or be shot?

He was alleged to be in a Moscow prison where he was considering the alternative of being shot as a spy, or joining the Russian Navy. He was said to have decided on the latter course—on condition that he never had to undertake missions against a British ship.

Another rumour, this time credited to Russian officers in Berlin, said that Crabb had been held underwater by a powerful magnetic device under the Russian cruiser, and had drowned.

Yet another suggestion was that Crabb was killed by a limpet mine planted on the ship by a fanatical Russian emigré group. It had blown up as he bravely tried to carry it away and disarm it.

But the rumour that gained most credence was that the British war hero had joined the Russians, in spite of his pronouncedly right-wing views in political matters.

This rumour gained strength from an unexpected source outside Great Britain.

A Russian forces magazine which reached the West carried a picture of a group of Soviet naval officers, one of whom was a Lieutenant Lvev Lvovich Korablov, an instructor in underwater operations. Although the photograph was rather blurred, Korablov was identified as Crabb by the missing frogman's ex-wife Margaret and one of his colleagues from wartime days.

Crabb's supposed reappearance in Russia was backed up by another report: that sailors from the *Ordzhenikidze* had described how the ship's hospital was sealed off during the return journey from Britain, with an unknown and heavily guarded patient inside.

If Crabb is alive in the Soviet Union it is difficult to understand why the Russians have never attempted to make any propaganda capital out of it.

If Korablov is Crabb, whose body was washed up in Chichester Harbour? This is a question that is never likely to be answered satisfactorily.

Faked body theory

Those who believe Crabb is alive suggest that a suitable body was procured by the Russians, given a leg scar, matured for a suitable period in sea water, then 'planted' —minus head and hands.

Another, somewhat melodramatic, theory is that the SIS itself disposed of the unfortunate Crabb when they realised that the Prime Minister's wrath would descend on them if the mission went ahead as planned.

Ultimately, the simplest and most likely explanation to most of us may be that Commander Lionel Crabb drowned because his equipment was faulty.

LOST GOLD REEF OF THE AUSTRALIAN DESERT

FAR OUT beyond the Petermann Range in the burning desert of central Australia lies the gold reef of Harold Bell Lasseter.

Lasseter, a stocky bushman, claimed to have found the reef in 1897, but it took him 14 years to raise funds for an expedition. That first trek was so hazardous that it had been abandoned. It was not until 1930 that he was able to finance a second party to dig out the riches he had seen.

One by one, the gold-hunters fell victim to the desert until Lasseter, alone except for two camels, was left to press on to his goal. He became sand-blinded and his body was found later in a cave, dead from starvation. But his legend, and the legend of his reef, lives on—glinting and tempting in the sun beyond the Petermann mountains.

THREE WISE MEN AND A STAR

The horoscope that changed the world

The Star of Bethlehem, said by the New Testament to have guided the three Magi to the birthplace of Christ, has puzzled scholars for centuries. What kind of phenomenon could, as described by Matthew, have appeared in the east and moved before the wise men, 'till it came and stood over where the young child was'?

One popular theory is that Halley's Comet, seen in the Holy Land around the time of Christ's birth, might have been taken as an omen by the Magi. But there are several objections to this idea which are difficult to overcome.

The comet is now known to have appeared over the Middle East in 11 BC, showing up brightest at $31\frac{1}{2}°$ North celestial latitude—the precise latitude of Bethlehem.

Report to Herod

It would have shone over the town and been visible to everyone. Why then, according to Matthew, would Herod have had to *ask* where the child was?

Having come from the east and 'seen' the star, Matthew says, the Magi reported to Herod who asked them to find the child, and: 'When they had heard the king, they departed; and, lo, the star, which they saw in the east, went before them, till it came and stood over where the young child was.'

And, of course, Halley's Comet, or any other comet for that matter, would not have behaved in this way—moving on ahead, then hovering over one spot.

In any case, Christ is believed to have been born at the time of the Romans' Imperial Census which, according to most historians, was in 4 BC. There are no records of any comets being seen anywhere in the world that year.

Another theory about the Star of Bethlehem is that it might have been a supernova—an exploding star, bright enough to remain visible for several months, even in daylight. But there is no evidence of such an event being seen around the time of Christ's birth.

Certainly, if such a spectacular heavenly display had occurred, not only would other contemporary chroniclers and figures have seen it—including Herod—but the Romans and Chinese would undoubtedly have recorded it.

A large meteor, or meteors, streaking across the sky, perhaps? Improbable, because meteors are visible only for seconds and are certainly incapable of hovering, or even appearing to do so.

A more probable theory, and one that is gaining ground in theological circles, is that the Magi were astrologers and had calculated that a particular star was in the ascendant, or rising in the east, and foretold the birth of a Messiah.

The Dead Sea Scrolls—a collection of ancient writings belonging to a little-known religious group and first discovered in caves by the north-west corner of the Dead Sea in 1947—give this theory some substance. Among the fragments of the Scrolls is a document giving the signs of the Zodiac, and another outlining the influence of the stars and planets on those born in various segments of the Zodiac.

The Scrolls also refer to a Teacher of Righteousness, or Prince of Light, who has been identified by some scholars with both John the Baptist and Jesus.

It could be, therefore, that contemporary astrologers would be watching the heavens and trying to calculate the necessary planetary conjunctions they believed would herald the birth of a Messiah.

Cardinal's theory

The late Jesuit scholar Cardinal Danielou accepted the theory that the star was one in a Messianic horoscope.

Danielou considered the Magi's statement, 'We have seen his star in the east', to be an allusion to a star at its rising, or in the ascendant—the most important factor in casting any horoscope.

He wrote: 'In those Jewish circles of the day in which astrology was accepted and the Messiah hoped for, there was speculation about which star he would be born under. From this it becomes clear that, as soon as a combination foretold in one of the previously prepared horoscopes actually took place, then people would believe that the Messiah had been born and start to look for his birthplace.'

This is perhaps just what the Magi, or astrologers, were doing when they visited Herod.

Adventures beyond the material world

Footsteps into the unknown

— • —

THE FLYING DUTCHMAN
Legend of a ship that never reached port

A burnished haze of heat hung over the blue waters of False Bay, a seaside playground on the tip of South Africa. It was a blazingly hot day in March, 1939, and on the sunbleached sands of Glencairn beach some 60 people relaxed beside the warm waters of the Indian Ocean.

Suddenly, out of the haze sailed a fine full-rigged Eastindiaman such as had not been seen in the waters off the Cape for several centuries. Those who noticed her called out to others, and soon everyone on the beach stood in an excited group, chattering at the edge of the sea.

Vanished without trace

According to a newspaper report on the following day, the ship 'with all her sails drawing well, although there was not a breath of wind at the time, appeared to be standing towards Muizenberg'.

The *British South Africa Annual* of 1939 reported: 'With uncanny volition the ship sailed steadily on as the Glencairn beachfolk, shaken from their lethargy, stood about keenly discussing the whys and wherefores of the vessel which seemed to be bent on self-destruction somewhere on the sands of Strandfontein. Just as the excitement reached its climax, however, the mystery ship vanished into thin air as strangely as it had come.'

In the days following the appearance of the phantom ship, several theories were advanced. One was that the watchers at Glencairn had seen a mirage and that

the mystery ship was, by some accident of light refraction, the image of a ship sailing several hundred miles away.

But, as those who had sighted the ship pointed out, the broad, squat hull and high poop, and even the rigging, were unlike that of any modern sailing ship. It was unmistakably a 17th-century merchantman.

Mrs Helene Tydell was among the crowd of witnesses on the beach that day. 'Let the sceptics say what they will, that ship was none other than the *Flying Dutchman*,' she said.

Even before it inspired Wagner to write his opera, 'Der Fliegende Holländer', the *Flying Dutchman* legend had been known to countless generations of sailors around the world. Old records show that in 1680, a Dutch Eastindiaman captained by Hendrik Van der Decken, sailed from Amsterdam for the Dutch East Indies settlement at Batavia. Van der Decken, a man of fearless and adventurous disposition, apparently had few scruples and an unsavoury reputation. But he was a skilled seaman and the owners had few qualms about giving him command of the vessel, in spite of his boasts in the waterfront wineshops that he would return with a fortune.

All seems to have gone well with Van der Decken and his crew as they sailed south through sunny tropical seas but, near the Cape of Good Hope, a sudden tropical gale tore the sails to shreds and wrecked the rudder. As days stretched into weeks, the vessel was tossed about off the Cape, unable to make headway against the battering force of a south-easterly gale. According to legend, Van der Decken became increasingly furious as every trick of navigation and seamanship he tried failed to bring him around the Cape.

Cursed the Almighty

Taking advantage of Van der Decken's frenzied state of mind, the Devil suggested to him in a dream that he should defy the Almighty's attempt to stop him rounding the Cape. In a rage, the Dutch sea captain took up the challenge:

> *With frantic mien the appalling oath he took,*
> *And loudly cried above the tempest's din:*
> *'My destined course and resolute career*
> *The power of God I thus defy to stay*
> *Nor shall the Fiend of Hell awake my fear*
> *Though I should cruise until the Judgment Day.'*

Who first quoted the captain's words is not known. But retribution came swiftly as the Angel of the Lord commanded that Van der Decken should roam the seas forever 'until the trump of God shall rend the sky'.

The ship would eventually founder and the crew would die, but Van der Decken must keep his vigil until Doomsday.

Van der Decken and his ship never reached Batavia. Since 1680 there have been countless sightings of his ship reported. Any ship that sights the phantom is said soon to encounter bad luck.

This was the case when the late George V, a midshipman on HMS *Bacchante*, saw the phantom ship and a figure in ancient dress on her poop as the *Bacchante* sailed 50 miles off the Cape. Next day, a member of the crew fell from the rigging and was killed.

The last recorded Cape sighting was in September 1942, when four people sitting on their balcony in Mouille Point, Cape Town, saw the ghostly Eastindiaman sail into Table Bay and disappear behind Robben Island.

Scientific view

Scientists continue to insist that what they, George V and the people of Glencairn beach saw were mirages, and that other ships have been sighted in that way. A mail ship of the P & O line bound for India was once spotted at Aden. Her log showed later that she was at least 200 miles away at the time.

But science has not yet been able to explain the constant similarities of detail given by those who have seen the Eastindiaman—or the fact that ships of her type last sailed more than 200 years ago.

SHIP OF ILL-OMEN *Long before it inspired Wagner to write his opera, 'Der Fliegende Holländer', the Flying Dutchman legend was known to generations of sailors as a portent of disaster.*

THE ANGELS OF MONS

Did a phantom army save the British from certain death?

A month after the bitterly fought Battle of Mons in the First World War, a report appeared in the London *Evening News* which caused a sensation at the time and has created controversy ever since.

The report, by a Welsh-born journalist and author, Arthur Machen, told how the tiny British Expeditionary Force, outnumbered by three to one, were apparently saved by heavenly reinforcements. The Angel, or Angels of Mons (accounts varied between one and a platoon), suddenly stood between them and the Germans. Understandably, the enemy fell back in confusion.

The battle took place on August 26, 1914, and when the report appeared in September, most of the survivors were still in France. In May the following year, a clergyman's daughter at Clifton, Bristol, published anonymously in a parish magazine, what she claimed was a sworn statement by a British officer.

In it the officer said that while his company was in retreat from Mons, a unit of German cavalry came rapidly after them. He made for a place where the company might stand and fight—but the Germans got there first.

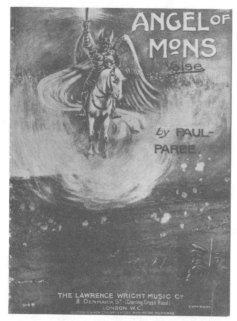

RIDERS IN THE SKY *The legend of the angels that saved the British army in retreat became so popular that a waltz was written on the theme.*

Expecting almost certain death, the British turned and saw to their astonishment a troop of angels between them and the enemy. The German horses were terrified and stampeded in all directions.

An Army chaplain, the Rev. C. M. Chavasse, brother of Noel Chavasse, VC, and later Bishop of Rochester, recorded that he had heard similar accounts from a brigadier-general and two of his officers.

A lieutenant-colonel described how, during the retreat, his battalion was escorted for 20 minutes by a squadron of phantom cavalry.

From the German side came an account that their men refused to charge a point where the British line was broken because of the presence of a large number of troops. According to Allied records, there was not a single British soldier in the area.

An imaginative writer

What is notable about all the Mons reports is that not one of them is first-hand. In each case, the officers from whom the reports originated wished to remain anonymous, feeling that they might be accused of having an over-active imagination—a possible hindrance to promotion.

Years later Machen, himself a writer of stories of horror and the supernatural, and a one-time member of the mystical society known as the Hermetic Order of the Golden Dawn, admitted that his original account had been no more than a piece of imaginative writing.

So the mystery becomes even more compelling. Despite the denial, scores of returning soldiers did reminisce about the strange events at Mons, and investigators did come to believe that something supernatural had indeed taken place.

Did the returning soldiers seize upon and support a story that appealed to them? Or did something—a mirage, perhaps—happen that made both the British and the Germans believe they had seen a spectral army of angels?

Whatever the explanation, the British did achieve something like a miracle. Despite overwhelming odds and heavy casualties, the retreat was successfully accomplished and the BEF remained an effective fighting force.

WHEN THE DEVIL WALKED IN DEVON

What else could leave a 100 mile trail of hoofprints?

All over southern England, the winter of 1854–5 was the coldest in living memory. Overnight, on February 9, there had been a severe frost and 2 in. of snow blanketed the County of Devon. The River Exe was frozen over and birds were trapped where they had stood in the ice.

When dawn came, the snow lay white, smooth and even, marked only by bird and animal tracks and, across about 100 miles of the county, a trail of mysterious footprints. They zigzagged through five parishes, across gardens, over rooftops, haystacks, walls and in and out of barns.

They were 4 in. long, $2\frac{3}{4}$ in. wide and 8 in. apart, and appeared to have been made by a creature with hooves, walking upright on two legs.

To the country people of the area, there was no doubt about the cause of the footprints. They had been made by the cloven hooves of the Devil.

Hooves of fire

The weird prints began in the middle of a garden in the parish of Totnes and ended as mysteriously as they had started, in a field at Littleham. In one village they led into a shed and out at the other side. Whatever made them had gone through a 6 in. diameter hole.

In another village, the creature appeared to have crawled through a drainpipe, leaving tracks at both ends.

In some places, the marks seemed to have been made by fiery hooves in the hard-frozen snow or, as at Woodbury, by a hot iron outside the door of the church.

Hundreds of people saw the prints and scores of letters poured in to newspapers in which people debated what could have caused them.

Near the village of Dawlish, the trail led into dense bracken and undergrowth. When dogs were brought in to flush out the thicket, they are said to have retreated, howling dismally.

Many theories

The naturalist Sir Richard Owen, in a letter to the *Illustrated London News*, suggested the prints were those of a badger. He pointed out that the badger places its hind feet in the marks left by its forefeet. Although it hibernates, it sometimes ventures out in search of food.

Other suggestions included a fox, an otter, cranes, wild cats, a donkey or a pony with a broken shoe. One amateur naturalist even suggested that the prints resembled those of a kangaroo and that the animal might have escaped from a travelling menagerie, then returned to its cage without anyone noticing its absence.

Rats, rabbits, squirrels and toads were also suggested as possible culprits.

A vicar, the Rev. Henry Fudsen, gave a sermon in which he declared the prints to be the paw marks of several cats.

One group of villagers, believing there might be a wild beast at large, set out with pitchforks and bludgeons to track it down, but without success.

But local people were not convinced. Many refused to go out after sunset, and children hid in closets and cupboards, terrified by the fireside gossip they had heard: that the Devil had walked in Devon that winter night.

THE ILLUSTRATED LONDON NEWS

FOOT-MARKS ON THE SNOW, IN DEVON.

(From a Correspondent.)

As many of your readers have perused, I have no doubt, with much interest, the paragraph which appeared in several of the papers of last week, relative to the mysterious foot-marks left upon the snow during the night of Thursday, the 8th, in the parishes of Exmouth, Lympstone, and Woodbury, as also in Dawlish, Torquay, Totnes, and other places on the other side of the estuary of the Exe, in the county of Devon, extending over a tract of country of thirty or forty miles, or probably more; and as the paragraph I allude to does not fully detail the mysterious affair, it may probably be interesting to many to have a more particular account—which I think this unusual occurrence well deserves. The marks which appeared on the snow (which lay very thinly on the ground at the time), and which were seen on the Friday morning, to all appearance were the perfect impression of a donkey's hoof—the length 4 inches by 2¾ inches; but, instead of progressing as that animal would have done (or indeed as any other would have done), feet, right and left, it appeared that foot had followed foot, in *a single line*; the distance from each tread being eight inches, or rather more—the foot-marks in every parish being exactly the same size, and the steps the same length. This mysterious visitor generally only passed once down or across each garden or courtyard, and did so in nearly all the houses in many parts of the several towns above mentioned, as also in the farms scattered about; this regular track passing in some instances over the roofs of houses, and hayricks, and very high walls (one fourteen feet), without displacing the snow on either side or altering the distance between the feet, and passing on as if the wall had not been any impediment. The gardens with high fences or walls, and gates locked, were equally visited as those open and unprotected. Now, when we consider the distance that must have been gone over to have left these marks—I may say in almost every garden, on door-steps, through the extensive woods of Luscombe, upon commons, in enclosures and farms—the actual progress must have exceeded a hundred miles. It is very easy for people to laugh at these appearances, and account for them in an idle way. At present no satisfactory solution has been given. No known animal could have traversed this extent of country in one night, besides having to cross an estuary of the sea two miles broad. Neither does any known animal walk in a *line* of single footsteps, not even man.

Birds could not have left these marks, as no bird's-foot leaves the impression.

TRACKING THE DEVIL *The mysterious hoofprints across 100 miles of Devon drew lots of correspondence (above) in the newspapers.*

VOICE IN THE NIGHT

For 400 years she has mourned her children

At the stroke of midnight an eerie cry that has echoed through more than four centuries is said to be heard in the heart of Mexico City.

The mournful voice is that of a grief-stricken woman, who wails: 'Oh, my children, my pitiful, wretched children.'

She is La Llorona, the Wailing Woman. Wearing a torn and blood-stained gown, she haunts the night, wailing her grief.

According to Mexican legend, dating back to 1550, the voice belongs to Doña Luisa de Olveros, a Spanish-Indian of outstanding beauty, who took as her lover a nobleman, Don Nuño de Montesclaros. She bore him two children, loved him deeply and prayed for the day when she would become his bride.

But Don Nuño did not return her feelings and, once his passion had died, began to neglect her.

Lonely and puzzled, Luisa finally decided one night to walk to the palatial home of the wealthy and influential Montesclaros family in the hope of seeing her lover and begging him to come back.

She found him—but to her horror he was in the centre of a lavish party, celebrating his marriage that day to a Spanish noblewoman.

Luisa rushed to him in tears, but he pushed her away, coldly telling her that because of her Indian blood she was unacceptable and could never have become his wife.

Hysterical, she ran home to her children and killed them with a small dagger which had been a present from her lover.

She fled from the house, covered with her children's blood, and dashed through the streets screaming, until she was arrested and thrown into prison. She was convicted of sorcery.

Doña Luisa de Olveros was publicly hanged in Mexico City and, as final humiliation, her body was left swinging in 'public mockery' for six hours. Every night since then, her ghostly cries have rung out and will continue to, so the legend says, until the end of time.

FISHER'S REVENGE

The murderer was caught by his victim's ghost

On a dark winter's evening in 1826, James Farley, a highly respected farmer of Cambelltown, New South Wales, was walking near a house belonging to a man named Frederick Fisher. There he saw a figure sitting on a railing and pointing to a spot in Fisher's paddock. So sinister was the figure, that Farley fled, convinced he had seen a ghost.

Fisher was a paroled convict who had become a prosperous farmer. Some time before when he had been imprisoned for debt, he had transferred his assets to a friend, another ex-convict, named George Worrall, in order to prevent them being seized by his creditors. After six months in gaol he had returned unexpectedly.

On June 26, 1826, some months before Farley saw the ghost, Fisher had been observed leaving a Cambelltown pub after a long drinking session, and had not been seen since. Worrall circulated the perfectly reasonable story that Fisher had returned to England on the ship, *Lady Vincent*. But three months after Fisher's disappearance the authorities became suspicious and inserted a notice in the *Sydney Gazette* which offered a reward of £20 for the discovery of Fisher's body.

Worrall was questioned by the police because he had been seen wearing trousers known to have belonged to Fisher. He accused four other men of murdering his friend, saying that he had seen them do it. This unlikely tale deepened official suspicion and Worrall was arrested.

It was at this point that Farley saw the ghost. On Farley's insistence, a Constable Newland went to the paddock with an aborigine tracker. He found traces of human blood on a rail and, at the spot that the ghost had indicated, discovered Fisher's savagely battered body in a shallow marshy grave.

Worrall was convicted of the murder and, before his execution, admitted to a clergyman that he had killed Fisher, but said the blow was accidental.

BARNEY DUFFY'S CURSE

Two soldiers ignored it . . . and died

Barney Duffy was a giant of a man. He towered over the two young soldiers, uttering a terrible curse: 'Take me or report me, ye red-coated, lily-livered lice! Aye! And then I'll hang —but hear me curse on ye! So surely as ye do this, before me corpse has hung a week on King's Town gallows, ye'll meet a violent death, the pair of ye!'

Duffy, an Irishman, had been imprisoned by the British on Norfolk Island, in the Pacific Ocean, 900 miles north-east of Sydney. The island is one of the most beautiful in the world, but its past is a long tale of blood.

Scores of its present residents claim they have seen ghosts—ghosts of the descendants of the *Bounty* mutineers, who outgrew tiny Pitcairn Island and moved to Norfolk in the 19th century, and ghosts of rebellious Irish convicts, hanged there after the British authorities shipped them from Botany Bay.

The convict's life was a continuous nightmare. Men got 50 lashes for possessing tobacco or singing. They ate with their fingers and drank water from buckets. Those sentenced to hang thanked God for deliverance, while the remainder prayed not for freedom but for death.

Barney Duffy escaped from this hell and hid in a hollow pine in the thick rain forest. He emerged at night to raid the vegetable gardens of the settlement. His beard and hair were long and matted, and he had just a few rags to cover himself when the two soldiers, who were out fishing, discovered him.

They shrugged off his curse and pushed him back to the settlement with their muskets. Duffy was hanged, and two days later the soldiers went to fish at the same spot near the hollow pine.

Shortly after, a foot patrol found their bodies, battered and broken, drifting in the tide near by.

To this day Norfolk Island maps show Barney Duffy Gully—where two soldiers ignored Barney Duffy's curse and paid with their lives.

WHOSE IMAGE?

Photographic evidence of Christ's death

In a reliquary in the chapel of the Dukes of Savoy at Turin Cathedral, lies a piece of cloth, measuring 13 ft by 3½ ft, which faintly bears the back and front images of a man.

Every 33 years—the supposed age of Christ at his death—the cloth is put on display and thousands of pilgrims flock to see it. They believe that they are gazing on the features of Jesus Christ.

The Holy Shroud of Turin is one of the most closely guarded and controversial Christian relics in the world. If it is genuine, it is certainly the most precious.

It is believed to be the linen in which Christ's body was placed in the tomb, after His crucifixion. His image appears to have imprinted itself on the cloth, as if it were a photographic plate.

Whether the shroud is genuinely that of Christ or not, it has been the subject of many investigations, which have uncovered some amazing facts and posed many more intriguing questions.

The shroud is believed to have been kept in hiding for three centuries during the early Christian persecutions. Later, it was acquired for the Treasury of the Byzantine rulers of Constantinople, where it remained until the city fell in 1204.

It was taken by Crusaders to Besançon Cathedral, in the French province of Doubs, where it narrowly escaped being destroyed by fire in 1349.

Finally, the shroud was presented to the Dukes of Savoy in 1432. After being slightly damaged in another fire, this time at the ducal palace, it was removed to the cathedral at Turin, where the dukes had another residence. It has been kept there since 1578.

The first photographs

In 1898, Secondo Pia, an archaeological photographer, took the first crude pictures of the shroud, and found to his surprise, that his negative plates gave a more positive, clearer, image of the

379

IS THIS THE FACE OF CHRIST? *The image captured in the age-old piece of cloth treasured at Turin Cathedral is certainly remarkable. Is it also a photographic record of Christ's death?*

figure that appeared to be on the cloth.

Dr Yves Delage, a distinguished French physician, began an investigation into the relic and, in 1902, presented his findings to the French Academy of Sciences.

His colleague, Paul Vignon, suggested that the stains on the shroud were caused by perspiration and spices, with which the cloth was impregnated.

Dr Delage reported that the image was a perfectly detailed portrayal of the body of a man who had undergone a brutal series of tortures, culminating in the agony of crucifixion.

The face bore the marks of several blows; the nose was injured; there was severe bruising and swelling of the right cheek; the right eyelid was sharply contracted; bloodstains on the forehead and back of the head indicated that the skin had been punctured by sharp instruments.

The whole body, with the exception of the face, hands and feet, was covered in marks suggesting scourging by a two-thonged lash, studded with balls of lead or bone, and administered by two people. These marks were particularly severe on the chest and abdomen. The shoulders had wounds consistent with carrying a heavy object. Both knees were cut, as if from heavy falls. There were bloodstained wounds, which could have been caused by nails, in both hands and the feet.

Wrist wounds

The hand wounds were through the wrists, just behind the heel of the hand. A large wound on the right side, between the fifth and sixth ribs, was clear, and there was a corresponding stain of blood and a colourless liquid, possibly fluid from a pierced lung.

The body had been sprinkled with powdered aloes. Traces of this remained but, contrary to Jewish custom, the body had not been washed or anointed—perhaps indicative of a hasty burial.

Dr Delage summed up by saying: 'On the one hand we have the shroud, probably impregnated with aloes, which brings us to the East, outside Egypt, and a crucified man who has been scourged. On the other, we have an account, pertaining to history, legend and tradition, showing Christ undergoing in Judaea the same treatment as we decipher on the body whose image is on the shroud.'

His report sparked off a controversy which has never really died down. Critics claim the shroud is a fake, the work of an extremely clever artist.

But Dr Delage pointed out that the shroud bore no apparent traces of pigment. As it had been authenticated since the 14th century, if the image was a fake there must have existed an unknown artist 'capable of executing a work hardly within the power of the greatest Renaissance painters'.

He also said that it seemed impossible for anyone to paint a negative image with such accuracy. Why, he asked, should anyone go to such lengths? And particularly in a time when photography was an art yet undreamt of?

In 1931, another photographer, Guiseppe Enrie, was allowed to take pictures of the shroud. After studying his plates, which were far superior to those of 1898, he declared: 'The imprint is not the work of an artist. The biggest enlargements establish that there is no trace of any dye whatsoever on the fabric.'

X-ray examination

Conventions were formed in Germany and Italy and the members made a deep study of the shroud and its religious implications. In 1959 the German convention petitioned Pope John XXIII to allow a small portion of the shroud to be removed for chemical and microscopic examination, X-rays, infra-red and ultra-violet rays and, most important, dating by radio-carbon process.

Their appeal was dismissed by Cardinal Maurilio Fossati, Archbishop of Turin. No reason was given.

Kurt Berna, the German writer, who has made a study of the shroud, points out that if the shroud is that of Christ, the bloodstains indicate that His heart was still beating *after He was taken down from the cross*. If His heart had stopped beating, the wounds would have ceased to bleed and any blood outside the body would have quickly congealed, long before it was wrapped in its shroud.

This proposition has enormous religious implications for Christians and Jews, whose Old Testament prophesied that the Messiah would die on the cross.

Berna says that Christ was not killed by the crucifixion, nor by the spear thrust into His side. He claims that photographic reconstruction shows that a lance thrust into the body as indicated on the shroud would not have pierced the heart.

And he believes that Jesus might merely have lost consciousness and stopped breathing because of the torture inflicted upon Him, loss of blood, or the fumes of the vinegar offered to Him by a Roman centurion.

Revived by cold

Believing Him to be dead, the executioners allowed Him to be removed and placed in a tomb.

It is there, Berna suggests, that aloes and ointments, and the cold atmosphere, might have revived Him, allowing Him to appear alive to the disciples before the Ascension.

Berna also makes much of the fact that the nail wounds on the shroud image are through the wrist. He says this lends authenticity to the shroud, because if, as popularly believed, nails had been driven through the palms, they would have torn out because of the weight of the body.

Other medical experts, who have examined photographs of the shroud, have noted the muscular deformities on the image which, they say, are consistent with the effects of crucifixion.

Dr David Willis, a police surgeon from Guildford in Surrey, England, noted that the thumbs of the image were sharply retracted—the exact result of having nails driven through the median nerve which runs down the centre of the wrist.

Those who are convinced of the shroud's authenticity point out that anatomical details such as these are not likely to be reproduced by an artist. They ask: Could even a Michelangelo depict with such fine accuracy a body which had gone through such agony and distortion?

Only when the Turin authorities allow a full scientific analysis can the many mysteries be solved.

THE WOMAN WITH WILLPOWER

An amazing case of mind over matter

The young girl-soldier in the Russian Red Army was bored. A front-line fighter at 14, she had been wounded by a German shell-fragment just as the Second World War was nearing its end, and recovery was proving a long business.

'I was very angry and upset one day,' Ninel Kulagina later recalled. 'I was walking towards a cupboard when suddenly a jug moved to the edge of the shelf fell and smashed to bits.'

Other, similar things happened—lights went on and off, doors opened and closed and crockery moved on tables, all with no visible human intervention. At first Ninel thought of poltergeists—the mischievous spirits that sometimes plague human beings, especially teenage girls. But she sensed that the force moving the objects came from inside her.

She practised concentrating and learnt how to focus her power. One of the first scientists to take an interest in her was Edward Naumov. He scattered a box of matches on a bench and she clasped her hands over them, shaking with the strain. Suddenly, all the matches moved in a body to the edge of the bench, then fell one by one to the floor.

Many more tests followed, and more than 60 films were made of Ninel in action. In perhaps the most notable test that was filmed, a raw egg was broken into a glass tank filled with saline solution. By intense concentration, she separated the white from the yolk and moved the two apart—though she was standing several feet from the tank at the time.

Instruments connected to Ninel showed that she was under considerable emotional and mental stress.

Dr Genady Sergeyev, who conducted the experiment, also measured the electrostatic field around Ninel. At the moment that she started to separate the yolk and the white, the field began to pulse at the rate of four cycles a second.

Dr Sergeyev deduced that these vibrations acted like magnetic waves. 'The moment these magnetic vibrations, or waves, occur, they cause the object she focuses on, even if it is something non-magnetic, to act as if magnetised,' he recorded. 'It causes the object to be attracted to her or repelled by her.'

THE MIRACULOUS MONK

An Italian padre who could be seen in two places at once

General Luigi Cadorna, Chief of the Italian General Staff, was in despair after a crushing defeat of his armies by the Germans in Slovenia in November 1917.

He sat in his tent holding his service revolver and contemplating suicide. Suddenly, a monk appeared and admonished him: 'Don't be so stupid!'—then vanished utterly.

Years after the First World War, the general visited the church of San Giovanni Rotondo at Foggia in Central Italy. He saw a monk, whom he recognised as the one who had appeared in his tent.

As the monk passed, he told the general 'You had a lucky escape, my friend.'

The monk was Padre Pio, a humble peasant priest who has since become famous as a worker of miracles, as a clairvoyant, stigmatic—and, since his death in 1968, a possible but controversial choice for canonisation.

What makes the story of the general so remarkable is that, for the entire duration of the war, Padre Pio never left his friary at Foggia.

Born in the village of Pietrelcina, near Benevento, in 1887, the son of a poor farmer, Padre Pio entered a Capuchin monastery at the age of 17. For 11 years he quietly studied and went about his duties with his fellow novices.

Then, on September 20, 1915, he complained of pains in his hands, feet and right side. Doctors could find no physical explanation. On September 20, 1918, while praying at the altar of the church at Foggia, he collapsed in agony. Fellow monks found him unconscious, and bleeding from his hands, feet and side—wounds closely corresponding to those suffered by

Christ on the Cross. Padre Pio was examined by doctors of several denominations but none could give a satisfactory explanation for his injuries.

Such wounds, called stigmata, have appeared, apparently involuntarily, on a number of people during the Christian era, and have been accepted by the devout as marks of sanctity.

The most common manifestations are bleeding from the hands and feet and from the right or left side. Bruises on the shoulders represent the agony of carrying the cross, while bleeding from the brow closely resemble the injuries inflicted by the crown of thorns.

Other stigmatics have felt the chafing of the ropes that bound Christ to the cross, while others have been scarred by the weals of the scourge.

THE MARK OF CHRIST *A rare photograph of Padre Pio. The stigma on his right hand can be clearly seen.*

Medical theories

Doctors have long ago dismissed the idea that stigmata arise from any physical cause. They, and theologians, have observed that most stigmatics are people given to brooding intensely upon the sufferings of Christ. And the most common explanation is that auto-suggestion is involved.

The Roman Catholic Church has put forward three possible causes for stigmata; divine revelation, diabolic intervention to confuse believers; and conscious or unconscious suggestion. None can be proved.

Whatever the cause in Padre Pio's case, he carried on his duties and became famous throughout the Catholic world as a kind and gentle confessor.

Avoided publicity

Never did he try to capitalise on the strange phenomenon of his stigmata, and he always tried to avoid publicity or any hint of notoriety—even to the extent of covering his hands in public. Nevertheless, money was sent to him and his friary from all over the world. In 1956 a hospital which cost nearly £1 million, and completely paid for out of donations, was opened at Foggia.

Padre Pio's home village of Pietrelcina also began to prosper as pilgrims flocked to his birthplace.

Twice he was suspended from his duties by the Vatican to which his fame was an embarrassment, particularly because of the money sent to him. Eventually the padre was absolved from his vows of poverty, provided that all money sent to him was willed to the Holy See. Meanwhile, the padre's fame for his clairvoyance and other powers continued to spread.

On January 20, 1936, three men visiting the friary were approached by Padre Pio, who said: 'Please pray with me for a soul who is soon to appear before the tribunal of God.'

They obeyed, and were then told by the priest that they had been praying for King George V of England, who had died at the time they were praying.

In the 1920s, a Monsignor Damiani, of Salto, in Uruguay, met Padre Pio, and was so impressed that he vowed he wanted to die in the priest's presence.

Padre Pio told him: 'You will die in your native land—but do not be afraid.' Consoled, Damiani returned to Uruguay.

A deathbed mystery

Then, in 1942, the Archbishop of Montevideo was awakened late at night by a Capuchin monk, who urged him to go to the bedside of Damiani.

When he got there, Damiani was dead. But by the bed was a slip of paper on which was written: 'Padre Pio came.'

It was not until 1949 that the archbishop met Padre Pio—and recognised him as the Capuchin who had summoned him to Damiani's bedside.

When he died, on September 28, 1968, Padre Pio's followers began to demand that he be canonised—demands not yet acceded to.

GHOST ON THE PROW

Dead or alive, he could not leave his ship

A German U-boat drifting aimlessly off Ireland was a target too good to miss in July 1918. The American submarine which spotted her was manoeuvring for the attack when a huge explosion seized the U-boat and sent her to the bottom with all hands.

What caused that explosion will never be known, but for the U-65 it was the final blow in a series of disasters.

For she was a jinx ship. Even before she had left the building yard at Bruges in Belgium, two years earlier, she had already claimed one life. A dockyard worker was killed when hit by a girder that was being lowered into place for the hull. On her first sea trials, the engine-room filled with fumes and three men suffocated.

As it was wartime, news of the deaths was kept within the German Admiralty. More trials with a pack of sister ships were without incident at first—until the captain of U-65 ordered her first dive.

The captain sent a sailor forward for a routine inspection of the hatches. The sea was calm and there was very little wind, but instead of making the inspection, inexplicably, he stepped overboard and was swept away in the wash.

The silent crew gazed nervously at each other as the captain closed hatches to dive. He gave the order to level-off at 30 ft but the U-65 continued down until she struck the sea bed, where she refused to budge. For 12 hours she lay there as the water seeped in. And for the second time she began to fill with battery fumes. Then once again, for some unexplained reason, she lifted from the bottom and rose to the surface.

After an overhaul back in Bruges, the U-65 was passed fit for service and re-fuelling and arming began. During this operation, a torpedo warhead exploded and took the death toll to 11. One of the victims was the second lieutenant.

As the U-65 was towed into dry dock, an hysterical crewman swore he saw the dead officer standing, arms folded, on the prow of the ship. Before she sailed for duty again another seaman had deserted after reporting that he, too, had seen the dead officer in the same place.

Repaired, the U-65 sailed for the Dover Straits and, during its tour of duty, reports of more sightings of the officer did little to increase morale. The duty officer was found trembling on the bridge after he saw the ghost and watched as the figure faded from sight.

The crew were all thankful when their ship returned to base, although it was under aerial attack. As the captain walked down the gangway he was struck and killed by a splinter from a bomb.

The Imperial Navy took the case so seriously they had the U-65 exorcised by a priest. But, on the next tour of duty, a gunner went mad, the chief engineer broke his leg and there was a suicide.

On the morning of July 10, 1918, she was spotted drifting off the Cape Clear coast of south-west Ireland by the American submarine, L-2.

When the captain of the L-2 looked through his periscope, he was puzzled by a lone figure, standing with arms crossed on the prow of the ship. Then came the shattering explosion which ripped the U-65 from stem to stern.

Loyal even in death, the lieutenant had stayed with his comrades to the end.

BATTLE TRAPPED IN TIME?

The women who heard a battle nine years late

Just before dawn on August 19, 1942, Canadian and British troops attacked the German-held port of Dieppe in Normandy, in a full-scale rehearsal for D-Day. It was a raid from which the Allies learnt much, but at a terrible cost. Of a total of 6086 men who landed, 3623 were killed or wounded. Just before dawn nine years later on August 4, 1951, two English women on holiday near Dieppe were awakened by the sound of gunfire. What happened in the next three hours was like listening to a battle that had become trapped in time. The women heard an uncannily accurate repetition of events of nine years before. Their account of the savage battle for Dieppe was confirmed from military records.

The two women, who were sisters-in-law, were staying at Puys, a seaside village near Dieppe, which had been one of three landing points for the assault.

Below is shown how the two women's description of the events of August 4, 1951, compares with the official Allied records.

No one else in the area heard anything unusual. Although the women had read accounts of the battle, a British Society for Psychical Research investigation in 1952 was satisfied that 'the experience must be rated as a genuine psychic experience'.

About 4 a.m.: the women hear men's cries 'as if above a storm', with distinct sounds of gunfire and dive-bombing steadily becoming louder.	*3.47 a.m.: Allied assault vessels exchanged fire with German ships. Troops manning beach defences were probably shouting to each other.*
4.50: abrupt silence.	*4.50: zero hour for troop landings at Puys, but the operation was running 17 minutes behind schedule and firing may have stopped at this point.*
5.07: waves of loud noise—mainly dive-bombers—but some faint cries in the background.	*5.07: landing craft beached at Puys under heavy fire, then destroyers bombarded Dieppe with shells while aircraft attacked seafront buildings.*
5.40: silence again.	*5.40: naval bombardment stopped.*
5.50: sound of aircraft in large numbers, with fainter background noises.	*5.50: Allied air reinforcements arrived and encountered German aircraft.*
6.00: all noise died away. 6.25: more cries, gradually becoming fainter. 6.55: uninterrupted silence.	*8.30: attack repulsed with appalling Allied casualties. Survivors surrendered.*

SYMBOLS OF DEFEAT *Burning wrecks of an Allied tank and landing craft on a Dieppe beach record the disastrous landing in 1942 in preparation for invasion. Allied casualties were 59·5 per cent.*

LIFE AFTER DEATH? *About 70 years after being declared dead, Dorothy Eady was still living in the ruins of the temple built by Seti I for the god Osiris.*

PRIESTESS OF THE NILE

The reincarnation of a little girl who 'died' in a fall

On the banks of the Nile near an ancient temple built to the god Osiris by Pharaoh Seti I, lives an elderly Englishwoman. Dorothy Eady, who 'died' when she was three years old, is deeply convinced that she has been reborn as an Egyptian priestess.

Dorothy was born in 1903 into a wealthy South London family. But in later life she called herself Um Seti, the reincarnation of a woman who served at King Seti's court. Her strange journey into the distant past, which she described in 1973, began as a child after she fell down a stairway and was declared dead by the family doctor. When the doctor returned with a nurse to lay out the body, he found the little girl very much alive and well.

Soon afterwards, Dorothy took to hiding under tables and behind furniture. She bewildered her parents with demands to be 'taken home'. One day the family visited the British Museum and, in the Egyptian galleries, Dorothy ran wild.

For no apparent reason she began kissing the feet of statues, clinging to mummy cases and screaming, in a voice which her mother recalled as sounding 'strange and old', that she wanted to be left with 'my people'.

On another occasion, Dorothy was shown a photograph of the temple built by Seti I. She immediately told her father that the temple was her 'real' home—a conviction she never lost.

Dorothy claimed that she had known Seti, and that he was a kindly man. As her convictions grew, Dorothy began to learn how to read hieroglyphics at the British Museum. She astounded her teacher with her ability to learn the symbols, and explained she was not learning a new language, only re-learning a language she had forgotten.

In 1930 Dorothy married an Egyptian and went to live in Egypt. Their only child, a boy, they named Seti, and Dorothy called herself Um Seti—mother of Seti.

For 20 years she worked as an archaeological research assistant. In 1952 she made her first pilgrimage to Abydos, the site of Seti's temple and the tomb of Osiris.

A 'homecoming'

She was quite unable to read modern Egyptian, but when her train stopped near a range of limestone hills, she knew she had arrived at the right place.

Dorothy described her first sighting of the temple as a 'homecoming'. In 1954 she returned to Abydos to live out her life. She helped with the upkeep of the temple and prayed daily to Osiris—which made her his sole living devotee.

By 1973 she had even obtained permission from the temple curators that when she died she would be buried in the grounds of the temple she called 'home'.

But belief in reincarnation is by no means unique. Many people at some time have the feeling they have done something or been somewhere in a previous life, but cannot explain how or when.

In 1956, during a two-hour sitting with hypnotherapist Arnall Bloxham, of Cardiff, a teenage English girl, Ann Ockenden, suddenly began talking of a previous life as a man in a land where people were decorated with scars and animal teeth.

Reborn after three centuries

Another of Bloxham's clients claimed she was the daughter of Charles I and Queen Henrietta Maria. Although this anonymous woman had not studied history, she was able to give accurate details of the court of French King Louis XIV, where she and her 'brother', Charles II, lived in exile.

Arthur Guirdham, an English psychiatrist, has recorded the story of a woman he calls Mrs Smith.

From her teens, Mrs Smith had recurrent dreams of a former life as the wife of a 13th-century French Cathar preacher. The Cathars were a heretical Christian sect which soon became the subject of much persecution by the Inquisition. History records that most of the Cathar preachers and followers were killed in a massacre. And Mrs Smith's most fearsome nightmare was that of being burnt to death at the stake.

Mrs Smith knew nothing of the Cathars, but in 1944 she described the clothes they wore. She described them as green or blue robes—which they were.

INNER FIRES

Strange cases of human incendiary bombs

On an October evening in the late 1950s, a pretty 19-year-old secretary, dancing with her boy-friend in a London discotheque, suddenly burst into flames.

As though driven by an inner storm, fire burst furiously from her back and chest, enveloping her head and igniting her hair. In seconds she was a human torch, and before her horrified companion

and other people on the floor could beat out the flames, she was dead.

With his burnt hands swathed in bandages, her boy-friend testified at the inquest: 'I saw no one smoking on the dance floor. There were no candles on the tables and I did not see her dress catch fire from anything. I know it sounds incredible, but it appeared to me that the flames burst outwards, as if they originated within her body.' Other witnesses agreed with him, and the mystified coroner's verdict was eventually 'Death by misadventure, caused by a fire of unknown origin'.

Rare, but real

Such terrifying cases of spontaneous human combustion are fortunately rare—but they do occur, and have been reported throughout history. In north Essex, England, in the 17th century, an elderly woman was found burnt to death in her cottage. But though the heat must have been intense, nothing else in the cottage—not so much as the bedclothes on which she lay—was even scorched.

'No man knoweth what this doth portend,' said one observer; he then hinted darkly at Divine Retribution, though for what he did not say.

Nearer our own time, a Yorkshire building contractor was driving past one of his construction sites and waved through the car window; a moment later, he simply burst into flames. Similarly, a Cheshire man was found totally incinerated in the cab of his truck.

The London *Daily Telegraph* reported: 'Police witnesses testified they had found the petrol tank full and unharmed by fire, the doors of the cab opened easily, but the interior was "a veritable furnace". The coroner's jury declared they were unable to determine how the accident occurred.'

Reynold's News, a few years later, recorded the tragic death of a west London man who, while walking along the street, 'appeared to explode. His clothes burnt fiercely, his hair was burnt off, and the rubber-soled boots melted on his feet.'

Costly damage

Not always, it appears, are these human incendiary bombs only self-destructive. The late Professor Robin Beach, of Brooklyn, founder of the scientific detective agency Robin Beach Engineers Associated, believed that these unfortunate people are inadvertently responsible for fire damage costing millions of dollars each year. One of his first clients was an Ohio factory-owner whose plant was suddenly bedevilled with as many as eight small fires daily.

Professor Beach's solution was to persuade each of the factory's employees in turn to step on to a metal plate while holding an electrode; at the same time,

he took readings from an electrostatic voltmeter.

One of the workers was a young woman recently employed; when she stepped on to the metal plate, the meter showed a tremendous jump. She registered 30,000 volts of electrostatic electricity and a resistance of 500,000 ohms. Wisely, Professor Beach recommended that she be transferred to some part of the factory where she would not come in contact with combustible materials.

The professor explained that under certain conditions—walking on carpets during dry winter weather, for example—almost anyone can build up an electrostatic charge of as much as 20,000 volts. Hence the shock we sometimes experience when touching a car door or other metal surface. Usually, the electricity is harmlessly discharged through the tips of the hair; however, the professor maintains, there are some people—maybe one in 100,000—whose abnormally dry skin permits them to generate as much as 30,000 volts at a time.

Danger to others

In certain circumstances, such people may be highly dangerous. They may, for example, have been the detonators that touched off explosions in hospital operating theatres whose atmosphere contained an admixture of anaesthetic vapour and air.

In addition, the professor is convinced that workers in ordnance factories and petroleum refineries should be tested to discover whether they have the type of skin which retains electric charges more persistently than others.

He quoted an instance in which a man proved to be a hazard to himself: 'In one case I investigated, a driver decided to see if the battery of his car needed filling with water. It was a dry, cold fall day and the man walked a short distance on a concrete driveway, raised the hood of his car, and unscrewed the caps of the battery. There was an immediate explosion as he touched off the hydrogen gas escaping from the battery of the recently parked car. He was severely injured.'

Diet remedy

Happily, it seems that the dry skin condition that leads to such tragedies may be corrected by diet and vitamins after consultation with a physician.

But while Professor Beach's ingenious theories may well account for many mysterious fires and explosions hitherto ascribed to arson or sabotage, a strong element of mystery remains. Did the unfortunate girl on the dance floor really burst into flames from 'within', as her companion testified? Electrical engineers have pointed out that no known form of electrostatic discharge could possibly have such an effect. The fate of the old woman in her cottage, and that of the truck driver, are also in flat contradiction of natural law; both bodies were utterly consumed by fire, yet their inflammable surroundings were completely undamaged by the flames that had engulfed them.

Are there then human beings who possess complex physiological and psychological conditions which make them potential victims of spontaneous combustion—or even living time bombs?

THE ELUSIVE BRIDEY MURPHY

A case of reincarnation . . . or a total recall of childhood?

When a Colorado businessman and amateur hypnotist put a local housewife into a trance, it sparked off some startling revelations—and launched a search for a woman who had supposedly died the best part of a century earlier.

The housewife was called Ruth Simmons (her real name has never been revealed) of Pueblo, Colorado and, speaking as 'Bridey Murphy', in 1952, she told the story of her childhood, marriage, death and funeral in 19th-century Ireland—and her rebirth in the United States 59 years later.

The hypnotist was Morey Bernstein, who wrote the best-selling book on the case, *The Search for Bridey Murphy*, which was published in 1956.

Bernstein used a technique called hypnotic regression, during which the subject is gradually taken back to childhood. He then attempted to take Ruth back one step further, before birth, and suddenly was astonished to find he was listening to Bridey Murphy.

The rambling tale began in 1806 when Bridey was eight years old and living in a house in Cork. She was the daughter of Duncan Murphy, a barrister, and his wife Kathleen. At the age of 17, she married lawyer Sean Brian McCarthy and moved to Belfast.

Saw her own funeral

Bridey told of a fall that caused her death—and of watching her own funeral, describing the tombstone and the state of being in life after death.

It was, she recalled, a feeling of neither pain nor happiness. Somehow, she was reborn in America, although Bridey was not clear how this event had happened.

Ruth Simmons herself was born in the Middle West in 1923, had never been to Ireland and did not speak with even the slightest hint of an Irish accent.

The 'facts' related by Bridey were not fully checked before the publication of Bernstein's book. However, once the book had become a best-seller, almost every detail was thoroughly checked by reporters who were sent to Ireland to track down the background of this elusive woman.

No official records

It was then that the first doubts about the 'reincarnation' began to appear.

Bridey gave her birthday as December 20, 1798, in Cork, and the year of her death as 1864. There was no official record of either event. Neither was there any record of a wooden house, called The Meadows, in which she said she lived. Indeed, most houses in Ireland are built of brick or stone.

She pronounced her husband's name as 'See-an', but said it could also be 'Shawn'. Sean is usually pronounced 'Shawn' in Ireland. Brian, which is what Bridey preferred to call her husband, was the middle name of the man to whom Ruth Simmons was married.

But some of the details did tally. For instance, her descriptions of the Antrim coastline were accurate. So, too, was her account of a journey from Belfast to Cork. She said she went to St Theresa's Church. There is one where she said it was—but it was not built until 1911.

The young Bridey shopped for provisions with a grocer named Farr. It was discovered that such a shop had existed.

Despite the holes in Bridey's story, it

was still a remarkably detailed account of life in 19th-century Ireland—information unlikely to have come the way of Ruth Simmons.

The case was studied by psychiatrists and pyschologists, who had used hypnosis in treatment for many years.

Many subjects, in deep hypnosis, can be highly suggestible and will act on the slightest hint given to them, seeking to supply the answer they subconsciously believe the hypnotist wishes to hear.

Such hypnosis is largely a matter of releasing relevant details from the brain's incredible capacity for storing information. For instance, the subject can speak in a foreign language not used since childhood, and in which he would not be able to converse in normal conscious life.

Not telling the truth

A subject can even quote verbatim from a long-forgotten childhood book. However, someone under hypnosis is not automatically telling the truth even if she is seeking to give a satisfactory response.

Bernstein admitted that, while she was under hypnosis, he did tell Ruth Simmons what he wanted, and that it was then that she became Bridey Murphy.

The experts who examined the case of Ruth Simmons came to the conclusion that the best way to arrive at the truth was not to check back to Ireland, but to her own childhood and her relationship with her parents.

The book stated that Ruth Simmons was brought up by a Norwegian uncle and his German-Scottish-Irish wife. True enough, but it did not say that her actual parents were both part-Irish and that she had lived with them until she had reached the age of three.

Scientists are satisfied that nothing Bridey Murphy said cannot be explained as a memory of Ruth's long-forgotten childhood. And they believe that the riddle would be unravelled if Ruth would allow her own infancy to be examined under hypnosis.

GHOST FACES ON THE KITCHEN FLOOR

AN ELDERLY WOMAN and her infant grandchild were sitting in the kitchen of their village home when suddenly the child cried out excitedly.

The innocent eyes of the child had seen nothing more than a diverting new game; but it was a 'game' that terrified the old lady, and developed into a mystery for which scientists, despite every test, have as yet been unable to find any natural explanation.

It happened in the village of Bélmez, not far from the city of Cordoba in Southern Spain, on a hot morning of August 1971.

Wider and wider

What the child had seen was a human face which had spontaneously imprinted itself on the pink floor tiles—a face with troubled features, infinitely sad. No recognisable pigment of any kind had formed the image, and when the family tried to rub it out, they were horrified to find that the eyes only opened wider and the expression grew even more sorrowful.

Alarmed and bewildered, the owner of the house tore up the floor and replaced the sinister tiles with concrete. But three weeks later a second face emerged, this time with even more clearly defined features.

The affair had taken a turn far beyond the grasp of the simple village folk, and now the local authorities became involved. They ordered a section of the floor where the faces had appeared to be cut away, and an official inquiry began. Workmen dug the floor up, uncovering the remains of a medieval cemetery.

Meanwhile, a third apparition took place, then a fourth, then a series of faces all together. The kitchen was locked and sealed. Four more faces, including that of a woman, appeared just as mysteriously in another part of the house. But they were the last: the phenomenon melted away as inexplicably as it had begun.

All this time the curious apparitions had attracted experts of one kind and another to the house. Even the most cynical of them were unable to prove that the images were the work of a human hand. Their puzzlement was enhanced by the evidence of ultra-sensitive microphones planted in the house.

Strange languages

These microphones had recorded sounds not audible to the ear—voices speaking strange languages, agonised moans matching the torment in the eyes of the faces on the floor.

No one yet has come forward with a really satisfying explanation of the Faces of Bélmez. All the experts have been able to suggest is that the house was once the scene of some tragic and terrible incident, perhaps connected with some form of medieval witchcraft.

THE CARBON-COPY SCHOOL-MARM

Her 'double' caused no end of trouble

People who protest that they cannot be in two places at once might ponder the strange case of Madame Sage. She was a schoolteacher, and her way to overcome the difficulty was to have a double—or so it was said.

When she was working at a girls' school in Livonia, Russia, in 1845, it was remarked that there appeared to be really *two* Madame Sages. One, for instance, would be sitting facing her class while the other was writing on the blackboard. Two pupils once saw her sitting indoors and at the same time picking flowers outside.

The mysterious duplicates were noted not only by her possibly over-imaginative pupils. A friend was reading one day to the schoolmistress, who was in bed with a cold, while a facsimile apparently walked round the room.

After 18 months or so the gossip became too much for the school governors, who demanded to know what was going on. Yes, she told them, it was quite true. She could project an image of herself by will-power. The trick, she had found, was a great aid in maintaining discipline: she could keep an eye on her class when her back was turned.

But the governors were not amused. She was sacked—not, she later confessed, for the first time.

There is no record of the teacher-in-duplicate's first name. She was always referred to just as Madame Sage—whether because she was a married woman or simply because she was a 'school-marm' is not recorded.

A pity: her husband, if any, could have written a fascinating memoir of his life with the two Madame Sages.

These are just two of the mysterious Faces of Bélmez—the one on the left probably that of a woman. These and other human faces began to appear on the kitchen-floor tiles of a cottage in Spain in 1971. Despite a most exhaustive scientific inquiry no one has ever been able to supply a completely satisfactory natural explanation.

THE MAN WITH TWO LIVES

Gestures, handwriting and memories all differed

A man called A. J. Brown rented a storeroom at East Main St, Norristown, Pennsylvania, at the beginning of February 1887. He lived in the rear half and traded in the front, selling confectionery, stationery and several other inexpensive items.

On Sunday, March 13, Mr Brown went to the local Methodist Church, then retired to bed as usual.

At five the next morning he was awoken by what he thought was the sound of a pistol firing. He opened his eyes, but could make no sense of his surroundings.

He felt weak, as though he had been drugged, and recognised nothing out of the window of the room.

For some two hours, in mounting distress, he lay and tried to remember how he, Ansel Bourne, came to be in this strange room.

Finally he opened the door to see the owner of the house, a Mr Earle.

'Where am I?' he asked his astonished landlord. 'You're all right, Mr Brown,' was the reply.

'But my name isn't Brown,' said Bourne.

The landlord told him which town he was in, and the date, the 14th.

'Does time run backwards here?' he asked. 'When I left home, it was the 17th.'

'The 17th of what?' asked Earle.

'Of January.'

'It's the 14th of March.'

Last recollection

Earle called a doctor and Bourne insisted the last thing he remembered was the wagons in Broad St, Providence, Rhode Island, after he had left a nephew's shop, now two months and 230 miles away.

The nephew was contacted and came to collect him. His family, who had reported him missing, asked him about his strange experience, but he could remember nothing of it. He could not imagine why he, a carpenter, preacher and farmer, should set up in a business he knew nothing about and had no interest in whatsoever.

Three years later, Professor William James, of Harvard, heard of the case and examined Bourne. Under hypnosis, Bourne said his name was Albert John Brown and detailed his journey to Pennsylvania on January 17, 1887. He remembered setting up a small shop a couple of weeks later, but he was confused and remembered little clearly about his life before the move to Pennsylvania.

He knew he had suffered in his life and that his wife had died in 1881 — as Bourne's wife had. His memory of events after March 13 was clouded.

Facial expressions

Professor James established that the personalities of Bourne and Brown were distinct and quite different, each with his own gestures, facial expressions and handwriting. As hypnosis progressed, the personality of A. J. Brown faded away, never to return.

It was the second tribulation that Bourne had faced. The first came on October 28, 1857, when he went for a walk near his home in Westerly, Rhode Island, and the idea came into his head that he ought to go to church, although he had earlier drifted away from the Baptist Church. But he said to himself he would rather be struck deaf and dumb than go to church.

Struck blind

A few moments later he felt dizzy and sat down by the roadside as, it seemed to him, a powerful hand drew something over his head, face and body, and all power of sight, hearing and speech went from him. He was convinced God had granted his wish and blinded him as well.

His sight returned after a day and on November 11 he had friends carry him into a local chapel, where he proclaimed his conversion. The following Sunday he stood in the middle of the congregation, held up his hands to heaven, and instantly regained his hearing and speech. This experience led to his becoming a preacher — a calling he followed for many years.

After his wife died, in his middle 50s, he resumed his trade as a carpenter, began farming, and by 1887 had saved enough to buy some land. He drew $551 from the bank and went to visit his nephew in Providence. How he was transformed to A. J. Brown is not known. But it was with the $551 that he set himself up in business in Norristown.

NOVELS WRITTEN FROM THE GRAVE

The woman whose books were 'ghosted'

Mrs J. H. Curran, of St Louis, Missouri, was no scholar. She had little knowledge of history, only a slight interest in books, and even less idea of the intricacies of language history.

Yet from her poured a stream of writings that astonished the most eminent academics on both sides of the Atlantic.

Mrs Curran, despite a dislike for spiritualism and mediums, was persuaded to take part in a séance. On July 8, 1913, her hand on the ouija board traced out the name Patience Worth. From that time onwards, Mrs Curran and Patience Worth —whoever she was—became good and inseparable friends.

Through the writings or speech of Mrs Curran, when in a trance, Patience Worth first told of her birth in Dorset, England, in the 17th century. She detailed the emigration of her parents to America and her eventual death at the hands of an Indian war party. Then, in frequent sittings over a number of years, Patience dictated a set of historical novels in a variety of literary styles. They ranged from *The Sorry Tale*, set in the time of Christ, to *Hope Trueblood*, a novel of the 19th century.

Critical acclaim

Hope Trueblood received wide acclaim from the critics. The correspondent of *The Athenaeum*, who was unaware of the way in which the book was written, wrote enthusiastically of 'Definite and clear-cut characterisation, good dialogue and arresting runs of expression, deep but restrained feeling.'

Mrs Curran could write two or more novels simultaneously as they were 'dictated' by Patience Worth. She would write a chapter on one book then do the same with a totally different subject, and always continue the first book without losing the theme.

Nor was she limited to novels. She could compose at will and reply in period prose to various subjects put to her. It was that remarkable knowledge of language and style that led to her most highly acclaimed work—*Telka*—a novel of medieval England, written in the English of the time, which Mrs Curran had never studied.

The intelligence and wit of Patience Worth continued to astonish psychologists. But to Mrs Curran, she was just a wonderful friend who told fascinating stories of days long ago.

TRAVELLER IN TIME *Mrs J. H. Curran, whose séances with a 17th-century girl produced some remarkable novels.*

HANGED—BECAUSE OF A STRANGER'S DREAM

WHEN SHAUN COTT disappeared from the Maitland district of New South Wales last century, it was assumed he had joined the gold rush—until a newcomer to the area had a vivid dream which led the police to dig up part of the farm where Cott had worked. They found his body, with its skull battered in. Cott's employer was hanged for the murder, which would never have been discovered—but for the dream of a stranger.

THE CROSS-CORRESPONDENCES

Did three men make contact from beyond the grave?

Thousands of miles apart, five women, none of whom knew each other, sat down and tried to communicate with the dead. The method they chose was automatic writing, by which the medium, in a state of trance, is apparently able to write down messages from the other world.

At first, the messages each received appeared garbled, often meaningless. But when compared later, the scripts appeared to provide links with three dead men.

All three had been founders of the British Society for Psychical Research—Henry Sidgwick, Frederic Myers and Edmund Gurney. All were dead by 1901 when the three ladies, completely independently, began their experiments.

In England, Mrs A. W. Verrall, a classical scholar at Cambridge University, who had known the three men, received fragments of messages purportedly from Myers.

Later in America, Mrs Leonora Piper began to receive similar messages signed 'Myers'. In India Mrs Alice Fleming, a sister of the author Rudyard Kipling, began to receive messages, as did her daughter, Helen. Back in England, a Mrs Willett, of Cornwall also found herself scribbling down messages from people she had never heard of.

Over the next 30 years, some 3000 messages—which became known as the cross-correspondences—were produced, and their contents were carefully investigated and annotated by the society.

A collective consciousness

From the different sitters, there emerged a complex pattern of fragmentary messages, largely based upon classical literature. Apart from Mrs Verrall, none of the others had much knowledge of, nor interest in, the classics.

The dead men, on the other hand, had all been classical scholars.

Scientists, scholars and businessmen who examined the scripts found in them a sense of purpose that seemed to be the product of a collective conscious mind.

It was considered impossible that the writers had collaborated in such a complex hoax. If there had been any unconscious telepathic communication, it

contained a fantastically complicated series of classical cross-references that only Mrs Verrall was capable of understanding.

In 1903 Mrs Holland produced a script saying that 'F' (Frederic Myers) wished to speak to some old friends. The message went on to describe Mrs Verrall, of whom Mrs Holland had never heard.

It ended: 'It is like entrusting a message on which infinite importance depends, to a sleeping person—get a proof—try for a proof if you feel this is a waste of time without. Send this to Mrs Verrall, 5 Selwyn Gardens, Cambridge.'

Obscure references

Despite Mrs Holland's ignorance of Mrs Verrall's existence, the address was correct. Mrs Holland, in fact, sent the script to the Society for Psychical Research, which then began to link up all the scripts.

Eventually, an American researcher, G. B. Dorr, devised a test. He asked 'Myers', through Mrs Piper, what the word 'Lethe' meant to him. The responses were so detailed and included such obscure references that only the most dedicated classicist could have discovered their origin and relevance. The answers were well outside Mrs Piper's experience.

Some time later, in England, the physicist Sir Oliver Lodge, also a psychical researcher, put the same question to Mrs Willett, who was unaware of the American test. As well as responding with the same classical allusions, her automatic script spelt out 'Dorr'—the name of the American investigator.

Mrs Fleming's scripts in India often contained frustrated and anguished passages, indicating the sender's desperate desire to communicate.

Behind frosted glass

Through her, 'Myers' wrote: 'The nearest simile I can find to express the difficulties of sending a message is that I appear to be standing behind a sheet of frosted glass —which blurs sight and deadens sound— dictating feebly to a reluctant and obtuse secretary. A feeling of terrible impotence burdens me.'

Later, 'Myers' wrote: 'Yet another attempt to run the blockade—to strive to get a message through. How can I make you docile enough . . . how can I convince them?'

Mrs Piper in America and Mrs Willett in Cornwall received similar messages.

Mrs Willett's scripts eventually suggested she try to make mental conversation with the three men. She developed this technique so that a second person could hold conversations, through her, with Myers, Gurney and Sidgwick.

Topics of discussion went far beyond Mrs Willett's normal interests and intellectual capacity.

'Sidgwick' spoke with Lord Balfour, brother of the Prime Minister, about three conflicting theories on the relation of mind and body. 'Gurney' spoke of the origins of the human soul.

Discussion of the scripts continued for many years, and no one has yet been able to explain satisfactorily how the communications came about.

Many theories have been advanced, from the continued existence of personalities beyond death to the notion of a psychic plane in which ideas alone survive, waiting to be picked up by anyone sensitive enough to receive them. But when the ladies died, their correspondents spoke no more.

THE GHOST WHO MOVED HOUSE

For almost a century she mourned her lost love

Rosina Despard was getting ready for bed at her father's house in Cheltenham, Gloucestershire, England. As she undressed, she thought she heard her mother's footsteps near the door.

But when she opened it, the corridor outside was empty. She looked along the passage and there, standing silently at the head of the stairs, she saw a woman in a long, black dress, holding a handkerchief to her face. After a few seconds, the woman descended the stairs, Rosina's candle went out and she saw no more.

That was in June 1882. During the next seven years, the phantom in black was seen quite frequently by various members of the Despard household, who appear to have accepted it almost as one of the family. On one occasion, Rosina watched it for half an hour then, touched by the figure's obvious distress, tried to speak to it. She received no reply and it vanished, its head pathetically bowed.

Dinner at the Despards' could be an unnerving affair, due to the figure's ability of appearing to one or two people in the room while remaining invisible to the others. Sometimes it would suddenly stand between two guests who, oblivious of its presence, would go on gaily chattering. Try as they might, Rosina and her father—to whom the phantom most frequently appeared—were unable to prevent a certain flagging in their own conversations.

All these appearances were carefully recorded by Rosina, who also tried to discover the ghost's identity. The most likely candidate seems to have been a Mrs Imogen Swinhoe, who had been the mistress of a previous occupant of the house. Expelled by her lover after a quarrel, she had died elsewhere in poverty and misery in 1878.

The appearances seem to have ceased in 1889, possibly after an exorcism requested by Mr Despard. Though the case aroused considerable interest at the time and was carefully investigated by the Society for Psychical Research, lack of further evidence caused it to fade from the public mind until even Cheltenham had forgotten the story.

After 69 years

Then, in 1958, the most extraordinary thing happened. A man living in a flat a few houses along the street from the building once owned by the Despards, woke up one night to see a woman silhouetted against his bedroom window. She was dressed in late Victorian costume, her head was bowed, and she appeared to be sobbing quietly into a handkerchief held to her face. When the man cried out in alarm, she vanished.

The man had never heard of the ghost and had little interest in the supernatural. This lack was amply compensated during the next few years by the woman in black. Often she would be seen flitting down the staircase, or wandering through the rooms, weeping piteously into her handkerchief. Obviously, time had not assuaged her grief; but why she should have moved house remains a mystery.

DANTE'S GHOST LED THE SEARCH

How the missing parts of 'The Divine Comedy' were recovered

When Dante Alighieri died in 1321, parts of the manuscript of his masterpiece, 'The Divine Comedy', were missing. For months his sons, Jacopo and Piero, searched the house and all their father's papers.

They had given up hope when Jacopo dreamt he saw his father dressed in white and bathed in an ethereal light. He asked the vision if the poem had been completed. Dante nodded and showed Jacopo a secret place in his old chamber.

With a lawyer friend of Dante's as a witness, Jacopo went to the place indicated in the dream. There was a small blind fixed to the wall. Lifting it they found a small window.

Inside were some papers covered with mould. Carefully they lifted them out, brushed off the mould, read the words of Dante—and 'The Divine Comedy' was complete. But for a ghostly vision in a dream, one of the world's greatest poems would have remained unfinished.

14TH-CENTURY GENIUS *But for his son's dream, Dante's masterpiece would be incomplete.*

DANTES ALIGHERIVS
Ex Pinacotheca Comitis Danielis Lisca Patricii Veronensis, pictus quondam a Bernardo India celebri pictore.

MRS WILMOT CROSSES THE SEA

Apparition seen by a husband and his cabin companion

Bound from Liverpool to New York in 1863, the *City of Limerick* ran into a fierce North Atlantic storm. For over a week it raged and, at home, fears grew for the lives of those on board.

At last the storm began to abate and Mr Wilmot, one of the passengers, was able to enjoy a night's sleep. He dreamt that he saw his wife, wearing her night-clothes, entering his state-room. She hesitated at first when she realised that it was a shared cabin and that another man was staring at her from the bunk set above and slightly back from her husband's. Then she went to her husband's bedside, kissed him and left quietly.

Wilmot awoke to find the man above staring down at him. The man, a Mr Tait, was shocked that Wilmot should have had a lady visit him in such a way. He described Mrs Wilmot's actions exactly as they had occurred in Wilmot's dream.

When Wilmot eventually arrived home, his wife surprised him by asking if he'd had a visit from her the week before. She described how at the height of her anxiety, at four o'clock one morning, she had felt she was going out to find him.

The wife's dream

She had crossed the dark, heaving sea and come to a steamship. Having gone aboard, she had walked down below decks at the stern of the ship and found her husband's state-room.

'Tell me', she asked him, 'do they ever have state-rooms like the one I saw, where the upper berth extends further back from the lower one? A man was in the upper berth, looking right at me, and for a moment I was afraid to go in, but soon I went up to the side of your berth, bent down and kissed you, and embraced you, and then went away.'

396

MUSIC FROM THE IMMORTALS

Beethoven and Bach dictated works to London widow

When Igor Stravinsky appeared to Mrs Rosemary Brown 14 months after his death and dictated 60 lines of music, she was not surprised. For he was, she said, the 20th dead composer or author to use her extraordinary talent.

Rosemary was only seven years old when she was introduced to the world of dead musicians. A spirit with long white hair and a flowing black cassock appeared and told her he was a composer, and would make her a famous musician one day. Rosemary did not know who he was until, about ten years later, she saw a picture of Franz Liszt.

Rosemary's mother and grandmother were psychic, and she herself displayed psychic powers at an early age. She told her parents of events before her birth, and when asked how she could know, she replied that her 'visitors' had told her.

Liszt, however, was not among them. He did not reappear until 1964, by which time Rosemary had married and brought up two children. Living in a Victorian terraced house in Balham, South London, she was now a seemingly unexceptional middle-aged widow.

Before 1964 she had paid little attention to music and had had little instruction in it. After the war she had bought a second-hand piano and taken lessons for a year. But a neighbour, once a church organist, was not impressed. 'She could just about struggle through a hymn,' he said.

Then in 1964 Liszt renewed contact and original compositions began flooding in from great musicians of the past. Mrs Brown transcribed pieces from Beethoven, Bach, Chopin, Schubert, Rachmaninov and, of course, Liszt himself.

These included a 40-page Schubert sonata, a Fantaisie Impromptu in three movements by Chopin, 12 songs by Schubert and two sonatas by Beethoven as well as his 10th and 11th Symphonies, both of them unfinished.

Each composer had his own way of dictating to Mrs Brown. Liszt controlled

THE MELODIES LINGER ON *Widow Rosemary Brown at work on the scores she said were dictated to her by dead composers. Behind her are the opening bars of a piece 'sung' to her by Schubert.*

her hands for a few bars at a time, and then she wrote down the notes. Others, like Chopin, told her the notes and pushed her hands on to the right keys.

Schubert tried to sing his compositions to her 'but he hasn't got a very good voice'. Beethoven and Bach simply dictated the notes—a method she disliked since she had no idea of what the finished product would sound like.

They all spoke to Rosemary in English, which did not surprise her. 'Why shouldn't they have gone on learning on the other side?' she asked. But when agitated, they were liable to relapse into their native tongues. 'Mein Gott!' Beethoven exclaimed when they were hard at work and the doorbell rang.

What the critics said

The opinions of musical critics were varied on the merit of Rosemary's transcriptions. But most agreed that in their style they bore a great resemblance to the composers' published works.

Forgeries and imitations have frequently been made in the past, but con-

FRANZ LISZT *It was Liszt's first visit to Rosemary Brown in 1964 that started her transcribing the works of great composers, long-since dead.*

siderable musical knowledge is required for this. Rosemary's musical knowledge was such that she was unable to play many of the pieces dictated to her, although she became more proficient at the piano under instruction by Brahms. He drilled her in finger exercises while Rachmaninov and Liszt attended to her style.

Rosemary was thoroughly investigated by musicians and psychologists. None could find any way in which she could be cheating, and all who met her were said to dismiss the idea after only a few minutes.

How she did it

Maurice Barbanell, editor of the London-based *Psychic News*, said: 'She appears to be a medium who is both clairvoyant and clairaudient. It is comparable to what hundreds of other mediums have done—the only difference is that you have some famous composers involved.'

Other explanations were put forward. One was that composers had left behind them unknown, written music and that Rosemary was able to read these sheets, unwittingly using a form of telepathy.

Another suggestion was that she picked up music from people around her by telepathy. However, she did not spend her time in the company of musicians who might be composing works in the manner of Bach and Brahms.

Of the music itself, Richard Rodney Bennett, the British composer, said: 'A lot of people can improvise, but you couldn't fake music like this without years of training. I couldn't have faked some of the Beethoven myself.'

What musicians felt

Hephzibah Menuhin, the concert pianist and sister of Yehudi, was also impressed. She insisted: 'There is no question but that she is a very sincere woman. The music is absolutely in the style of these composers.'

Alan Rich, music critic of *New York* magazine, took a different line. Having heard a privately issued record of piano pieces by the spirits of Bach, Beethoven, Chopin, Debussy, Liszt and Schubert, Rich concluded that they were just sub-standard reworkings of some of their better known compositions.

However, the record contained only the simpler pieces. Richard Rodney Bennett found other compositions to be subtler and far more complex.

GIRL WHO FETCHED THE DOCTOR

She begged help for her mother—a month after her own death

Doctor S. Weir Mitchell, an eminent 19th-century nerve specialist in Philadelphia, fell asleep in his chair one winter evening after an exhausting day's work in his surgery.

Awakened by the ringing of his doorbell, he found a thin, shivering girl on the doorstep, pulling a threadbare shawl around her shoulders. She begged him to come and treat her mother who, she explained, was desperately ill.

The doctor followed her through the snowy streets to an old tenement, where the girl led him upstairs.

There, the doctor found a sick woman —whom he recognised as a former servant of his household. He diagnosed her condition as pneumonia and sent for the medicines she needed. Mitchell then made the woman as comfortable as he could— and congratulated her on having such a dutiful daughter.

Daughter was dead

To this, the old woman looked up with surprise and said: 'My daughter died a month ago. Her shoes and shawl are there in that little cupboard.'

The doctor looked and found the same shawl as that which had been draped over the shoulders of the pathetic girl who rang his doorbell. It was folded and dry, and could not possibly have been worn outside that night.

The girl who had showed him in was nowhere to be found.

THE SHATTERED DREAM OF XANADU

Insensitive behaviour of the person from Porlock

Samuel Taylor Coleridge's famous poem 'Kubla Khan' has been surrounded by mystery ever since it was published in 1816, 20 years after it was written and when he needed money.

Coleridge explained that the 54 lines were a mere fragment of a glorious vision inspired by an opium dream. The dream had been shattered by an interruption and the rest of the poem had been lost forever.

It came to him while he was staying at a lonely Exmoor farmhouse, recuperating from an illness. He had taken two grains of opium for medicinal purposes (he was in fact an addict). On awaking he began to put down the poem in an ecstasy of inspiration.

When he got to:

For he on honey dew has fed,
And drunk the milk of Paradise

he was interrupted by an insurance salesman from the nearby town of Porlock. Desperately he tried to get rid of the man, but somehow he was detained for an hour, talking mundane finance.

Try as he might, Coleridge could never recapture his vision of the legendary world of Xanadu. All that was left was the first fragment of 'Kubla Khan', which for 20 years he did not consider worth publishing.

PARADISE LOST *Coleridge, the poet whose drug-induced dream vanished when he was interrupted by the awful Man from Porlock.*

MESSAGE ACROSS THE SEA

A dream that sent a ship on a life-saving mission

The captain of a ship crossing the Atlantic to Newfoundland in 1828, glanced through the open door of a cabin adjoining his own and saw a man standing in the shadows. He had never seen him before.

He was not one of the crew, and no passengers were being carried on that voyage. Certain that he had trapped a stowaway, the captain burst into the cabin, but as he did so, the figure disappeared from sight.

All the evidence that remained was a scrawled message on the cabin wall: 'Steer to the north-west.'

The captain was considerably shaken, but at the same time, so impressed by the stranger's message that he altered course according to the scribbled instructions.

After a few hours, his vessel came across a foundering ship. The only person aboard was the man whom the captain had encountered in the cabin of his own ship. He said that he had just awoken from a deep sleep during which he had dreamt that he was about to be rescued.

THE NIGHTMARE OF BORODINO

The countess who dreamt that her husband died in battle

As Napoleon's armies advanced into Russia in 1812, the wife of a Russian general, Count Toutschkoff, had a dream. She saw herself in a room at an inn, in a town that she did not know.

Into the room came her father, holding her small son by the hand. Sorrowfully, he told her that her husband had been killed by the French. 'Your happiness is at an end,' he said. 'He has fallen. He has fallen at Borodino.'

Twice more the dream came to her and in the end she told her husband. Together they searched maps but they could not find a mention of Borodino anywhere.

But on September 7, 1812, the retreating Russian armies turned and defied the French—at a village called Borodino, 70 miles west of Moscow. They were heavily defeated.

Countess Toutschkoff and her family stayed at an inn only a few miles from the battlefront, while her husband commanded the reserves. The next morning her father entered the room holding her small son by the hand.

'He has fallen,' he stammered. 'He has fallen at Borodino.'

PREPARING FOR AN EXPENSIVE BATTLE *Officers of the French cavalry prepare for the next round in the Battle of Borodino, which was to cost more than 30,000 French and 45,000 Russian lives.*

A VISION OF VICTORY AT SEA

Two weeks before battle, a pope thanked God for success

The treasurer's voice droned on as he went through the accounts of the papal states. Suddenly, Pope Pius V stood up, opened a window and stared out. After a few moments he relaxed, and turned back to his senior Vatican officials with eyes shining.

'Leave all this for now,' he said, waving towards the ledgers and financial statements, strewn about the table, 'We must go and give thanks to God. Victory has gone to the Christian fleet.'

The business-like treasurer made a note of the strange incident in the minutes. It happened, he wrote, just before 5 p.m. on October 7, 1571.

Exactly a fortnight later, on October 21, a messenger galloped into Rome from Venice with news of an historic naval victory.

A Christian fleet, under Don John of Austria, had trounced the Turkish fleet at Lepanto. According to the official report, it had become clear that victory was theirs just before 5 p.m. on October 7.

POPE WITH A MESSAGE *During the battle, depicted at the top of this engraving, Pius V prayed for a Christian victory.*

A GHOSTLY WARNING

The ugly man who saved a lord's life

In the 1880s, Lord Dufferin, British Ambassador in Paris, was on holiday at a friend's country home in Ireland. One night he awoke suddenly, unaccountably startled from a deep sleep.

Getting up and going to the window, Lord Dufferin looked out on the lawn to see, in the moonlight, a hunched figure staggering under the weight of a coffin-like object. Dufferin went outside and called: 'What have you got there?'

The man lifted his head from beneath his burden, and Lord Dufferin saw a wizened, ugly face that utterly repelled him. When Lord Dufferin asked the man where he was taking the coffin, the figure disappeared, seeming to pass through him.

Next morning, he told the experience to his host, who was at a loss to explain the strange apparition.

A few years later, in the 1890s, Lord Dufferin was back in Paris to attend an international diplomatic reception at the Grand Hotel.

But just as he and his private secretary were about to enter the lift, Dufferin recoiled and refused to step inside. The lift operator was none other than the wizened, ugly little man he had seen carrying the coffin on his friend's estate in Ireland, years before.

The lift ascended, without Lord Dufferin and his secretary. The ambassador went to the reception desk to inquire the identity of the strange man.

As the lift reached the fifth floor its cable snapped and, with a resounding crash, plunged to the bottom of its shaft, killing all the occupants.

The accident was reported in the Press and recorded by the British Society for Psychical Research, but the ambassador was unable to discover the identity of the liftman who turned out to be his saviour. Neither the management of the hotel, nor the accident investigators could find any record of the man's name or background.

401

A SCENT OF VIOLETS

Was the empress guided from beyond the grave?

Bent upon the subjugation of the fierce Zulus, the British Army invaded Zululand in 1879. The campaign opened with the virtual annihilation of a British column at Isandhlwana—a disgrace which even the heroic defence of Rorke's Drift failed to expunge.

Reinforcements were rushed from England, among them the Prince Imperial of France, only son of exiled Napoleon III and the former Empress Eugénie.

The young prince, strictly enjoined to take no unnecessary risks, was permitted to join a column in the front line. Riding into an ambush of Zulus, the prince's mount, Fate, reared and tossed him to the ground. The Zulus closed in with spears poised and stabbed the prince and two fellow officers to death.

The prince's body was recovered and sent back to England. A year later, Queen Victoria gave permission for Eugénie to visit Zululand to see the place where her son had died.

Grass and shrubs covered the cairn of stones which marked the spot and for some time it could not be found. Then Eugénie cried out: 'I smell violets; they were always his favourite flower.' She ran unerringly to where her son had fallen.

THE PRINCE IMPERIAL *Zulu warriors surrounded the prince as he tried to remount his horse. Minutes later he was dead.*

THE END OF HMS 'VICTORIA' *A photograph, taken from HMS* Collingwood, *shows the* Victoria *sliding bow first beneath the sea. To the left is HMS* Nile *which rescued survivors.*

THE LAST VOYAGE HOME

He died at sea—yet guests spoke to him in London

At precisely 3.34 p.m. on June 22, 1893, the Royal Navy flagship, *Victoria*, was rammed and later sank. She went down off the Mediterranean port of Tripoli with the loss of many lives, including that of her commander—Admiral Sir George Tryon.

A naval board of inquiry heard that the *Victoria* was rammed by another ship in the same squadron—*Camperdown*—during a difficult manoeuvre ordered by Sir George. The manoeuvre meant that two columns of ships, including the *Victoria* and *Camperdown*, turned inwards towards each other. Only when Sir George saw that a collision was imminent did he order the *Victoria* 'Full astern'.

No one knows what made Sir George, an experienced and level-headed sailor, order such a disastrous manoeuvre. But as his ship went down, survivors heard him say: 'It is all my fault.'

At the time of the collision, Lady Tryon was giving a party in her home at Eaton Square in London. Shortly after 3.30, guests saw the unmistakable figure of the admiral stride across the drawing-room.

When the guests politely remarked that it was nice that Sir George could be present, Lady Tryon, who had not seen the figure, told them that her husband was with his ship. Some of the guests later claimed to have spoken to the figure and were perfectly certain he was Sir George,

although it is not recorded whether he replied or not.

The admiral was never seen again, and the mystery remains unsolved. Perhaps, knowing that he was about to die, Sir George turned his thoughts to his wife and home . . . somehow projecting a fleeting image of himself in the drawing-room.

ADMIRAL ON THE BRIDGE *A contemporary engraving shows Admiral Sir George Tryon going down with his ship, HMS* Victoria.

PREMATURE FLIGHT *It is now thought that the 777 ft R101 was launched too soon. It had not been sufficiently tested when it set off on the non-stop flight to India, which the British government hoped would coincide with a Commonwealth conference on transport.*

MEN WHO FELT THEY WERE DOOMED

The chilling story behind Britain's airship disaster

On October 4, 1930, the pride of British aeronautical engineering, the R101 airship, left England on its maiden, non-stop voyage to India. The weather was not good. As the R101 crossed the Channel she was tossed and buffeted by ever stronger gusts of wind. Visibility was reduced to nil, and the airship, travelling at about 1000 ft, bucked in unintentional swoops, losing 200–300 ft at a time, which the crew regained only with the utmost difficulty. At 2.5 a.m. the following morning the cigar-shaped vessel crashed at the edge of a wood near Beauvais in Northern France and burst into flames.

Only six of her crew and passengers,

who were all accommodated in a gondola-like compartment slung under the airship's belly, escaped. Forty-eight other people died.

The $5\frac{1}{2}$ million cu. ft of hydrogen that had lifted the 777 ft long ship contributed to the inferno that sent flames shooting 300 ft into the air.

The disaster gave rise to much speculation, many inquiries and eventually an official report. But in addition to these aspects of the tragedy, a more chilling side emerged.

Investigators discovered that five years earlier, while the airship was still in its design stage, Sir Sefton Brancker, Director of Civil Aviation, had consulted an

WRECKAGE OF A DREAM *The pride of British aviation, the R101 had been equipped with all the passenger amenities of an ocean liner. When it crashed in a wood near Beauvais in France, 48 people died and airship development was at an end.*

astrologer. He had been told that there was nothing to be seen in his life after six years. Together with Lord Thomson, the Secretary of State for Air, Sir Sefton was killed.

They heard how, when one of the riggers who flew in the airship, Mr Walter Radcliffe, left home on the morning of October 4, his young son began to cry: 'I haven't got a daddy.'

Mr Radcliffe did return home once more that day after checking some of the girders, but he left again to go on the flight . . . and was killed.

The Captain's wife knew

When a friend went to the home of the R101's captain, Flight Lieutenant Carmichael 'Bird' Irwin, to inform his wife of his death, Mrs Irwin said: 'It's all right. You needn't worry. I know. You see, Bird is Irish and I'm Scottish. We both knew he wasn't coming back again.'

Even stranger was the fact that at the exact time of the crash, the switchboard operator at the Cardington base heard a click on the telephone line connected to Irwin's office. A duty officer went to investigate and found the office empty.

Most puzzling of all, however, was the report of a séance held in London three days after the tragedy. The medium, Mrs Eileen Garrett, in a trance, spoke in a man's voice and mentioned the name 'Irwin'.

The voice listed technical defects in the airship that were not known publicly until the following year when the results of the official inquiry were published.

Three weeks later Mrs Garrett is reported to have received more messages from Irwin and others who died. One of the voices was said to have been that of Sir Sefton.

THE 'UNSINKABLE' *When the liner* Titanic *left Southampton on her maiden voyage in 1912, a novel and a short story had both foretold her fate with uncanny accuracy. But her tragedy helped to save a later ship—a tramp steamer bound for Canada from Tyneside, in 1935.*

THE FICTION THAT CAME TRUE

Strange case of the two 'Titanics'

Afloating palace sailed from Southampton in 1898 on her maiden voyage. She was the biggest and grandest liner ever built, and rich passengers savoured her luxury as they journeyed to America. But the ship never reached her destination: her hull was ripped open by an iceberg and she sank with heavy loss of life.

That liner existed only on paper, in the imagination of a novelist called Morgan Robertson. The name he gave to his fictional ship was *Titan*, and the book's title was *Futility*.

Both the fiction and the futility were to turn into terrifying fact. Fourteen years later a real luxury liner set out on a similar maiden voyage. She too was laden with rich passengers. She too rammed an iceberg and sank; and, as in Robertson's novel, the loss of life was fearful because there were not enough lifeboats. It was the night of April 14, 1912. The ship was the RMS *Titanic*.

Passenger's preview of doom

In many other ways than the similarity of their names the *Titan* of Robertson's novel was a near duplicate of the real *Titanic*. They were roughly the same size, had the same speed and the same carrying capacity of about 3000 people. Both were

'unsinkable'. And both sank in exactly the same spot in the North Atlantic.

But the strange coincidences do not end there. The famous journalist W. T. Stead published, in 1892, a short story which proved to be an uncanny preview of the *Titanic* disaster. Stead was a Spiritualist: he was also one of the 1513 people who died when the *Titanic* went down.

Backward recollection

Neither Robertson's horror novel nor Stead's prophetic story served as a warning to *Titanic*'s captain in 1912. But a backward recollection of that appalling tragedy did save another ship in similar circumstances 23 years later.

A young seaman called William Reeves was standing watch in the bow of a tramp steamer, Canada-bound from Tyneside in 1935. It was April—the month of the iceberg disasters, real and fictional—and young Reeves had brooded deeply on them. His watch was due to end at midnight. This, he knew, was the time *Titanic* had hit the iceberg. Then, as now, the sea had been calm.

These thoughts took shape and swelled into omens in the seaman's mind as he stood his lonely watch. His tired, bloodshot eyes strained ahead for any sign of danger, but there was nothing to be seen;

EYEWITNESS *As the* Titanic *sank, these sketches were made from an overturned lifeboat by a Mr John B. Thayer. No other survivor spoke of the ship breaking in half, however. Having torn a 300 ft gash in her side, she went down in 2 hr 40 min., taking 1513 people with her.*

nothing but a horizonless, impenetrable gloom. He was scared to shout an alarm, fearing his shipmates' ridicule. He was scared not to.

Then suddenly he remembered the exact date the *Titanic* went down—April 14, 1912. The coincidence was terrifying: it was the day he had been born. Reeves's mounting sense of doom flared into panic-stricken certainty. He shouted out a danger warning, and the helmsman rang

the signal: engines full astern. The ship churned to a halt—just yards from a huge iceberg that towered menacingly out of the blackness of the night.

More deadly icebergs crowded in a-round the tramp steamer, and it took nine days for Newfoundland icebreakers to smash a way clear.

The name of the little ship that came so near to sharing the *Titanic*'s fate? She was called the *Titanian*.

CROSSWORD STARTED A SPY SCARE

Clues led to vital secrets of D-Day invasion

Solutions to the popular crossword puzzle in the *Daily Telegraph* gave a nasty headache to security officers who were responsible for guarding the secrets of the planned invasion of Europe by the Allies in June 1944.

Members of MI5, Britain's counter-espionage service, who used to wile away their spare moments in this pastime, noticed that some of the clues appeared to give away vital codenames invented to cloak the mightiest seaborne attack of all time.

The answer to the clue 'one of the U.S.' turned out to be, for instance, UTAH, and another, OMAHA—beaches on which the American armies were to land. Another answer was MULBERRY, the floating harbours that would accommodate supply ships. NEPTUNE was the naval support.

Most suspicious of all, there was a clue about 'some big-wig' which produced the answer OVERLORD, the codeword invented to describe the entire operation.

MI5 was in a flap. Was the *Telegraph* crossword being used to tip off the Germans? Two officers were sent to Leather-head, in Surrey, to find out. There they interviewed the compiler of the puzzles, Leonard Dawe, a 54-year-old teacher.

Why, they demanded, had he chosen these five words for his solutions? Why not? replied Dawe, somewhat indignant. Was there any law against choosing whatever words he liked?

Dawe's patent honesty convinced MI5. He had no knowledge of the coming D-Day invasion strategy.

His crossword solutions were just an-other of life's astonishing coincidences.

LINCOLN'S DREAM

The President foresaw his own death

People who claim their dreams come true are seldom taken seriously. And even President Abraham Lincoln, when he experienced precognition in 1865, was not immediately believed by his associates.

Lincoln recounted his dream to a close friend, Ward Hill Lamon, who wrote down the President's words that same evening.

'About ten days ago I retired very late . . . I soon began to dream. There seemed to be a deathlike stillness about me. Then I heard subdued sobs, as if a number of people were weeping. I thought I left my bed and wandered downstairs.

There, the silence was broken by the same pitiful sobbing, but the mourners were invisible. I went from room to room. No living person was in sight but the same mournful sounds of distress met me as I passed along . . . I was puzzled and alarmed . . . Determined to find the cause of a state of things so mysterious and so shocking, I kept on until I arrived at the East Room. There I met with a sickening surprise. Before me was a catafalque, on which rested a corpse wrapped in funeral vestments. Around it were stationed soldiers who were acting as guards and there was a throng of people, some gazing mournfully upon the corpse, whose face was covered, others weeping pitifully.

"Who is dead in the White House?" I demanded of one of the soldiers. "The President," was his answer. "He was killed by an assassin."'

A few days after that account, on April 14, Lincoln was shot dead by John Wilkes Booth at Ford's Theatre in Washington. His body was taken to lie in state in the East Room of the White House.

DEATHS OF THE PRESIDENTS

How fate linked the destinies of Lincoln and Kennedy

The assassinations of Presidents Abraham Lincoln and John Fitzgerald Kennedy were linked by an amazing series of coincidences.

Abraham Lincoln was first elected to Congress in 1846. John Kennedy followed exactly 100 years later. Lincoln was elected as the 16th President of the United States on November 6, 1860. Kennedy was elected to be the Republic's 35th President on November 8, 1960. After their deaths they were both succeeded by Southerners named Johnson. Andrew Johnson was born in 1808, Lyndon Johnson in 1908.

Both Southerners

John Wilkes Booth, the man who killed Lincoln, was born in 1838, while Lee Harvey Oswald, Kennedy's killer, was born in 1939. Both men were Southerners, and both were themselves shot before they could come to trial.

Booth committed his crime in a theatre and then ran to a barn. Oswald pulled the trigger on Kennedy from the window of a warehouse—and ran to a theatre.

On the day he was assassinated Lincoln told a guard, William H. Crook: 'I believe there are men who want to take my life . . . And I have no doubt they will do it . . . If it is to be done, it is impossible to prevent it.'

Kennedy's fatalistic view

And Kennedy unsuspectingly told his wife, Jackie, and his personal adviser Ken O'Donnell: 'If somebody wants to shoot me from a window with a rifle, nobody can stop it. So why worry about it?'

'Some day' proved to be that day. He was shot a few hours later.

Lincoln and Kennedy were both historic civil rights campaigners, and both were shot on a Friday, in the back of the head. Their wives were with them.

The Ford coincidence

Lincoln was shot in Ford's Theatre. Kennedy was shot in an automobile made by the Ford Motor Company—a Lincoln.

One final, unhappy coincidence is that Kennedy had a secretary named Evelyn Lincoln, who is said to have strongly advised him against going to Dallas.

THE WITCHDOCTOR'S CURSE

When a judge was sentenced in his own court

Witchcraft and magic still play a significant part in the lives of many tribal Africans, even some of those who have now settled in urban communities. They still believe that a curse, particularly a death curse, can be broken only by the invocation of stronger spirits, and the help of an even stronger witchdoctor.

Anthropologists insist that the curse merely creates a death wish which the victim fulfils. However, there are instances in which white people, who are not usually psychologically affected by witchcraft or magic, have been the victims of such curses.

There have been two spectacular cases in Rhodesia in the last 33 years.

A witchdoctor appeared before Salisbury High Court in 1949, and was gaoled for two years for illegally practising his craft. The old man simply shrugged his shoulders, fatalistically accepting his punishment. But he burst into a furious temper when the judge ordered his charms and medicines to be destroyed.

He screamed a curse that lions would return to the streets of the city. By 1949 Salisbury was an established, modern, sophisticated city and lions had not been seen in its streets for 50 years.

However, three weeks later a pride of lions, an adult male and female and three almost fully grown cubs, strolled nonchalantly across a street just 2 miles from the city centre.

Pets slaughtered

A few days later they attacked a tame goat in the garden of a house 1 mile away, under the horrified gaze of the family on the veranda.

The chain of events went on, with dogs and cattle being slaughtered. A hunt was launched, poison was put down—all without success. After a week of siege, the lions moved away and were next seen in Mazoe, 16 miles away, causing havoc at a gold mine.

The lions made two kills at a farm, in spite of two hunters who sat up all night waiting for them. All the hunters bagged that night was a pedigree bull which had wandered over to investigate the bleats of a goat staked out as lion bait.

After this the lions were never seen or heard of again.

Seven years before, Adrian Brooks had had an encounter with witchcraft. He was an enthusiastic young graduate who had been posted to the Government Administrative Office at Kasama in Northern Rhodesia—now Zambia.

Superstitious tribesmen

This was the small, administrative headquarters for the deeply superstitious Wemba tribe. For the tribesmen, a spirit lurks behind every tree, and there is an occult reason for even the most everyday happening.

Brooks was District Officer at Kasama and quickly settled into the routine. He was a keen amateur photographer and spent his free time looking for unusual subjects, pictures of which he might be able to sell.

After three months, he learnt from a tribesman of the Wembas' sacred burial ground of the paramount chiefs. It was in a secret place, which had never been visited by a white man.

The burial ritual has been handed down over the centuries. The chief's body is placed in a royal hut and watched over until the flesh has rotted from the bones. The skeleton is then buried in a sitting position, with its hand sticking out of the ground, held upright by a forked stick, so that passers-by can shake hands with the dead chief.

Deadly picture

The sacred grove is guarded by two elderly witchdoctors. In spite of their vehement protests, Brooks walked in and started taking photographs with an air of nonchalance which further angered the guardians of the grove. When he left they warned him that he had angered the spirits and would soon be dead.

Brooks was not at all worried, and when he got back to Kasama he joked about the curse with a macabre relish.

Three days later he was standing outside his office building when the flagpole crashed down and killed him. The official report stated that termites had been eating the base of the pole and it had fallen just as Brooks paused below it.

THE MOST HAUNTED HOUSE? *For the better part of a century, Borley Rectory, Essex, was allegedly bedevilled by a phantom nun, a headless coachman and showers of stones that came from nowhere.*

ENGLAND'S MOST HAUNTED HOUSE

Monastic chants, strange scribbling and a slap on the face

Borley rectory was a damp, rambling Victorian building on the north bank of the River Stour in Essex. It was the most haunted house in England.

For more than a century there were sightings of phantom coaches, a nun and a headless man. There were poltergeists throwing things about, mysterious footsteps, objects appearing and disappearing, bells ringing, writing on walls and, from Borley church near by, weird monastic chantings and organ music.

The rectory was built in 1863 for the Rev. Henry Dawson Ellis Bull, on the reputed site of a medieval monastery. As

WALL MESSAGES *The first may mean 'Marianne get help. (To die unrep)entant bothers me.' The capitals are Mrs Foyster's replies.*

soon as he, his wife and their 14 children moved in, the happenings started. Footsteps and taps were heard in the night. Bells rang, and voices whispered.

One daughter was awakened by a slap in the face; another saw the dark figure of an old man in a tall hat by her bed. One frequent visitor saw a nun several times. No one was harmed but the experiences were unnerving.

The vicar's son, Harry Bull, took over the rectory in 1892 and stayed until 1927. In that period a headless man was seen in the bushes; a phantom coach appeared; a cook reported that a locked door was open every morning; and four of Mr Bull's sisters together saw a young nun who disappeared without trace.

In 1929 poltergeists, the mischievous spirits that toss things about, were recorded at Borley for the first time. Among the objects which appeared inexplicably were pebbles, keys and medals, one with the head of St Ignatius engraved on it and the word 'Roma' beneath a design of two human figures.

Between 1930 and 1935, the rectory was in the hands of the Rev. Lionel Algernon Foyster, his wife Marianne and their daughter Adelaide. Messages were scribbled on walls and scraps of paper; footsteps were heard. A voice called out Marianne's name and an invisible assailant attacked her, the first recorded time that someone was harmed. There were also strange smells, especially of lavender. Many of the scribblings on the wall were illegible, but one appeared to say 'Marianne get help'.

Edwin Whitehouse, who later became a Benedictine monk, visited the rectory with his aunt and uncle during 1931. On one occasion a fire started in the skirting board of an unused room. As the flames were put out, a flint the size of a hen's egg fell to the floor. Later, when the vicar was conducting a service of exorcism in his room, Edwin and his aunt were hit by falling stones.

The experts move in

In 1937 Harry Price, founder of Britain's National Laboratory of Psychical Research, advertised in *The Times* for people of leisure and intelligence, intrepid, critical and unbiased, to join a rota of observers. From more than 200 people who applied, he chose 40.

Ellice Howe, an Oxford graduate, saw objects move. Others reported unexplained noises. Commander A. B. Campbell, of the BBC 'Brains Trust' team, was hit by a piece of soap in a sealed room. Dr C. E. M. Joad, the philosopher, another member of the team, reported that a thermometer recorded a sudden and inexplicable drop of 10 degrees.

The rectory was burnt to the ground in 1939. On the night of the fire, two mysterious figures were seen leaving the building—although the only person known to have been in it was the new owner, a Captain Gregson. Several people saw the figure of a young girl at an upstairs window.

But still the phenomena continued. A chauffeur, Herbert Mayes, heard the thunder of hooves approach and pass him close to the rectory when there was nothing to be seen.

During the wartime blackout, air-raid wardens were summoned many times to deal with lights seen in the windows.

In 1943 the site was excavated. At a depth of 3 or 4 ft, workers found fragments of a woman's skull and pendants bearing religious symbols.

As late as 1961 torches, car headlights and camera flashes all failed during an investigation.

Other researchers into Borley rectory have learnt at séances that, in the 17th century, a young French nun, Marie Lairre, was induced to leave her convent at Le Havre to marry one of the Waldegraves of Borley, a landed family. They were told that she was strangled by her fiancé on May 17, 1667, in a building standing on the rectory site.

Her body, according to the spirit messages, was buried in the cellar.

ODD BEHAVIOUR OF POLTERGEISTS

Why should they prefer the company of youngsters?

A curious conclusion has been reached by researchers investigating poltergeists, the spirits which traditionally cause 'bumps in the night'. It seems that they prefer to operate when young children or teenagers are present.

Their name is a combination of the German words 'Polter' (noise or racket) and 'Geist' (spirit). They are reputed to send objects flying across rooms, shatter pottery and make weird noises after dark.

In November 1967 a German lawyer, Herr Adam, was practising in the Bavarian town of Rosenheim, when all sorts of inexplicable happenings occurred.

Herr Adam was a respected member of the community with little knowledge of the supernatural. Suddenly light-bulbs in his office began to shatter, lamp-shades fell off and all four telephone lines rang without reason.

Baffled, he called in technical experts who installed a recording device to check the electricity supply. At times it showed such surges in the current that the needle ripped the graph paper—but not once did the power overload blow a fuse.

So Herr Adam had recourse to Professor Hans Bender, an expert in parapsychology, specialising in telepathy, clairvoyance and extra-sensory perception. Bender set traps to see if the incidents were the work of a hoaxer, but all proved negative.

After interviewing all available witnesses, he suggested that the events might have been connected with poltergeists, and attention focused on Herr Adam's clerk, a 19-year-old girl named Anne-Marie. A check on dates showed that the events began about the same time as Anne-Marie began working in the office. They stopped while she was away briefly and resumed upon her return. When Herr Adam, with this knowledge, said to her, 'Now all we need is for the pictures on the wall to move', the pictures indeed did just that.

Anne-Marie was tested by doctors and psychologists who found nothing unusual. Attempts to induce psychokinesis, the ability to move objects by concentration, all proved futile. All that is known for certain is that the events ceased when Anne-Marie left the office and took another job. It was reported that the disruptions continued at her next office but only in a minor way.

Another poltergeist case began on February 3, 1958, in the house of James Herrmann, Seaford, Long Island, only 25 miles from New York. There were two children in the Herrmann family—Lucille, aged 13, and James 12.

Holy water spilt

The phenomena began when a bottle of holy water with a screw cap became unstoppered and the contents spilt out on a bedroom floor. In the bathroom, a similarly capped bottle of shampoo also spilt, as did a bottle of medicine and other bottles down in the kitchen and basement.

While cleaning his teeth in the bathroom, Mr Herrmann clearly saw a bottle of medicine slide 18 in. across a level ledge and smash into the hand-basin. No human hand had been near the bottle and there was nothing in the bathroom that could have propelled it.

Something weird

A sceptical but polite police officer, James Hughes, was called to the house and interviewed the family. While he sat with them in the living-room, more bottles began to pop their caps. Hughes returned to his police station with the report that 'something weird' was happening at the Herrmanns', and a detective, Joseph Tozzi, joined the case.

Even today, says Tozzi, he does not believe in the supernatural, but he can offer no explanation for what he saw.

On one occasion, he was at the house when a porcelain figure flew across the dining-room and smashed against a desk. The strain proved too much for the Herrmanns and they went to stay with relatives, taking the two children with them. Nothing happened while they were away, but on the night of their return another glass bowl flew into the air and smashed.

Neither the Rosenheim nor the Seaford events can be explained. They are just part of the unfathomable that makes human lives more fascinating.

COFFINS THAT KEPT MOVING

The tomb mystery scared Barbados 150 years ago

In the 18th century, the Walronds, a rich family of planters, built a rock-hewn tomb at Christ Church, Barbados. It was sealed with a massive marble door—more a fortress than a tomb.

One family member to be interred there was Mrs Thomasina Goddard, in 1807. A year later the vault was taken over by the Chase family—also slave-owning planters—who purchased it to bury two daughters in 1808 and 1812.

When the tomb was opened again in 1812 to receive the body of their father, Thomas Chase, the girls' lead coffins had been stood on end upside down. There was no sign of a break-in.

Nor was there in 1816, when the tomb was again opened for the body of a boy

relative. But the Chase coffins had again been wildly disarranged.

That of Thomas, which had taken eight men to carry, was leaning upright against a wall of the vault.

By the time of the next funeral, eight weeks later, word of the strange tomb had got around and a huge crowd turned up for the ceremony. They were not disappointed. Although the tomb was sealed, the four Chase coffins inside were once more in disarray.

The Governor of Barbados, Lord Combermere, now took a hand. In 1819 he supervised the orderly restacking of the coffins and had seals put round the door slab. But the following year, after reports of noises, he visited the site again.

NO PEACE FOR THE DEAD *On the several occasions that this tomb in Barbados was opened to put in another coffin, those already inside had been disturbed. The cause remains a mystery.*

His seals were intact. But the lead coffins were in their customary jumbled confusion. Only the little crumbling, wooden coffin of Mrs Goddard still lay peacefully in its corner.

No explanation seemed to fit the case. Negro slaves could not have moved the coffins in revenge without leaving some trace. There was no trace of flooding. And earthquakes would hardly have shaken one tomb without disturbing others in the surrounding area.

Sir Arthur Conan Doyle, creator of Sherlock Holmes, suggested that super-natural forces moved the coffins in pro-test at their lead construction, which prevented the speedy decay of the bodies inside. He thought these forces might have been strengthened by the fact that Thomas Chase and one of his daughters had committed suicide.

Whatever the reason, the moving coffins caused such mass concern all over Bar-bados that the tomb was emptied of all its occupants 150 years ago.

It remains empty to this day, except for the litter, blown in by the wind through the gaps in the bars of the door.

URI GELLER'S PERPLEXING POWER

Spoons bent under the forces of his will

Uri Geller, a quietly spoken Israeli, caused a stir in the scientific world of the 1970s by what appeared to be remarkable mental powers.

He seemed to bend a variety of metal objects including forks, spoons and keys, by just stroking them or on occasions merely concentrating on them. He ap-parently made watches stop or go, bend or twist their hands and sometimes break off completely, by nothing more than passing his hands over them.

Geller, who became a household word in his native country, America and Britain, could not explain his 'powers'. He said: 'I just feel it must come from some external source.'

He added: 'Perhaps everybody has got this within them, but it requires a certain power to trigger if off. I am sure, though, the power must come from an intelligent form of energy.'

He was born in Tel Aviv in 1946, and even at the age of three he knew he could 'do things', including reading people's minds. In 1969 he demonstrated his powers before a school audience.

After this first public performance he was asked to appear all over Israel. Some of his critics said he was no more than a brilliant conjurer, but even the most sceptical had to admit that he could per-form the most astounding and amazing feats.

In Germany in 1972 he snapped the heads off spoons and left knives and forks slowly bending as he walked away. Watches stopped, started and broke in his presence and keys bent. Even more impressive, he drove a car blindfolded through the crowded streets of Munich.

Finally he stopped a cable car, made it hover over a 140 metre drop in the Chiemgau mountains and then moved it forward and backward to his silent command.

Scientists baffled

Scientists at the Max Planck Institute for Plasma Physics described his powers as 'a phenomenon which in theoretical physics cannot yet be explained'.

Geller's fame spread to America and a research scientist, Andrija Puharich, who then worked for the New York University Medical Centre, went to Israel to decide for himself whether or not Uri Geller's powers were genuine. As a result of their meeting, Geller agreed to go to America to demonstrate his abilities under strict scientific conditions.

Scientists at the Stanford Research Institute at Menlo Park, California, which does research work for the US Government, organised strict experiments for Geller to carry out. They also took a film of him performing his feats.

At the institute Geller was asked to pick out from ten small metal cylinders the one that contained a metal ball. After a few moments' concentration and passing his hands across them, he was able to pick out the correct cylinder. Another test consisted of selecting which one of the metal cylinders contained water and again he was able to pick the right one. This was repeated with various items and under varying conditions.

Geller was not always able to perform just as he wanted to, but he knew when he could by a kind of 'uplift'. One test

at Stanford was duplicating shapes hidden from Geller's view. In one case he drew a cluster of round shapes not knowing what they were—the test picture was of a bunch of grapes and he had drawn the same number of round objects as there were grapes in the picture.

He said he saw the pictures on a kind of television screen in his mind. Although many believed that his talents were genuine, no theory has yet emerged to explain what forces he used. Geller said that he was interested in performing to 'sympathetic' audiences or small friendly gatherings. He claimed he needed the energy of others to generate his mental forces efficiently.

Dr Puharich, who spent a great deal of time with Geller, said: 'It is a fact that there is an outer-space intelligence that exists independent of any form we know and that operates through Uri and around Uri.'

Influence on TV

That 'intelligence' must have been operating strongly the night Geller appeared on British television in 1973. For after performing his feats before scientists and a studio audience, hundreds of people rang, jamming the BBC TV centre switchboards, to say that metal objects in their own homes had bent and broken while Geller was on television.

They also reported that watches which had not worked for many years had suddenly, and for no apparent reason, started ticking as they watched their televisions.

Geller now travels the world as an entertainer, hoping that one day scientists will be able to explain what lies behind his strange powers.

SURGEON WITH A KITCHEN KNIFE

Brazil's country bumpkin who healed tens of thousands

The surgeon was an illiterate Brazilian peasant. His only surgical instrument, an old kitchen knife. The operation, for the removal of a cataract from an eye, was painless and completely successful. It was another miracle cure performed by Zé Arigó— 'Joe From-the-Sticks'.

Born in the Brazilian town of Congonhas do Campo, in the state of Minas Gerais, Zé was one of a family of ten children. His

real name was José Pedro de Freitas, but he was nicknamed Arigó because he never lost his peasant accent and rough, country-bumpkin manners.

In his boyhood, Zé knew the taste of poverty—made more bitter by the knowledge that the family had seen better days; his grandfather had been a prosperous landowner and mine-owner, but the family business went to pieces after his father inherited his share.

'I used to sleep on piles of banana leaves, or against the leather of a pack-saddle,' Zé Arigó once told a reporter. 'But that was when the pumas weren't nosing about, for then I used to sleep in the forks of trees, with my arms round the trunk just like a monkey, and trembling with fear.

'I looked after cattle, led a troop of donkeys or an ox-cart. I only left my father's house to get married. I was 21, and all I had in this world was a cheap three-piece striped suit.'

But he did have a mystical talent that became more evident as he grew older. At first, his nights were tortured by a mysterious voice and strange visions of a man in a medical gown, wreathed in mist, consulting other doctors and carrying out interminable operations.

Eventually, in 1955, the spirit announced itself as 'Dr Fritz', a German surgeon who died in the First World War. From that moment, Zé was transformed into a great healer.

Every day up to 1500 people would flock to his surgery, a small room with a rough table and chair. They came from all parts of Brazil looking for miraculous cures—and Zé provided them. The blind regained their sight; the lame threw away their crutches.

Doctors baffled

Thousands were treated, and not one died or had his or her condition worsened because of Zé's ministrations. Doctors from Rio de Janeiro, São Paulo University and Minas Gerais Medical Academy watched him at work. They were baffled by his methods, but all agreed that they were successful.

Zé's routine never varied. Rising at 6 a.m., he would go to the Jesus of Nazareth Spiritualist Centre, where his patients awaited him. He would ask them to leave the waiting-room for a few moments. When they returned, they found the country bumpkin turned into a professional man, Dr Fritz. When 'possessed' by the character of his beloved Dr Fritz, he spoke Portuguese with a pronounced German accent and could converse with ease in perfect German.

All he asked his patients was their name and address. He did not inquire about their symptoms—indeed, he stopped them if they started to elaborate on what was troubling them. 'I know that already,' he would say. He was invariably right.

One of God's remedies

On one occasion when a journalist, Rosinha Sarda, was present, a young man came to him. Zé told him: 'I am not going to prescribe any human remedies. Your own doctor has already done so. Instead, I am going to give you one of God's remedies.'

He wrote on his prescription pad: 'Every day, on waking and at six in the evening, pray. On going to bed read a chapter of the Bible.' When the young man had gone, he said: 'He has not long for this world. He has advanced cancer and does not know it.' Rosinha Sarda checked soon after and found the young man had died.

Twice Zé was prosecuted by the local medical association and found guilty of being a 'charlatan', but no one was able to show he was guilty of anything other than practising medicine without a licence.

After the first conviction he was pardoned; the second time he served eight months in prison. Not a single patient out of all the thousands he had treated would go into the witness box against him. They and other well-wishers sent him a total of $840,000, but he sent it all back—Dr Fritz would never accept a fee.

Zé Arigó was killed in a road accident on January 11, 1971, on his way to his smallholding where he loved to tend his roses. Some months before the accident he had said: 'Arigó will not be here much longer. His mission on earth is coming to an end.'

MAKING A DEADLY POINT

MANY AUSTRALIAN Aborigines still believe that they can kill an enemy by pointing a human or kangaroo bone at him, while singing a death chant. They think that this will implant an invisible splinter of bone in the victim's body, even though he might be miles away. Often the enemy dies out of sheer terror. His only hope is that a magician will go through the motions of removing the invisible bone.

Dismissed as travellers' tales—but were they true?

Legendary lands and beasts

───────●───────

THE LETTUCE-EATING DRAGON

An image that varied between East and West

In the West the dragon, spiky-tailed, scaly and breathing fire, represents evil. But in Far Eastern philosophy, dragons were largely benevolent creatures, though they also symbolised rain, mist and wind.

Every river and stream in Korea had its own dragon. In northern and central China dragons were rain gods, moistening the rice paddies and forming clouds with their breath. Two fought in a pool in Liang, in 503 BC, and spat out fog that blanketed the entire landscape.

From ancient times floods, tempests and thunderstorms were supposedly caused by dragons fighting in the air or on the rivers. Beautiful pebbles lying by mountain brooks were thought of as dragons' eggs, which split open in thunderstorms, releasing the young into the sky.

Dragons raised whirlwinds on land and waterspouts at sea. As they left their smoking burrows in the ground and climbed through the air, the pressure of their feet on the clouds brought rain.

Chinese dragons came in different colours: black for destruction and the thunder dragon of the imperial household, yellow for luck, and azure to announce the birth of great men. (On the night Confucius was born, two azure dragons came to his mother's house.)

SCALE DRAWING *This tapestry from a Polish castle is a fine example of the Renaissance conception of a dragon. In the West all dragons were bad; in the East a good dragon could be man's best friend.*

They could also change their shapes. They could glow in the dark, become invisible at will, shrivel to the size of caterpillars, or expand until the skies and the land were blotted out. They rested at the bottom of the sea in pearl palaces, and spoke in pleasant voices like tinkling copper trinkets.

Dragon bones, a popular feature of Chinese traditional medicine, were almost certainly fossils of prehistoric animals, and most apothecaries stocked them in ground or powdered form.

Sparring-partners for heroes

In the West, man-eating dragons often guarded treasure at the bottom of the sea, or underground. They flew at night, spitting fire or poison, as a warning of war or other disasters.

The story of the dragon-slayer has many gory variations. It was the crowning achievement of nearly every ancient hero—Siegfried, Sigurd, Beowulf, St George, St Michael, Arthur, Tristan and even the gentle Lancelot—to kill a wicked dragon.

Legends abounded. Blacksmith John Smith of Deerhurst, Gloucestershire, fed milk to one greedy monster. It drank the lot and lay down in the sun with its scales ruffled up—and the burly blacksmith cut off its head.

A dragon-slayer at Lyminster, Sussex, fed his enemy a poisoned pudding so big it had to be transported on a cart. The dragon gulped it down—cart, horses, pudding and all.

In most of the legends dragons dine off maidens, but the early-17th-century writer, Topsell, in his *Historie of Foure-Footed Beastes*, gives them a more wholesome diet: 'They greatlie preserve their health (as Aristotle affirmeth) by eating of Wild lettice, for that they make them to vomit, and cast fooreth of theyr stomacke whatsoever meate offendeth them, and they are most speciallie offended by eating Apples, for theyr bodies are much subject to be filled with winde, and therefore they never eate Apples, but first they eate wild lettice.'

Alarming as they seemed to be, there were friendly dragons. The Roman writer, Pliny, mentions a man called Thoas of Arcadia, who was saved from a robbers' attack by his pet dragon.

Dragon legends were common to so many lands that the question arises: What were they? Artists' impressions are extraordinarily close to science's careful reconstruction of dinosaurs.

A remarkable guess

Dinosaurs vanished from the earth 70 million years ago, and man's immediate ancestors did not appear until some $2\frac{1}{2}$ million years ago. So the dragon legends cannot be a folk memory of the time when monsters ruled the planet. The likeliest origin of the legend is that ancient man, coming across the fossilised bones of dinosaurs, decided that they must belong to some gigantic, terrifying, lizard-like creature. The remarkable thing is how close to the truth they were.

HEADSTRONG HYDRA *An 18th-century attempt to explain the mythical and terrible hydra in zoological terms.*

PHOENIX: BIRD OF IMMORTALITY

Rebirth in a funeral pyre of wild cinnamon

The phoenix, most beautiful of fabulous creatures, symbolised hope and the continuity of life after death.

Clad in feathers of red and gold, the colour of the rising sun, it had a melodious voice which became mournful with approaching death. Other creatures were then so overcome by its beauty and sadness that they fell dead themselves.

According to legend, only one phoenix could live at a time. The Greek poet Hesiod, writing in the 8th century BC, said it lived nine times the lifespan of the

LIFE FROM FIRE *As flames bear away the spirit of one phoenix, another rises in splendour from the ashes.*

long-living raven. Other estimates went up to 97,200 years.

When the bird felt death approaching, it built itself a pyre of wild cinnamon and died in the flames. But from the ashes there then arose a new phoenix, which tenderly encased its parent's remains in an egg of myrrh and flew with them to the Egyptian city of Heliopolis, where it laid them on the Altar of the Sun.

These ashes were said to have the power of bringing a dead man back to life. The profligate Roman emperor Elagabalus (AD 204–22) decided to eat phoenix meat in order to achieve immortality. He dined off a bird of paradise, sent in place of a phoenix, but the substitute did not work. He was murdered shortly afterwards.

Scholars now think that the germ of the legend came from the Orient, and was adopted by the sun-worshipping priests of Heliopolis as an allegory of the sun's daily setting and rebirth.

Like all great myths, it stirs deep chords in man. In Christian art the resurrected phoenix became a popular symbol of Christ risen from the grave.

Strangely, its name may come from a misunderstanding by Herodotus, the Greek historian of the 5th century BC. In his account of the bird he may have mistakenly given it the name 'phoenix' because of the palm tree (Greek: *phoinix*) on which it was customarily pictured sitting in those days.

BEAUTIFUL SEA MAIDENS

Mermaids had long tresses and fish-tails, but no souls

The mermaid caught in Belfast Lough in Northern Ireland in AD 558 had an unusual past. Three hundred years earlier she had been a little girl called Liban, whose family died in a flood. She lived for a year beneath the waves, gradually being transformed into a mermaid.

The mermaid eventually gave herself away by singing beneath the waves. She was overheard, and a party of men rowed into the lake and caught her in a net. They called her *Murgen*, which means

'sea-born', and displayed her in a tank of water for everyone to see. She was baptised and when she died she was called 'St Murgen'. Many miracles were attributed to her.

In 1403 another mermaid was stranded on mud-flats near Edam, in West Friesland. According to a 17th-century historian, she was befriended by village women who 'cleansed her of the sea-mosse, which did stick about her'. She never learnt to speak, but lived for 15 years and was given a full Christian burial in the local churchyard when she died.

The beautiful mermaid of the Holy Island of Iona, off Scotland, every day visited an unknown saint who lived there. She was in love with him and wanted the soul that mermaids lack.

The saint told her that to gain a soul she must renounce the sea. This was impossible, so she left in despair and never returned. But her tears remained and formed the grey-green pebbles which are found only on the island.

Mermaids appear in the oldest legends of some of the world's oldest cultures. The Philistines and the Babylonians of Biblical times worshipped fish-tailed gods. Mermaids appear on Phoenician and Corinthian coins. Alexander the Great, it was said, had several adventures with beautiful sea maidens, visiting the bottom of the sea in a glass globe. The Roman writer Pliny recounts how an officer of Augustus Caesar saw many mermaids 'cast upon the sands and lying dead' on a beach in far away Gaul.

In folk tradition, mermaid stories are often pathetic. The mermaids are lonely, occasionally taking human form for a night to join in village fun. Sometimes a man will seize their magic cap or belt, preventing their return to the sea, often with disastrous consequences.

Marriages with humans are seldom happy, although some coastal people, notably in north-west Scotland and Cornwall, have claimed that they had mermaids for ancestors.

SAILOR'S TRAP *A mermaid in an 18th-century woodcut, combing her tresses to lure sailors.*

In the Middle Ages, distinguished French families tampered with their pedigrees to claim ancestry from the mermaid Mélusine, wife of Raymonde, a relative of the Count of Poitiers.

Typically, their love story had a tragic ending. A condition of the marriage was that Raymonde should leave Mélusine alone on Saturdays. For years they lived happily together. But one Saturday, egged on by family gossip, he peeped at his wife through the bathroom keyhole.

THE LITTLE MERMAID *The statue that sits at the entrance of Copenhagen harbour, as a memorial to Hans Andersen's fairy tale, was made by the Danish sculptor Edvard Eriksen. It is felt to symbolise the port's seafaring tradition.*

She was sitting in the bath, partially transformed with a fish's tail.

Mélusine cried out in dismay and fled through the window. Raymonde never saw her again, though she would return at night to suckle her babies. Nurses saw a gleaming figure with a blue-and-white scaly tail hovering over the cradles.

Sailors returning from far-off lands and seas often told of seeing mermaids and 'sea wives'. A detailed description of a 'see wyf' found in the East Indies appears in a lavishly illustrated work on marine life in the Indian seas, published in Amsterdam in 1717. It reads: 'See wyf. A monster resembling a siren, caught near the island of Borne in the Department of Ambione. It was 59 inches long and in proportion as an eel. It lived on land, in a vat full of water, during four days seven hours. From time to time, it uttered little cries like those of a mouse. It would not eat, though it was offered small fish, shells, crabs, lobsters etc.'

The multi-coloured mermaid

The creature had seaweed-coloured hair, olive-tinted skin and olive webbing between the fingers. Around its waist was an orange fringe of hair bordered with blue. Its fins were green and it had a grey face. A delicate row of pink hairs ran along the tail.

An African who posed as a mermaid had a more serious purpose—to save his life. King Chen, a 14th-century ruler of Benin (now part of Nigeria), became paralysed in his legs—and tribal custom demanded that kings who grew old and sickly should be put to death.

But the wily King Chen claimed he was the reincarnation of a sea god and that he had legs like a mud fish. This gave him an excuse not to walk, and to hide his legs. There is a statue of him in this form in the British Museum.

A profitable myth

Perhaps no one found the mermaid myth more profitable than the enterprising London taxidermist who in the 1830s manufactured a hideous creature he said was half-fish, half-human. It was displayed in a London hall, and sold to two Italian brothers for about £10,000. A naturalist of the time complained that the creature was a monkey stitched on to the skin of a fish.

This monkey-and-fish combination was also the basis of a flourishing trade in mermaids by which 19th-century Japanese fishermen supplemented their incomes. Many specimens found their way to Europe to be exhibited in travelling circuses and fairs.

The mermaid legend almost certainly goes back to the fish-tailed gods of early civilisations. But probably it owes most to those creatures of the sea which seem almost human.

In tropical waters, sea mammals, such as the dugong and the manatee, rise up in the water as they suckle their young— perhaps the origin of a constant theme of the mermaid nursing her child.

In colder regions there are the seals which love to bask on the rocks uttering strange cries.

Credulity, wishful thinking, mistaken identity . . . whatever the origins, the mermaid myth dies hard. In 1961 the Manx Tourist Board offered a prize to anyone who could bring in a mermaid from the sea—alive of course.

WORM THAT TERRORISED DURHAM

PEOPLE in Durham still sing of the 'worm'—old English for dragon—which terrorised the county in the Middle Ages. It all began when the young heir to Lambton Castle went fishing on a Sunday. He caught an eel-like creature, which he threw down a well.

In the well the 'worm' grew to enormous size, and when the young knight went off on a crusade it broke out and devoured men and beasts. Every night it would sleep wound three times round Lambton Hill, now called Worm Hill.

Young Lambton managed to slay the dragon on his return from the crusade, but only by promising a witch he would kill the first creature he met after his victory. Unfortunately it was his father, who was first on the scene. Young Lambton refused to kill him and, because of this, the Lambton family was put under the witch's curse—a curse said to be effective still.

THE ISLAND-SIZED KRAKEN

Nightmare of fishermen in the northern seas

The fishermen's nets were stretched almost to breaking point. Something was making the water teem with shoals of fish. The men worked feverishly, knowing that the invisible creature terrifying the fish could at any moment rise from the sea and swallow their ship whole. Or it might choose to pluck them one by one from the deck.

They knew it was the kraken, the biggest of the giant sea monsters.

Many such stories abound in Norway's literature, for legend has it that fishermen over the centuries have been terrorised by the sudden appearance and disappearance of the leviathan.

The back of a fully grown kraken was about 1½ miles long. With its bumpy spine and tentacles floating like strands of seaweed, it was often mistaken for a good-sized island.

A bishop's living church

Several writers have described the kraken, kraxen or sea-korven.

Bishop Pontoppidan of Bergen, Norway, wrote in 1755 that floating islands which appeared and disappeared suddenly in the northern seas were certainly kraken.

The Bishop of Midaros found a kraken on the shore. Thinking it to be a rock, he set up an altar on its back and celebrated Mass. The creature waited respectfully until the bishop had finished and then quietly slipped into the sea and vanished. Modern sceptics tend to dismiss the kraken, saying that witnesses had probably been confused by sightings of giant squid. But in the vast depths of the sea, who knows? Perhaps as Tennyson wrote:

Below the thunders of the upper deep;
Far, far beneath in the abysmal sea
His ancient, dreamless, uninvaded sleep
The kraken sleepeth . . .

NORWEGIAN SEA-DRAGON *A kraken about to devour a terrified human victim.*

GIANT SNAKE OF THE DEEPS

'A great head rose out of the water . . .'

Tales of gigantic monsters lurking deep below the waves have been passed down through successive generations of fishermen and sailors in almost every country in the world. But no monster has been better authenticated than the giant sea-serpent which is said to have its lair off the east coast of Brazil.

One of the most reliable accounts of its appearance came in 1905 when two members of the British Royal Zoological Society were travelling on the steamship *Valhalla* off the coast of Brazil.

The two men—Meade Waldo and Michael Nicholl—were on deck when they saw what at first appeared to be a rock. Waldo later wrote: 'I looked and immediately saw a large fin or frill sticking out of the water, dark seaweed brown in colour, somewhat crinkled at the edge.

'It was apparently about 6 ft in length and projected from 18 in. to 2 ft from the water. I could see under the water to the rear of the frill, the shape of a considerable body. A great head and neck rose out of the water in front of the frill. The neck

A SEA-SERPENT *with hairy neck and undulating coils, by a 19th-century artist. It closely resembles modern ideas—and even photographs—of the Loch Ness Monster.*

appeared about the thickness of a man's body. The head had a very turtle-like appearance, as had also the eye.'

Commotion in the water

'I could see the line of the mouth, but we were sailing pretty fast and quickly drew away from the object. It moved its neck from side to side in a peculiar manner; the colour of the head and neck was dark brown above and whitish below.'

The monster seems to have made another appearance within 14 hours, for Nicholl reported 'a great commotion in the water'. The first and third mates of the *Valhalla* also saw it.

Nicholl wrote: 'At first they thought it was a rock awash about 100–150 yds away, but they soon made out that it was something moving and going slightly faster than the ship, which was at that time doing about $8\frac{1}{2}$ knots. One of the crew who was on lookout saw it too. Although there was a bright moon at the time they could not make out anything of the creature itself, owing to the amount of wash it was making; but they say that from the commotion in the water it looked as if a submarine was going along just below the surface.'

A head like a horse

The monster disappeared after several minutes. John Lockhart, who in 1924 wrote about the sightings in *Mysteries of the Sea* commented:

'Most of the witnesses agree on certain outstanding features: it is a long serpentine creature; it has a series of humps; its head is rather like a horse's; its colour is dark on top and light below; it moves by undulations up and down; it appears during the summer months.' But Lockhart

added: 'It is harmless, for it never actually attacked anybody.'

The *Valhalla* account tied in with previous sightings made centuries earlier—also describing a long, serpentine animal which snaked through the sea.

In the 4th century BC Aristotle wrote of large serpents off Libya: 'Mariners sailing along the coast have told how they have seen the bones of many oxen which, it was apparent to them, had been devoured by the serpents. And as their ships sailed on, the serpents came to attack them, some of them throwing themselves on a trireme and capsizing it.'

The serpent as weather prophet

In 1555 the Archbishop of Uppsala in Sweden, Olaus Magnus, described a sea-serpent measuring 200 ft long and 20 ft thick. It had hair hanging from its neck and sharp scales.

Another Norwegian, a missionary called Hans Egede, wrote of a 'terrible sea monster' he saw in 1734 near Greenland. 'It had a long, sharp snout, and blew like a whale, had broad, large flippers, and the body, as it were, covered with a hard skin, and it was very wrinkled and uneven on its skin; moreover, on the lower part it was formed like a snake, and when it went under the water again, it cast itself backwards, and in doing so it raised its tail above the water, a whole ship-length from its body. That evening we had very bad weather.'

Unknown to science

Reports of sea-serpents in the 19th century were centred on 'the animal of Stronsa' in the Orkneys in 1808. The carcass of a monster was seen by fishermen, and experts inspected the body.

Some said that the animal was unknown to science, others that the remains were those of a basking shark. For years controversy raged, but learned opinion finally agreed that the carcass was indeed that of a basking shark.

Captain M'Quhae's monster

The most famous sea-serpent 'spotting' was in 1848 by the captain and crew of HMS *Daedalus* off the African coast in the Atlantic. Captain Peter M'Quhae reported that he saw an enormous serpent. 'Its head and shoulders kept about 4 ft constantly above the surface of the sea.

It had no fins, but something like a mane of a horse, or rather a bunch of seaweed, washed about its back,' said the captain. Zoologists were not convinced that the legendary serpent had been sighted, and explained the 'monster' away as a large species of seal, or a squid.

But while some zoologists dismiss the sea-serpent as pure folklore, others equally qualified maintain that somewhere in the vastness of the world's oceans there may exist at least one such creature—perhaps the last remaining descendant of the gigantic animals that ruled the earth for millions of years before man appeared.

STORM RAISER IN MONK'S ROBES

SEA-GOING men as far apart as Scandinavia and the Orient once told stories of a strange creature which could raise storms. They called it the sea monk or sea bishop.

The sea monk of Norway was a small and normally inoffensive animal, despite its frightening appearance. It got its name from its monk's cowl and tonsured head. It had fins for arms, and a human face, although of a crude kind.

The Far Eastern variety is sometimes referred to as the sea bonze—a bonze is a Buddhist monk. Sailors feared it, for as well as causing storms it sometimes attacked their junks and capsized them.

Sailors performed a ritual dance whenever a sea monk threatened. On every junk there was at least one deckhand who was specially trained to ward off the creature by waving a stick decked in red streamers.

It has been suggested that the sea monk was conjured up by imaginative seamen who had glimpsed skates or rays. The underside of the ray, with its strangely shaped gills and mouth, bears a faint resemblance to a deformed human face.

The sea bishop, one of several creatures conjured up by seamen—possibly after glimpsing the strange-looking underside of skates and rays.

The sea monk, frightening to look at but rather inoffensive as monsters went. Sailors believed its one fault was a tendency to raise storms.

DOES THE CAMERA LIE? *This photograph, taken in 1972, seems to show the Loch Ness Monster heading towards the right with its hump protruding well above the surface.*

THE LOCH'S ELUSIVE MONSTER

An underwater camera may have solved the 1400 year enigma

Loch Ness, in Scotland, is the reputed home of a monster that has been chronicled, with varying degrees of credibility, over the past 1400 years. The loch is the largest sheet of fresh water in Britain and perhaps the most sinister, even when the sun shines on its murky, peat-stained waters.

Those waters are so deep—more than 900 ft in parts—that they would engulf most of the world's tallest buildings.

Some of the stories about the Loch Ness Monster appear equally tall. The earliest of them goes back to about AD 565, when the monster was said to have been sighted by the Irish saint, Columba. According to his biographer, St Adamnan, writing a century later, a disciple of Columba was swimming across the mile-wide loch, to fetch a boat for his master from the opposite shore, when the monster suddenly rose to the surface 'with a great roar and open mouth'.

The onlookers, converts and heathen alike, were, according to Adamnan, 'stricken with very great terror'. But St Columba, making the sign of the Cross and invoking the Almighty, is said to have

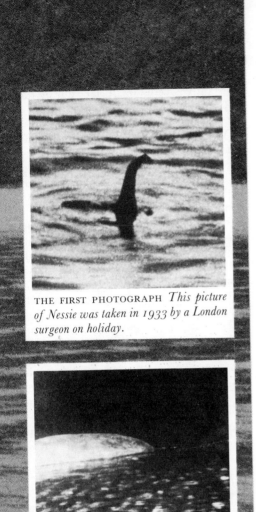

THE FIRST PHOTOGRAPH *This picture of Nessie was taken in 1933 by a London surgeon on holiday.*

EARLY RISER *A monster-like object photographed by torchlight on the loch one dawn in May 1960.*

connection with the spate of sightings reported around that time. There were frequent explosions as engineers blasted a path for the road.

Did the noise disturb the monster from the depths of the loch? Or was it just that, with the coming of the road, new vistas were opened up, enabling tourists to see, for the first time in centuries, something that had always been living in the water?

Whatever the answer, that first photograph was published in the London *Daily Mail* and provoked an argument that was to rage for years.

Sceptics claim that it portrays either a mass of decaying vegetable matter lifted to the surface by trapped gases, or the tip of the tail of a diving otter photographed out of scale.

On the other hand, true believers in the monster say that the picture tallies with the description given by many people who claim to have seen the creature and that, in any case, an eminent surgeon would hardly be likely to risk his reputation for a hoax.

The last argument may indicate a touching faith in the gravity of the medical profession. All the same, it remains a fact that many of the people who are convinced they have seen the monster belong to groups normally considered to be truthful witnesses: schoolmasters, naval officers, Benedictine monks, one Nobel prize-winner, two town clerks and many dour Scottish professional men, none of them inclined by nature to risk ridicule or to court publicity for its own sake.

Surprised forestry worker

While naturalists and zoologists tended to steer clear of the argument, bolder spirits pressed on with the search for more evidence. Sometimes this appeared to those who were not looking, such as Lachlan Stuart, a forestry worker who lived beside the loch. In 1951 when he went out one morning at 6.30 to milk his cows he noticed a disturbance on the water, and three humps appeared, moving in line towards the shore.

Stuart ran back to the house, grabbed his small box camera and a family friend to back up the evidence of his own eyes. He managed to take one picture before the monster (if such it was) vanished and the camera shutter jammed.

Stuart's picture, taken from a range of

repelled the monster with the words: 'Think not to go further, nor touch thou that man. Quick, go back . . .' The beast obeyed, and has never hurt anyone since.

Adamnan's account may have been a powerful argument for the efficacy of prayer, but it was somewhat vague as a portrait of the monster. Indeed, no clear picture of it emerged until 14 centuries —and innumerable sightings—later. Then, in 1933, a London surgeon, driving past the loch on holiday, secured the first photograph of a monster—or what was claimed to be one. It showed a long neck, arched over the water from a thick body and was taken, according to the surgeon, from a distance of 200 to 300 yds, near Invermoriston.

At that point, the road runs 200 ft above the loch. The road was then newly built, which may have had some kind of

MONSTER BELT *Lake monsters are said to live within a wide belt across the world.*

60 yds, got wide publicity, as the surgeon's had done 18 years before. But by and large, people remained sceptical of this and other photographic evidence.

The first moving pictures of something that might have been 'Nessie', as the monster was now affectionately known, came in 1960. The cameraman was Tim Dinsdale, an aviation engineer, who was so convinced of his film's authenticity that he gave up his career to live in a small boat on the loch, in full-time pursuit of the elusive monster.

Dinsdale's enthusiasm fired others, and helped to pave the way for a more scientific approach to the question of whether the monster really exists. In 1961, the Loch Ness Phenomena Investigation Bureau was formed, at the instigation of two naturalists and David James, a Member of Parliament, who became the bureau's organiser.

He collated, checked and published all the reports of sightings and enlisted students and other volunteers to man, during the summer months, the 36 in. cameras set up at strategic points around the 24 mile loch.

Submarines and television

The range of one camera overlapped the next, so that observation was complete—as well as continuous. But the evidence they yielded has been inconclusive. So has that of British and Japanese television crews, who hoped to record the monster's activities with the aid of the most modern scientific equipment.

One such expedition, in 1969, deployed the Vickers' submersible *Pisces*, with low-light-level underwater cameras, closed-circuit TV and videotape recording machines. There was also a one-man American submarine, the *Viperfish*, and a team of sonar experts. Elevated cameras

constantly covered the surface during the day, and a 'night-sight' camera was used for ship patrols after dark.

More bizarre items of equipment included a noise-making machine, lent by the Royal Navy, with which it was hoped to disturb the monster. In addition, an evil-smelling bait of suitably monstrous proportions was dangled in the loch. The bait weighed half a hundredweight, and was compounded of dried animal blood, snake hormone and other fearsome ingredients which it was hoped might have some appeal to 'Nessie'.

But the beast remained coy as ever. No sight or sound of her appeared on either camera or sonar gear, and this particular expedition's sole contribution to the world's knowledge of 'Nessie' and her habitat came from the submersible *Pisces*. Diving off Castle Urquhart, her crew took a sounding which showed the loch to be 950 ft deep at that point—200 ft deeper than was supposed. The *Pisces*, on this dive, also found a vast underwater cavern.

Lair discovered?

The monster's lair? Maybe—but of the monster, no sign. The expedition left, with its leader lamenting that, for him, it was the 'end of a legend'.

In November 1975, however, an American research team produced new photographic evidence that impressed sceptical experts and caused Sir Peter Scott, the naturalist, to say that the monster existed.

Mr Robert Rines, president of the Massachusetts Academy of Applied Sciences, led the team that operated a 16 mm. motor-driven camera, suspended 45 ft below a boat, and took pictures by searchlight every 75 seconds.

Several seemed to show a red-brown beast about 12 ft long, with a hideous head and an arching neck about 8 ft long. Mr James proclaimed that they established the monster's existence 'beyond reasonable doubt', and appealed unsuccessfully to the British Government to protect it under the Conservation of Wild Creatures Act.

Many experts, although impressed, said the evidence was far from conclusive, but Sir Peter was convinced that a family of prehistoric plesiosaurs—a species of fish-eating reptiles that have been officially extinct for 70 million years—had survived or could have survived in the loch.

The monster's advocates have always argued that when the last Ice Age ended, 10,000–15,000 years ago, sea levels must have been raised considerably by the melting ice. Floodwater could have swept a number of plesiosaurs into the newly formed loch.

Whether or not this is so, the Loch Ness Monster is not unique. Reports of similar creatures have come from other lochs in the Western Highlands.

Some are just as fearsome as the one St Columba encountered. An early Scottish historian, Hector Boece, wrote in 1527 of the creature that emerged from Gairloch in Ross and Cromarty: 'a terrible beast as big as a greyhound, (that) struck down great trees and slew three men with three strokes of his tail.'

Loch Morar is the traditional lair of a monster, known locally as Mhorag. Descriptions of it vary: 'about the size of an Indian elephant'; 'about 30 ft long with four humps'; 'about 20 ft long, with snake-like head and four legs.'

In Ireland, too, lake monsters are an accepted part of local zoology—and mythology. Similar shadowy creatures have been reported in the Scandinavian countries, in Iceland and across the Atlantic—but still in roughly the same latitude—in British Columbia.

The demon Ogopogo

There, in the south-central part of the province, lies Lake Okanagan, a sheet of water thrown up by the retreating Ice Age and inhabited (it is said) by a water demon named Ogopogo. The Indians, who appeased the demon with ritual offerings of livestock, called it Naitaka and left crude drawings of the creature on stone. These show a long-necked animal remarkably like the photographs and descriptions of 'Nessie'.

Reported sightings of Ogopogo are no more conclusive than those of 'Nessie', but are enough to prompt the question: is there a 'monster belt' across the Northern Hemisphere, where supposedly extinct creatures can be found?

THE GREEDY GULO

ONE OF the most useful of mythical beasts was the gulo of northern Sweden, which looked like a big dog with a cat's face (inset). According to Olaus Magnus, Archbishop of Uppsala in 1555, the Swedes used its thick, brown hair to make caps, its guts for strings for musical instruments, its hooves to cure vertigo and earache.

But, he said, the gulo had one fault—a voracious appetite. 'He devours so much that, finding a straight (narrow) passage between trees, he passes between them, that he may discharge his body by violence.'

The animal's appetite suggests that the myth may have been based on the gluttonous wolverine (photograph).

THE TENDER TRAP *The only way to capture a unicorn—according to medieval scholars—was to use a virgin as bait. Her purity induced the beast to lay its head on her lap.*

DEADLY ENEMY OF THE ROYAL LION

A unicorn could impale three elephants on its horn

On the royal arms of Britain the lion and the unicorn have been together since Scotland and England were first united under James I. Before that the English shield was supported by a lion and a dragon. The unicorn came from Scotland, whose arms were supported by two of those noble beasts.

To bring the lion and the unicorn together at all was taking a risk, for though the medieval heyday of unicorn-spotting was past, the beasts were still considered to be deadly enemies. One 17th-century author has a lively description of their battles: 'Wherefore as soon as ever a Lion seeth a Unicorn, he runneth to a tree for succour, that so when the Unicorn maketh force at him, he may not only avoid his horn but also destroy him; for the Unicorn in the swiftness of his course runneth against a tree wherein his sharp horn sticketh fast.' He added cheerfully: 'Then the Lion seeth the Unicorn fastened by the horn, without any danger at all he falleth on him and killeth him.'

Other ancient writers also mentioned some of the unicorn's problems. For instance, it was credited with such remarkable strength that it could impale and carry away three elephants on its horn. However, it was unable to shake them off and usually died either from

starvation or from the stench as the elephants rotted. Unicorn hunters had to go to the mountains or deserts to find their quarry, and an encounter with the beast might daunt the stoutest heart: 'There was nothing more horrible than the voice or braying of it, for the voice is strained above measure.' Also, it 'biteth like a lion and kicketh like a horse'—and had no fear of iron weapons.

The unicorn was very bad-tempered with its own kind, even with the females, 'except when it burneth in lust for procreation'. But with other animals it was 'sociable, delighting in their company'.

Antidote to poison

Unicorn leather boots were believed to ensure sound legs and protection from plague, and a paste of egg yolk and unicorn liver healed leprosy. But of all its admirable parts, the most useful was the horn. If a man drank from one, it would relieve epilepsy and stomach troubles. Moreover, it could neutralise poison. If a serpent's venom had spoilt a drinking hole, the unicorn only needed to stir it with his horn to make the water pure again.

During the Renaissance, when assassination by poison was a daily hazard, cups made of 'unicorn horn'—probably narwhal or rhinoceros tusk—were used as a protection against deadly drinks, for the horn was supposed to sweat and change colour in the presence of poison. Venomous insects would not dare to cross a line marked out with it, and poisonous plants or animals anywhere near would burst and die.

Needless to say, a horn with such properties was enormously expensive. The German traveller Paul Hentzner claimed that he saw one among Queen Elizabeth's crown jewels in 1598 which was valued at £100,000, a colossal sum in those days.

Frauds were common when such profits were to be made. A Venetian recipe for fake unicorn horns was 'compounded with lime and sope and peradventure with earth or some stone'.

There was only one way to tame a unicorn. Isidore of Seville described it in the early 7th century. A maid had to get him to lay his head on her lap. Then, said Isidore, he 'leaveth all his fireness and sleepeth in that wise'. Sadly, Isidore went on, the trusting beast is then 'slain with darts of hunters'.

Did unicorns ever exist? Possibly they were a confused blend of several animals, garbled together in travellers' tales. The Greek, Ctesias, who described one in 400 BC, probably saw a rhinoceros. The rhinoceros horn was an ancient Chinese cure for poison.

It might also have been an oryx—a large long-horned antelope—seen in profile with one horn broken off. And Queen Elizabeth's valuable horn was almost certainly the tusk of a narwhal, a small whale which grows one tooth to a great length, twisted spirally and pointed like the legendary unicorn's horn.

MONSTER FROM THE AUSTRALIAN SWAMPS

ABORIGINES sitting around camp fires in the Australian outback still tell tales of the bunyip—the monster from the swamps which terrified both Aborigines and many early settlers.

Pioneers believed the bunyip was a creature 'terrible in appearance, with a voracious appetite for human flesh. Its booming voice in the night filled their minds with fear'.

For them it was a living fossil, a huge water beast which had survived from prehistoric times by lurking in deep swamps, lakes and lagoons. To the Aborigines, it was a creature of many different shapes: a bullock with a long, maned neck, a head like an emu's and a body covered with fur or feathers. It was often depicted in their drawings as having a horse-like tail, flippers and the tusks of a walrus.

Aborigines also believed in a monstrous snake called Myndie or Mindi, which would extend its body for 10 miles to devour people who broke tribal laws or wandered beyond their totem boundaries—the tribal areas which they believed were protected by their gods.

But early settlers also believed in the bunyip of the swamps, and some claimed to have seen it. Horsemen fording a river near present-day Canberra in 1886 saw a whitish creature about the size of a dog, with 'the face of a child', and threw stones at it. A similar beast, in New South Wales, disappeared with a grunting noise into a lagoon when it was fired on.

Sadly, however, the bunyip appears to be just a legend. In lonely places, the booming cry of the bittern and the odd sighting of a seal might combine to create monsters.

Though the Maoris of New Zealand had never heard of the bunyip they did have an equivalent—the taniwha, a giant man-eating monster which took the form of a lizard, snake or fish. It lived everywhere—in springs, rivers, lakes, caves and mountains.

The beast also had supernatural powers. It could fly through the air and transform itself into other creatures.

The origins of the taniwha legends are obscure, and no white man has ever claimed to have seen one. But it has been suggested that the taniwha represents some folk-memory of the man-eating crocodiles of the Western Pacific region. There, the name for the crocodile is Moko-tolo, and the Maori uses the same word, moko, for all lizards and for the taniwha.

The horror of the Australian swamps is credited with widely different forms. One aboriginal artist drew the nightmare beast.

GUARDIAN OF THE TREASURE

Only one man braved the great snake's cavern

Somewhere in the Richtersveld, an area of scrubland in the middle of South Africa, is a cavern which, according to legend, is crammed with diamonds. There is only one problem: the cavern is guarded by the Grootslang, or Great Snake of the Orange River, a fearsome 40 ft long serpent with enormous gems in its eye-sockets.

Guides are reluctant to take expeditions to the cavern, known as the 'Wonder Hole' or 'Bottomless Pit'. Only one man, a tough prospector, is said to have tried to explore the hole, which local tribes say is connected to the sea 40 miles away. He used a winch and cable to reach a ledge far below. Tunnels led off the ledge and there was a strong smell of sulphur. He dropped his electric torch when bats flew in his face and he was hauled back to the surface; he did not try again.

Some travellers claim to have caught glimpses of the Grootslang, and reports of sightings occasionally appear in South African newspapers. Witnesses confirm the beast's length as 40 ft and tell of 3 ft wide tracks in the muddy banks of the Orange River. A party of prospectors once followed the track for miles before it finally disappeared into the river. The natives say that the Grootslang is a spirit snake, and anyone who encounters it is overcome by a sense of evil.

Does a giant snake live in the Orange River country? If so, it could only be a python and, although it is not impossible that one of these reptiles might attain a length of 40 ft, it is fairly unlikely. The longest African python reliably recorded was 32 ft, but this was a freak.

Pythons 25 ft long have been shot in the area, and one of these, if seen at close quarters, would be sufficiently alarming to make exaggeration understandable. However, the natives maintain that there is only one Grootslang.

WHEN YOUR HOME IS POSSESSED BY FOXES

PEOPLE who suddenly start to overeat, talk gibberish and fret about whether their face is getting longer may be possessed by goblin foxes. At least that is the widely believed Japanese theory.

Stories of these goblin foxes are popular throughout Japan, and there are even present-day reports of people being 'possessed', or taken over, by them. Families in some rural areas are said to keep foxes for practising sorcery against the less well-equipped members of the community.

In 1963 the priest of a temple near Tottori described how to identify families keeping foxes. 'It is easy,' he said. 'You can see the foxes sitting in rows along the eaves, shading their eyes with their paws, or playing together in front of the house.'

People buying a fox-owner's property inherit the stigma of being involved in such fearful behaviour, and purchasers are hard to find even when prices have tumbled to rock-bottom.

The treatment for possession is a drastic one. Within living memory, a woman was treated by having all food stopped, pepper sprinkled in her eyes, nose and mouth, a rub-down with red-hot sticks and holes bored in her breast and abdomen. Whether the treatment was successful is not known, as the patient died within three days.

A Japanese print shows ghostly foxes joining in a spiritualists' session of table-turning with cheerful gusto and abandon.

MAN'S BEST FRIENDS

A nation that even looked like dogs

Many dog-owners are proud of their pet's pedigree. But the Koniagas, a tribe of North American Indians, trace their own pedigree back to a dog. And the legend of a breed of men with dogs' heads is a recurring one in many different civilisations.

One of the best accounts is in the medieval writings of Sir John Mandeville. 'Men go by the sea ocean, by many isles, unto an isle that is clept (called) Nacumera, that is a good isle and fair.

'And it is in compass about, more than a thousand miles. And all the men and women of that isle have hounds' heads, and they be clept Cynocephales (Greek for "dog heads").'

Marco Polo said these people lived in the Andaman Islands in the Bay of Bengal, but the whole idea of dog-men probably grew out of early sightings of baboons which have projecting, dog-like muzzles.

Pictures of St Christopher in Eastern art sometimes show him with a dog's head. According to legend, he was unusually handsome and, because he was constantly pestered by women, he prayed to be given a dog's head as protection. It is possible that the tale originated in early Christian times, when the Egyptian cult of the dog-headed god, Anubis, may have been confused with stories of St Christopher.

CANONISED CANINE *A Byzantine painted icon of St Christopher shows how pre-Christian gods were assimilated into the new faith as saints.*

KALLIKANTZAROI

The Greeks have a word for unpleasant goblins

It used to be a serious matter for Greek couples to have a child born at Christmas. Although Christmas itself was a happy time, it meant that the baby had been conceived on March 25—the Feast of the Annunciation, when the angel told Mary that she would bear Jesus.

Great care was needed to stop such a baby becoming a Kallikantzaros, or goblin. It might have to be strapped up with garlic. An even less pleasant charm was to singe its toenails, but then these goblins are singularly unpleasant. Some are so tall that their loins are level with the roof tops. They have big heads and, in general, are black and hairy, with bloodshot eyes and long curved nails. Fortunately they are occupied for most of the year hacking away with axes at the tree which holds up the world. But each year, just as they are about to chop the tree down, the birthday of Christ comes round again and the tree miraculously renews itself.

The goblins get into a terrible rage and rush out above ground to create havoc for the 12 days of Christmas. During the day they hide in damp, dirty places, making their meals off snakes and worms.

But once it is dark, they emerge to swarm down chimneys and wreck houses, tearing to pieces anyone they meet. To stop them, Greeks still hang a pig's jaw in the house or throw an old shoe on the fire—the smell puts them off.

431

VAMPIRES GALORE!

Cause and cure varied from country to country

Travellers who visited remote parts of Transylvania in the 16th century returned with strange and horrifying tales of creatures that were neither living nor dead . . . creatures that left their haunts at night and feasted on human blood.

These monsters went by various names: *vurculac, wampyr* . . . and vampire. Although similar creatures are recorded in Greek, Roman and Hebrew mythology, the story of the vampire stems almost entirely from Eastern Europe: from the Carpathian mountains, Transylvania and Wallachia, and from neighbouring areas in the Balkans.

At the root of the vampire myth lie two concepts. First, that an evil spirit can take over a corpse and use it for its own malevolent purposes. Second, that the soul of a person considered too wicked to be allowed into the realm of the dead can continue to inhabit his own body—in the guise of a vampire.

The mythology of the vampire is remarkably detailed—and specific. The Transylvanian species, for instance, is said to be easily recognisable by its gaunt appearance and deathly pale complexion.

It is said to have full, red lips and pointed canine teeth; gleaming eyes with a hypnotic gaze; long, sharp fingernails; eyebrows that meet; and hair on the palms of its hands.

Its breath is said to be foul and its diet of blood—so it is claimed—endows it with superhuman strength, despite its cadaverous, emaciated appearance.

In addition to these characteristics, some European vampires are said to have red hair and a harelip.

The Russian vampire—according to legend—has a purple face and is believed to have been, in human form, one who rebelled against the Church, or was perhaps a witch.

The vampire stories abound with a wealth of detail. Those found in Bulgaria had only one nostril . . . the Bavarian variety slept with its left eye open and its thumbs linked—and was held responsible for cattle plague.

The Moravian vampire was addicted to throwing off its shroud—and attacking its victims in the nude. Albanian vampires wore high-heeled shoes, and the Brazilian type had feet that were plush-covered, which presumably indicated a velvet tread.

The Chinese vampire, according to its chroniclers, drew its strength from the light of the moon; the American species—from the Rocky Mountains—was said to suck the blood from its victims' ears through its nose; and the Mexican vampire was recognisable by its fleshless skull.

Accounts of the vampire's powers vary from country to country. But the monster

THE VEGETABLE LAMB OF TARTARY

HALF PLANT, half animal, the Vegetable Lamb of Tartary stems from the Middle Ages—a traveller's tale from the Far East. Its full name: *Planta Tartarica Barometz*—the word 'barometz' being the Tartar name for lamb.

The fruit of this animal-tree was cotton, but European travellers, who knew nothing of cotton at that time, took it for wool—a fabric they did know.

Wool, they reasoned, came from sheep. So arose the legend of the Vegetable Lamb of Tartary. The cotton was considered to be the fleece of lambs growing from the tree or attached to it by their navels.

It was said the plant bent to let the lambs graze and that when they had eaten all the grass around, the lambs and the plant died.

has been credited with the ability to assume a variety of animal shapes—such as those of bats and wolves—and with the power to control all the creatures of the night.

Methods of combating vampires seem to be as numerous as the species themselves. Some Rumanians believe that the best day to tackle a vampire is Saturday—the one day when it is powerless to leave its grave. The method of disposal? Pour a basin of boiling water into a hole near the grave. Such a hole, Rumanians believe, is a sure sign that the occupant of the grave is a vampire.

Chalk and holy water

Others claim that vampires can be discouraged by sprinkling chalk and holy water, but those in favour of more direct methods prefer to drive a wooden or iron stake through the creature's heart as it rests by day in its grave. To make absolutely sure, cut off the vampire's head with a sexton's spade and fill the mouth with garlic.

The rays of the sun are said to be fatal to a vampire, and a crucifix is also held to be a powerful deterrent.

In Eastern Europe, the search for a vampire's grave involved a ritual in which a virgin boy, riding a black virgin stallion, was led through a churchyard.

The tomb where the stallion first halted was presumed to be that of the vampire.

The vampire's origins varied considerably from country to country. In Rumanian tradition, if a vampire stares at a pregnant woman, there is a strong chance that her child will become a vampire—one of the so-called undead. So will a corpse over which a cat has jumped—or a dead person with a wound that has not been scalded with hot water.

But by far the most common method of joining the clan is to become a vampire's victim. Once the nocturnal visitor has drained the blood of its human prey, the victim dies and, in turn, is condemned to walk the night as one of the undead.

In Serbia, in 1727, it was reported that a peasant, Arnold Paole, had fallen from a cart and broken his neck. From then on, his neighbours declared that Paole entered houses in the village at night—and that those people he visited always died. Paole's body was exhumed and his shroud was found to be saturated with blood. The corpse was burnt by the

EARLY-VICTORIAN VAMPIRE *Fifty years before* Dracula *was written, a vampire named Varney left its imprint on British bookshelves.*

villagers and Paole's ashes were scattered.

By the late 18th century, when Gothic romances became popular, the vampire was an ideal character for stories set in mist-shrouded castles. In the early 1800s, the vampire made its first appearance on the stage. Writers such as Alexandre Dumas churned out blood-curdling plays about the exploits of these creatures.

Bram Stoker's classic

In 1847 a spine-chilling novel—*Varney the Vampire* or *The Feast of Blood*—helped to propagate the cult in Britain. But it was not until 50 years later that Bram Stoker, a relatively unknown Irish writer, a former civil servant and business manager of the actor Sir Henry Irving, launched his classic story, *Dracula*, upon the world.

Stoker apparently based his character on Vlad the Impaler, a medieval tyrant of Wallachia, who had a penchant for impaling his enemies alive. Vlad was known as Draculaea, son of the Devil.

Since then, in plays, in novels—and in films frequently repeated on television—the blood-drinking Transylvanian count has assured the vampire its immortality—at least in the world of popular entertainment.

BIG BAD WEREWOLVES

Even a king could come under suspicion

Even he who is pure of heart
And says his prayers by night
May become a wolf when the wolfbane blooms
And the moon is full and bright.

So runs an ancient rhyme describing the risk run even by good and honest people of becoming werewolves.

What vampires are to Transylvania, werewolves are to Northern and Western Europe. The werewolf legends may have sprung from myths of the Norse gods who were said to change into animal forms, such as the bear and the wolf.

Later, during the 16th-century witch-hunts, the idea that a witch could change into a wolf was grafted on to the list of creatures—toads, cats and hares—whose forms witches were said to assume.

In his human form, it is not easy to distinguish a werewolf from a vampire, since they share many characteristics. These include eyebrows that meet, claw-like fingernails, small ears that may be slightly pointed and hair growing on the palms. But there is one slight difference: a werewolf's third finger on each hand is supposed to be as long as, or longer than, the second finger.

Transformed, the creature appears either as an extra large wolf, moving on all fours, or as an extremely hairy biped, retaining recognisable, although particularly repulsive, human facial features and clawed hands. In either of these shapes, it tears out the throats of its animal or human victims and then devours the flesh raw.

Internal hair

In 16th-century Italy, it was believed that some werewolves grew hair internally, and in 1541 at least one suspect died under the scalpels of his examiners.

England's unpopular King John, who reigned from 1199 to 1216, was said to have been a werewolf. A Norman chronicle describes how monks, hearing sounds from

WORRIED MAN *A 15th-century German print shows a werewolf attacking its victim. The recurring legends seem to have sprung from the myths of the Norse gods who changed themselves into animals.*

434

his grave, dug him up and took his body out of consecrated ground:

'Thus the ill presage of his surname Lackland was completely realised, for he lost in his lifetime almost all the domains under his suzerainty, and even after death he could not keep peaceful possession of his tomb.'

There are many ways in which man may become a werewolf. The medieval churchman Gervase of Tilbury said that stripping naked and rolling in the sand under a full moon was an effective method.

But in Italian folklore, being conceived at the time of a new moon or simply sleeping outdoors under a full moon on a Friday is enough to create a vampire.

In Ireland, St Patrick is said to have cursed an entire clan who displeased him by their lack of faith; every seven years, they turned into werewolves.

Some European legends say that drinking from a stream from which a wolf has drunk, being bitten by a rabid wolf or simply eating the wolfbane plant will cause the transformation.

The methods used to deal with werewolves are equally varied. French-Canadian lore advocates an exorcism by speaking the name of Christ, or calling the werewolf three times by his true Christian name.

In France, it was said that the *loupgarou*, as the werewolf was known, could be defeated by taking three drops of blood from the creature during its wolf period.

But by far the best-known method of freeing a human from the curse of the werewolf is to shoot the creature with a silver bullet, preferably consecrated silver, such as a crucifix from a church.

Were-leopards

Practically every nation has its lore of were-creatures. In Africa, some primitive people believe in men who become were-leopards, in Asia the were-tiger is feared by the superstitious, and Scandinavians believed in people who hunted as bears.

Strangely, some of these weird stories may be founded on fact. Odd cases, fortunately rare, have been reported of people who believed they were animals, and who attempted to drink blood and eat raw flesh; this condition is known as Zoanthropic paranoia.

WEREWOLVES' GATHERING *This 19th-century print shows the werewolves of Normandy, in France. They were believed to steal into cemeteries and dig up corpses to devour.*

THE BEAST OF GÉVAUDAN

FROM 1764 to 1767 an unknown monster terrorised shepherds and shepherdesses who worked in the fields near the Auvergne mountains in southern central France. Known as the Beast of Gévaudan, the creature was held responsible for the savage deaths of 40 people and vicious attacks on more than 110. Local people claimed that the creature was red, covered with scales and had a mouth the size of a lion's. It could run at tremendous speed and evade any trap or hunter.

In 1767 an unusually large wolf was killed and the attacks ceased. But to this day, no one is certain whether some other beast—or human—was responsible.

STRANGE GIANT *This shy creature hurried away when rancher Roger Patterson started to film it near Eureka, California, in 1967. Is Patterson's film genuine? Was it the legendary Bigfoot he saw?*

HUNTING THE YETI
Mountain men give it many names

In every mountain range in the world, there are stories of a strange shambling, man-like creature; of footprints too large to belong to any human; of isolated communities living in fear of a monster that goes by many names.

In the Himalayas, he is called the Yeti. Elsewhere in Asia, from the Gobi Desert in the north to Assam in the south, he goes by the name of Meti, Shookpa, Mi-go, or Kang-Mi. To people living in remote, wooded parts of the American north-west, he is Bigfoot. In the foothills of the Canadian Rockies, he is known as the Sasquatch.

Whatever the name, the description is roughly the same: Height, up to 10 ft; weight, about 300 lb.; appearance, hairy and apelike, but walks upright on two legs; species, unknown.

Seen in 1832

In one form or another, yetis have been in and out of the public eye since as long ago as 1832, when Nepal's first British Resident, B. H. Hodson, described a hitherto unknown creature which 'moved erectly, was covered in long, dark hair

and had no tail'. But it was not until 1951, when the British mountaineer Eric Shipton published a series of photographs of humanoid footprints, 13 in. long and 8 in. wide, taken in the Gauri Sankar range of the Himalayas, that the yeti, or Abominable Snowman, became an international household name.

Too large for bear

Shipton said the tracks were too large to have been made by a bear and too fresh to have been enlarged by melting. 'What really made my flesh creep,' he added, 'was that where we had to jump crevasses you could see clearly where the creature had dug its toes in.'

Yeti-hunting became a popular pastime. Sherpas were happy to relate stories of these giant creatures of the mountains, and monasteries in many parts of the Himalayas turned up bones, skins and scalps allegedly of yetis.

A conical scalp from Khumjung village in Nepal was triumphantly displayed in the West. But it was analysed as skin and hair similar to that of a Nepalese goat.

No one has ever managed to capture a

yeti, but the clues continue to accumulate year after year:

In 1948 a Norwegian uranium prospector, Jan Frostis, claimed he was attacked and his shoulder badly mauled by one of two yetis he encountered near Zemu Gap, in the Himalayan state of Sikkim.

A fragment of skin, the joint of an index finger and a thumb from a mummified hand were found at Pangboche, Nepal, in the 1950s. It was thought by some zoologists and anthropologists to be 'almost human' and 'similar in some respects to that of Neanderthal man'.

Thomas Slick, a Texas oilman who co-sponsored a 1957 yeti-hunt, was told by scores of Nepalese villagers that yetis had battered to death at least five people in the preceding four years.

An expedition sponsored by the London *Daily Mail* found footprints and droppings which, when analysed, were found to contain the diet of a creature which, like man, lived on part animal, part vegetable matter.

Prehistoric ape theory

One theory about yetis is that they could be descendants of *Gigantopithecus*, a prehistoric giant ape, remains of which were found by Dutch palaeontologist Ralph von Koenigswald. In the 1930s von Koenigswald found teeth in various parts of Asia which would have belonged to an ape between 11 and 13 ft tall.

It has been argued that if giant apes such as these could not compete for survival with man in the forests, they may have taken to remote, mountainous regions to avoid annihilation.

Sceptics have pointed out that 'clues' such as teeth could be left by bears, Langur monkeys, Himalayan foxes, grey wolves or snow leopards. Others have suggested that yetis are hallucinations caused by lack of oxygen at high altitudes.

But not all the evidence has been satisfactorily dismissed. Nor have the sceptics been able to explain the sightings of similar creatures in the American north-west.

Literally hundreds of sighting reports have poured into Canadian newspapers and broadcasting stations. In 1973 a Canadian publishing company offered a $100,000 reward to anyone who could bring in a Sasquatch alive.

In 1967 rancher Roger Patterson, of Yakima, Washington, shot 29 ft of 16 mm film of a tall, hairy creature, walking upright, 125 yds away across a creek near Eureka, California. He got a blurred, brief sequence of the animal—a female with pendulous breasts—taking long strides, swinging its arms and turning briefly to look at the camera, before disappearing into the woods.

Trail of river slime

Recently, Bigfoot, as Californians call him, seems to have put in appearances in southern Illinois. From Murphysboro, a small community on the banks of the Big Muddy River, came reports of a huge ape-like creature.

At midnight on June 25, 1973, a couple sitting in a parked car heard weird shrieks from nearby woods. Lumbering towards them came an 8 ft figure, covered in light-coloured hair and matted with mud. The couple drove off and reported the incident to the police.

Other sightings of what became known as the Murphysboro Mud Monster followed. Two teenagers said it smelled of foul river slime.

Workers on a nearby fairground said they saw the monster gazing at some tethered ponies.

Police chief Toby Berger ordered searches, but all that was found was a trail of crushed grass, broken trees and gobs of black slime.

Tony Stevens, editor of *The Southern Illinoisan*, said: 'This is no hoax. This is hunting country and anyone who goes around in an animal costume is going to get his butt shot off.'

The mystery remains, from the Himalayas to the Rockies, from the Gobi Desert to southern Illinois. There have also been reports of ape-like, hairy men in regions of Africa and South America.

The ancient legend

The legend of wild half-men is universal, reaching from the satyrs and centaurs of Greek mythology to Tarzan and similar heroes of modern fiction.

Harlan Sorkin, an expert in yeti-lore from St Louis, Missouri, believes that the creature is the result of a gene deviation in a species of large ape.

He comments: 'The gorilla was not discovered until the early 1800s. Can you imagine what people thought when they first saw it?'

DROWNED CITIES

The sea takes revenge for royal crimes

Seas around Britain have drowned at least three flourishing kingdoms, according to legend. One was Tyno Helig, which· is said to have stretched northwards from Gwynedd under what is now Conway Bay.

Tyno Helig was apparently destroyed in the 6th century as divine retribution for the sins of its rulers, who lived in Llya Helig Palace, 2 miles out from the present Welsh coastline.

One version of the legend says that it was the crimes of King Helig ap Glannawg that brought disaster to his land. The sea swept in, drowning everyone except the king and his sons, who were spared to lead more upright lives.

For centuries, people living on that part of the Welsh coast insisted that the ruins of the palace could be seen beneath the sea at low tide. However, in 1939 an underwater investigation proved that the 'ruins'—covering 5 acres—were a natural rock formation, which had been submerged during the Iron Age.

Victim to human failings

A similar investigation in Cardigan Bay destroyed some of the legend of another 'lost' land—the Lowland Hundred. This, too, was said to have perished through human failings. The story of the Lowland Hundred may well be a localised version of the Tyno Helig legend.

HORSE REMEMBERED *The coat of arms of the Trevellyan family depicts the white horse on which their ancestor escaped from Lyonesse.*

According to tradition, the Lowland Hundred was a fertile and prosperous territory, 40 miles long and 20 miles wide, connecting what is now Bardsey Island with the present coast. It was defended from the sea by a system of embankments and sluices.

Sluices opened

The main city was Caer Gwyddno, where the lord of the territory, Gwyddno Garanhir, held court early in the 6th century. It was there that a great feast was held one night—and during the festivities the sluice gates were opened either through carelessness or as a drunken prank. The whole land was drowned along with all but a handful of its inhabitants.

Seven miles west of Land's End a group of rocks called the Seven Stones is referred to by some Cornish fishermen as 'The Town'. It is said to be the site of the capital of Lyonesse, a flourishing kingdom which, according to legend, once connected Cornwall with the Scilly Isles. Lyonesse—called Lethowstow in Cornish—had many prosperous villages and no less than 140 churches.

The sea apparently began encroaching on Lyonesse at an alarming rate some time in the 5th century AD, yet only a man named Trevellyan realised the potential danger. He sent his family to Cornwall for safety. Soon afterwards the land was swallowed up by the Atlantic, but Trevellyan reached Cornwall on horseback—the sole survivor of the catastrophe.

In the 16th century there were reports of fishermen hauling up window frames and other parts of buildings near the Seven Stones, which gave rise to the belief that Lyonesse's capital lay there.

Although Lyonesse, Tyno Helig and the Lowland Hundred belong to mythology, parts of all three areas were inhabited at one time. Traces of human occupation have been found on submerged salt-flats between the Scilly Isles and off the coasts of Cornwall and Wales.

The people who lived there would have been gradually driven further inland and their accounts of abandoned hamlets being engulfed by waves were, perhaps, embellished by the fertile imagination of their descendants.

LOST CONTINENTS
Which one was the Garden of Eden?

Stories of lost continents and cities have stirred men's minds for centuries. To this day the search goes on for the island of Atlantis, which was supposedly destroyed by earthquakes and tidal waves in 1500 BC. But if the legend is to be believed two vastly bigger civilisations have vanished without trace—also victims of natural disasters. They are the continents of Lemuria and Mu, each one credited with being the original Garden of Eden.

The theory that Lemuria once covered a huge area of what is now the Indian Ocean gained scholarly support in the mid-19th century, to explain similarities in animal and plant life on continents separated by thousands of miles of sea.

The British zoologist P. L. Sclater coined the name Lemuria from the lemur family of animals which are found in Africa, southern India and Malaya. He claimed that the lemurs must have been split up when the sea swamped their central homeland—an area that presumably stretched from the Malagasy Republic across the south coast of Asia to the Malay archipelago.

Fossil links

This theory was backed up by the finding of similar animal fossils in the South African province of Natal and Southern India. Nineteenth-century evolutionists such as England's Thomas Huxley expressed their belief in Lemuria, and the German biologist Ernst Haeckel went a step further by suggesting that the vanished continent had been 'the probable cradle of the human race'. From this developed the idea that Lemuria was Eden.

The lost continent of Mu was supposed to have been situated in the Pacific. According to Colonel James Churchward, the Anglo-American who first told the world of Mu in 1870, this continent was 6000 miles long and 3000 miles wide, with its centre just south of the Equator.

Ancient language

Churchward claimed to have learnt about Mu in India during the famine of 1866. He described how a Hindu priest taught him an ancient language, Naacal, which was apparently the original tongue of all mankind. The colonel was then able to decipher the story of Mu on ancient stone tablets hidden in the priest's temple.

The tablets revealed that man first developed in Mu 2 million years ago, and a sophisticated race of 64 million people had evolved. Then the continent was completely destroyed in a single volcanic eruption. But there were some survivors, and from them sprang all the world's present races.

Both Lemuria and Mu may well have existed, for earthquakes, floods and volcanic eruptions have changed the face of the earth many times. Certainly continents thousands of miles apart were once joined together, which accounts for plants and animals of the same species being found in different parts of the world. It is now known that this is due to continental drift—masses of land moving away from each other. But the continents drifted apart long before man's first appearance.

BUSHMAN'S PARADISE

THE BUSHMEN of South Africa's Kalahari Desert are poor by the world's standards, but there is a legend that they know of a secret oasis, hidden among the Kalahari's burning dunes, where huge diamonds lie on the ground in enormous quantities. There is a story that only one white man, a soldier lost from his patrol in the desert, has ever seen the fabulous oasis. He was captured and taken there by Bushmen, the primitive tribesmen who inhabit the fringes of the Kalahari. But he escaped and raised money for an expedition to make his fortune.

He was found dead weeks later, with a Bushman's arrow through his heart. And in his pocket was a map showing the route to the Bushman's Paradise—and several rough diamonds. No one has yet read the map successfully, so the diamond oasis still awaits discovery.

WHO IS THE MAN IN THE MOON?

CHILDREN OF THE Western world have translated the markings on the moon as a human face which half-seriously they have dubbed the Man in the Moon.

According to a German tale, he is an old man who offended God by cutting sticks on a Sunday and was swept up to eternal imprisonment on the moon. Another story labels him as a Christmas Eve cabbage thief, who on each anniversary turns around and reveals his bundle of cabbage to the world.

A Puritan yarn claims that he is being punished for using brambles and thorns to block the path to church.

One of the many punishments which tradition has heaped upon Judas Iscariot is that of being imprisoned upon the moon.

To the Masai of Kenya, the markings show a woman's face with swollen lips and a missing eye. These injuries were inflicted in a quarrel, by her husband, the sun.

The Chinese tell gentler tales. They see the Man in the Moon as a toad, a rabbit pounding rice, or an old man who binds married couples with a silken cord.

THE KINGDOM OF PRESTER JOHN

Somewhere was a country where poverty and vice were unknown

Early this century, Portuguese missionaries in Ethiopia reported finding ancient Christian banners and swords that had been handed down from generation to generation, with the story that they had once belonged to a god-like Christian king.

Could this king have been the legendary Prester John? For centuries, stories persisted of a fabulously wealthy priest-king and his mysterious land in the East, where peace and justice reigned and poverty and vice were unknown.

It was also a land of marvels. In the Middle Ages, Prester John is said to have written: 'In one region grows no poisonous herb, nor does the querulous frog ever quack in it; no scorpion exists, nor does the serpent glide amongst the grass.'

Getting there was a frightening ordeal. In the desert were wild men 'hideous to look on, for they be horned, and they speak nought, but they grunt, as pigs'. Then came vicious pygmies, giants, and finally a race 'who feed on the flesh of men and of prematurely born animals, and never fear death.

'When any of these people die, their friends and relations eat him ravenously, for they regard it as a main duty to munch human flesh. We lead them at our pleasure against our foes and neither man nor beast is left undevoured. When all our foes are eaten, then we return with our hosts home again.'

Prester John's palace was built of crystal and roofed with precious gems. A magic mirror gave him a warning of any plotting that was being done in the realm.

Fountain of youth

The king slept on a bed of sapphires. His robes were made of salamander wool and cleaned in fire. Dragons were saddled and ridden through the air. The fountain of youth was available to all, and the king himself was 562 years old.

Prester John, whose name meant John the Priest, was said to be leader of the Nestorians, an early Christian sect, and descended from one of the three kings who visited the infant Jesus.

The stories about him seem to have been started by Bishop Hugh of Gebal (modern Lebanon) in 1145. Christians of the Nestorian sect played some part in the conquests of the Mongol conqueror, Yeh-lu Tah-shih, and the bishop may have deliberately confused the reports to make it seem the conquerors were Christian.

Then, in 1165, a forged letter circulated throughout the courts of Europe. Several copies of the letter exist, one in the British Museum. It purports to have been written by Prester John himself. Addressed to the Byzantine Emperor Manuel, it refers to Prester John as ruler of India and 'Lord of Lords'.

In 1177 Pope Alexander III sent a letter to 'John the illustrious and Magnificent King of the Indies'. It gave Prester John permission to build a shrine in Rome, thus uniting the Christian Church.

Nothing more was heard of the legend until 1221, when information reached

CHRISTIAN KING *The Portuguese cartographer Diogo Homem's atlas of 1558 shows Prester John presiding over his kingdom. For centuries travellers sought this land of milk and honey.*

Rome from a prominent churchman—the Bishop of Acre—who shed new light on the mystery by reporting that King David of India was alleged to be a grandson of John. This David was probably none other than Genghis Khan.

So strong did the renewed rumours become, travellers such as Giovanni da Montecorvino and Marco Polo joined the unfruitful search.

After the middle of the 14th century, the search was directed towards Abyssinia, now Ethiopia, and Prester John was believed to be its Christian ruler.

Some modern scholars have suggested that 'John' is merely an incorrect rendering of 'Zan', the royal title of Ethiopia. The country has been Christian since the 4th century, and about 1270 the present royal line was founded, claiming its descent from King Solomon and the Queen of Sheba.

BLACK STUMP AND CROOKED MICK

BEYOND the Black Stump . . . To many Australians, this phrase conjures up a land where the improbable becomes likely, and reality shades into fantasy.

There may never have been an actual black stump to mark the border of the wild outback, even though some people say it stood between Gunbar and Crow's Nest Tank in New South Wales.

Beyond it lies the Speewah, a mythical sheep station of enormous size. The wandering sheep-shearers of the 1870s and 1880s told of mighty deeds done on the Speewah, especially by Crooked Mick.

Mick was the mythical shearer who worked at such a clip that his shears ran hot and had to be stood in the water pot to cool. He ate two sheep at each meal, and when he was fencing he used an axe in each hand or dug holes for posts with a shovel in one hand and a crowbar in the other to save time.

THE FORTUNATE ISLES

The dream lands to the west

Men have always dreamt of earthly paradises—places of great peace and beauty, where there is no war or poverty and there is justice for everyone; islands where there was permanent respite from the cares of the world.

Despite the efforts of the medieval Church to discourage such popular mythology, belief in some kind of western paradise was still widespread among people at all levels of society. The Celts, in particular, believed in the Isles of the Dead—another world where men's immortal souls could find eternal peace.

Poets and minstrels spread their versions of these imaginary lands, and strange flotsam from far across the seas washed up on the western coasts of Europe may have helped to make the dream appear more real.

From the ancient Greeks to the Celts and Anglo-Saxons, these paradises, generally thought of as islands somewhere in the west, beyond the setting sun, were known variously as Meropis, Ogygia, the Fortunate Isles, the Garden of the Hesperides and Avalon. To the Scottish and Irish Celts in particular, it was known as Tir nan Og—The Land of Youth.

When the legendary King Arthur, who is believed to have reigned over the Britons before the Saxon conquest, was about to die, he was reputedly carried off in a barge to the Isle of Avalon, the Celtic Isle of the Blessed.

Glastonbury, in Somerset, is often associated with the Isle of Avalon and with the stories of Arthur's passing.

In 1190 what were believed to be the remains of Arthur and Queen Guinevere were found in the ancient cemetery of Glastonbury Abbey. They were put in the abbey church, in a tomb that was rediscovered in 1931.

Arthur's court

Glastonbury Tor, a curious conical hill set in rich meadows, was surrounded by swamps and marshes around AD 500, the assumed time of Arthur, and is probably what was thought to be the Isle of Avalon.

Camelot was Arthur's legendary court, and speculation has placed it at several different sites in Britain.

In *Morte d'Arthur*, Sir Thomas Malory suggests Camelot was at Winchester, but other suggestions, based on local folklore, have placed Camelot at Colchester, for which the Roman name was Camulodunum, and near Tintagel, in Cornwall, where the River Camel and the market town of Camelford are situated.

Cadbury Castle

But the most popular site, backed to a certain extent by archaeological evidence, is Cadbury Castle, in Somerset. The castle—the remains of a fortified hill—is near the village of Queen Camel, and John Leland, an antiquarian of Henry VIII's reign, wrote that local people often referred to the hill on which the fort was found as 'Camalat'.

It has also been claimed that the nearby River Cam was the scene of King Arthur's last battle, Camlann, which is referred to in *Annales Cambriae*, written by the 9th-century British historian, Nennius.

It is said that farm labourers once unearthed a large number of skeletons in a mass grave west of Cadbury Castle, as if a battle had once taken place there.

The legend of Arthur being only wounded in the battle, eventually recovering and returning to rule in a golden age, has a parallel in another medieval myth of the land of Ogygia.

Plutarch (born AD 46), the Greek writer-philosopher, wrote that Ogygia was in the west, a place of enchanting beauty beneath the setting sun.

There, it is said, sleeps Cronus, the Greek Titan god, who castrated his father Uranus and devoured most of his children for fear of being usurped. Like Arthur, Cronus would one day awaken to rule in a golden age.

Ancient Greek poetry says that Ogygia is a land where youth reigns; a land of plenty where the golden age lasts forever.

Glass palace

There, a glass palace floats to receive the souls of the blessed. Youths and maidens are said to dance on soft, dewy grass. Trees are laden with apples, and cows can fill ponds at one milking.

Stories of a distant island paradise became so popular in medieval Europe that it eventually became the subject of burlesque and, in France, was nicknamed 'Cockaigne', or 'land of cakes'.

A 13th-century English poem describes Cockaigne as being west of Spain, while a French one said roast geese go down the streets of Cockaigne and there is a fountain of youth there.

Apple paradise

But despite the fun-poking, the myth of a happy western land held its own in the popular imagination among medieval peoples. Germans called it Engel-land (since England lay to the west), and Slav people dreamt of an apple-orchard paradise to be found in a far distant land in the west.

The Irish and Scottish Celts believed that Tir nan Og was a city of palaces either somewhere beneath the Atlantic or at the bottom of an unknown lake.

This creation was also adopted into the mythology of Norse people who invaded Ireland and took back legends to their homelands.

They called it Ireland hit Mikla (Greater Ireland) and believed it lay west of the Ireland they knew.

WAS THIS CAMELOT? *Rising out of green Somerset fields, the ancient fortified hill of Cadbury Castle is backed by both local legend and modern archaeology as the seat of King Arthur.*

THERE IS A HAPPY LAND

Age-old ideas of life after death

The twin concepts of Heaven and Hell have fascinated man since his earliest days. Certainly, cultures all over the world have shared a common belief in the promise of eternal peace and happiness for those who have lived virtuously—and the awful threat of eternal agony for those who have transgressed.

The classic vision of Heaven and Hell has, in modern times, tended to become a cliché, and few clergymen now subscribe to the picture of angels, harps and haloes —or the alternative fate of an underground inferno.

However, all believe in the life hereafter. No one, of course, can possibly know exactly what this entails. Men's dreams of what lay beyond the grave were often a reflection of earthly desires. Desert peoples envisaged cool fountains; Viking warriors, the company of heroes.

Garden of Eden

The word Paradise was originally Persian, later borrowed by the Greeks, and means literally 'the land of the blessed'. It denoted the enclosed pleasure gardens of the Persian kings, and the name was adopted for the Garden of Eden. Later,

New Testament writers applied it to Heaven, celestial abode of the blessed Christian dead. In most mythologies and religions, this is located somewhere in the sky.

The Indian Vedic religion placed it in the outer sky, a realm of light. This Paradise, too, was an enhancement of the individual's earthly lot, with 'music, sexual fulfilment, no pain and no care'.

The dwelling of angels

Hinduism also has its Paradise up above the clouds, while Buddhism has a graded series in a vague, non-astronomical heaven in the sky.

Christianity borrowed heavily from both Hebrew and Greek religions. From Judaism came that region of the sky where God and his angels dwelt. From Greece came the spiritual journeyings.

The idea of seven heavens—the seventh and last being the ultimate in joy—is also Greek. Elysium was the home of the blessed of Greek mythology. Hence, the Elysian fields of the poets. According to Homer, most famous of the poets of ancient Greece, these lay 'at the world's end'. Other Greeks were more precise about its location—it was out over the

CHINESE VIEW *Souls of the just were allowed to enter the dwelling place of the immortals as a reward for a good life. This design appears on an 18th-century porcelain dish.*

MEDIEVAL CONCEPT *This detail from the painting 'The Seven Deadly Sins', by Hieronymus Bosch, shows an early medieval concept of Heaven and the Seat of Judgment.*

GRADES OF HEAVEN *Maha-yana Buddhism teaches a series of graded Paradises, but its followers aim at release from personality, not enjoyment in Paradise.*

PATHS TO HEAVEN AND TO HELL *Nineteenth-century American Christians had a clear idea of the ways to everlasting life or damnation.*

Atlantic, where 'the bounteous earth beareth honey-sweet fruit, fresh thrice a year'.

Scandinavia's vision of Valhalla, the Viking's version of Heaven, was slightly less restful, as Wagner's mighty operas depicted. Valhalla was the hall of the slain in Nordic mythology. The great palace of Asgard was said to have 450 gates so wide that 800 slain warriors could enter abreast. Inside, the god Odin feasted with the heroes brought to Valhalla by the Valkyries, his handmaidens. They rode resplendent into battle to select those of the dead worthy of dining with Odin.

There was obviously no peace even for the brave, for once the dead were in Valhalla, they had to fight all day. But those who fell in battle were always restored in good time for the evening feast with their warlike god.

The Yang and the Yin

Ancient Chinese philosophy evolved a gentle interpretation of the natural order thousands of years before Christ.

Many different heavens evolved where the dead journeyed to live together in happiness. The most important were the Isles of the Blest—in the Eastern Sea—and the Western Paradise, in the Turkestan mountains.

To them, the universe contained two interacting forces, the Yang and the Yin. Yang was the positive, or masculine, force —it was warm, active, hard, bright, procreative and steadfast.

Negative qualities

Yin was negative, or feminine—and was represented as wet, cold, passive, soft, mysterious, dim and changeable.

Their eternal intercourse brought into being Heaven, which was predominantly Yang, and Earth, which was predominantly Yin. While the dualism of other philosophies—such as good and evil— are always in conflict, Yang and Yin were invariably in accord.

Taoism is at the root of Chinese philosophy. It is a 'way' or a 'road', and understanding of Tao is the very secret of life.

JUDGMENT DAY *A Japanese view of the fate of sinners.*

FROZEN HELL *Dante imagined Hell to be a frozen lake where all feelings died.*

The unity of Heaven and Earth is possible only when Tao is allowed to take its natural course. In time Taoism took on occult and magical overtones and became a dreamland ruled by a fairy queen.

Islam, youngest of the great religions, is also the simplest, revering a single supreme God, known as Allah. The word Islam itself means 'submission'—to God's will. The word Moslem means 'he who submits'. Islamic belief is that God spoke through Mohammed, the prophet of Allah.

Mohammed himself set down the first units of the Koran, the Islamic 'Bible', although whether it was completed in his lifetime is not known.

Delights of Heaven

The Koran vividly describes the delights of Heaven. It offers gardens, fountains, wine and lovely virgins. Those who enter are at last allowed to drink the wine they were forbidden on earth, and—rather uncharitably—to laugh at the sufferings of the unbelievers.

Buddhists do not share the common belief in Paradise. They—and all living things—are bound instead to countless cycles of birth, death and rebirth.

Buddhism, which is the religion of followers of Gautama Buddha, sprang up in north India in the 6th century BC, and seeks to show man the way to deliverance from the pain of life. Only when a man surmounts his cravings and physical desires can he turn to the basic Buddhist concept of Nirvana—a state in which total peace is attained.

In early China, Japan and Tibet, however, one particular sect of Buddhists believed in 'The Great Western Paradise'. This is described in an ancient text that has survived, as 'a place surrounded by radiant beams and brilliant jewels of untold price . . . Buddha sits on his lotus seat like a gold mountain in the midst of all the glories, surrounded by his saints'.

Threat of brimstone

Hell can be many things, but traditionally it has been portrayed through the ages of

WINGED DEMONS *The damned, tormented by the winged demons of Hell, in a detail from Signorelli's 'Last Judgment'. It is based on Dante's journey through the nine circles of Hell.*

Judaism and Christianity as the grisly and terrifying means of keeping prospective sinners in line.

This was the threat of certain eternal damnation, preferably in flames, and much ingenuity was used to depict doom and torture as a cogent reason for avoiding atheism, immorality and crime.

A more modern view of Hell would be Sartre's vision in his play *Huis Clos*, translated 'Closed Circle', in which Hell was quite simply two women and a man locked forever in a small room.

However, the early Christians totally accepted the threat of brimstone, which would account for the popularity of the *Apocalypse of Peter* in the 2nd century AD.

It says: 'And some were there hanging by their tongues; and these were they that blasphemed the way of righteousness, and under them was laid fire flaming and tormenting them . . . And in another place were gravel-stones sharper than swords or any spit, heated with fire, and men and women clad in filthy rags rolled upon them in torment . . . Beside them shall be girls clad in darkness for a garment, and they shall be sore chastised and their flesh shall be torn in pieces. These are they that kept not their virginity until they were given in marriage.'

Homer, pessimistically, depicted a dreary darkness to which all, or very nearly all, the dead must go. This was the home of Hades, the god of death, ruling as the *Iliad* put it, 'hateful chambers of decay that fill the gods themselves with horror'. The Greeks were so terrified of death that they were reluctant even to name it.

River of death

The Styx, an Arcadian stream, became the main river of the underworld. The dead were ferried across it by Charon, whose toll was a coin placed in the mouth or hand of the corpse.

For Islam, too, the picture was gloomy. Hell featured 'coverings of fire . . . pestilential winds . . . scalding water'.

DAY OF WRATH *The 15th-century German artist Lochner depicts the terrors and joys of Judgment Day. Demons devour the damned while angels usher the blessed into Paradise.*

part

4

Contents

Hoaxes, frauds and forgeries

Tricksters who rocked and shocked the world

Hoaxes,
frauds and forgeries

———— ∙ ————

BUNGA-BUNGA

The supreme prank of a great practical joker

It was an awesome display of Britain's sea power. Line upon line of battleships and cruisers of the Home and Atlantic Fleets lay at anchor across the wide sweep of Weymouth Bay in Dorset. In their midst loomed the vast bulk of the flagship, HMS *Dreadnought*, the Royal Navy's mightiest battleship.

On this February day in 1910 she was gay with flags and bunting in honour of a visit by a group of Abyssinian princes, accompanied by a high-ranking Foreign Office official and an interpreter.

Protocol was strictly observed. The visitors were piped aboard and welcomed by officers in cocked hats and full dress, and naval ingenuity quickly overcame naval ignorance of the flag and national anthem of Abyssinia. The standard of Zanzibar was run up instead, while the Royal Marine Band played Zanzibar's national anthem. The guests were too polite to comment on this. In fact they were full of admiration for everything they saw, and occasionally threw up their arms and shouted 'Bunga-bunga' in delight at the marvels of modern naval architecture.

Only one thing looked like marring the highly successful visit. The admiral refused to provide prayer mats for the party's sunset devotions. Embarrassment was avoided by not sounding the sunset bugle call, thus abolishing sunset for that day.

At the end of the visit, crowds milled around the train at Weymouth station as the guests waited for their return jour-

ney to London. It was noted that the chief prince had his face turned away as he waved his last farewells from the carriage window. This was because he had just sneezed and had blown away half of his moustache.

That sneeze almost gave away one of the most audacious hoaxes planned and executed by William Horace de Vere Cole, the greatest practical joker of his age.

The 'princes' who trod the decks in flowing costumes were: Anthony Buxton, well known as a public school and university cricketer; Duncan Grant, an artist; Guy Ridley, a judge's son; Virginia Woolf, the novelist, who played a slender prince; and her brother, Adrian, who posed as the party's German interpreter.

Herbert Cholmondeley, the man from the Foreign Office, was Cole himself.

Cole, a wealthy man-about-town, had a lively creative mind and great planning ability. He exploited these gifts in the execution of his outrageous hoaxes, which sent Europe into gales of laughter.

When planning the *Dreadnought* affair he decided that it would be impossible for the 'princes' to learn Abyssinian. So he ordered visiting cards to be printed in Swahili, and instructed his fellow hoaxers to make up a language of their own as they went along.

Cole persuaded Willy Clarkson, actress Sarah Bernhardt's make-up man, to disguise the party. Willy warned him, however, that the make-up would be ruined if any of the 'coloured' hoaxers started to

450

ADRIAN STEPHEN

ANTHONY
BUXTON

WILLIAM COLE

VIRGINIA WOOLF

DUNCAN
GRANT

GUY RIDLEY

THE ABYSSINIAN 'PRINCES' *This is one of the photographs that William Horace de Vere Cole sent to newspapers to show the group of Abyssinian 'princes' who paid a ceremonial visit to the* Dreadnought. *All Europe rocked at the Navy's discomfiture.*

eat—a warning which caused some complications later.

On the morning of the visit, Cole donned his morning dress and went along to Paddington, announcing himself as Herbert Cholmondeley of the Foreign Office. He demanded a special train to take the princes to Weymouth, and an official committee to see them off.

The station-master protested at the short notice, but agreed to add a special coach to a scheduled train. Then he put on his top hat, collected an honour guard of ticket inspectors, and greeted the dusky princes on a hastily laid red carpet.

Meanwhile, another conspirator sent a telegram in the name of the Foreign Office to the Admiral of the Fleet, ordering him to lay on facilities for the distinguished visitors.

The admiral was annoyed by this interruption to the fleet's routine, but everything went well until tea was served in the *Dreadnought*'s wardroom.

The man from the Foreign Office set to with a will, and so too did the German interpreter. But the princes, aware of the precarious state of their make-up, refused to eat even one slice of cake.

When officers questioned Cole about the princes' lack of appetite, he explained that the Abyssinians were strict about having only two meals a day, and that they had already had their quota.

The crisis was only just over when a more alarming threat to the hoaxers arose. The chief staff officer, who knew nothing about the visit, suddenly walked into the wardroom and was startled to hear the heavy German accent of the interpreter.

Cole was appalled, for the staff officer was related to Virginia Woolf and himself, and knew them both well. But he need not have worried; the officer was far too concerned that a possible German spy had been able to inspect all the secrets of the mighty *Dreadnought*.

He was about to tell the admiral of his disquiet, when Cole hastily gathered the party together and announced they would have to leave for their sunset prayers ashore.

Cole still had a few refinements to add. On the train back to London he explained to the buffet-car attendants that, according to Abyssinian custom, the princes could receive food only from people wearing grey kid gloves. When the train stopped at Reading an attendant was sent off to buy the gloves, so that the royal visitors might eat their dinner.

451

THE MEDICINE MAN

His success as a surgeon led to his downfall

Everybody wants to be somebody. But Ferdinand Waldo Demara went a stage further. He wanted to be almost everybody.

Demara, one of the great impostors of all time, successfully posed as theologian, psychologist, doctor of philosophy, prison officer, teacher and surgeon.

In 1941, after deserting from both the US Army and Navy, he used the name of Dr Robert Linton French, a doctor of philosophy, and joined a Trappist monastery in Kentucky. He introduced himself as a man who was sick of war and wanted only the peace of a religious order.

Demara submitted to all the disciplines except frugality. He began to steal food and then, by happy chance, was sent to work in the vineyards where he and another monk guzzled grapes and let their vows of silence go by default.

Unfortunately, their sins found them out. The other brother confessed and remained in the monastery, but Demara decided he had had enough and left.

Exposed by brilliance

Unlike most impostors, whose deceptions are exposed by flaws in their schemes, Demara's downfall came about as a result of his brilliance.

This was in 1952, when he was in the middle of his most spectacular escapade. Demara had used the credentials of a doctor friend to get a commission as a surgeon-lieutenant in the Royal Canadian Navy during the Korean war.

He had met the doctor, Joseph C. Cyr, when he was posing as a physician turned theology student in New Brunswick.

Young Dr Cyr wanted an American medical licence in Maine, so that he could practise in both Canada and the United States. Demara offered to present the doctor's papers to the Maine medical board. Instead, he used the papers to get himself accepted in the navy as Dr Cyr.

His first task as medical officer on board HMCS *Cayuga* was to pull a tooth from the captain, Commander James Plomer. Demara, who had never pulled a tooth before, sat up all night reading a book on dentistry. In the morning he gave the captain a shot of novocaine and deftly removed the tooth.

From then on he revealed an amazing talent for medicine and surgery. His first serious case came when three wounded South Korean soldiers were brought on board. One had a bullet lodged near his heart. Before the eyes of many of the crew Demara went to work as if he had been a surgeon for years. Twelve hours later the soldier was able to leave the ship. A week later the *Cayuga* was again in the area, and Demara went ashore to find that his patient was making good progress.

While ashore Demara was shocked by the lack of medical care and facilities, so he set up a clinic. Alone he performed operations and amputations daily.

Portrait of a hero

Unfortunately for him, one of the *Cayuga*'s officers handled the navy's public relations in the Far East. This was a story not to be missed. The officer prepared a Press and radio release, describing the achievements of the heroic young doctor.

Less than a week after the story appeared

THE DAY THE CHANNEL CAUGHT FIRE

BY THE end of September 1940, everyone in Britain had heard the story. The Germans had attempted to invade and, as a result, the entire English Channel was choked with charred German corpses. Waiting until the last possible moment, the defenders had, at the touch of a button, flooded the coastal waters with petrol and set the sea ablaze. Doubters who wondered if there was sufficient petrol in all Britain for such a task were ignored. Everyone knew someone who had actually seen the bodies. To this day, no one knows how the story began. The Germans never attempted an invasion, and though the British experimented with submerged oil pipes as a means of defence, the idea was quietly abandoned. Yet even now many people remember the day when the Channel was set on fire.

in American and Canadian newspapers, Demara was called to the captain's cabin. In embarrassed tones Commander Plomer told him that he had received a message saying: 'We have information that Joseph C. Cyr, surgeon-lieutenant 0-17669, is an impostor. Remove from active duty immediately, repeat immediately. Conduct investigation and report facts to Chief of Naval Staff, Ottawa.'

The story had been published in New Brunswick where it was read by Dr Cyr. He identified the navy's brilliant surgeon as the man he had known and admired as Dr Cecil B. Hamann. To make matters worse, the real Dr Hamann, who lived in Kentucky, denounced Demara as the man who had been expelled from St Louis University for cheating.

Demara was returned to Canada to face a naval inquiry board. He was discharged with all the pay due to him and told to leave the country.

That was by no means the end of Demara's escapades. Soon after leaving Canada he sold his story to a magazine, then drifted from town to town until, in Houston, Texas, he read a recruiting advertisement for the prison service. He applied for a job as a prison officer, under the name of Ben W. Jones, and used a number of earlier aliases as references.

As usual, he found that he had a flair for the job. He organised writing classes and sports days for the inmates.

His work quickly brought him to the attention of the director of the Texas Prison System, O. B. Ellis, who asked him to try out his progressive ideas at Huntsville Prison, which housed the state's toughest criminals.

Demara threw himself wholeheartedly into his new role, organising classes, arranging film shows and establishing a meaningful routine for the prisoners.

At the height of Demara's success, disaster was not far behind. One day a prisoner was reading a magazine when he discovered that Ben W. Jones was Ferdinand Waldo Demara, alias Joseph C. Cyr, alias Cecil B. Hamann and others.

Ellis called a meeting of prison officials to confront Demara. They showed him the magazine and Demara flatly denied that he was the man in the article. He accused the officials of taking a prisoner's word against his, and challenged anybody who disbelieved him to a duel.

But Demara did not bluster for long. He packed his bags and left.

Ellis, like most of Demara's employers, has admitted that if Demara could return with genuine credentials he would take him back. 'He was one of the best prospects ever to serve in the prison service,' he has said.

Why did a man with such undoubted talents not study for genuine qualifications? When this question was once put to Demara, he replied cheerily: 'Rascality, pure rascality.'

In the end he became an ordained minister of the Church. At last the Great Impostor had an identity of his own.

VICTIMS OF ARROGANCE

The Prussian officer was an odd type—but orders were orders

The elderly Prussian captain marched smartly up to a platoon of soldiers on a Berlin street and began to bark orders imperiously. He stopped a bus bound for the outlying Köpenick district and hustled the men aboard.

There, he marched them briskly to the office of Köpenick's mayor and snapped: 'You are under arrest!'

Intimidated by the overbearing, authoritative manner of the officer, the mayor managed to ask, timidly: 'Where is your warrant?'

'My warrant,' roared the captain, 'is the men I command.'

The mayor, himself a reserve officer, wondered why the captain wore his cap badge upside-down and was so old. But he kept his curiosity to himself.

The captain then ordered the borough treasurer to hand over all the cash in the treasury—4000 marks, worth about £650 today—and issued an 'official' receipt.

The mayor, his wife, the treasurer and the deputy mayor were then marched outside the town hall and held under guard. The captain ordered the men to stay at their posts for half an hour—and marched away with the 4000 marks.

The captain was in fact Wilhelm Voigt, a cobbler and ex-convict, who had

STRANGE PROCESSION *Cobbler and ex-convict Wilhelm Voigt marched his commandeered platoon to the town hall of Köpenick. His haul was only £650.*

THE CARTOONIST'S VIEW *Voigt's attempt to mock the Prussians' deep respect for anything in uniform was eagerly seized upon by contemporary cartoonists.*

exploited the Prussian awe of uniformed authority to rob Köpenick of its petty cash in October 1906.

Ten days later, when the police arrived at Voigt's attic home, they found the uniform wrapped in a bundle. Voigt did not resist arrest, but asked only to be allowed to finish his breakfast.

Voigt, who explained that he had learnt to mimic the speech and mannerisms of Prussian officers while mending their boots as an apprentice in Tilsit, was jailed for four years.

His exploit had attracted great public sympathy and affection, however, and he was pardoned by the Kaiser after serving half his sentence. Voigt retired in comfort to Luxembourg on a life pension, given to him by a rich Berlin dowager who had been impressed by his sheer audacity.

DOWNFALL OF GOOD OLD STAN

The hoaxer who made the mistake of playing straight

Stanley Clifford Weyman was known as a pleasant fellow, a smooth talker with an ability to influence people. 'Good old Stan' is how he is remembered by most of those who knew him.

Good old Stan, alias Stephen Weinberg, posed, among other things, as the US consul in Morocco, Peruvian ambassador to the USA, Rumanian consul-general in New York, Serbian military attaché in Washington, and State Department protocol expert.

In 1948 he was released from prison after serving a seven-year sentence for organising schemes for men to dodge the draft into the US Forces.

Pretending to be a former journalist, he got a job as a news agency reporter at the United Nations in New York. Every day he broadcast reports on the United Nations for a small radio station, and once a week brought international celebrities to the microphone.

He told members of the Thailand delegation that he worked with the US Office of Strategic Services in their country during the war—though, in fact, he spent most of the war in jail.

The Thais were impressed, and asked him to become their press officer, a post carrying diplomatic status. After years of

diplomatic self-appointment it seemed a dream come true for Weinberg.

He wrote to the US State Department in 1951, asking if his American citizenship would be affected if he took the post. That led to his undoing. The department checked on his past—and his whole list of deceptions was revealed.

Weinberg could not take the diplomatic job and, to add to his misery, the news agency sacked him. Good old Stan's one attempt to play it straight had led him to disaster.

RISE OF MARVIN HEWITT

The 'academic' who wrote his own references

Given the right references and enough self-confidence, it is possible to go far in the academic world. Marvin Hewitt had both, for he wrote the references himself. Though he had left school at 17 without completing his studies, he posed as a doctor of philosophy in physics and lectured at several American universities for eight years.

Hewitt had an obsession for mathematics, but his family was not rich enough for him to go to university. On leaving school he worked in factories and goods yards for six years, before he saw an advertisement for a school teacher. He described himself as a university graduate and taught for a term, but already he was more ambitious.

In 1945 he took a name from a university staff list and used it to become an aerodynamicist at an aircraft factory. But the name he chose was so well known that it was only a matter of time before he was found out.

Hewitt moved to Philadelphia College

of Pharmacy and Science, where he taught physics as Julius Ashkin of Columbia University.

The following year he went to a State Teachers' College in Minnesota, where he impressed the college president with his impeccable—but imaginative—references. Here, he made something of an academic name for himself. This was unfortunate, because the real Julius Ashkin wrote to him gently suggesting that the masquerade should end.

Hewitt was not a man to give up easily. He successively became George Hewitt, 'formerly research director of the Radio Corporation of America', Clifford Berry, PhD, and Kenneth Yates, PhD. Once again his obsession for taking other people's names caught him out. Somebody discovered that the real Kenneth Yates was working for an oil company.

This time the newspapers picked up the story, and the publicity was so great that Marvin Hewitt had no alternative but to find work outside the universities.

THE GREATEST LIAR IN THE WORLD

THE STORY by Louis de Rougement of '30 years among the cannibals of Australia' caused a sensation. Scientific societies invited him to give lectures on his experiences, and a waxworks model of him was placed in Madame Tussaud's in London. In 1898 Louis described in the magazine *Wide World* how, after being shipwrecked off the north-west coast of Australia, he had taken part in cannibal feasts; built a house of pearl shells; sent off fleets of pelicans carrying messages in six languages and had ridden on 600 lb. turtles. He also claimed to have cured himself of fever by sleeping in the body of a dead buffalo. When exposed as a fraud, the unabashed Louis cashed in again by giving lectures in South Africa, describing himself as 'The Greatest Liar on Earth'.

THE TICHBORNE CLAIMANT

A racehorse that changed into a carthorse

For 11 years the Dowager Lady Tichborne had waited for her son to return from the dead. Now the miracle had happened. In her hands she held a letter that seemed to justify the waiting and her faith.

The letter from Australia appeared to be from her long-lost son, Sir Roger Charles Doughty Tichborne, heir to the Tichborne estates in Hampshire and descendant of a family dating back 200 years before the Norman Conquest. Though the hand-writing was crude and the language smacked more of London's East End and the Australian Bush than the drawing-room, Lady Tichborne was pathetically eager to be convinced that the letter came from Sir Roger.

She had last seen him in March 1854, after he had resigned his commission as an officer of the Sixth Dragoons. A love affair with his cousin Katherine had broken up, and he decided to set off on a long tour of South America and Mexico to get her completely out of his mind.

By the following month he had reached Rio de Janeiro, which he left aboard the *Bella* of Liverpool. The ship was never seen again. As the months wore on, all hope of survivors disappeared. The letters Roger had asked to be directed to Kingston, Jamaica, remained uncollected. Eventually, Lloyd's of London wrote off the *Bella* as lost, and settled insurance claims.

Roger's French-born mother, Henriette, refused to abandon hope and, after the death of her husband, Sir James, clung more and more stubbornly to the conviction that her son was still alive.

She placed advertisements in several newspapers in South America and Australia, offering a reward for information. One of them was seen by Arthur Orton.

The youngest of 12 children, he had been forced to leave his overcrowded home in Wapping, in London's East End, and go to sea. In 1849 he deserted his ship in Valparaiso, and some time later re-

THE CLAIMANT *Arthur Orton weighed 24 stone when he first claimed to be Sir Roger Tichborne in 1866. He had wavy fair hair and no tattoo marks. He could not speak French.*

THE HEIR *Sir Roger Tichborne weighed under 9 stone before he disappeared at sea in 1854. He had straight dark hair and a tattoo on his left arm. He spoke French fluently.*

turned to England, using the name Joseph M. Orton. In 1852 he departed again, this time for Australia.

There he was alleged to have been a member of a horse-stealing gang. He next turned up as a cattle slaughterer in Wagga Wagga, and it was there in 1865 that he read Lady Tichborne's advertisement and began his long deception.

Orton was about to file a bankruptcy petition when he confessed to his solicitor that he had property in England. He also hinted that he had been shipwrecked. The solicitor, who had also seen the advertisement, was interested.

After Orton was seen carving the initials 'RCT' on trees, posts and even on his pipe, it was hardly surprising that his solicitor should ask him: 'Are you Roger Tichborne?' The impostor allowed himself to be persuaded to write to Lady Tichborne about his 'inheritance'.

Deeply involved

Orton was by now far too deeply involved to back out as he had already raised about £20,000 on the strength of his 'expectations'. In 1866 he, his wife and baby daughter set sail for England.

Soon after he arrived he travelled to Hampshire and quietly tried to familiarise himself with his 'home' surroundings, and at the same time enlist the support of the Tichborne locals.

He met with little success. The village blacksmith dismissed Orton's suggestion that he was Sir Roger: 'If you are, you've changed from a racehorse to a carthorse!'

Sir Roger had weighed under 9 stone, had a long, sallow face with straight dark hair, and he had a tattoo on his left arm. Orton was 24 stone with a large, round face and fair wavy hair. He had no tattoo.

In spite of this glaring disparity, Orton decided to meet Lady Tichborne. She was then living in Paris, and eventually it was there, in Orton's hotel bedroom, that their meeting took place on a January afternoon. Orton said he was ill, and the room was kept darkened.

He spoke to her of his grandfather, whom the real Roger had never seen, wrongly said he had served in the ranks of the army, and even referred to his school, Stonyhurst, as Winchester.

His blunders were glaring and, to anyone but a grief-stricken and self-deluding old woman, completely damning. But without hesitation she accepted him as her son. 'He confuses everything as in a dream,' she fondly observed, and made him an allowance of £1000 a year.

The rest of the family, their friends and servants refused to have anything to do with him, but this did not deter Orton. He began a legal action claiming the Tichborne estates, worth between £20,000 and £25,000, from the trustees of the infant Sir Alfred Tichborne, posthumous son of Roger's younger brother. Before the case came to court, his case was drastically weakened by the sudden death of Lady Tichborne. Orton had lost his most influential supporter, but undeterred he determined to press on with the case.

While he awaited the court hearing, Orton engaged as servants two men who had been in Roger's regiment. With their help he memorised many details of regimental life so well that 30 of the dead man's brother officers were willing to swear that he was Sir Roger despite his extraordinary change in appearance.

He produced more than 100 witnesses who testified that he was the real Sir Roger. None was really close to the family, but they made a powerful showing against the 17 who spoke against him.

Inevitably it was his rough way of speaking that condemned him. 'I would have won if only I could have kept my mouth shut,' he said later.

The case went on for 102 days and cost the Tichborne family £90,000. After losing the action, Orton was charged with perjury. He was jailed for 14 years.

Loyal supporters

Amazingly, the discredited Orton still had supporters. Dr Kenealy, the barrister who defended him, tried to turn the case into a national issue, and his vehement defence led to his being disbarred for unprofessional conduct.

Orton completed 10 of his 14-year sentence and, after his release, arranged a tour of public meetings in a vain attempt to regain sympathy. He also appeared as a music-hall turn, and later worked in a public house and a tobacconist's shop. With poverty facing him he sold his 'confession' to The People newspaper for £3000. Even then he died penniless.

Even in death, Orton was able to inspire the belief of one unknown person, for there is an inscription on his grave:

'Sir Roger Charles Doughty Tichborne; born 5 January 1829; died 1 April 1898.'

THE NECKLACE OF FATE

A jewel that led to revolution

The most brazen confidence trick in history had its beginnings in 1772, when Mme du Barry, mistress of the ageing Louis XV, demanded that her doting royal lover should buy her the most expensive diamond necklace in the world.

Louis could refuse her nothing, and commissioned Böhmer, the court jeweller, to search Europe for the finest diamonds in existence. Böhmer was delighted. He bought some 600 stones and strung them together in a necklace whose price of 2 million livres (about £3 million by today's reckoning) was almost as breathtaking as its vulgarity.

Proudly, Böhmer awaited the summons to Versailles; but, unfortunately, the king fell victim to a smallpox epidemic and died. Ruin stared the jeweller in the face. Neither the new king, Louis XVI, nor his 20-year-old queen, Marie Antoinette, had any use for a necklace 'like a scarf'.

For years, Böhmer besieged the palace. Each time the queen gave birth to a child, he would hurry to Versailles, hoping that she would change her mind and buy the necklace for the christening. But she never did.

The cardinal and the adventuress

Marie Antoinette's distaste for the necklace was exceeded only by her loathing of Cardinal de Rohan, who during her girlhood had been French ambassador to the court of her mother, the Empress of Austria. Indeed, the objects of her dislike had much in common; to the queen, both were worldly, pretentious and immoral. De Rohan's affairs were notorious throughout Europe. A courtier as well as a prince of the Church, he had amassed a fortune in bribes, much of which he spent on his mistresses. He was well aware that the queen despised him, and more than anything else he wanted to ingratiate himself with her.

It is at this point that Jeanne de la Motte, self-styled countess, enters the story. She was born Jeanne de Saint-Remy, and was apparently a genuine descendant of the Valois, the old royal family of France. Her husband, de la Motte, was a penniless army officer who, on the strength of his wife's royal blood,

awarded himself the title of a count.

It was said of Jeanne that she could charm people into believing anything, and she used all her wiles to convince Cardinal de Rohan that she had such influence with the queen that she could restore him to royal favour. Jeanne's gentle persuasion extended over several months. With the aid of a forger, she produced a number of letters, apparently in the queen's handwriting, proving that Marie Antoinette's heart had softened towards the cardinal.

Then she brought out her masterstroke. She found a girl who somewhat resembled the queen, and arranged that the cardinal should meet her late one night in a dark grove in the grounds of Versailles.

All de Rohan could see was a silhouette of the same height and build as the queen and, as he knelt in adoration, it pressed a rose into his hand and flitted away into the darkness.

The cardinal was overjoyed. Not only had the queen forgiven him, but she was

HOAXER'S VICTIM *Marie Antoinette, born Maria Antionetta, daughter of the Empress Maria Theresa of Austria, was already despised by the Paris mob even before the scandal of the necklace and the cardinal. She was guillotined in 1793.*

apparently in love with him as well. So when he received a note from her beseeching him to buy the necklace on her behalf, he was delighted to comply. Naturally, the transaction would be secret, and the only go-between permitted was the queen's dearest and most trusted friend, the Countess de la Motte.

So the cardinal bought the necklace and passed it to Jeanne, whose husband promptly carried it off to London. There it was broken up, and the stones sold to several Bond Street jewellers. Wisely, the 'count' remained in England, but Jeanne continued to live in Paris where, with the money her husband sent her, she bought a house and carriages, and entertained her lovers in grand style.

Outraged queen

It took about six months before the cardinal summoned sufficient courage to ask the queen why she did not wear the necklace. Marie Antoinette was outraged and, instead of hushing the matter up, demanded that it should be put before Parliament. Jeanne was arrested, found guilty, branded with a 'V' for *voleuse*, or thief, and thrown into prison.

The court rocked with laughter, but the scandal took the French people by storm. Marie Antoinette was already unpopular, and the mob was entirely prepared to believe that the cardinal was her lover who had bought her fabulous presents while Frenchmen starved. Riots broke out, and Jeanne, who was considered to be an innocent scapegoat, mysteriously vanished from prison, probably with the aid of revolutionaries. She fled to England, where she wrote to the newspapers protesting her innocence and insisting on the queen's guilt.

Gunpowder of revolution

Undoubtedly, the necklace affair was one of the sparks that touched off the gunpowder of revolution. In 1793, when Marie Antoinette was on trial for her life, she was asked about her connection with Jeanne de la Motte; her protests that she had never met her were howled down. The queen, already unpopular, was guillotined.

There was no means of confirmation one way or the other, for Jeanne had died two years earlier, having jumped from the window of her lodgings off the Edgware Road in London in an attempt to avoid her many creditors.

SPARK OF REVOLUTION *Six hundred of the finest diamonds were used to create the world's most expensive necklace for Mme du Barry, mistress of Louis XV. Yet no one ever wore it; after it was stolen, the necklace was broken up and the stones were sold in London.*

THE END OF THE AFFAIR
From a Paris window, the artist David made this sketch of the doomed Queen Marie Antoinette on her way to the guillotine. At her trial she was accused of being Cardinal de Rohan's mistress, and of conspiring with him to steal the necklace. Both charges were probably untrue, but it made little difference; the mob was determined to have her head.

THE PROTOCOLS OF ZION

The most damaging fraud in history

One summer day in 1903 the citizens of the Russian capital of St Petersburg were startled by the news in their morning paper. It claimed to have unmasked a sinister plot by a small group of men to seize power and rule the world by force. Cities were to be bombed and opponents wiped out by injecting them with dreadful diseases.

The myth of the great Jewish conspiracy had been born. It all sounds far-fetched now, but many Russians believed the story and it soon spread to other countries. People were still believing it more than 30 years later, when Adolf Hitler turned it into Nazi gospel.

The 'Protocols of the Elders of Zion' forgery helped to pave the way for the murder of millions of Jews.

The item in the St Petersburg newspaper had been entitled: 'A programme for world conquest by the Jews. Minutes of a meeting of the Elders of Zion.' The editor of the paper, a well-known anti-Semite, did not reveal the source of his information, but claimed that it was a translation of a document originally written in French.

The forgery professed to be a series of lectures, in which a member of a secret Jewish society outlined their plot to achieve world domination. This ambitious plot was apparently well under way.

The rot spreads

In the early stages, the liberal democracies of Europe were to be undermined and Christian morality discredited by propaganda. Jewish businessmen would stir industrial unrest by keeping prices high. And then, when the Gentile society collapsed, the bombs and germs would be thrown into battle.

So widely accepted did this nonsense become that in 1905, just two years after the 'Protocols' were published, the Metropolitan of Moscow ordered them to be quoted in every church in the city, as a warning to the faithful.

But it was after the First World War that the 'Protocols' really spread. In Britain, *The Times* commented on them, though it also published a refutation. In Germany a translation appeared in 1920 and rapidly sold 100,000 copies.

Who was the forger who created this

PROLOGUE TO MURDER *The theory, based on a forgery, of a worldwide Jewish conspiracy spread in the 1920s and 1930s. This Spanish pamphlet is typical.*

TSAR'S MAN IN PARIS *Pyotr Ivanovich Rachkovsky, head of the Russian secret service abroad, was the most likely author of the forgery used extensively by the Nazis.*

evil hoax? There are two main suspects. Ilya Tsion, an elderly Russian political journalist living in Paris at the time, may have done it to discredit political opponents. Tsion was an extreme reactionary, and some of the views in the 'Protocols' were very close to his own. He may have written them as a means of impressing the tsar with the danger of the liberals.

A far more likely candidate, however, is Pyotr Ivanovich Rachkovsky, head of the tsarist secret service abroad. Rachkovsky was the author of several anti-Semitic tracts, and certainly believed in the existence of a worldwide Jewish con-

spiracy, particularly directed at Russia. He had many enemies, and some passages in the 'Protocols' may be oblique references to them. One enemy, a Jewish Russian official in Paris called Effron, was even mentioned by name.

Rachkovsky had his headquarters in Paris for 18 years, until he was recalled in 1902. And when a Russian official arrived to wind up the Paris office after the revolution of 1917, one of Rachkovsky's former aides admitted that the 'Protocols' had been forged in Paris. And the man who gave the order? Pyotr Ivanovich Rachkovsky.

THE DOCUMENT THAT SPLIT THE CHURCH
Strange case of the Donation of Constantine

For 600 years, popes of the Church of Rome used the Donation of Constantine (Constitutum Constantini) to support their claim to be the rulers of Christendom.

Constantine was the first Roman emperor to be converted to Christianity. He was said to have made the gift of half his empire, in AD 315, in gratitude for his religious conversion and for his miraculous cure from leprosy. The Donation— the document that recorded the gift— gave to the See of Rome spiritual authority over all the churches of the earth, and temporal authority over Rome, all Italy and the western world. Those who tried to overthrow it would 'be burned in the lower hell and shall perish with the devil and all the impious'.

The 3000-word Donation first became known in the 9th century, and it was a powerful weapon in the dispute between the Eastern and Western Churches. This

quarrel culminated in the separation of the Eastern Orthodox Church and the Church of Rome in 1054.

No fewer than ten popes cited the document, and its authenticity remained unquestioned until the 15th century. Then, Nicholas of Cusa (1401–64), the greatest ecclesiastical scholar of his age, pointed out that Bishop Eusebius of Caesarea, Constantine's contemporary and biographer, had not mentioned the emperor's gift.

Now the document is almost universally regarded as a forgery, probably made in Rome in about AD 760. And the forgery was not even particularly clever. For example, it gives the Roman See authority over Constantinople before that city had been founded!

Small wonder that the French philosopher Voltaire described it as 'the boldest and most magnificent forgery which deceived the world for centuries'.

GUARD OF DISHONOUR
The agony of Captain Dreyfus

There was a spy in the French Army, and Captain Alfred Dreyfus was the perfect suspect. Hard-working and conscientious, his ability aroused jealousy in his fellow officers—and in the anti-Semitic mood of the times, the fact that he was both rich and a Jew ensured his unpopularity.

He was arrested in 1894 after a letter

addressed to the German military attaché in Paris, Colonel Max von Schwarzkoppen, fell into the hands of the French General Staff. The letter listed a number of military secrets which the author offered for sale.

The General Staff, aware that a traitor was passing secrets to the Germans, needed a scapegoat. On the evidence available,

461

SPY TRIAL *Captain Alfred Dreyfus leaving the court martial building at Rennes, in France, after the first day's hearing. He was charged with spying for Germany.*

they decided that he must be a junior gunnery officer who had served in several camps before joining the General Staff. Dreyfus filled all these requirements and, since his hand-writing also resembled that in the letter, he was arrested.

Yet, at his court martial, it seemed that the prosecution had little enough to go on. Dreyfus had a first-class military record, handwriting experts doubted whether he *had* written the incriminating letter; and a police report that he was a gambler turned out to refer to another man of the same name.

Just as it seemed that the court had no choice but to acquit Dreyfus, Commander Hubert Joseph Henry, the intelligence officer who had conducted the preliminary inquiry, intervened. A sealed packet was shown to the judges.

Inside that packet were documents that put Dreyfus's guilt beyond doubt— especially an 'intercepted' letter from the Italian military attaché, Panizzardi, to his German counterpart, von Schwarz-koppen. It referred to the traitor in the French War Office as 'that dirty dog, "D"'.

Dreyfus was found guilty and sentenced to imprisonment for life on Devil's Island.

Proof was a forgery

Yet the truth was that Commander Henry, convinced of Dreyfus's guilt, and anxious to see a traitor punished, had written the Panizzardi letter himself.

Only two years after the court martial,

it became apparent to the General Staff that French military secrets were still being passed to the Germans. The Dreyfus file was reopened, and the new investigating officer, Colonel Picquart, began to have grave misgivings.

Picquart's probings, however, worried senior officers, who thought the honour and reputation of the army more important than the fate of one Jewish officer. So Picquart was posted to Tunisia—while Henry tried to cover up his own guilt by removing some of the Dreyfus papers and tampering with the Panizzardi letter.

That proved his undoing—for Picquart had already had the documents photographed. The forgery came to light, and Henry himself was arrested and charged. He confessed, and a few days afterwards committed suicide in prison.

In a last letter to his wife, he claimed that he had copied the letter from an authentic original.

That was four years after the arrest of Dreyfus. Another eight years passed before Dreyfus's innocence was established—in 1906, when the real spy in the French War Office, a Franco-Hungarian officer named Esterhazy, fled to London.

Within weeks the highest court in France, the Cour de Cassation, annulled the conviction against Dreyfus. He was reinstated and decorated with the Legion of Honour. In the First World War, he was recalled to active service. He died in Paris in 1935, at the age of 76.

MAJOR WILLIAM MARTIN, RM

The dead man who won a battle

The Briton who lies in a Spanish cemetery may have done little enough for his country in his lifetime. Yet, in death, this pneumonia victim of the damp English autumn fooled Nazi intelligence, and helped to save thousands of lives.

In 1942, as the North African campaign drew to a close, it became obvious to the Germans that the next objective of the Allies would be Sicily. Therefore, it was a matter of desperate urgency to convince them that they were wrong.

A solution was put forward by Royal Naval Intelligence. They suggested that a body, ostensibly that of a courier killed in a plane crash, and carrying misleading but apparently top-secret papers, should be allowed to drift ashore on the coast of neutral Spain. Almost certainly, it was felt, local German agents would get a glimpse of the papers.

The first task was to find a corpse whose cause of death could be taken as drowning. The pneumonia victim's body was obtained in return for a promise that his true identity would never be revealed.

He was 'reborn' as Major William Martin, Royal Marines. Among the papers he carried was a letter from the Vice-Chief of the Imperial General Staff to General Alexander, commanding the 18th Army Group in Africa. It explained why he could not have his own way, and that the invasion target was not Sicily, but somewhere in the western Mediterranean.

Major Martin also carried a message from Lord Mountbatten to Admiral of the Fleet, Sir Andrew Cunningham. An apparently indiscreet sentence was included, hinting that Sardinia was the proposed invasion area: 'He might bring some sardines with him—they are on points (rationed) here!'

The major sailed on his first and last assignment on April 19, 1943, hidden in the torpedo compartment of HM Submarine *Seraph*.

Eleven nights later, bare-headed officers gently lowered the body over the side. At dawn the following morning, the tide washed it towards Huelva, where

IN NAME ONLY *Documents which helped to establish the existence of Major Martin of the Royal Marines—his Naval Identity Card, a pass to Combined Operations Headquarters, and the stubs of two tickets to a London show for eight days before his 'death'. The vital documents were in a briefcase chained to his wrist.*

it was discovered by a fisherman. The Spanish authorities informed the British vice-consul, and Major Martin was buried with full military honours. But there was no word of the documents.

An alarmed formal demand was made to Spain, and the papers were eventually returned on May 13. Scientific tests proved that the envelopes had been opened, but it was not until after the war that Major Martin's contribution was fully realised. Even Hitler had concluded that the attack would be directed mainly against Sardinia.

The German High Command scattered its forces and left gaps that the Allies were able to exploit. The invasion of Sicily was opposed by an Italian force and only two German divisions.

The Allies' task was made easier too by the Germans diverting motor-torpedo boats and mine-layers, in anticipation of a totally fictitious invasion of Greece. As a result, Allied losses on the beaches were reduced, and the invasion was successful.

SHIP OF PREY

The windjammer that went to war

To anyone who went aboard the *Maletta* in Hamburg in 1916, she appeared a normal, three-masted windjammer of about 1500 tons. Stacks of timber lined the decks, stamped with the names of Norwegian lumber yards.

The crew's clothing, aged and worn, bore Norwegian labels. Pictures of the King and Queen of Norway hung on the saloon and cabin walls. And among the crew's effects were family snapshots of home towns and villages, with letters from relatives in Norway. Even the captain's underwear was embroidered: Captain Knudsen of the *Maletta*.

But behind the elaborate façade lay one of the most daring wartime ploys of all time. The *Maletta*, alias the *Walter*, alias the *Hero*, was in fact the *Seeadler* ('Sea Eagle'), a warship of the Imperial German Navy.

Its mission: to run the British blockade in the North Sea, head south through the Atlantic and attack Allied shipping in the Pacific. For during the First World War the Germans were convinced the only way to beat the British was by cutting her trade routes. Warships proved too expensive, so merchant ships were armed and set against merchant ships.

These commerce raiders achieved successes, but British surveillance was constantly improving, and by 1916 the blockade was highly effective.

Then the German Admiralty realised they had a near-perfect secret weapon in their possession . . . a sailing ship, the *Pass of Balmaha*, built in Glasgow in 1888 and captured by a U-boat in 1915. The innocent-looking vessel was fitted with auxiliary engines and two 4·2 in. guns

concealed by foldaway railings, and re-named *Seeadler*. She was given a largely Norwegian-speaking German crew of 57 men and six officers, and put under the command of Count Felix von Luckner.

The deck of the wardroom was mounted on a hydraulic lift so that, at the touch of a button, the officers could disappear to the deck below and attempt to re-take the ship should she be boarded and captured. The ship was riddled with secret passages and compartments, including quarters for prisoners.

Von Luckner, meanwhile, took a job as a longshoreman in Copenhagen, where a Norwegian ship called the *Maletta* was unloading a cargo of wheat. He studied the vessel, a three-master like *Seeadler*, and managed to steal the ship's log.

Seeadler was now renamed the *Maletta*. Her forged papers even included a letter from a British naval officer warning of the dangers of German raiders. If *Seeadler* were boarded, seaman Hugo Schmidt was to play Jeanette, Captain Knudsen's wife—wearing powder, wig and padding.

On December 23, 1916, *Seeadler* ran the British blockade and a hurricane-force gale without incident. South of Iceland she was boarded and given clearance by a British inspection party—then off she sailed into the Atlantic.

First strike

On January 9 *Seeadler* made her first strike. The target was a British freighter, the 3628 ton *Gladys Royal*, taking coal to Buenos Aires.

Norwegian flags flying, *Seeadler* moved in using her auxiliary engines to increase manoeuvrability. Deception was neces-

'SEA EAGLE' UNDER SAIL *Despite her innocent appearance she was a warship of the Imperial German Navy, fitted with 4·2 in. guns and auxiliary engines. Below decks she was riddled with secret passages.*

BORN ADVENTURER *Count von Luckner. He masqueraded as a Norwegian.*

THE END OF A RAIDER *The* Seeadler *lies dismasted and smashed on a reef at the Pacific Island of Mopeha in 1917 after being hit by a freak wave.*

sary until the last instant before attack—to prevent the possibility of a detailed radio message being sent by the victim. As the British ship came within range, von Luckner gave the order.

Down came the Norwegian flag and up went the black, white and red ensign of the Imperial German Navy. The breakaway railing on the port side went clattering to the deck and the 4·2 in. gun slid out. A shell was fired across the bows of the *Gladys Royal* and von Luckner sent a prize crew aboard.

At dusk, when von Luckner considered it safe to do so, the 26 man crew of the *Gladys Royal* was moved to the sailing ship. The *Gladys Royal* was then sunk with explosive charges.

The next day, *Seeadler* brought her complement of prisoners to 50, capturing and scuttling the *Lundy Island*, a 3095 ton steam freighter from West Hartlepool, carrying a cargo of sugar.

From January 21 to March 21, *Seeadler* captured and sank ten more vessels. Altogether a total of 40,000 tons of Allied shipping had been destroyed.

Von Luckner treated his prisoners courteously, toasting them in champagne and sometimes allowing the captured officers the freedom of his ship. The only casualty was an American officer, who died of his wounds after von Luckner opened fire on the freighter *Horngacth*.

Eventually, *Seeadler* could hold no more prisoners. Von Luckner decided to transfer all his captives to a French sailing ship, the *Cambronne*, while he headed for the Pacific.

The *Cambronne* reached Rio and, as von Luckner had anticipated, alerted the British. Cruisers were sent after *Seeadler*. But even then it was not the British Navy that ended the *Seeadler*'s career.

In August 1917, von Luckner stopped at the island of Mopeha, in the Pacific, to take on rations. While he and the crew were ashore, a freak wave swept in and wrecked *Seeadler* on the island's reefs.

Von Luckner refused to accept defeat. He set off with a party of five in one of *Seeadler*'s 18 ft motor cutters to try to capture another ship. After a long and arduous journey, the mission ended at last when the Germans were captured in the Fiji Islands by the crew of a British steamer.

FORCES' FAVOURITES

The story of Black Radio

The forces' radio station Gustav Siegfried Eins—GS1—had a special appeal to German troops during the Second World War. As well as its excellent news coverage and highly popular disc-jockey programmes, the station also mounted its own outspoken crusades on behalf of the ordinary soldier. The troops quickly discovered they could learn a great deal from these broadcasts by reading between the lines.

There was the time, for example, when GS1 launched a bitter condemnation of profiteering 'while our brave troops are freezing to death in Russia'. To soldiers who dreaded a posting to Russia, the profiteering was unimportant; what mattered was the official confirmation of winter conditions on the Eastern Front.

Again, the station inspired more disquiet than admiration when it praised the skill of doctors at camps housing civilians bombed out of German cities. Dedicated work had reduced the cholera and typhus death rate to an average of only 60 a week, the troops were told.

The outspokenness that made Gustav Siegfried Eins so popular was adopted by two later stations—Atlantiksender and Soldatensender Calais—broadcasting to German forces in Occupied Europe. However, their patriotism sometimes tended to create trouble for commanders.

One topic which regularly roused the wrath of the broadcasters was desertion. They deplored in detail the methods used by disillusioned soldiers to enter neutral countries when they were on the run.

Nevertheless, there was sympathy for listeners with genuine reasons for wanting to leave their posts. Bulletins kept them informed of the extent of Allied raids on Germany, and men with families in the bombed cities were advised how to apply for compassionate leave.

The information contained in the broadcasts was always confirmed by the forces' newspaper *News for the Troops*, delivered to the front by air.

Truth and falsehood

These services for the German soldier were not provided by the Wehrmacht, however. Radio stations and newspaper were both the brainchildren of Allied Intelligence. The radio stations, based in England, were so powerful that they drowned out real forces' broadcasts. They owed their success as propaganda instruments to a careful blending of truth and falsehood, which was used to play upon the anxieties of soldiers far from home.

News for the Troops, which closely resembled a real German forces' paper, was dropped each night by British aircraft. It too followed a similar policy of interlarding truth with fiction.

Goebbels, head of the German propaganda machine, admitted that the fake information service gave him a lot to worry about. But as one propagandist to another, he paid the supreme compliment. The service's hints on sabotage, desertion and dodging-the-column were translated into English, and dropped by the Germans behind the British and American lines.

THE FORGER WHO HAD TO PROVE IT

IT WAS most embarrassing for Parisian Jean de Sperati. The French Customs had intercepted a consignment of postage stamps he was sending to a Lisbon dealer, and accused him of evading export duties. At his trial in 1942, Dr Edmond Locard, the country's leading criminologist, gave evidence that the stamps were extremely rare, and suggested a value of Fr. 223,400 (about £20,000). Only de Sperati knew that the stamps were worthless forgeries he had printed himself. To avoid being convicted, he had to prove the stamps were counterfeit and so not subject to tax. He confessed that he had been a successful stamp forger for more than 30 years. On this occasion he was acquitted, but in 1952 was sentenced to two years' jail for fraud. His advanced years, however, saved him from serving the sentence. Ironically, collectors now prize his forgeries for themselves, and they are worth thousands of pounds.

THE MONEY-MAKERS

Prisoners who produced £140 million in cash

A few days after the German surrender in 1945, a lorry loaded with notes worth £21 million was handed over to US counter-espionage officers. More notes were reported floating in the Enns River in Austria.

A Bank of England official flew to Frankfurt to examine them and pieced together the amazing story of Operation Bernhard, a gigantic Nazi hoax that almost wrecked Britain's economy.

For almost two years during the war an alarming number of near-perfect forgeries, in batches of £100,000, had appeared in London from Zurich, Lisbon, Stockholm and other neutral cities. The Bank believed a gang was responsible but the capture in Edinburgh of a German spy carrying some of the finest forgeries ever seen, convinced the experts that they were up against the German government.

Until the lorryload of notes the Bank had no lead, but now the German officer in charge of the lorry said that he had been given the money by an SS man near Redl Zipf, Austria. There, in a mountain tunnel, officials found presses and machinery—but no plates, paper or records.

Operation Bernhard, named after Major Bernhard Kruger who directed it, was the brainchild of Gestapo chief Himmler. The aim was to break Britain's economy but Reichsbank civil servants rebelled at the idea of forgery.

So Kruger recruited engravers and printers from concentration camps. They were promised preferential treatment, sworn to secrecy and put to work at Sachsenhausen Camp near Berlin.

Plates were made and the Bank of England's paper was reproduced. The first batch of forged notes was sent to Gestapo agents in neutral countries. Banks accepted them without question.

When the tide of battle turned against Germany, Himmler decided to wind up the operation, but Kruger persuaded him to move it into the Alps. He argued that the forgers could provide escaping Nazis with forged money and documents.

By the time the move was completed, the Allies were closing in. The plates were destroyed but the forgers could not bring themselves to dispose of Kruger's hoard of notes. It was these that were found in the lorries, on their way to be buried for later recovery.

The Bank of England calculated that Kruger's operation had produced almost 9 million notes—about £140 million. For a time, some were found on the black market but no one ever found Major Bernhard Kruger.

THE SECRET OF DR JAMES BARRY

DR JAMES BARRY, a retired army surgeon, died in London on July 25, 1865, at the age of 73. Throughout his long and distinguished career, spent mainly in the West Indies, South Africa and India, he had been a popular and efficient officer. In his younger days, his dashing good looks had gained him the reputation of being something of a lady's man, and on one occasion it was said he had quarrelled with a brother-officer over a woman and fought a duel with him.

It was only on his death that the amazing truth about Dr Barry was discovered.

Dr Barry was a woman. Not only that, a post-mortem examination revealed that, at some time in youth, Dr Barry had given birth to a child.

To this day, the true identity of Dr Barry remains a mystery. In 1808, at the age of 16, she had been accepted as a medical student at Edinburgh University in the name of James Barry. Even in student days, apparently, no one had suspected that Barry was a girl.

It seems possible that, disillusioned by being jilted early in her life, she decided to spend the rest of her days as a man.

What happened to the child is another secret which she took with her to the tomb. This, in the absence of any other information, was inscribed with the name she had borne through most of her life—Dr James Barry.

THE ACADEMIC HOAXER
He caused the repainting of a submarine fleet

Reginald Jones, professor of natural philosophy at Aberdeen University and scientific adviser to successive British governments, is one of the world's most successful practical jokers. His feats range from persuading a distinguished academic to drop his telephone into a bucket of water to tricking German bombers on to a wrong flight path.

When Jones was a research fellow at Oxford in the 1930s, he telephoned an eminent doctor of philosophy several times and hung up as soon as he got an answer. Then he called again, this time as a telephone engineer reporting a fault on the line. When the victim agreed that there must be one, Jones suggested that 'a leak to earth' was the cause. His victim co-operated in all sorts of suggested remedies—from tapping the phone with his fountain pen to standing on one leg and hitting the receiver with a rubber. Finally, Jones talked the man into lowering the phone into a bucket of water.

Professor Jones's jokes are never malicious, and have sometimes been of value to his country. When he worked for Air Ministry Intelligence during the war, he discovered that the Germans were using directional beams from the Continent to guide their bombers on to British targets.

A less original scientist would have jammed the beams, but Jones had one signal duplicated and sent out from London. The result was that the German planes went off course and dropped their bombs on to empty fields.

Another of Jones's wartime hoaxes concerned a navigational device called H2S, which helped Allied bombers to seek out U-boats. The Germans realised that the RAF had something new, but Jones put them off the scent. He 'invented' an infra-red beam to locate submarines and made sure that news of it was fed to the enemy. The entire U-boat fleet was repainted with special paint to counteract the non-existent rays.

A LICENCE TO PRINT MONEY
Forgery on the grand scale

It was the most fantastic fraud in Portuguese history. Two hundred thousand counterfeit banknotes—each to the value of 500 Escudos, about £5—flooded the country, and they were perfect in every detail.

The man who planned this gigantic swindle was Arthur Virgilio Alves Reis, an official in Portugal's colonial service. Reis first practised the art of forgery when he obtained a job as an engineer in Angola, by presenting a diploma from the non-existent 'Oxford University Polytechnic'.

In 1924 he learnt that some of the Bank of Portugal's notes were printed by the British firm of Waterlow and Sons. Out of this, and his discovery that the bank had no procedure for checking for duplicate notes, his plan was born.

He chose three confederates—Karel Marang van Ysselveere, a Dutch merchant; José Bandeira, brother of the Portuguese Minister to the Hague; and Gustav Hennies, a German businessman.

Marang and Bandeira began as innocent dupes. Reis told them he had authority to arrange a loan for Angola, and showed them an official-looking contract.

The contract bore the forged signatures of the High Commissioner of Angola and the Portuguese Minister of Finance. The men were impressed, and agreed to assist Reis on a commission basis.

Karel Marang travelled to London to negotiate the printing of the notes with Sir William Waterlow. He took the contract with him, together with a letter of introduction from José Bandeira's brother. He explained to Sir William that for political reasons the printing of the notes had to be kept secret. Sir William said that he understood, but would need authorisation from the Governor of the Bank of Portugal. Marang assured him that the necessary papers would be dispatched from Lisbon immediately.

During the next few weeks a series of imposing documents arrived at the offices of Waterlow and Sons. A letter from the

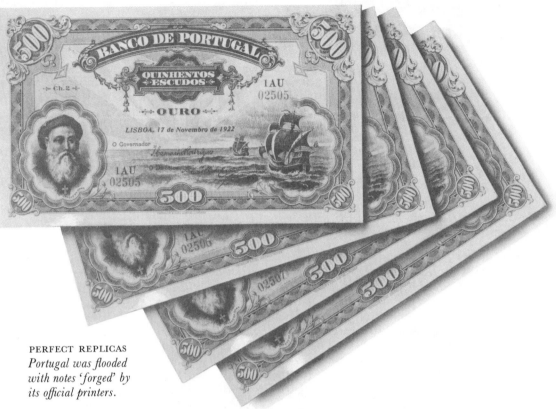

PERFECT REPLICAS
*Portugal was flooded
with notes 'forged' by
its official printers.*

Governor of the Bank of Portugal, contracts signed by the High Commissioner of Angola and prominent Portuguese bankers—all brilliantly forged by Reis.

The letter from the governor explained that, as the notes would be circulated only in Angola, they could be printed on the same plates and with the same serial numbers as a previous issue.

Sir William was told that the Bank of Angola would overprint the word 'Angola' on the new notes to avoid confusion.

When the notes had been printed they were passed to Marang, who took them to Lisbon. There were no problems with the customs officials, for Marang was also the Consul-General of Persia at the Hague—with diplomatic immunity.

Reis opened accounts in the branch offices of the big banks, and later made withdrawals at other branches. He exchanged the counterfeit notes for foreign currency, bought blocks of shares in industrial concerns, and within months had built his assets into a financial empire. Finally, he became so powerful that he opened his own bank—the Bank of Angola and Metropole.

But by June 1925 the increase of 500 Escudo notes in circulation gave rise to rumours of counterfeiting, and the Bank

of Portugal started an investigation. The counterfeit notes passed all forgery tests, but when inspectors raided the Oporto branch of the Bank of Angola and Metropole they found packets of new notes bearing the same serial numbers as some already in circulation.

Arrested, but undaunted

The game was up, and Reis was arrested. Even then he fabricated documents which suggested that the Governor of the Bank of Portugal and some of the directors were responsible for the fraud, and that he was a victim of a political plot. So convincing were the documents that they delayed his trial for five years.

But in May 1930 he was tried and found guilty on his own confession, and sentenced to 20 years' imprisonment. Bandeira was also jailed for 20 years. Hennies fled to Germany, where he died in 1936, and Marang was tried in the Hague and sentenced to 11 months' jail for 'receiving stolen property'.

Reis was released from jail in 1945. An attempt to enter Brazil was refused, and he returned to Portugal. Reis died of a heart attack in 1955, aged 59—so poor that he asked to be buried in a bedsheet so that his son could inherit his only suit.

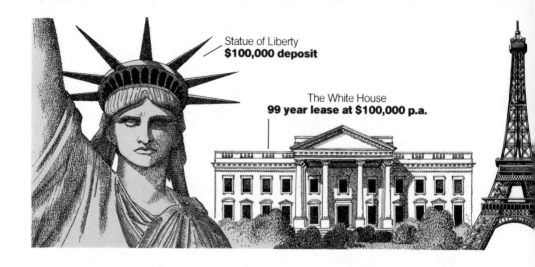

Statue of Liberty
$100,000 deposit

The White House
99 year lease at $100,000 p.a.

EVERYTHING HAS ITS PRICE

For sale—Big Ben and the Statue of Liberty

Arthur Furguson was a Scotsman with phenomenal selling ability though, like many another genius, he was unaware of the fact until one blinding moment when opportunity and inspiration combined. Furguson's moment occurred in Trafalgar Square one sunny morning in the 1920s. The source of his inspiration was a rich American from Iowa, whom he discovered gazing reverently at Nelson's Column.

Furguson appointed himself temporary guide to the square. The statue on the column was, he explained, that of Admiral Lord Nelson, England's greatest hero. Such a shame, he mused. The place would not be the same without it. But Britain's debts were soaring and it had to go— column, statue, lions and fountains.

The American was sympathetic, and inquired the price. A mere £6000, sighed Furguson. Of course, it would have to be the right buyer—someone who would appreciate these great monuments of Britain's former glory.

By an odd coincidence, it was Furguson himself who had been entrusted with the sad task of making the sale, which had to be kept secret.

The American begged Furguson to help him jump the queue, and at last he consented to telephone his superiors for instructions. He returned within minutes. It was agreed. Britain was prepared to accept a cheque right away and complete the whole deal without further delay. Ever anxious to help, Furguson gave his client the name and address of a reliable firm who would dismantle the square ready for shipping.

The American handed him a cheque, the receipt was presented and the men parted company. Furguson immediately cashed the cheque while his customer got in touch with the contractors. They were reluctant to accept the job and told him why. But it was not until he had received an assurance from Scotland Yard that the buyer would believe he had been duped.

That summer season in London was a happy one for Arthur Furguson. The police, however, were not so pleased; one American complained that he had paid £1000 for Big Ben, while another bewailed the fact that he had made a £2000 down-payment on Buckingham Palace and had been unable to complete the purchase.

It all led Furguson to the conclusion that since Americans had been his best customers, he should continue his operations in their country.

Westward Ho!

In 1925 he went to Washington, where he leased the White House to a cattle rancher for 99 years at the give-away price of $100,000 a year—the first year's rental payable in advance.

Furguson's nest egg was now sufficiently large for him to begin considering retirement. But vanity would not allow him to slip quietly from the scene without some truly grand finale to his career.

He found his ideal victim—an Australian from Sydney—and Furguson soared to new heights of inventiveness. New York harbour was to be widened and the Statue of Liberty was in the way. Mere sentimental attachment could not be allowed to impede the march of progress, and the Government was prepared to sell the monument to anyone willing to take it away.

Eiffel Tower
—sold for scrap, price unknown

Big Ben
£1000

Buckingham Palace
£2000 down payment

Nelson's Column
£6000 including lions

The Australian spent the next few days trying to raise the $100,000 deposit from Sydney. Furguson never left his side, keeping him well away from anyone to whom he might be tempted to boast of the bargain he had made. But as a souvenir of the deal, Furguson kindly allowed himself to be photographed arm in arm with his buyer in front of the Statue of Liberty—soon to be his property.

There was a delay in getting the money through, and Furguson grew impatient—and the Australian suspicious. Finally, he took the photograph to the police. Here was the break the police wanted. They certainly knew about the super-salesman of great monuments, but until then he had always managed to escape them.

The Australian led them straight to the hapless Furguson, who was promptly arrested. He was jailed for five years, a small price to pay for the fortune he had made. He was released in 1930 and moved to Los Angeles, where he lived in luxury—paid for by a string of new confidence tricks—until his death in 1938.

THE MAN WHO SOLD THE EIFFEL TOWER

It seemed the chance of the century

Count Victor Lustig, a high official in the ministry responsible for public buildings, explained to the five Paris business men in his office that the Eiffel Tower was to be scrapped. The costs of its maintenance were enormous, and its preservation was no longer considered practical. The tower would amount to at least 7000 tons of high-grade iron, and the five men—scrap-metal merchants—were invited to submit sealed bids for the sale.

The bids arrived promptly, and the following day André Poisson, a self-made man of substance, was informed that his offer had been successful.

Within a week, Poisson had raised the money, and the final meeting was arranged. But why, he asked, were such important negotiations being carried out in an hotel and not at the ministry?

The Count ordered his American secretary, Dan Collins, from the room and explained: 'The life of a Government official is not easy. We must entertain, dress in fashion—yet all on pitifully small salaries. In letting a Government con-tract, it is customary for the official in charge to receive. . . .' Poisson understood at once; obviously such a suggestion, however delicately put, could not be made within the ministry's walls. He willingly handed over his certified cheque together with a wallet bulging with bank-notes, and left, triumphantly clutching the deed of sale.

Within an hour, the cheque was cashed—Lustig never revealed how much he had made—and he and Collins were sitting grinning at each other in a first-class compartment in the Vienna express.

Lustig, born in Bohemia, the son of a highly respected citizen, and Collins, a small-time American crook, stayed in one of Vienna's best hotels for a month, studying the Paris newspapers. But there was no report of the swindle.

The buyer, too embarrassed to report the hoax, had left the field clear for Lustig and Collins to sell the tower again. They did, but this time the victim went to the police. Although Lustig and Collins were never caught, the publicity almost certainly prevented a third sale.

EVEN CRIME IS COMPUTERISED

Tricksters with ultra-modern tools

For non-technical people, the computer is an incomprehensible mystery. But with its help experts have committed some highly successful frauds. Computers can be valuable and obedient accomplices.

An employee of a large bank in Minneapolis ordered the bank's computer to ignore all the cheques he drew on his own account. His fraud was discovered when the computer broke down and the bank was forced to revert to human accounting.

A Boston bank employee replaced the blank paying-in slips on the bank's counters with forms bearing his own account number. Ignoring the name and address on the form, the computer credited all these deposits to the employee's account.

Another American bank employee programmed the bank's computer to shave 10 cents off every account and add it to the last account on the books. Since customers' names were listed alphabetically, he then opened an account under an assumed name beginning with 'Z' and all went well until a Mr Zydel opened an account. He noticed that his balance kept inexplicably increasing. Being an honest man, he reported this, and inquiries exposed the fraud.

A large catering firm in London received a series of bills from a company in Tooting for supplies of smoked salmon and shellfish. The food never arrived, but the computer had paid £50,000

before a clerk noticed the unusual account number and checked to see that all was well. The thieves—one man in each of the companies—had programmed the computer to accept bills and make payments. Had they used an existing account number with a false name and address they might have avoided discovery.

The most successful computer crime arose after a big chemical combine, with its headquarters in London, decided to control the accounting for its three major divisions by means of a central computer system. The computer revealed that one division was selling chemicals to another division at the full market price, although the buying department should have been claiming a 40 per cent discount for bulk buying.

With this information, the chief programmer and the head of the buying department set up a fictitious subsidiary. This new branch bought all the chemicals at full discount and on extended credit terms. They then resold the supplies to the parent company at full price and on immediate-payment terms, and made a profit of £150,000 in two and a half years. Soon they were supplying 50 outside customers as well.

By the time the subsidiary was unmasked, it was undercutting the combine so efficiently that the executives who had originated the idea were employed as fee-earning consultants, to advise on the running of the once fraudulent operation.

THE BEST-LAID PLANS . . .

THE DREAM of every gambler is to know the result of a horse race before it starts. Politician Horatio Bottomley, himself a racehorse owner, hit on an audacious scheme to make this dream come true shortly before the First World War. The plan was simple: not only would he back every horse in a particular race, he would also own every horse and make sure that they finished in the right order.

Bottomley chose Belgium for his coup because racing rules there were not as strict as in Britain. He engaged six English jockeys to ride his team of horses at Blankenberg, a seaside town where the racecourse veered alongside the shore, and sand dunes sometimes obscured the horses.

The jockeys were given strict instructions—and Bottomley's associates in England laid heavy bets on the exact finishing order. But disaster struck midway through the race when thick sea mist swept over the course and the jockeys got hopelessly out of touch with each other. They crossed the finishing line in a jumble—and Bottomley's 'coup' cost him a fortune.

MADAME HUMBERT'S HALFPENNY

The story of an elusive inheritance

Thérèse Humbert, daughter-in-law of the French Minister of Justice, was a beautiful woman famed as much for the extravagance of her spending as for the parties that made her the most successful hostess in Paris. In eight weeks in 1897 she spent £1000 on flowers; and £4000 was by no means too much for her to pay for gowns in a season.

Born Thérèse Aurignac, the daughter of a hard-drinking peasant from the village of Bauzelles, near Toulouse, she later married the son of the Mayor of Toulouse, much to the consternation of his parents. Shortly afterwards, Madame Humbert claimed she had inherited a vast fortune in unusual circumstances.

In 1879, while sitting in a suburban train, she heard groans from the next compartment. While the train was still moving she climbed along the outside of the carriage and found Robert Henry Crawford, an American, suffering a heart attack. She made him comfortable and administered smelling salts. Crawford, sure that she had saved his life, took her name and address.

Two years later, Thérèse received a letter from Crawford's lawyers in New York enclosing a copy of his will in which she was named as a beneficiary. The other heirs were Thérèse's schoolgirl sister, Marie, and Crawford's two American nephews, Robert and Henry. Under the will, Henry Crawford was to marry Marie when she left school to keep the fortune in the family. Until the wedding, Thérèse was to guard the inheritance in a safe.

Raising a loan with the inheritance as security, Thérèse and her husband Frederic moved into a luxurious mansion in Paris's Avenue de la Grande Armée. To repay her loans, Thérèse Humbert raised larger loans at higher rates of interest.

In 1883 a newspaper article was published casting doubts on the existence of the Crawford fortune, although as Thérèse's father-in-law, by this time Minister of Justice, had himself publicly discussed the inheritance, considerable weight was lent to her story.

Shortly after the publication of the article, Thérèse announced that she had quarrelled with the Crawford family, who had started a lawsuit to enforce her to lodge the fortune with Credit Lyonnais. She eventually won the case and considerable public sympathy, the final judgment stating that the locked safe should remain in her keeping.

But after a casual conversation with Jules Bizat, a high official of the Bank of France, Thérèse found herself once again in trouble. Bizat asked Thérèse how the inheritance was invested. She replied that it was in Government Securities. Bizat checked with the bank to find out whether the securities had been cashed to collect the interest due. None had been cashed.

Confidence shattered

Thérèse Humbert then floated an insurance scheme called the Rente Viagère, which was so attractive that investors flocked to deposit thousands of pounds every day. Thérèse promptly withdrew the money to pay for her loans and buy enough Government Securities to allay the fears of her anxious creditors. But the confidence of the creditors was finally shattered when they calculated that the lawsuits with the Crawfords would have taken most of the inheritance, leaving too little to cover her expenditure.

The newspaper *Le Matin* again took up the story and called, in a series of scathing articles, for the opening of the safe. In 1902 Madame Humbert's creditors sued her, and the court ordered the safe to be opened.

Inside, they found a brick and an English halfpenny. Thérèse Humbert's story had been a hoax. The Crawfords had never existed. Accomplices—her brothers —had brought the lawsuit and posed as the Americans.

But by this time, Thérèse and her family had disappeared. Detectives searched the world and, finally, they were run to earth and arrested in Madrid in December 1902.

Returned to Paris for trial, Thérèse was imprisoned for five years. Her two brothers were sentenced to two and three years each. Frederic had died some years earlier, and the Minister of Justice and Marie had been innocent dupes.

The empty safe went on show for a year in a shop window in the Rue Blanche in Paris. The 20-year swindle was over.

THE ANCESTRESS OF MAN

Whose skull at Piltdown?

From the moment that Charles Darwin published his *Origin of Species*, in 1859, the entire scientific world was intrigued by the search for the 'missing link' that would prove his theory.

Darwin argued powerfully that men and apes were descended from a common ancestor. If so, said his critics, then why had no fossils of this creature ever been found? Because, replied his supporters, men simply have not looked hard enough.

It took 50 years of searching, but in 1912 the Darwinites· were triumphant. From a gravel pit near Piltdown Common, in East Sussex, were unearthed fragments of bone and teeth from a creature that seemed to be half man and half ape, and roamed the earth half a million years ago.

Respected lawyer

The discoverer was Charles Dawson, a highly respected lawyer, amateur geologist and fossil hunter from Lewes, the county town of East Sussex.

Dawson sent his first Piltdown finds— prehistoric flint tools, fossilised teeth and a fragment of unusually thick human skull—to his contact at the British Museum, the palaeontologist Dr Arthur Smith Woodward. And so excited was Woodward that he wasted little time in travelling down to Sussex to join Dawson at the gravel pit. It was the beginning of one of the most spectacularly successful partnerships in the history of excavation.

When, near to where the skull had lain, Dawson discovered the jaw of an ape, he and Woodward could hardly contain their excitement. For the teeth were worn in a way which, it seemed, could only be produced by the rotary action of a human jaw. Here were all the requirements for a missing link—a creature with the brain of a man, and the ability to use tools, but the appearance of an ape.

Painstaking reconstruction

With painstaking care, the experts reconstructed Piltdown Man's life story. He should, as it happened, have been called Piltdown Woman, for the remains were those of a female—and moreover, a dumb one; there was no ridge on the skull to anchor the speech muscles. From the way the teeth were worn, observed Dr Wood-

ward, she could only have been vegetarian.

The idea of a non-talking female was irresistible to a suffragette-conscious public. The *Daily Express* said: 'She could not cook. She could not talk. She could not wash. She could not light a fire.'

Highest honour

That sort of ridicule meant little to Dawson, for he was about to receive the highest honour in science—outranking even the Nobel Prize. Dr Woodward, with the authority of the British Museum, decided to name Piltdown Man after its discoverer. It went into the records—and posterity—as *Eoanthropus dawsoni*—Dawson's Dawn Man.

And still Dawson's luck held. Teeth, bones and tools turned up at the gravel pit for the next three years, and in 1915 Dawson found the teeth and skull fragments of a second Piltdown man in a field 2 miles from the pit. All of these fragments were deeply stained, as if they had been buried for untold centuries.

Dawson died in 1916, aged 52, and the finds ceased. Woodward carried on digging for five more years, then gave up.

MONKEY BUSINESS *A reconstruction of the skull of 'Dawn Man', with the stained jaw compared with those of an ape (top) and man.*

But rumbles of dissent began as early as 1913, when David Waterston, Professor of Anatomy at King's College, London, claimed that the Piltdown jaw was practically identical with that of a chimpanzee.

The American palaeontologist William Howells was also to take a sceptical view, and there was also a disturbing story about the visitor who one day had walked into Dawson's office without knocking, and found him busy staining bones in a crucible. But most experts agreed that the skull and jaw belonged together; and the fragments were jealously guarded from doubters who would have scraped and probed at them.

Fluoride and the tooth test

It was not until 1949 that a young geologist at the museum, Dr Kenneth Oakley, was allowed to take minute samples from the bones and date them by a new chemical test. When bones lie buried they absorb fluoride from water in the ground, and the amount absorbed is a good indication of how long they have been buried.

Dr Oakley's tests showed that the skull and jawbone were a mere 50,000 years old. The idea of a missing link alive at the same time as the far more advanced Neanderthal Man raised nagging doubts.

One man who did something about

those doubts was Dr J. S. Weiner, an anthropologist at Oxford University. He tried to isolate all of the factors that made Piltdown Man so unlikely: a thick human skull and human teeth in an ape-like jaw, worn flat as if they had been filed. That was the answer!

Taking a chimpanzee tooth, Weiner filed and stained it, producing almost an exact replica of a Piltdown tooth. Dr Oakley helped him with further tests on the Piltdown fragments in 1953, and results proved conclusively that although the skull was a genuine fossil, the jaw was a cunningly stained fake. It belonged to a modern orang-utan, and the teeth had been filed down before staining.

The hoaxer has never been positively identified, but everything points to Dawson. He had access to fossils and enough knowledge of anatomy and chemistry to fake and stain the fragments found at Piltdown. There were no further discoveries after his death. And Dawson was the only man in the entire hoax with anything to gain. He did not need money, but Piltdown Man brought something which he valued far higher—fame.

Or did he begin simply with the idea of pulling the dignified leg of the British Museum, then lose his nerve when the joke thrust him into the limelight?

PALAEONTOLOGICAL LEG-PULL *A group of experts examine the 'historical find'. Dawson stands third from right, and on his left is Dr Arthur Smith Woodward of the British Museum, who followed up the find. The group portrait was made in 1915 to mark the occasion.*

THE BOY WHO WROTE SHAKESPEARE

'When this solemn mockery is o'er'

Drury Lane Theatre was packed to capacity on the night of April 2, 1796. Every available seat in the theatre had been booked and those who had paid for boxes, only to find the seats allocated several times over, scrambled over the lowest tier to fight for a place.

John Kemble, a renowned actor, was creating the role of Vortigern in a newly discovered play by William Shakespeare, *Vortigern and Rowena*, the love story of Vortigern, a British ruler, and Rowena, daughter of Hengist, leader of the Saxon invaders of Britain in 450.

The whole event, sensational as it was, would have been acknowledged as all the more extraordinary had the public then known that Shakespeare's play was, in fact, the work of 17-year-old William Henry Ireland.

Young Ireland, son of a London book engraver, was taken to Stratford-upon-Avon during his early teens. Greatly moved by this visit to Shakespeare's birthplace, he began his first few simple forgeries. On blank sheets of paper taken from Elizabethan folios, using ink artificially aged, he started with the Bard's autograph on a lease. He explained to his delighted father that a wealthy man he had met, knowing of the boy's interest in old papers, had given him documents handed down by his ancestors.

Encouraged by success

Encouraged by that success, in 1795 Ireland produced an original manuscript of *King Lear* and parts of *Hamlet*, both entirely in forged Elizabethan handwriting. Incredibly, experts and critics alike were willing to testify to the genuineness of the documents. Kneeling before them, James Boswell, biographer of Dr Johnson, said: 'I now kiss the invaluable relics of our bard, and thanks to God that I have lived to see them.'

When the idea of an entirely new play dawned on Ireland, he tried for several days to think of a suitable subject. Then, as he later described it, 'a large drawing executed by Mr S. Ireland (his father) representing Rowena in the act of presenting wine to Vortigern, which hung over the chimney-piece in Mr Ireland's study, suddenly attracted my attention'.

Rashly the boy mentioned that he had discovered the play before even a line had been written, and from then on his father persistently asked to see it.

Ireland was so ignorant about the length and form of a Shakespearian play, that he chose one at random and counted the lines. He did not name the play he used as a model, but it was unfortunate for him that it was unusually long, 2800 lines in all. In two months, the young forger produced a play of identical length. He claimed that he had copied it from the original.

When the dramatist Richard Sheridan read the play, he remarked: 'There are certainly some bold ideas, but they are crude and undigested. It is very odd: one would be led to think that Shakespeare must have been very young when he wrote the play. As to the doubting whether it be really his or not, who can possibly look at the papers, and not believe them ancient?'

Although he questioned the play's quality, he did not doubt its authenticity and bought it for £300 and a share of the profits from its production on the stage.

The leading actor, John Kemble, suspected that the play was a fraud, and tried unsuccessfully to have it staged on April Fool's Night. He did, finally, manage to have a play entitled *The Lie of the Day* included on the bill.

On the first night, Kemble was delivering a solemn monologue to Death:
And with rude laughter and fantastic tricks
Thou clapp'st thy rattling fingers to thy sides.
Then Kemble paused and spoke the next line in 'sepulchral tone of voice':
And when this solemn mockery is o'er . . .
The audience got the point. Reporting on the evening later, Ireland said there was a howl from the pit that lasted ten minutes. At last it died down and Kemble once more took the centre of the stage. Before ending the speech he repeated that line 'with a solemn grimace'.

The game was up for Ireland. The doubters came forward and Edmund Malone, a renowned Shakespearian expert, denounced *Vortigern* as a fraud. The run at Drury Lane was abruptly finished after the first, sensational, night.

His father was blamed for the forgeries

Shakespeare's real signature, on a document.

and Ireland confessed. But many people felt he was trying to protect his father, and Mr Ireland, himself, believed that William had made a false confession to shield some unknown culprit.

The boy stuck to his previous plan of writing Shakespearian plays covering every reign, from William the Conqueror to Elizabeth I. But his *Henry II* aroused no interest. He wrote several novels and poetry under his own name before he died in 1835. But only his forged Shakespearian plays are remembered, and are now on display in the British Museum.

THE LOUVRE'S GOLDEN FORGERY

Ancient tiara was only one year old

For seven years a priceless gold tiara held a prominent place in the Louvre. It had been found on the site of the town of Olbia, in southern Russia, and was inscribed in Greek: 'The Senate and People of Olbia to the Great Invincible Saitaphernes.'

The Louvre paid 200,000 francs for the tiara—£88,000 in today's values. It went on display on April 1, 1896.

It was in a remarkable state of preservation for an object believed to be 2200 years old. And so it should have been—it had been made only a few months earlier.

In 1895 Schapschelle Hochmann, a Rumanian wheat dealer, commissioned a goldsmith, Israel Rouchomovsky, to make a gold tiara in antique style.

Hochmann paid Rouchomovsky 2000 roubles (about £3500) for the work, took the tiara and—carefully so that the decorative panels would be undamaged—battered it to simulate age.

The tiara would still have been on display to this day, had not a Montmartre painter, known as Elina, falsely claimed to have created it. A friend of Rouchomovsky, living in Paris, who had seen the goldsmith fashioning the tiara, would not allow an unknown artist to steal the glory, so he exposed the fraud.

The once priceless work now appears only in rare Louvre exhibitions of fakes.

ETRUSCAN WITHOUT A THUMB

Italian gang made three mistakes in their forgery

The giant clay figure of an Etruscan warrior was more than 7 ft tall and weighed more than 1000 lb. It almost filled the room in which it had been created by three Italian sculptors.

Glaze and colouring were added to the figure, and the scaffolding surrounding it gently removed. Then the workmen stood back, admired their work—and pushed it over, smashing it on the floor.

Their next move was even stranger. They began to piece the fragments together again. The end result, with its cracks and scratches, was an Etruscan statue, which the Metropolitan Museum of Art in New York bought in 1918 for $40,000, then a fabulous sum.

And it was not until 40 years later that the museum learnt it had been hoaxed by forgers. The forging ring was begun by the brothers Pio and Alfonso Riccardi, and three of their six sons.

The Etruscans were a highly civilised people living in middle Italy, who were eventually conquered by the Romans and absorbed into their empire. Their relics, still being found today, are highly prized by museums and private collectors.

It was Pio's eldest son Riccardo who planned the giant statue, which became known as the Big Warrior—and it was not the first masterpiece to be created by the team. They began their career when Roman art dealer Domenico Fuschini hired them, first to forge fragments of Etruscan pottery and later complete vases.

Two-horse chariot

Having mastered the technique, the team then produced their first major forgery—a complete bronze chariot. In December 1908, the British Museum was told that a *biga*—a two-horse chariot—had been found on an Etruscan site at Orvieto, Italy. After its supposed burial of 2500 years it needed cleaning—and the museum was told the work was being carried out by the Riccardis.

The museum bought the chariot from

THE OLD WARRIOR *Cleverly fashioned after ancient models, the forgery is now listed in the Metropolitan Museum as '20th-century AD in style of 5th-century BC Etruscan work'. The severed thumb can clearly be seen.*

Fuschini, and officially announced its acquisition in 1912. The same year, the Riccardis moved their business from the outskirts of Rome to Orvieto. Pio died soon afterwards.

But the Riccardis—helped by a master sculptor called Alfredo Fioravanti—were quickly back at work, this time on a statue called the Old Warrior. The figure, which stands 6 ft 7½ in. high, wears a plumed helmet, a breastplate, and armour on its calves. It is naked from breastplate to knees, and the right arm and left thumb are missing. The forgers had argued about the positioning of the right arm so much, that, in the end, they discarded it.

Once completed, the statue was sold to the Metropolitan Museum, which also acquired the gang's next major forgery— a piece called the Colossal Head, which was 4 ft 7 in. high from the neck to the top of its helmet. Experts who examined it later thought it formed part of a statue 23 ft high. The price for the two works amounted to only a few hundred dollars.

The next forgery was the Big Warrior —which was the last to be completed by the gang. Ricardo Riccardi was killed when he was thrown from a horse before the statue was completed. After the figure had been sold to the Metropolitan Museum, the gang split up.

Colour gives the clue

The museum put the three pieces on show in February 1933. Many Italian experts doubted their authenticity, but it was not until 1937, when the museum published a paper about them, that the conflict came into the open.

Even so, it was not until another 22 years passed that the museum began an inquiry into the allegations. After exhaustive tests, it was found that the glaze of the three pieces contained manganese —a colouring agent that was unknown in the Etruscan era, about 800 BC.

Vents for airing

But the museum authorities were still not convinced they had been hoaxed. The proof they sought came a year later, from experts who examined genuine Etruscan artefacts. They found that the Etruscans always made and 'baked' their pottery in one piece, and that to do so, vents were always left in statues to allow proper airing when they were in the kiln.

The Riccardis had made their statues in sections and had not left any vents— a mistake which showed the statues to be clever fakes.

But it was left to Alfredo Fioravanti, the man who had helped make the statues, to put the issue beyond doubt. On January 5, 1960, the craftsman, who was then aged 75, went to the American consul in Rome and signed a confession.

And to prove he was telling the truth he took from his pocket the missing left thumb of the Old Warrior—a souvenir he had kept for more than 40 years.

THE COUNTERFEIT GENIUS
He produced masterpieces to order

Most forgers of fine art are masters of one particular style or material. The forger who fakes a passable Matisse will usually bungle an imitation of another artist. But not Alceo Dossena.

Dossena was an Italian restorer of broken statuary who, in 1916, turned his remarkable talents to forgery. He produced fake sculptures, in styles ranging from ancient Greek statuary to Gothic figures in wood. He could work in stone, bronze and terracotta.

So prodigious were Dossena's talents, that art critics and connoisseurs often found his imitations superior to the genuine article. Dossena's artistic efforts in the style of Simone Martini (c. 1283–1344) were particularly remarkable. Martini was a painter, but never, so far as was known, a sculptor. Dossena studied his painting of 'The Annunciation', and translated the portrait into a seated Madonna in wood. Experts acclaimed it as a major discovery, and art historians hastily modified their lectures.

Part of Dossena's triumph was due to his skill in finding authentic materials and in ageing his pieces. Genuine Gothic wood sculpture, for instance, was often gilded or painted. To simulate this, Dossena soaked the paint from old but relatively worthless statuary and picture frames. He used the wood to create new statues and carefully re-applied the flecks of paint. To give his 'ancient' marble sculptures the appearance of antiquity, he dipped them in an acid formula whose composition he never revealed. This process produced a discoloration and hard-

MASTER HOAXER *Museums and galleries are still believed to display fake sculptures by Alceo Dossena, seen here modelling figures in clay.*

ness in depth which completely fooled the museums' experts.

In the 1920s, Dossena's fakes were displayed in the greatest museums and art collections of the Western world. Although suspicion was eventually aroused by the sheer volume of newly discovered masterpieces, no one suspected that they had all been created by a single artist. The Cleveland Museum of Art, for instance, owned a wooden 'Madonna and Child' in the style of Giovanni Pisano (*c.* 1245–1314) which had been carved by Dossena. In 1927, when the sculpture was X-rayed, 20th-century nails were revealed inside, causing it to be hastily removed from display. Then, in the very same month, another Dossena fake, a marble 'Athena', was bought by the same museum for $120,000.

When Dossena finally confessed to forging several famous sculptures, both dealers and museum consultants refused to believe him. In fact, even today, there are probably some of his works in galleries and collections which are still attributed to the Old Masters.

PRIDE GOES BEFORE A FRAUD
Medieval frescoes painted by a modern master

On September 2, 1951, Dietrich Fey, head of a firm of art restorers, proudly escorted the West German Chancellor, Konrad Adenauer, around the newly restored frescoes of the Marienkirche, in the Baltic port of Lübeck. It was the church's 700th anniversary.

Christians and art lovers throughout Germany celebrated the event, and the government issued 2 million postage stamps depicting the 'medieval' frescoes.

The following year when Lothar Malskat, an unknown artist from Königsberg, and a member of Fey's team, suddenly announced that the frescoes were entirely his own invention, nobody believed him.

Enraged by this slur on his artistic integrity, Malskat instructed his lawyer to file charges against himself and Fey. During their trial, the story emerged.

When the Marienkirche (the Evangelical Lutheran Church of St Mary) was damaged by an incendiary bomb in 1942, the peeling whitewash uncovered huge figures of saints on the walls of the nave.

The bomb destroyed the roof, and by the time it was replaced the frescoes had suffered from years of exposure, and only faint traces of the paintings remained.

The West German Association for the Preservation of Ancient Monuments gave £20,000 towards the cost of restoration and, despite a warning from the provincial curate that Fey could not be trusted, Fey's team was given the contract.

Fey and Malskat worked behind closed doors.

At their trial Malskat produced a film, revealing that the walls were almost bare when work was started. The frescoes had been done completely from Malskat's imagination.

Some of the figures were inspired by photographs of Marlene Dietrich, and by Malskat's sister, Frieda. Also depicted were Rasputin, the 'mad monk' of the tsar's court, and Genghis Khan, the Mongol 'scourge of God'—both wearing haloes.

The reason for Malskat's seemingly unnecessary confession was simple: it was

A CELEBRATED FRAUD
German authorities were so impressed by the 're-storation' of a church's frescoes by Lothar Malskat, that 2 million commemorative stamps were issued, depicting the paintings. Today the stamps are collectors' items, worth about £1000 per 100.

pride. Malskat was furious that Fey should receive the glory that belonged to him. Also, Fey became steadily richer, while Malskat's demands for a half-share in the profits from this and other forgeries were met with blank refusals.

Fey was sentenced to 20 months' imprisonment, while Malskat received only 18 months. But financially, Malskat was still the loser, although he did later manage to make an honest living.

He was commissioned to do imitation 14th-century decorations for a restaurant in Stockholm, and continued to paint in the Gothic, Romantic and Byzantine styles, of which he was master.

MONA LISAS TO ORDER

The day Leonardo's masterpiece was stolen

In 1911 no fewer than six Americans each paid $300,000 (then about £75,000) for the Mona Lisa, and each became the proud possessor of nothing more than a clever fake. All six paintings were the work of the master forger, Yves Chaudron.

What made the rich Americans believe they had the real thing was the fact that the Mona Lisa had been stolen that year from the Louvre, in Paris.

It was the culmination of a series of art forgeries which had begun at the turn of the century, all perpetrated by the self-styled Marquis Eduardo de Valfierno and his accomplice, Chaudron.

Valfierno had started his career by selling faked old masters to rich Argentinian widows. He offered them as memorial bequests which the widows could place in churches.

Chaudron, a former picture restorer, specialised in copies of paintings by the Spanish artist, Bartolomé Esteban Murillo.

When the pair had saturated Argentina with fake Murillos, they moved to Mexico City where Valfierno's sales technique was perfected.

First, Valfierno would sneak Chaudron's copy of a painting into the back of the frame of the original. Then, a prospective buyer would be taken to the gallery, shown the painting and, while no one was looking, would be urged to mark the back of the picture.

In this way, he was told, he would be sure that the painting eventually delivered to him was the one he had seen hanging. In fact, he would have marked the back of Chaudron's copy.

Valfierno also had a series of faked Press cuttings reporting the theft of various paintings, which he would send to his clients. The fact that the original was still hanging in the gallery he would explain away, by saying the authorities had put up a copy.

How much Valfierno made in this way is not clear, but it enabled the pair to depart for Paris.

Using the same techniques, Valfierno went to work on selling paintings 'stolen' from the Louvre. This time he would supply clients with forged documents on Louvre paper, including a confidential report that a masterpiece had been stolen and a copy substituted.

481

ENIGMA VARIATION *Confusion over the subject of the Louvre's portrait is complicated by the similarity of Mona Lisa del Giocondo's name to the nickname of Medici's mistress, 'La Gioconda'.*

After three years Valfierno, Chaudron and three confidence men with whom they had teamed up managed to convince an American that they could steal the Mona Lisa for him—and delivered to him one of Chaudron's clever copies.

This particular triumph made the gang so self-confident that they decided to sell a whole series of Mona Lisas—and to steal the original.

Valfierno recruited Vincenzo Perugia, an Italian small-time criminal, who had worked as a glazier on a protective glass box for the Mona Lisa. He knew exactly how the painting was hung.

On Monday, August 21, 1911, a day when the gallery was closed for cleaning, Perugia and two accomplices dressed as workmen. After spending the previous night hiding in a storeroom, they walked casually to the Salon Carré, took the 18 lb. portrait and walked out.

Over the next few months, six US buyers each surrendered $300,000, convinced they had the original.

But the gang did not make any money from the masterpiece itself. Perugia stole it from them and, in November 1913, offered to sell it to a Florentine art dealer. The dealer became suspicious, Perugia was caught and jailed and the painting was returned to the Louvre.

THE OTHER MONA LISA

A woman whose nickname was 'Smiler'

The face of the Mona Lisa smiles mysteriously down, not only from the wall of the Louvre, in Paris, but from the wall of a flat in Kensington, London. The latter is not a reproduction, says its custodian Dr Henry Pulitzer, but another version by the master himself, Leonardo da Vinci.

While there are more than 60 alleged Mona Lisas catalogued throughout the world, Dr Pulitzer, inventor, scientist and art connoisseur, is convinced of the authenticity of this other Mona Lisa.

Leonardo, he points out, habitually did two or more versions of his portraits. The original sitter was Mona Lisa del Giocondo, wife of a Florentine nobleman.

At the time she was mourning the death of her baby daughter, and wore a transparent veil during the sittings.

Leonardo spent four years on the portrait, and eventually left it with the Giocondos. Then, shortly before he went to France, at the invitation of Francis I, Guiliano de Medici asked him to paint a portrait of his current mistress, Constanza d'Avalos. Coincidentally, Constanza not only resembled Mona Lisa slightly, but also was nicknamed 'La Gioconda'—

PORTRAIT OF A PORTRAIT *This sketch, by Raphael, was made while Leonardo was still working on his masterpiece. Several features, such as the two columns, are similar to the painting (below) owned by a Swiss syndicate and kept by Dr Henry Pulitzer in his flat in Kensington, London.*

TOPLESS GIOCONDA *There are more than 60 alleged Mona Lisas on catalogue. This semi-nude portrait, 'La Belle Gabrielle', is in the collection of Lord Spencer of Althorpe, Northamptonshire, and is attributed to the school of Leonardo da Vinci.*

LONDON'S MONA LISA *This version bears fingerprints which match up with those on other authenticated paintings by Leonardo. It is thought to be of Mona Lisa del Giocondo, while the Louvre version is of Constanza d'Avalos, 'La Gioconda'.*

which means, approximately, 'Smiler'.

Leonardo adapted his alternative version of Mona Lisa del Giocondo's portrait, turning the face into that of Constanza.

But no sooner had he completed the

<hr>

TRADEMARKS OF A MASTER

ONE OF LEONARDO's trademarks was that he held his paintbrush in his left hand and sometimes smoothed in the paint with his right hand to achieve a particular effect. His fingerprints (above) show up clearly, and have become a recognised way of authenticating his work.

Experts have compared the fingerprints on a version of the Mona Lisa, jointly owned by a Swiss syndicate and London scientist Dr Henry Pulitzer, with those on other da Vinci paintings. The verdict was that the painting in the possession of Dr Pulitzer is an authentic Leonardo. The portrait, which bears a resemblance to that in the Louvre, is of Mona Lisa del Giocondo.

<hr>

work, than Medici dropped his mistress in favour of a profitable marriage and so did not buy the picture.

It was this second portrait, Dr Pulitzer says, which Leonardo took with him, along with all his other unsold works, to Paris. It is this version—of Constanza—Dr Pulitzer maintains, which graces the walls of the Louvre.

The other portrait—of Giocondo's wife, who was 19 years younger than 'La Gioconda'—stayed with the Florentine family until it eventually found its way to England, and was bought early this century by William Blaker, art connoisseur and curator of the Holburne of Menstrie Museum of Art, Bath, and more recently by a Swiss syndicate, of which Dr Pulitzer is a member.

Dr Pulitzer has had the painting examined by microscopic photography techniques, and says that fingerprints on the canvas match up with those on other authenticated works of Leonardo.

Another pointer to the painting's authenticity is a sketch by Raphael, made while Leonardo was still working on the portrait in his studio.

Raphael's sketch shows features, including two columns in the background, which are on the painting in London, but not on the version in the Louvre.

Also, the younger girl in the London portrait is wearing a fine, transparent veil of mourning.

REVENGE OF AN UNDERRATED ARTIST

How Van Meegeren ruined his critics' reputations

Crowds flocked to Rotterdam's Boymans Museum in 1937, to see its latest exhibit—'Christ and the Disciples at Emmaus'—painted by Jan Vermeer, the 17th-century Dutch master.

This was an important discovery. At that time only 36 other works by Vermeer were known. Dr Abraham Bredius, a renowned art authority and the man credited with its discovery, basked in the glory of his greatest moment.

Only one other man in the excited throng matched his happiness. He was Hans van Meegeren, and he alone could truly appreciate the subtlety of the painting's colour and composition—because he had painted the picture himself. This was Van Meegeren's special moment,

a time to savour his revenge on the so-called experts and critics whom he considered beneath contempt.

His hostility dated back to his early days when, as a highly promising painter in his own right, he had refused to bribe a corrupt critic to obtain a favourable review. Later, his work was savaged by the man and he was ignored by the critics in general.

In May 1945, after the fall of Nazi Germany, Hermann Goering's priceless collection of looted art treasures was found at Berchtesgaden, his home on the Obersalzburg, and hidden in a salt mine near Konigsee. There were 1200 paintings, among them 'Woman Taken in Adultery' signed by Vermeer. What dis-

FORGER'S MASTERPIECE *Hans van Meegeren's 'Christ and the Disciples at Emmaus', which he passed off as a Vermeer. He had spent four years learning how to age paintings artificially.*

tinguished it was the fact that it was one of the few paintings that Goering had not stolen. Someone in Amsterdam had sold it to Goering's agent for about £150,000.

The Dutch police followed an intricate trail that led them to Van Meegeren, then a wealthy night-club owner. His money had come from selling his collection of six Vermeers—five to Dutch museums, the sixth to Goering. Van Meegeren told police that he bought the painting from an Italian family and had sold it in good faith. How could he know it would eventually fall into Nazi hands?

The sceptical authorities were unimpressed. Van Meegeren was arrested and after three weeks in custody, under constant interrogation, and with the threat of execution for collaborating with the Germans, he cracked.

'Fools,' he yelled. 'You are like the rest of them. I sold no Vermeer to the Germans—only a Van Meegeren, painted to look like a Vermeer. I have not collaborated with the Germans, I have duped them.' More was to come.

He confessed to forging 14 Dutch masterpieces by Hals, Hooch and Vermeer, including 'Christ and the Disciples at Emmaus'. This sensation was enough to shake the reputation of Bredius and all the other connoisseurs, as Van Meegeren intended.

The experts called him a liar. They could do little else, for his confessions threatened them with professional ruin.

'Prove your wild tale,' they challenged. 'Paint Emmaus again.'

Van Meegeren went one better and offered to paint a 'brand new Vermeer'. And so he embarked on what was to be his last picture, 'Young Christ Teaching in the Temple'. He worked in a locked and barred studio, under the ever-present eyes of a panel of official witnesses. He was allowed his usual arsenal of chemicals to reproduce the pigments of Vermeer's day, but his work was so impressive that he did not need even to finish it. The collaboration charge against him was dropped.

However, he was brought to trial in 1947, accused of forging signatures. His forgeries hung on the courtroom walls, and after a one-day trial Van Meegeren was found guilty and returned home to await sentence. Two weeks later the judge sentenced him to one year in prison, but before he could begin his term, he had a heart attack. Six weeks later Van Meegeren died, aged 58.

An ironical touch to the affair was that Van Meegeren, the master forger, had himself been duped by a master criminal. Goering paid him for his forged Vermeer with forged banknotes.

As a youth, the artist had boasted that his work was destined to adorn the walls of Holland's greatest museums and galleries and, indeed, for a time, they did. In his own way, he had proved himself the equal of the old masters.

Brilliant, original thinkers—or charlatans?

Eccentrics and prophecies

THE SPENDTHRIFT SQUIRE

He bombarded his friends with bundles of money

Guests had already gathered for dinner when the host made his entrance—riding on a bear. Even they were startled, although they had learnt to expect eccentricities from the celebrated John Mytton, a hard-hunting Shropshire squire.

But their amusement turned to alarm when Mytton spurred his steed and was bitten savagely in the leg—a typical ending to one of his escapades.

On one occasion, he drove his gig at high speed into a rabbit warren to see if the vehicle would overturn. It did. In the further pursuit of knowledge, he determined to prove that a horse and carriage are unable to jump a closed toll-gate. He was correct.

Sport and drink—he got through about eight bottles of port a day and nearly as much brandy—were the twin passions of his life. He would hunt wearing the thinnest of clothes, or none at all, in the coldest weather.

Mytton was much admired for his generosity. He would toss bundles of notes to his friends and servants, or hurl the money into a hedge. His father had left him £60,000 in cash and an income of about £10,000 a year; but he dissipated the entire fortune in less than 15 years.

It was a wonder it had lasted so long. In 1834 he died in the debtors' prison of the King's Bench; he was 37. His body was returned to his old family home, Halston Hall in Shropshire, and there, in the presence of 3000 friends and hunting companions, he was laid to rest.

BEAR-BACK RIDER *Guests leap for safety as their host, John Mytton, rides in to dinner on a ferocious bear. However, it was the prankster and not his victims who came off worst.*

STRANGE COMPANY *Lord Bridgewater astonished Paris by giving dinner parties for dogs. But though he was an animal lover, he also liked to shoot captive game birds in his garden.*

DINNER WITH THE EARL

His guests were dogs, dressed as men and women

The French were not surprised that the *milord* living in Paris was unusually fond of animals. They expected such bizarre conduct of an Englishman. But they raised their eyebrows a little when they heard he gave dinner parties for dogs dressed in the height of fashion, even down to fancy miniature shoes.

Nor did it accord with their ideas of English sportsmanship that Francis Henry Egerton, 8th Earl of Bridgewater, should keep partridges and pigeons with clipped wings in his garden so that he could still shoot them despite his failing eyesight.

Strangely, this odd nobleman was an extremely learned scholar, a connoisseur and patron of the arts and a fellow of the Royal Society. He was the donor of an important collection—the Egerton Manuscripts—to the British Museum.

Yet this was the eccentric who wore each pair of his shoes once only, and then had them arranged in rows so that he could measure the passing of time.

And to return a book he had borrowed, he would send a sumptuous carriage attended by four liveried footmen.

He never married and, with his death in 1829, the title became extinct.

COUNTRY CAPERS *An engraving published in 1840 showing Jemmy in his carriage with odometer on the axle ; hunting on the bull Jupiter ; out shooting with dog and pig ; and Jupiter in a bull-fight.*

12 MAIDS ALL IN A ROW

Jemmy wanted his funeral to be a happy occasion

Guests at parties 200 years ago in Rawcliffe, Yorkshire, were often unnerved when they realised that their drinks were being served from the host's favourite coffin. But usually they got used to the idea and moved on to inspect his second-best coffin.

This had folding doors and a window and stood on its end. When visitors climbed into it the doors closed automatically and could not be opened from the inside. Men had to pay a penny to be released and women had to surrender one of their garters.

The man who devised this odd hospitality was James, or 'Jemmy', Hirst, who had the reputation of being the most eccentric man in England. His fame reached London, and George III commanded him to attend court. Jemmy did not hurry off immediately; he informed His Majesty that he was very busy teaching an otter to swim, but would call on him in due course.

When he did arrive, it was in great style. His wickerwork carriage was painted like a rainbow and he wore a lambskin cap, 9 ft in circumference, an otter-skin coat lined with red flannel, a waistcoat of drake's feathers, patchwork breeches, red-and-white striped stockings and shoes with huge silver buckles.

The king was delighted with Jemmy and restocked the wine cabinet in his carriage from the royal cellars.

Jemmy, who was born in Rawcliffe in 1738, gave early signs of his love of the bizarre. He rode his teacher's pig and trained it to jump low hurdles. But his tricks led to his expulsion from school, and he became apprenticed to a tanner. He fell in love with his master's daughter and was broken-hearted when she died.

He returned to his father's farm where he saddled a bull named Jupiter, and from that day forward rarely rode a horse. He rode Jupiter to hounds and generally wore the same kind of clothes as those in which he visited the king.

But for all his eccentricities, he was a shrewd businessman and quickly built up a fortune dealing in farm produce.

The wickerwork carriage which he designed was originally pulled by Jupiter, but he had it extended for sleeping in. It was then pulled by two mules.

On one occasion, however, he had sails rigged on the carriage and 'sailed' into Pontefract, where a sudden gust blew him and the carriage into a draper's window. He also fitted the wheels with an odometer he invented, a clock-like device that rang a bell once a mile.

Before he died, at the age of 91, he left instructions that his coffin should be carried by 12 old maids, to the accompaniment of a fiddler and bagpiper.

Sadly, only two women could be found who would swear on oath to their maidenly status; the vicar banned the fiddler; and the piper was allowed to play only solemn music.

MANUFACTURER OF MONSTERS

The man who improved on nature

Pope Pius VII was extremely annoyed. Some young jackanapes of an Englishman had climbed St Peter's, Rome, and left his gloves on top of the lightning conductor. They must be removed at once. But who would dare to carry out His Holiness's wishes? Sadly, only that same jackanapes had the courage. So Charles Waterton, a good Roman Catholic, penitently re-climbed St Peter's and brought down his gloves.

That was in 1817 when Waterton was 25, and this was the first time he caught the public eye. He then went travelling in the West Indies and North and South America, observing wildlife, collecting birds and eventually writing a best-selling book on his travels in Latin America and the natural history of the region, on which he became the acknowledged expert.

Again, he showed his physical courage. In South America, Waterton caught an alligator by riding on its back and seizing its front legs. Helpless in this judo hold, the animal was dragged ashore. Later he cut its throat and skinned it.

As an experiment, on one of his expeditions, he tried to get a vampire bat to bite his big toe by sleeping with his foot dangling out of his hammock. However, the bat ignored him, choosing instead to bite his native servant.

When he returned to his home, Walton Hall, in Yorkshire, he built a 9 ft high wall encircling 3 miles of his estate to make it one of the world's first bird and wildlife sanctuaries.

His interests as a naturalist had made him an accomplished taxidermist and he built up a whole museum of stuffed birds and animals.

Not content with nature

But he was not content with animals as nature had created them. He took different parts of birds and animals and amalgamated them into his own monsters. In the case of his celebrated 'Nondescript', he contorted the face of a red howler monkey, convincing many people that he had stuffed a human head.

To many of these home-made monsters he gave the names of well-known Protestant personalities.

But this was not his only eccentricity.

One of his favourite pranks was to hide under a hall table until a guest had put down his coat, then leap out to bite the astonished visitor.

After the death of his wife, he slept on the bare floor with a block of wood for a pillow. He rose at 3 a.m. each day, and spent the time before breakfasting at 8 a.m. reading and praying.

Then he would spend the rest of the day studying wildlife. When he was over 80 —he lived to 83—he would shin up trees to examine birds' nests.

He scrambled up 'like an adolescent gorilla', according to a contemporary.

A flying machine

One of the eccentric squire's projects was the construction of a flying machine. It took a great deal of persuasion by his friends and servants before he gave up the idea of testing the machine by leaping from an outhouse roof.

It was this kind of unusual activity that brought about his death. He fell while carrying a huge log and died of his injuries ten days later. He was buried with great ceremony and a fleet of funeral boats escorted his body across the lake on his estate.

His valuable natural history collection was presented to Stonyhurst College.

CHARLES WATERTON IN 1834 *Despite appearances, he was the forerunner of the wildlife preservation societies of today.*

THE AGE OF FOLLIES

When wealthy men erected buildings—for fun

Mr Paulet St John was riding across the Hampshire downs, in southern England, enjoying the air. His thoughts were miles away. Suddenly, almost under his horse's hooves, a deep pit opened up. He had not noticed it, but fortunately his horse had—and saved both itself and its rider with a fantastic 25 ft leap to the opposite rim.

A monument to that amazing leap can still be seen, a 30 ft pyramid at Farley Down, Hampshire. Mr St John renamed the horse Beware Chalk Pit and raised the pyramid to mark its grave after it died. For, as an 18th-century gentleman, he shared the prevailing taste for 'follies'—buildings which served little purpose except to indulge the extravagant whim of a wealthy landowner.

The great age of English folly building lasted through the 18th and 19th centuries, but some were built even later. The 140 ft Gothic tower outside Faringdon, in Berkshire, for example, was built by Lord Berners in 1935. But he had difficulty obtaining planning permission. When a visitor complained that the folly was so far from the house it could be seen only through a telescope, Berners replied that, as a retired admiral, he would not dream of viewing the countryside any other way.

MCCAIG'S COLOSSEUM AT OBAN *It was built to provide work for local men in times of unemployment and hardship.*

WEST WYCOMBE CHURCH *A sphere was built over the belfry for meetings of Sir Francis Dashwood's infamous Hell-Fire Club.*

Sir Francis Dashwood built this strange mausoleum at High Wycombe, Bucks.

A dwelling at Clayton on the London-Brighton main railway line.

The 'Disgrace of Edinburgh', never completed because money ran out.

The tomb of an 18th-century horse on Farley Down, Hampshire.

A modern folly, completed in 1935 by Lord Berners at Faringdon, Berks.

The chimneys of Morwenstow Rectory in Cornwall are replicas of church towers.

TRIANGULAR LODGE *Sir Thomas Tresham, fascinated by the number three, put up the lodge in 1593 at Rushton, Northants.*

BURTON PYNSENT COLUMN, SOMERSET
When a cow climbed the spiral staircase inside and plunged to its death, the tower was closed.

ASHTON MEMORIAL, LANCASTER
Imposing and costly, its purpose is unclear as there is little room to move inside.

MEMORIAL IN OTLEY CHURCHYARD, YORKS
In honour of men who died building a tunnel.

THE ELEPHANT THAT WAS FORGOTTEN

LITTLE SURVIVES of the work of the 18th-century French architect Charles Ribart, which is a pity because, in an age when the fashion was for grandeur, he was an architect with a sense of fun.

In 1758 Ribart planned an amazing addition to the Champs Élysées, in Paris, to be constructed where the Arc de Triomphe now stands. It was a building on three levels, in the shape of an elephant with a ballroom, and entry through a spiral staircase in the elephant's underbelly.

The building was to have air conditioning and furniture that folded into the walls. The drainage system was incorporated in the elephant's trunk. But the French government was not amused and turned the plan down.

THE HERMIT WHO LOVED BEER

LIKE several other 18th-century English gentlemen, the Hon. Charles Hamilton felt that the landscaping of his estate would be incomplete without the melancholy presence of a hermit. So the Hon. Charles built a suitable retreat among the gnarled roots of trees and advertised. His terms were that the successful applicant would be given a Bible, spectacles, food and water, a mat and a robe. He must not cut his hair, beard or nails, nor speak to anyone for seven years, at the end of which time he would be given £700. But the man who got the job lasted only three weeks. He explained that he was lonely. But, apparently, he also had a taste for beer, and the prospect of seven years on water was more than he could endure.

LUDWIG, THE CASTLE BUILDER

The simple pleasures of a mad king

The groom at the royal riding school did not question the king's wishes. If his royal master chose to ride round and round the riding school from 8 p.m. to 3 a.m., it was obviously his duty to follow, changing the horses from time to time. And he enjoyed the pleasant stop for a picnic supper. The king was known for his generosity to servants who pleased him, and the loyal groom was rewarded with a gold watch and chain for attending His Majesty on this so-called gallop 'from Munich to Innsbruck'.

For the royal horseman was Ludwig II, the 'mad' King of Bavaria, and imaginary journeys calculated on the distance round the riding school were one of his simple pleasures. The inconvenient hour was dictated by the fact that Ludwig had chosen to reverse night and day, even having a moon painted on his bedroom ceiling to help the illusion.

And yet the start of his reign had seemed so promising when he succeeded to the throne after the death of his father, Maximilian II, on March 10, 1864.

Agreed, the family background was slightly odd. His grandfather, Ludwig I, had fallen in love with a 'Spanish' dancer, Lola Montez—in reality Mrs Eliza Gilbert—when he was 60, and squandered the national exchequer on her. And then there was his aunt, Princess Alexandra, a highly talented woman whose excessive concern for her health was based on the impression that she had swallowed a grand piano made of glass.

But the handsome 18-year-old monarch had captured the imagination of the Bavarians and immediately showed signs of wishing to be a conscientious ruler. However, he had heard Wagner's 'Lohengrin' at the age of 15 and been entranced by the whole Wagnerian world of Germanic legend.

At the time of Ludwig's accession, Wagner had gone into hiding to escape his many creditors. The king sent his secretary to find him and, on May 3, Wagner was finally run to ground.

The secretary delivered the king's message. Wagner was to go at once to Munich where all his debts would be paid, and he would be provided with everything that he needed so that he could continue his life's work without interruption or worry.

Thus began a deep friendship, in which Ludwig idolised the composer. He revelled in his company and threw himself into his artistic enterprises. But Wagner's extravagance was also of regal proportions. There were mutterings in Bavaria about how much his genius was costing. On one occasion, Wagner sent his mistress to draw one of the king's payments from the bank. It was paid in sacks of small coins so the lady had to convey it conspicuously in two cabs—whether the bank did this

NEUSCHWANSTEIN CASTLE *Though one of King Ludwig's most extravagant follies, the fairy-tale palace perched on a hill-top has become a great attraction for tourists in Bavaria.*

deliberately to stir up feeling against Wagner is not known.

But the composer also began to dabble in politics and it was put to Ludwig that he must choose between his private friendship and his public duty. Sadly, he decided he must accept his royal responsibilities and he asked Wagner to leave Munich. His devotion to the composer continued, however, until Wagner's death.

A sofa for a sentry

So far, the king was showing few signs of eccentricity—though there were odd incidents like sending out a sofa to one of the palace sentries when he thought he looked tired. He tried to take an interest in affairs of state and even became engaged to his cousin, Sophie, although, throughout his life, women held little attraction for him. In fact, he could not go through with the marriage.

It was about this time that he turned to the passion for which he is best remembered—the building of his castles. His mother, Queen Marie, had recorded that as a child he had loved playing with bricks and showed an aptitude for construction.

In 1868 he wrote to Wagner: 'I propose to rebuild the ancient castle ruins of Vorderhohenschwangau, near the Pollat Falls, in the genuine style of the old German knights' castles, and I must tell you how excited I am at the idea of living there.' It would, he said, be in the spirit of *Tannhäuser* and *Lohengrin*.

And so it began. This was to be Neuschwanstein, his fairy-tale castle perched on a giddy mountain pinnacle. But there was also the baroque splendour of Linderhof, and the opulence of Herrenchiemsee, a replica of Versailles. The king retreated into the dream world of his castles far from affairs of state.

He no longer contented himself with jaunts round the riding school but on winter nights went on wild drives through the mountains in a golden rococo sleigh, attended by coachmen, outriders and lackeys who were obliged to dress in the style of Louis XIV.

His lack of attention to affairs of state and boundless extravagance could not go on for ever. In June 1886 his uncle and heir Prince Luitpold had him declared insane and succeeded him as regent.

But the story was to end in mystery as well as tragedy. Ludwig was confined at Schloss Berg, outside Munich, on June 12, and the following day he set out on a walk with Dr Bernhard von Gudden, his personal physician. When they failed to return a search party was sent out and the two bodies were found floating in shallow water about 20 yds from the bank. Many theories of murder, suicide and accident have been put forward, but no one has proved conclusively how Ludwig's bizarre life came to its tragic end.

ANNA'S ICE PALACE

Chilly rebuff for an erring courtier

Anna Ivanovna, Empress of All the Russias, was a cold-hearted woman. So it was not wholly inappropriate that she should build a palace completely of ice, including towers, ballroom and bedroom.

It was 1740 and Europe was in the grip of the worst winter for 30 years. The Seine, Rhine, Danube and Thames froze solid for months and wine turned to ice in the glass even before roaring fires.

The design was entrusted to architect Peter Eropkin, who had just completed a plan for the rebuilding of St Petersburg. Hundreds of serfs and skilled artisans were put to work on the project.

The palace, 80 ft long, 33 ft high and 23 ft deep, was designed in Classical style.

The ice used was carefully chosen for its transparency, and each block was measured with compass and rule before being cut and lifted into position. The blocks were joined with water, which instantly froze, so that, in effect, the edifice became one single chunk of ice.

Ice trees were sculpted, some as tall as the palace; others were dwarf orange trees bearing ice fruit. Ice birds sitting in the trees were painted in their natural colours. Ice statues stood in niches and the windows were glazed with sheets of ice.

In the bed chamber was an elaborate, curtained four-poster, with mattress, quilt, two pillows and two nightcaps all carved out of ice. There was even a meticulously carved model clock as well as all the other usual furnishings that one would expect.

The most striking feature in the grounds was a life-size ice elephant ridden by an ice-man in Persian costume. From the elephant's trunk a 24 ft spout of water jetted during the day. At night petroleum was used so that the animal spouted flame. A trumpeter concealed inside its body simulated roars.

There were also six cannons and two mortars made of solid ice. The amount of gunpowder they could withstand was calculated carefully, and they were fired many times without damage either to themselves or the crowd.

The only thing not made of ice was a wooden fence placed round the palace to keep the curious public at bay. For this was not an extravagant but harmless folly for their amusement. The ice palace had been designed for a cruel jest.

Prince Michael Alexievich Golitsyn had angered the empress by marrying, without her permission, an Italian Roman Catholic, who died soon after the wedding. Anna made him court jester as a token of her displeasure.

This was not enough, however. She also ordained that he should re-marry, and the empress herself chose the bride— a particularly ugly Kalmuk serving woman. And the ice palace was for their honeymoon. The unhappy couple were paraded in a cage on the back of an elephant, leading a procession of the grotesque human beings Anna had gathered about her and an array of animals including bears and pigs. Then they were bedded down publicly in the icy bed chamber.

The ending of the story was not too unhappy, however. With the spring, the ice palace melted into the river and the empress died later that year. Prince Michael and his Kalmuk bride found they got on well together and lived happily ever after.

COOL RECEPTION *The drawing-room of Empress Anna's ice palace; a contemporary St Petersburg engraving.*

COLD COMFORT *Anna Ivanovna, the capricious Empress of Russia, ordered a prince who had incurred her displeasure to marry an ugly serving wench, and built an ice palace for their wedding night.*

THE FOLLY OF RICHES

The rise and fall of Fonthill Abbey

Put enormous wealth into the hands of an eccentric and allow him to indulge himself, and the results are likely to be prodigious—and foolish.

So it was with William Beckford, who constructed England's biggest and most extravagant folly.

In 1770, at the age of ten, he inherited about £1 million in cash, land and houses in England and sugar plantations in Jamaica with thousands of slaves. His income was £100,000 a year—a fabulous sum in the 18th century.

Beckford was brought up like a prince, studying music with Mozart and architecture with Sir William Cozens, designer of London's Somerset House.

At the age of 21, Beckford justified his expensive education by writing *Vathek*, a romantic novel, which earned praise from Byron. He is said to have written it in French in a single sitting of three days and two nights.

For a time Beckford was an MP, but spent most of his time on a Grand Tour of Europe, accompanied by a retinue of servants, including his own musicians.

Then, in 1794, he set about the fulfilment of his greatest ambition—the building of a Gothic 'abbey' at his Fonthill estate in Wiltshire.

Beckford's approach to the project was distinctly odd. To begin with, he built a 12 ft high wall around the entire estate to keep out prying eyes. Behind the wall he lived in seclusion, seldom admitting visitors. But each evening he would order dinner for 12, and sit at table alone, eating only a single dish.

If Beckford decided to take a morning stroll through the woods, he would expect the entire village to work all night cutting down trees to clear his path.

Lofty disregard

Fonthill Abbey was built with the same lofty disregard for expense. Hundreds of builders were kept at work day and night, and a further 400 men were diverted from working on St George's Chapel, Windsor, in order to complete Beckford's project.

If only he had left them to get on with the job, he might have had better results. But he would insist on directing the work.

WILLIAM BECKFORD'S IMPRACTICAL FANTASY *The lofty halls and soaring towers of Fonthill Abbey were in keeping with the romantic idealism of the day. But high towers call for firm foundations.*

His notions of man-management were more generous than practical. Each day, the builders were given an ever-increasing liquor ration as an incentive to finish on time; as a result, the workers were generally drunk and incapable.

Then he ordered a 400 ft wooden tower to be built so that he could see its effect on the design. He did not like it and had it pulled down.

Little chance

But the project had little chance from the start. Beckford was so impatient that he could not wait for proper foundations to be dug. Instead, the abbey was built on those laid for a small summer house.

Beckford vowed to eat Christmas dinner cooked in the abbey's kitchens. And so he did, though they collapsed as soon as the meal was over. The main tower also fell down in 1800.

In the words of a contemporary, Fonthill Abbey was 'a desert of magnificence, a glittering waste of laborious idleness, a cathedral turned into a toy shop'.

In 1822 Beckford came to the edge of ruin when he lost two of his Jamaican estates in a legal action and was forced to sell his dream house.

It was perhaps as well. Soon after the new tenant moved in, the main tower fell down again. Not surprisingly, little of Fonthill Abbey remains today.

THE OTHER MAN IN AN IRON MASK

Only war could break his resolve

Could a man walk round the world without showing his face? It was one of those idle questions that arose when members of London's National Sporting Club were gathered together after a good lunch in 1907. John Pierpont Morgan, the American millionaire, and the sporting peer, Lord Lonsdale, were arguing. Lonsdale said it could be done, Morgan said it could not.

The argument resulted in a wager of 100,000 dollars, and all that was needed was someone to attempt the feat. In that same company was Harry Bensley, a 31-year-old playboy with an annual income of £5000 which came from investments in Russia. He wanted to get away from the tedium of club life—and offered his services.

A stiff set of rules was drawn up, the main one being that, like the fictional character in the Dumas novel, Bensley would wear an iron mask at all times. In addition he would push a perambulator, set out with £1 in his pocket and take nothing but a change of underwear.

He had to pass through a specified number of British towns, and 125 towns in 18 other countries. He also had to find a wife on his journey, who was not to see his face; and to finance himself he would sell picture postcards. To ensure that he kept to the rules, a paid escort was to accompany him.

Harry set out on January 1, 1908. Wearing a 4½ lb. iron helmet and pushing a 200 lb. spindly wheeled pram, he left Trafalgar Square amid cheering crowds.

At Newmarket Races he met Edward VII, and sold him a postcard for £5. The amused king asked for his autograph, but this would have revealed his identity, known only to his backers, so Harry had to refuse.

At Bexleyheath, Kent, a zealous policeman arrested him for selling postcards without a licence. Harry appeared in court wearing his mask, and the angry magistrate ordered him to remove it. But when the wager was explained to him the magistrate allowed Harry to be charged as 'The man in the iron mask', and fined him only 2s 6d.

Harry Bensley spent six years pushing his pram across 12 countries, passing through New York, Montreal and Sydney. Two hundred offers of marriage poured in, some from titled ladies, but Harry declined them all.

In August 1914 he arrived in Genoa, Italy, with only six more countries to visit. But the Great War had broken out, and as a patriotic young man he felt he had to join the forces. The bet was called off. Harry was given a consolation prize of £4000, which he gave to charity.

He was one of the lucky ones who survived the war, but in 1917 his fortunes suffered a blow. His investments were lost in the Russian Revolution and he was penniless. He died in 1956, in a bed-sitting room at Brighton.

ELAGABALUS THE HORRIBLE

An emperor to whom rule was a joke

No one dared refuse an invitation to dine with the Roman emperor Elagabalus. But the best they could hope for was a thoroughly unpleasant evening—and the worst, a particularly nasty death.

For the young emperor devoted his short reign to playing elaborate practical jokes on some of his unfortunate subjects.

One of his greatest joys was to invite the seven fattest men in Rome to dinner. They were seated on air cushions which slaves then punctured, sending the fat men sprawling on the floor. Other guests would be served with artificial food made of glass, marble or ivory. Etiquette compelled them to eat it.

When real food was served, guests were likely to find spiders in the aspic or lions' dung in the pastry. Anyone who dined too well and fell asleep might wake up in a room filled with lions, leopards and bears. If he survived the shock, he would discover the animals were tame.

Elagabalus, who reigned from AD 218 to 222, was fond of animals and often his chariot was pulled by dogs, stags, lions or tigers. But he was equally likely to arrive at a state function in a wheelbarrow pulled by naked women.

Often he would order his slaves to gather spiders' webs, frogs, scorpions or poisonous snakes which he would send to his courtiers as gifts.

On one occasion he had the seemingly pleasant idea of showering his dinner guests with rose petals. He used so many that some of them suffocated.

The state coffers were emptied by his extravagances. He would order a magnificent bath to be built, use it once, then have it demolished.

But Rome did not approve of his high-living—nor did it share his sense of humour. Finally, his own Praetorian guard murdered him on the orders of his grandmother, and his body was bundled into the Tiber. He was just 17.

ELAGABALUS OF ROME *He served his dinner guests glass, and died by order of his grandmother at the hand of his own guard.*

THE WORLD OF DADAISM

Eccentricity as a way of life

During the First World War, a number of writers, artists and musicians banded together in a movement whose object was the destruction of the middle-class values which they believed had led Europe into war.

The movement was called 'Dadaism' and deliberate eccentricity was the life style of its members. Bourgeois standards were toppled in a campaign of insults waged against anyone not prepared to adopt their ways. The principal weapons in the battle were bizarre sculptures, paintings and verse which bewildered and offended much of the public.

The movement began in Zurich during 1916 with the foundation of the Cabaret Voltaire in a popular bar. It was a nightly 'happening' of gibberish recitals, punctuated by bells, drum rolls and shouts.

Dadaism evolved through confusion and contradiction of established beliefs. Even the name is obscure. A Frenchman named Hans Arp said: 'I declare that Tristan Tzara found the word on February 9, 1916 at 6 p.m. I was present with my 12 children when Tzara uttered this word which filled us with justified enthusiasm. I am convinced that this word is of no importance and that only imbeciles and Spanish professors can take an interest in dates.'

'Imbeciles' was one of the kinder words used by the staid Swiss Press in describing Russian born poet Tzara and his fellow 'artiste', the German Hugo Ball. Prancing about on stage clad in a blue cardboard cylinder and red collar, Ball was the first person known to use the flashing red lights so popular in present-day discotheques. But as suddenly as he had appeared, Ball opted out of the avant-garde and retreated to a semi-monastic life.

Spanning the Atlantic

Meanwhile, Dadaism swept the world. In New York the movement was led by Fabian Lloyd—who for reasons best known to himself adopted the name of Arthur Cravan. Earlier in Paris, Lloyd had startled the women attending an art lecture by taking off his clothes in what may have been one of the first 'streaks'. What happened to Lloyd is not known. He left Mexico in an attempt to sail a small boat to Buenos Aires and was never seen again.

A painter named Marcel Duchamp took over from Lloyd as leader of the movement. Duchamp's object was to shake off artistic convention in a deliberate 'anti-art' campaign, which included a version of the Mona Lisa with a moustache. Another of his works was a bicycle wheel attached to a chair and a snow shovel entitled 'In Advance of the Broken Arm'. Duchamp's masterpiece took him eight years to assemble. It was an abstract made of paint, wire, varnish and New York dust held between sheets of glass. On the way to a Brooklyn exhibition in 1923 the glass broke, but the undaunted Duchamp triumphantly announced the work as 'The Last Refinement' and put it on show. Everything he did was intended to be a rejection of art. Ironically, his works now fetch enormous prices.

During the mid-1920s, the Dadaist movement gradually dwindled out. The grand finale came in Paris with an all-in brawl as rival factions clashed. The Dadaists felt they had made their point and left the future for the world to decide.

AN EARLY DADA *Hugo Ball complete with cardboard suit appearing on stage at the Swiss Cabaret Voltaire.*

NAME YOUR POISON

GUSTAV III of Sweden believed that coffee was poison. To prove his theory, he sentenced a murderer to drink coffee every day until he died. To provide comparison, another murderer was pardoned on condition that he drink tea every day. Two doctors were appointed to supervise the experiment and see who died first. In the event the doctors were the first to die. Then the king was murdered in 1792. Finally, after many years, the first criminal died—at the age of 83. He was the tea drinker.

History suggests that the results of the experiment were disregarded. Coffee prohibition was reintroduced in Sweden in 1794 and again in 1822.

'AGAIN I DIE!' *One of Robert Coates's postures that reduced his audiences to helpless laughter. Over-elaborate costumes detracted nothing from the awfulness of his acting.*

HAM CAN BE JAM

Success comes to the world's worst actor

So bad an actor was Robert Coates that he became a star of Regency London. People travelled from far away to see if he really was as bad as they had heard. He did not disappoint them. His incompetence amounted almost to dramatic genius.

In one play, where Coates had to die, he drew a silk handkerchief from his pocket, spread it carefully on the stage and then laid his elaborate headdress upon it so that he might expire in style. This so enchanted the audience that they demanded encores and had him die several times over.

Coates was born in the West Indian island of Antigua in 1772, the son of a rich merchant and plantation owner. But it was in England, where he was brought up, that he acquired a passion for the theatre. For years he wore a bejewelled 'Romeo' costume without ever getting an invitation to play the part.

Finally, his opportunity arrived and on February 9, 1810, he made his first stage appearance—as Romeo. His début was in Bath, then a centre of the rich and fashionable world.

His acting was so appalling that he became an overnight hit.

Before long he had moved on to still greater success in London. There he rewrote Shakespeare, ad-libbed outrageously and addressed the audience in the middle of scenes, often threatening to cross the footlights and fight those who laughed too loudly.

But the laugh was really on the audience. Coates continually played to packed houses, which included such personalities as the Prince Regent. He became so prosperous that he could flaunt himself in a carriage shaped like a kettledrum, painted in brilliant colours and drawn by two white horses. On its side was emblazoned a heraldic cock with his motto: 'While I live I'll crow.'

And so he did to a robust 75, when he came to a dramatic end. Crossing a London street to retrieve his opera glasses left in a theatre, he was struck by a passing hansom cab and died soon afterwards.

COALS TO NEWCASTLE

Strange business deals led to a stranger home life

Although he was born too early to sell refrigerators to Eskimos, Timothy Dexter did manage to sell coals to Newcastle—and show a handsome profit from the deal.

He was born into a poor American family in 1747, and apprenticed to the leather trade. In Newburyport, Massachusetts, he first showed his financial acumen by marrying a widow with some property and going into business himself. But it was at the end of the War of Independence that he demonstrated the flair that was to make him a brilliantly successful entrepreneur.

He bought up a large amount of European currency which, due to the dearth of trade during the war, was almost valueless in America. As stability returned. it almost regained its pre-war value, and he found himself in possession of a fortune. With it he bought ships, and began his series of trading coups.

Dexter conceived what seemed to be the crazy idea of selling 40,000 warming pans to the sweltering islands of the West Indies. People thought he was throwing away his money, but in fact the pans fetched high prices for cooking and as ladles in the molasses industry.

He even got a good price for a consignment of mittens sent to the West Indies, for another trader bought them for re-export to Russia. Dexter had similar luck when he sent coal to Newcastle. Somebody pulled his leg by saying there was a huge market for coal there. But when Dexter fell for this and sent off several ships full of Virginian coal, he had the astonishing good fortune to land it in Newcastle during a miners' strike. As a result his cargoes were snapped up.

Rejected by polite society because of his lowly birth and *nouveau riche* ways, he decided to call himself 'Lord Timothy Dexter' and establish his own court in a sumptuous mansion. Besides his nagging wife, crazy daughter and alcoholic son, his 'courtiers' included a fortune-teller, a 6 ft 7 in. tall idiot whom he called 'The Dwarf', and a poet laureate appointed by himself. This 'laureate' was Jonathan Plummer, a former fishmonger and purveyor of pornography, whom he dressed in cocked hat and silver-buckled shoes.

Within the mansion he built up a collection of hundreds of watches and clocks. Then he set about turning the grounds into an outdoor museum by employing a ship's carver to make 40 life-sized wooden figures of such famous characters as William Pitt, Nelson, Benjamin Franklin, Washington—and himself.

Visitors to the collection would also view the tomb which he had built for himself, containing a magnificently decorated coffin and, among other funeral accoutrements, a speaking trumpet, a set of pipes with tobacco and, of course, a box of fireworks.

In later life Dexter wrote a book called *A Pickle for the Knowing Ones; or Plain Truths in a Homespun Dress.*

Published in 1802 it was distributed free, but so popular did it become that copies changed hands at high prices. It ran to eight editions.

Its main claim to fame—and it has been praised by such eminent critics as Oliver Wendell Holmes—is that it contained no punctuation whatsoever although interspersed with numerous capital letters, mostly in the wrong places. It related Dexter's experiences, and attacked politicians and the clergy.

The book suggested that what America needed was an emperor; and that Americans need look no further than Lord Timothy Dexter of Newburyport.

LORD TIMOTHY
In his garden he erected statues of the world's most famous men— including Lord Timothy Dexter.

501

THE EMPEROR WHO HURT NOBODY

Norton the First ruled San Francisco with a gentle hand

The editor of the *San Francisco Bulletin* was the first to hear about it. The down-and-out in the cast-off army colonel's blue-and-gold uniform told him quite simply: 'I am the Emperor of the United States.' The editor was amused and agreed to print his visitor's first proclamation on the front page. So began the fabulous reign of Joshua Abraham Norton—a reign that was to last for 20 years.

Once, Norton had headed a considerable commercial empire. He was born in London in 1819 and, two years later, moved with his family to South Africa where his father, a farmer and ship's chandler, helped to pioneer Grahamstown.

When his father died in 1848, Norton sold up and went to Brazil. Meanwhile, gold had been discovered in California.

In November 1849 Norton arrived in San Francisco with $40,000. He decided there was more money to be made in the booming city itself than in panning for gold. He opened a general store and dabbled in real estate.

Corner in rice

By 1853 he had piled up $250,000. But he got greedy. He decided to corner rice, buying up every cargo. The price soared from 5 to 50 cents a lb., but he still refused to sell. Without warning, a fleet of ships arrived from South America laden with rice and the market collapsed. Norton was ruined. Two years later he was bankrupt.

He still was when he issued his first proclamation in September 1859. A week later a second decree said that because of corruption in high places the President was deposed and Congress abolished. Henceforth he would rule in person.

San Francisco was delighted. Norton had become the city's favourite 'character'.

When Washington ignored his second decree, Emperor Norton ordered the commander-in-chief of the US Army to 'proceed with suitable force and clear the Halls of Congress'.

All states of the Union were ordered to send delegates to San Francisco's Hall of Music to pay homage and 'make such changes as are necessary in the law'.

This was soon followed by a declaration that, because the Mexicans were obviously unable to manage their own affairs, the emperor had assumed the role of 'Protector of Mexico'.

In a drab rooming house, with pictures of Napoleon and Queen Victoria on the wall, Emperor Norton held court. In the afternoons, he sauntered through the streets with two mongrel dogs at his heels, gravely acknowledging the bows of his subjects, inspecting drains and checking bus timetables. He attended a different church every Sunday—in order to prevent sectarian jealousy.

Theatres reserved a special seat for him and the audience would rise in respectful silence when he made his entry. Once an over-zealous young policeman arrested him for vagrancy and the whole city reacted angrily. The chief of police personally released Emperor Norton with profuse apologies. A city council deputation called on him and he graciously agreed to 'blot the incident from memory'.

When the Civil War broke out in 1861, he followed the course of the fighting with 'deep concern'. He summoned President Lincoln and Jefferson Davis, President of the Confederacy, to San Francisco so that he could mediate.

When neither of them turned up, or even replied, he ordered an end to hostilities pending the 'Imperial decision'.

All this time Norton was being kept by the citizens of San Francisco. He was given free board, free meals and free travel. He once 'abolished' the Central Pacific Railroad for refusing him a free meal in the dining car, and was only appeased by a gold pass for life and, of course, an abject public apology.

But he was always short of ready cash so he introduced a system of taxation: 25 to 50 cents a week for shopkeepers and $3 a week for banks. San Franciscans laughed—and most paid up.

A national disgrace

When his uniform grew faded and shabby, Norton decided that he should issue a proclamation: 'Know ye that we, Norton the First, have divers complaints from our liege subjects that our Imperial wardrobe is a national disgrace.'

An Edict.

His Imperial Majesty, Norton I., has issued the following edict to Hall McAllister, Esq.:

H. McALLISTER, EsQ.—You are hereby commanded to apply to the United States Supreme Court for a Writ of Error, so that we can legally proceed to the capitol, at Sacramento, and *burn up* the new Constitution.

Given under our hand and seal, this twenty-second day of May, A. D., 1879.   NORTON I. [SEAL.]

Dei Gratia Emperor of the United States, and Protector of Mexico.

THE EMPEROR'S NEW CLOTHES *When Norton issued edicts like the one shown above, they delighted San Francisco. And his appeal for a new 'Imperial wardrobe' was heavily subscribed.*

Next day the city council voted funds for a new outfit.

The people of San Francisco were loyal and true subjects. When he died on January 8, 1880, 10,000 citizens filed past his coffin in two days.

In 1934 a marble slab was placed on his grave in Woodlawn Cemetery with the simple inscription: 'Norton I, Emperor of the United States, Protector of Mexico, 1819-1880.'

The real explanation of the attraction which Joshua Norton held appeared in his obituary in a San Francisco paper: 'The Emperor Norton killed nobody, robbed nobody and deprived nobody of his country—which is more than can be said for most fellows in his trade.'

503

A HEARTY APPETITE

Dr Buckland ate anything—including royal relics

Crocodile with the orange juice was the breakfast often served at the home of gourmet extraordinaire, Frank Buckland who, as was well known, would eat anything.

Buckland, a 19th-century British surgeon and naturalist, was a founder member of the Society for the Acclimatisation of Animals in the United Kingdom—an organisation devoted to increasing the

BUCKLAND AT HOME *Caged monkeys for company. At Oxford he kept a menagerie in his room—including a tame bear.*

nation's food supplies by breeding anything from kangaroos to bison in the fields of England.

In 1862 Buckland was responsible for the society's annual dinner. It was a rare feast with a menu that catered for the most jaded of appetites. There was kangaroo meat from Australia, and South-East Asian trepang sea slug. The slug looked so repulsive that only a few were able even to sample it. On another occasion, Buckland complained that it was a pity earwigs were so 'horribly bitter'.

But despite this gastronomic setback, he persevered in his crusade. From mouse on toast—served to his fellow students at Oxford—he graduated to the 'delights' of boiled elephant's trunk, rhinoceros pie and a whole roast ostrich. The ostrich apparently gave the eminent zoologist, Sir Richard Owen, a severe case of indigestion, though Sir Richard's wife described it as tasting 'very much like coarse turkey'.

Another of Buckland's failures was broiled porpoise head. He said he could not stop it tasting like an oil-lamp wick. But he considered some of his food pioneering work so successful that he offered the recipes to the public in a magazine. Slug soup and garden snails were but two of his unsavory suggestions.

Buckland's worst dishes included stewed mole and bluebottles—even he admitted he could not eat those.

He had a passion for the unusual and exotic in anything. His collection of curiosities included Ben Jonson's heel-bone, a piece of skin from a frozen Siberian mammoth and a lock of hair from the head of Henry IV.

In 1878 he was given a four-poster bed which had once belonged to the 18th-century surgeon John Hunter. Hunter had been a lifelong hero of Buckland's so he promptly cut the bed up and made it into the chair which now stands in London's Royal College of Surgeons' museum.

Buckland also took a deep interest in royalty. During a meal with a friend he once confided: 'I have eaten many strange things in my lifetime but never before have I eaten the heart of a king.' On the plate was the heart of Louis XIV which had been plundered from the royal tomb during the French Revolution.

STRACHEY'S TIMELY RETURN

WILLIAM STRACHEY lived most of his life ahead of time—six hours ahead in fact. After five years in India he returned home to England and decided not to go back.

While in India, Strachey, an uncle of the English writer, Lytton Strachey, decided the only accurate clocks were in Calcutta. For the rest of his life he lived by Calcutta time which was six hours ahead of Greenwich.

He spent 56 years rising in the middle of the night and going to bed as other Englishmen were taking afternoon tea.

THE GOVERNOR WORE GOWNS

The queen's representative who went too far

The elaborately dressed aristocrat who opened the New York Assembly in 1702 on behalf of Queen Anne was fittingly regal. Spectators gasped at the extravagant hooped gown, the elegant headdress and fan. For dressed in the finest ladies' fashion of the day was none other than Lord Cornbury—governor-general of the colony.

When other officials at the ceremony

money lavishly, he was so mean to his wife that she was forced to steal.

But the most remarkable of the peer's foibles was his frequent habit of dressing up as a woman. Some of his closest acquaintances claimed that he was fulfilling a mysterious vow by wearing only female clothing for a month each year. Others suggested that the real reason was his conviction that he resembled the

DRESSED AS A MAN *Lord Cornbury, Queen Anne's cousin, preferred however to represent his monarch by wearing queenly attire in public.*

QUEEN ANNE'S REPRESENTATIVE *Some people thought that Cornbury (above) interpreted his appointment too literally.*

complained that the queen's representative had made them all a laughing stock, he replied: 'You are all very stupid people not to see the propriety of it all. In this place, and on this occasion, I represent a woman, and in all respects I ought to represent her as faithfully as I can.'

By royal appointment

Lord Cornbury was credited by some of his contemporaries with doing more to harm British rule in America than any other royal representative.

He was awarded the posts of captain-general and governor-in-general of New York and New Jersey solely because he was the queen's cousin.

He was hopelessly inefficient as an administrator and in his personal life there was a curious paradox: while he spent

monarch. The most widely accepted explanation was that when the queen ordered him to represent her in America, he took her quite literally.

A woman who knew him in New York said: 'He was a large man, seen frequently at night on the streets wearing a hoop skirt and headdress.'

One man wrote of Lord Cornbury: 'He is a spendthrift, a grafter, a bigoted oppressor and a drunken, vain fool.' Another writer was to report: 'He is a frivolous spendthrift, an impudent cheat and a detestable bigot.'

In 1708 Lord Cornbury was recalled to England, but was arrested and kept in custody until he paid his debts. But his talents were recognised in the end. In 1711 he was made a member of Her Majesty's Privy Council.

505

THE CURIOUS CURES OF DR GRAHAM

Magnetic treatment for impotence at £500 a night

In 1781 childless London couples were invited to cure their unfortunate state by spending a night together in the Celestial Bed—for fees of up to £500.

The proprietor of this remarkable device was Dr James Graham, an Edinburgh physician, who had created a fashionable cult of cures by magnetism and electricity.

His bizarre treatments became the rage of fashionable London, and he opened a Temple of Health in the Royal Terrace of the Adelphi. There, attended by negro servants, he administered special baths, sat his gullible patients on 'magnetic thrones' or gave them mild shocks in an electric chair.

At the Temple of Health his chief assistant was none other than the beautiful Emma Hart, later to become Lady Hamilton and Nelson's mistress. Dressed in scanty robes, she entertained the patients as 'The Rosy Goddess of Health'.

Of all Graham's equipment the Celestial Bed was the most splendid. An ornate couch standing on eight brass pillars, it owed its curative powers, he said in his advertisements, to 'about 15 cwt of compound magnets . . . continually pouring forth in an everlasting circle'.

The treatment does not appear to have worked. At any rate he was obliged to return to Edinburgh where he was sent to gaol as a lunatic.

DOCTOR OF FASHION *A contemporary engraving of Dr Graham, in a foppish suit of white linen, with a nosegay in his hand.*

REMEDY FOR CHILDLESSNESS *The scantily clad Rosy Goddess of Health reclining on Graham's Celestial Bed.*

BRIDES BY MAIL ORDER

How New England girls were brought to the West

An advertisement in 1865 in the *Seattle Puget Sound Herald* brought a wistful flutter to many a rough, tough heart. In those days Seattle was a pioneer town on the uncivilised Pacific coast, and almost all its inhabitants were men—single men.

The advertisement proposed a meeting

to devise ways of persuading young ladies to move out West. Lonely bachelors packed the meeting, and the discussion went on all night.

A few days later another advertisement appeared: 'I, Asa Mercer, of Seattle, Washington Territory, hereby agree to bring a suitable wife of good character and reputation from the East to Seattle on or before September, 1865, for each of the parties whose signatures are hereunto attached; they first paying me the sum of $300, with which to pay the passage of said ladies from the East and to compensate me for my trouble.'

By the time Mercer left on his mission of matrimony, he had the signatures on 500 firm orders.

But as the weeks went by, the customers became restive. Mercer was meeting with resistance from the staid New Englanders, who knew little of the West except that it was populated by roughnecks.

Nevertheless, he was a persuasive man and one after another girls came forward to volunteer. Of course, they did not admit to seeking husbands, but claimed they just wanted to visit the West out of feminine curiosity.

The 7000 mile journey by land and sea was not easy in those days. And in San Francisco the crew had to fight a pitched battle to stop the boatload of girls being hauled off by the local males.

When they arrived in Seattle, the town had spruced itself up as never before. The men were shaved, the taverns closed, the buildings newly whitewashed.

Within a week the first wedding took place, and soon every mail-order bride was married—including one lady who became Mrs Asa Mercer.

THE LADY WAS A CHAMP

John L. Sullivan ruled the ring until he met Hessie's haymaker

John L. Sullivan, the 'Boston Strong Boy', held the world heavyweight boxing crown from 1882 to 1892. During that time he was knocked out only once—by a woman.

Mrs Hessie Donahue was a big, handsome woman, married to Charles Converse, who ran a school for boxers in Worcester, Massachusetts. In 1892 Sullivan was touring theatres, boxing with several sparring partners, and he invited Charles Converse to join his company.

Converse agreed, and as an extra attraction Hessie was invited to spar with Sullivan. Hessie was well acquainted with the sport, for she had watched the boxers at her husband's school.

Hessie and Sullivan worked out an act. Sullivan would claim that he could lick any man in the house, and offered a reward to anyone beating him.

Having disposed of his challengers, usually with one punch, he would announce that he had been challenged by a woman, whereupon Hessie would enter the ring wearing boxing gloves and clad attractively in blouse, skirt, bloomers and long stockings.

One night in the third round Sullivan caught Hessie with a hard blow to the face. Seething with anger, she lashed out with a right to the jaw—and the world champion hit the canvas, where he stayed for a full minute.

The incident created a sensation, and although Hessie's punch had been a fluke it was decided to keep the knock-out in the act. Sullivan would hit Hessie all round the ring for three rounds, and at the end of the third round she would produce her knock-out punch. The referee would pronounce her the new champion, then Sullivan would bounce up laughing.

The act continued for several months, and always got a big laugh.

But on September 7, 1892, John L. entered the prizefighting ring in earnest, to defend his title against James J. Corbett—'Gentleman Jim'. After 21 gruelling rounds Sullivan was knocked out—for the first time in his career by a man.

HESSIE DONAHUE *Who would suspect that this dear old lady once lost her temper and floored the great John L. in the third round?*

THE HUMAN FLY

George Polley hit the heights

Many thousands of New Yorkers craned their necks to look up at the Woolworth Building—in 1920 the tallest in the world—where the tiny figure of a man was inching his way to the top.

He reached the 30th floor, and had 27 more floors to go, when a policeman stuck his head out of a window.

George Gibson Polley was promptly arrested—for climbing a building without an official permit!

Polley scaled 2000 buildings in the United States, without ever slipping or falling. He became known as 'The Human Fly', and was often hired by store-owners as part of the opening ceremony. He was able to command a fee of $200—in those days a princely sum.

His career started as a boy, when he was playing baseball in Richmond, Virginia. George hit a big shot, right on to the roof of a six-storey building. As it was the only ball they had, he climbed up to fetch it.

In 1910 his family moved to Chicago, and George got a job as a newspaper delivery boy. One day he saw an expensive suit in a store window.

'I'd stand on my head on top of this building for a suit like that,' he declared.

The store-owner laughed. 'If you did that I would give you the suit,' he said. George got his suit, and the episode attracted so much attention that a local theatre offered him a booking. He climbed buildings to attract crowds to the show.

The Human Fly performed his feats all over the USA. In Boston he climbed 500 ft up the Custom House, in Hartford he scaled three buildings in one day, and in Providence, Rhode Island, he wore a blindfold to shin up a flagpole.

His daredevil stunts were always backed up by sound, commonsense safety precautions, and he carefully inspected every building before a climb.

George Gibson Polley's career came to an end at the early age of 29 when he died, not from a fall, but from a brain tumour.

WHOOPS! *Part of George Polley's act was to pretend to slip. Here he is seen in mid-air, dropping from one window ledge to another.*

SAM, SAM, THE APOTHECARY'S MAN

IF SAMUEL JESSOP were alive today, he would probably have ruined the National Health Service, or any medical insurance company. Born in 1752, Jessop was the hypochondriac to end them all. A rich farmer of Heckington, Lincolnshire, he was unmarried and had no relatives. Jessop devoted his latter years to protecting his 'delicate' health, dosing himself with remedies of all kinds. During the years from 1795 to 1816 his apothecary supplied him with 226,934 pills—an average of 10,806 a year, or 29 every day. His best year was 1814, when he swallowed 51,590 pills. He also consumed 40,000 bottles of medicine. In spite of this massive medical intake, or, some would say, perhaps even because of it, Samuel Jessop survived until the age of 65.

THE STONY-HEARTED SCULPTOR

Joseph Nollekens, the popular miser

Misers are often lonely and obscure men whose wealth is revealed only after their death. Joseph Nollekens, however, was a popular sculptor with many friends, and known to possess a large fortune. Yet he lived the life of a pauper.

Born in Soho, London, in 1737, he worked in Rome repairing statues, which he then sold as perfect. He added to his income by smuggling stockings, gloves and lace inside hollow busts. His appearance was always ragged, and his table manners appalling.

Nollekens rose to be one of the most admired sculptors of his day. On his return to England he produced busts of George III, William Pitt, Dr Johnson and David Garrick. His austerity extended into his professional life, and he would deliberately model a bust with the head looking over the shoulder, so that he could use pieces of marble rejected by other sculptors as too small.

At home he would sit in the dark, and if guests came he would light a small fire —quickly put out when they left.

When dining at the Royal Academy he would stuff his pockets with pepper and salt from the table . . . and he would

A FRIEND AT COURT *Joseph Nollekens poses with one of his most famous and successful works, the bust of George III.*

scrounge pinches of snuff, saying he had left his snuff-box in another coat.

Mrs Nollekens was just as mean. She kept her servants on low pay and haggled with tradesmen over the most trivial items. She once traded in the handle of an old mop when buying a new one.

Joseph Nollekens died in 1823. He left a fortune of £200,000.

A WOMAN OF MEANS

Hetty Green, the richest 'Scrooge'

Hetty Green was one of America's richest women—and she was also one of the meanest.

She was the most wealthy of the Quaker Howland family, whose fortune was made in the whaling industry.

Although she inherited $833,332 from her father, plus $4 million in property and investments, she tried hard to add her Aunt Sylvia's fortune as well. She failed, after contesting the will with an apparently forged document.

With shrewd investments, and incredible meanness, she built herself up as a formidable operator who became known as the 'Queen of Wall Street'. Some rival investors, jealous of her success, substituted 'witch' for 'queen'. But there was nothing occult or magical about Hetty Green's

financial achievements . . . Just plain tight-fistedness!

She took it to amazing lengths, living in cheap boarding houses, wearing ancient, tatty and faded clothes, and riding around town in a carriage that had once been used as a henhouse.

Hetty begrudged even the expense of an office. Instead, she conducted her daily business sitting on the floor of her bank, surrounded by cheap trunks and suitcases full of her documents.

This little eccentricity was benignly overlooked by the bank—a tolerance no doubt influenced by the fact that their valued client kept a current balance of more than $2 million.

She became obsessed with the delusion that she was marked down to be kidnapped

FAMILY PORTRAIT *Hetty Green (seated) with her daughter Sylvia. With an income of $3 million a year they lived on the cheap.*

or robbed and went to ridiculous lengths to throw off her imaginary would-be attackers. Her routes were always circuitous, and she would double back on her tracks and even hide in doorways to evade the fortune hunters she was sure were always lurking.

Hetty was also convinced that her father and aunt had been poisoned by their enemies.

Surprisingly, in view of her extreme meanness, she was always remembered with great affection by her many friends.

However, she was not above criticising her friends for what she believed were totally unjustifiable extravagances. And it was one such incident that killed her.

The Countess Leary, one of her closest associates, was staying with her in 1916 when one of the servants lost patience and rounded on Hetty for criticising the countess's spending.

Such insolence was unheard of and was too much for poor Hetty. She suffered an apoplectic fit and died.

Her estate was estimated at $100 m.

LUCK OF THE DRAW

A Californian's remarkably accurate election predictions

Four weeks before the American Presidential election of 1956, a Californian paint manufacturer, Jack Swimmer, wrote down his predictions of the votes that would be cast for General Dwight D. Eisenhower:

In Los Angeles County, 1,218,462.

In California, 2,875,637.

In the whole country, 33,974,241.

He also wrote a cheque for $5000 and deposited both documents with a charity commissioner clerk in Los Angeles.

The clerk, Gordon Nesvig, sealed Swimmer's predictions in a brass container, put that in a wooden box and deposited the box in the safe of the sheriff, and a guard was mounted to ensure fair play.

After the election, newspapermen were called to the sheriff's office and the paper was taken out. Swimmer's predictions were 100 per cent accurate . . . down to the last digit.

He had offered the $5000 to charity if he had been wrong, but he was so delighted with his success that he handed over the money anyway.

Swimmer refused to reveal the secret of his success. It may have been an incredibly lucky guess, but previously he had accurately predicted the 1952 election results and the scores in a World Series baseball season.

PROPHETS WHO COULD NOT WAIT

A 2000-SEATER amphitheatre, costing £20,000, was built overlooking Sydney Harbour, Australia, in 1925, for the Second Coming of Christ. Members of 'The Order of the Star of the East', led by Hindu mystic Krishnamurti, believed that Christ would soon return to earth in human form and walk across the Pacific Ocean to the amphitheatre. When He did not arrive by 1929, the group dissolved, and a block of flats now occupies the site.

EUROPE'S GREATEST PROPHET

The uncanny words of Nostradamus

In the autumn of 1939, when Adolf Hitler was in the act of unleashing world war, the wife of his Minister of Propaganda, Josef Goebbels, drew his attention to a remarkable set of prophecies which had been made 400 years earlier.

Written by a Frenchman called Nostradamus, they seemed to predict the rise of Hitler, and even came near to mentioning him by name, when they referred to a German leader called 'Hister'.

Unfortunately for Hitler, even the most skilled interpretation of the prophecies could not predict success for the Third Reich—so the Propaganda Ministry composed fake verses. In 1940 the Luftwaffe dropped thousands of 'Nostradamus leaflets' over France and Belgium, announcing that Germany would be victorious, and prophesying that south-eastern France would be spared in the conflict. The aim was to ensure that refugees would not choke the roads leading to Paris and the Channel ports.

In retaliation, British Intelligence also made up 'Nostradamus writings' but these, of course, predicted an outright Allied victory over the Axis.

A revolutionary doctor

Michel de Nostredame—who later latinised his name to Nostradamus—was born in 1503 in St Rémy de Provence. His family were Jewish, but were converted to Christianity and the young Michel was brought up as a Catholic. He was a brilliant student, who first became famous as a skilled physician dealing with plague victims. Many of his successes in this field were undoubtedly due to his refusal to 'bleed' patients—a revolutionary concept in the early 16th century.

He was ahead of his time in other ways too. Nostradamus proclaimed that the earth circles the sun, 100 years before Galileo's findings.

His prophetic gifts came to light in 1555 when he published the first of ten books, all simply entitled *Centuries*. Each volume contained 100 predictions, all of which were written in verse form.

Nostradamus never made any secret of his technique for looking into the future. He placed a bowl of water on a brass tripod and gazed into it, in much the same way as a fortune-teller intently studies a crystal ball.

But occasionally his predictions came to him in spontaneous flashes of intuition. One day, when he was a young man and travelling in Italy, he fell on his knees before a passing monk named Felice Peretti. To the astonishment of the monk and onlookers alike, Nostradamus declared: 'I kneel before His Holiness.' In 1585 the monk became Pope Sixtus V.

And once when visited by Catherine de Medici he was intrigued by a boy in her entourage, proclaiming that he would one day be King of France. The boy was Henry of Navarre who became Henry IV.

Exhumation foretold

On another occasion a French nobleman tried to confound Nostradamus's prophetic powers. He asked him to predict the fate of two suckling pigs he had in his yard. The answer was that the nobleman would eat the black one, and a wolf the white one. The nobleman instantly ordered the white one to be killed for dinner that night. When dining later with Nostradamus, he was amazed when told that a tame wolf cub had carried off the meat of the white pig and that he was, after all, eating the black one.

The prophet predicted his own death in 1566, and before he died he had a date engraved on a small metal plate, instructing that this should be placed with him in his coffin. In 1700 the coffin was taken from the grave, where it had lain for 134 years, and was moved to a more prominent site. The plate was resting on the prophet's skeleton. It bore the date 1700.

To avoid being accused of witchcraft by the Inquisition, Nostradamus confused the dating of his predictions, and wrote in a bewildering mixture of anagrams, symbols, Old French, Latin and other languages. This deliberate confusion has led to some curious and widely varied interpretations of his prophecies. Even so, many of his predictions are uncannily close to the facts—enough to justify his reputation as the greatest prophet Europe has ever produced. On the following pages, his prophecies have been translated into modern English, but the names are in the original spelling.

HENRY II OF FRANCE

Before it became tragically true, no one at the French court dared mention Nostradamus's most notorious prediction, of how King Henry would die:

The young lion will overcome the elder
In a field of combat in a single fight.
He will pierce his eyes in their golden cage.
Two wounds in one, then dies a cruel death.

This was fulfilled four years later in 1559 when Henry, one of whose heraldic emblems was a lion, had a friendly joust with a young officer called Montgomery, captain of the French king's Scottish Guard. Montgomery's lance accidentally pierced the visor of Henry's gilt helmet, wounding him in the eye and throat. The king died after ten days of agony.

Nostradamus's successful prediction was a particularly cruel blow for Henry's widow, Catherine de Medici. She believed in the prophet implicitly, and had become his patron.

In gratitude, Nostradamus once created 'visions' of all France's future monarchs in a mirror at the palace. This was probably a trick using reflections of accomplices in an adjoining room, but the superstitious Catherine was deeply impressed, and her patronage for the prophet was assured. With his own prospects guaranteed, Nostradamus was able to carry on with his serious work of foretelling future events for all mankind on a grand scale.

He also accurately predicted that Catherine's three sons would die before their mother.

Henry II was the subject of an early example of Nostradamus's uncanny skill.

LOUIS XVI

The unsuccessful flight of Louis XVI and Marie Antoinette to Varennes in 1791 was graphically described in these words:

By night will come through the forest of Reines
Two partners by roundabout way;
The queen, the white stone,
The monk-king dressed in grey at Varennes,
The elected Capet causes tempest, fire
and bloody slicing.

The royal couple fled by night through the forest, having escaped from the queen's apartments. They lost their way and chose a bad route. The white stone is thought to refer to the diamond necklace affair which ruined the queen's reputation, but she was also in the habit of wearing white dresses.

The monk-king could be an allusion to the king's one-time impotence. It is known that at the time of his capture he was wearing grey clothes.

He was a member of the Capet royal line, and though he was not directly responsible for the guillotine executions ('bloody slicing'), he was a cause of the Revolution and the terror that followed.

In a linked verse, Nostradamus even named the man Saulce who sheltered the royal couple in their hour of crisis.

Louis XVI is arrested at Varennes. The event was foreseen in detail by the prophet.

NAPOLEON

The prophet foresaw the rise of Napoleon, whom he described as the first anti-Christ (the second was Hitler, and a third has apparently yet to appear).

Of Napoleon's rise to power and years as emperor, he wrote:

An emperor will be born near Italy,
Who will cost the Empire very dearly.

Napoleon certainly cost France dearly in both manpower and political strength until his eventual downfall.

Charles I awaiting his execution at the hands of the Roundheads.

CHARLES I

Nostradamus made several predictions about Charles I, of which the most comprehensive covers Charles, Archbishop Laud and Cromwell:

*The unworthy man is chased from the
English kingdom.
The counsellor through anger will be burnt.
His followers will stoop to such depths
That the Pretender will almost be received.*

Charles's irresponsibility lost him his kingdom. His counsellor, Archbishop Laud, was beheaded (not burned) in 1645. The followers who stooped so low were the Scots who sold the king back to Parliament in 1646, and the Pretender is presumably Oliver Cromwell, the Lord Protector, who was almost accepted as king.

Nostradamus's most accurate prediction regarding Charles was:

'*The Parliament of London will put their king to death. . . . He will die because of the shaven heads in council.*'

Clearly the prophet was referring to the Roundheads. Cromwell was described as 'more like a butcher than an English king'.

The prophet also mentioned 'The broken bridge, the city faint from fear'. This is thought to refer to Pontefract, whose name derives from the Latin *pons* (bridge) and *fractus* (broken). The town held out for Charles during two sieges by Cromwell's Parliamentary forces.

THE GREAT FIRE AND THE PLAGUE

Nostradamus rarely gave precise dates, but the Great Fire of London was an exception. He was very precise when he wrote:

*The blood of the just will be demanded of London
Burnt by fire in three times twenty plus six.*

The disaster occurred in 1666, and Nostradamus adopted the Italian habit of leaving out the first two digits in the date.

This is how he prophesied the Great Plague that ravaged London in 1665 — retribution, he suggested, for the murder of Charles I:

*The Great Plague of that maritime city
Shall not cease till death is avenged;
For the blood of the just taken and
condemned through innocence
And the great dame outraged by feigning saints.*

The 'feigning saints' in the last line appear to be the Puritans, and the 'great dame' is thought to be St Paul's Cathedral, which was destroyed in the fire.

The Great Fire of London proved to be the saviour of the doomed city.

Nostradamus also made this prediction of Napoleon's fate:

*The great Empire will soon be exchanged
for a small place,
Which will soon begin to grow.
A small place of tiny area in the middle of which
He will come to lay down his sceptre.*

Napoleon was exiled to the small island of Elba but escaped for 100 days, in which his empire grew again. He relinquished all power on the tiny island of St Helena in the South Atlantic.

Napoleon, emperor turned exile.

LOUIS PASTEUR

Nostradamus's prophesies about more recent events are just as remarkable. Here he predicts both a name and a date:

Pasteur will be celebrated as a godlike figure.
This is when the moon completes her great cycle.

Pasteur made a vital contribution to medical science when he founded the Pasteur Institute in 1889.

The lunar cycle about the earth takes 19 years to complete. One such lunar cycle was completed in 1889.

Louis Pasteur pioneered the use of inoculation to fight disease.

The Duke and Duchess of Windsor lived in exile after his abdication.

EDWARD VIII

Nostradamus foresaw the abdication of Edward VIII caused by his love for the divorced American Mrs Wallis Simpson. He wrote:

For not wanting to consent to the divorce,
Which afterwards will be recognised as unworthy,
The king of the islands will be forced to flee
And one put in his place who has no sign of kingship.

Because he insisted on marrying Mrs Simpson, Edward VIII was forced to abdicate the British throne on December 10, 1936. Mrs Simpson was considered 'unworthy' to be queen by many of the British people and 'the king of the islands' had to flee into exile. George VI, who had no training or experience in kingship, ascended the throne in his elder brother's stead.

GENERAL FRANCO

In describing the Spanish Civil War (1936-9) Nostradamus names the main protagonists, Primo de Rivera and Franco who helped depose him. The last line refers to Franco's temporary exile when he was not allowed to cross the Mediterranean to enter Spain:

From Castille, Franco will bring out the assembly.
The ambassadors will not agree and cause a schism.
The people of Rivera will be in the crowd,
And the great man will be denied entry to the gulf.

General Franco's exile and his part in the Spanish civil war struggle were predicted.

ADOLF HITLER

Nostradamus produced several extraordinarily accurate predictions about the Nazi leader. One verse sums up Hitler's life and even predicts the fact that his death in Berlin in 1945 would never be satisfactorily confirmed:

In the mountains of Austria near the Rhine
There will be born of simple parents
A man who will claim to defend Poland
and Hungary
And whose fate will never be certain.

Another verse describes the early years of the Second World War when the German armies swept across the Rhine into France. Though most of Europe was allied against him ('the greater part of the battlefield') Hitler, or 'Hister', was for a time only too successful:

Beast wild with hunger will cross the rivers,
The greater part of the battlefield will
be against Hister.

The prophet also warned of 'weapons

Adolf Hitler was foreseen by Nostradamus as the second anti-Christ.

heard in the skies' and 'machines of flying fire'—references to aircraft, bombing and the early V-weapons.

Nostradamus drew a vivid picture of what a wartime pilot would look like in an oxygen mask, helmet and goggles, describing him as 'half pig, half man when battles are fought in the skies'.

HIROSHIMA

The nuclear bombs dropped on Hiroshima and Nagasaki were forecast:

Near the harbour and in two cities will be two scourges the like of which have never been seen.

The two cities are on the sea and both the explosions and the radiation that followed were horrors the world had never experienced before.

The bomb at Nagasaki, one of 'two scourges the like of which have never been seen'.

ABOUT THE FUTURE

Nostradamus refers to a third war this century which will take place in the Northern Hemisphere after two great powers join in an alliance against the East. The prophet wrote:

When those of the Northern Pole
are united together
In the East will be great fear and dread . . .
One day the two great leaders will be friends,
The New Land will be at the height of its powers:
To the man of blood the number is repeated . . .

The man of blood is identified elsewhere as being the world's third anti-Christ who will emerge in China. The new land was a common term used in all of Nostradamus's predictions to refer to what we now call America.

Thus, Nostradamus seems to be suggesting war between China and a Russo-American alliance.

The prophet even gives a precise date for when the conflict will come—'when the cycle of the centuries is renewed'. He says:

In the year 1999 and seven months
From the sky will come the great king of terror . . .
Before and afterwards war reigns happily.

The Northern Hemisphere will suffer most. 'A very great famine caused by a pestilent wave will extend its long rain the length of the Arctic pole,' reads the terrifying prophecy.

515

WORLD WITHOUT END

Thousands believed when William Miller predicted Armageddon

On April 3, 1843, thousands of people assembled on hilltops in New England to await the end of the world. They were disappointed, but despite this setback many never lost their faith in the man who had predicted the cataclysm—William Miller, a farmer and former atheist who had taken to Doomsday predictions.

Having brooded upon the Books of Daniel and Revelation, Miller issued his first warnings in 1831. He became a preacher and travelled widely.

His predictions of approaching doom

DAY OF ATONEMENT *Some of William Miller's followers dressed in shrouds and waited in graveyards when he predicted the end of the world.*

were reinforced by shooting stars in 1833, haloes around the sun and a spectacular comet in 1843.

Then the *New York Herald* ran Miller's story that the world would be destroyed by fire on April 3. Fanatics were reported to have murdered relatives and committed suicide, believing the dead would be first through Heaven's gate.

Not-so-stupid idiot

In Westford the village 'idiot' blew a large horn and the Millerites screamed, 'Hallelujah, the time has come!' The idiot, who was clearly not so stupid, answered: 'You fools, go dig your potatoes. Angel Gabriel won't dig 'em for you!'

Undaunted, Miller revised the date to some time before March 22, 1844, and once more the Millerites believed. Some families dressed in shrouds and waited for the end in graveyards.

Several Millerites sold all they possessed—although it is not recorded what they planned to do with the money.

On March 22 he admitted that he had made a miscalculation and gave October 22 as the date of Armageddon. One farmer took his cows, dressed in white robes. 'It's a long trip,' he said knowingly. 'The kids will want milk.'

At last, on October 23, the Millerites began to doubt, especially those who had sold up. The world was still turning and Miller still had all his worldly goods.

The movement, which had once had up to 100,000 adherents, broke up. But some branches of the Adventist Church, derived from his teachings, survive today.

THE PROPHET WHO FORESAW HIS KILLER'S DOOM

A 16TH-CENTURY Scottish mystic known as the Brahan Seer prophesied many events, including the coming of railways . . . 'long strings of carriages without horses', and the Caledonian canal . . . 'ships will sail round the back of Tomnahurich Hill'. But, when he told the Countess of Seaforth, quite accurately, that her husband had a mistress in Paris, the countess ordered that the seer should be boiled in tar. He then prophesied doom for his executioners—that the last of the house would be deaf and dumb, and the inheritor would be 'a white-hooded lassie who would kill her sister'. In 1815 Francis Mackenzie, last of the line, died after an illness that made him deaf and dumb. His eldest daughter, wearing white in mourning for her own husband, inherited the estate. Later, when the daughter was driving a carriage, her sister was thrown out and killed.

SHOT IN THE DARK

John Williams dreamt of the premier's death in advance

Engineers and bankers are two groups of people unlikely to suffer from flights of fancy. John Williams was both a mining engineer and a banker yet on the night of May 2 or 3, 1812, he had one of the most remarkable precognitions ever recorded. He dreamt the full details of the scene in which a British Prime Minister was assassinated.

He told his dream to a writer, John Abercrombie, who published it in 1834 as follows: 'Mr Williams was in the House of Commons where he saw a small man in a blue coat and white waistcoat. Then, as he watched, a man in a brown coat with yellow buttons drew a pistol from his coat. He fired at the small man who fell, blood pouring from a wound a little below the left breast. Mr Williams heard clearly the report of the pistol, saw blood fly out and stain the waistcoat, saw the colour of the man's face change.'

The assassin was seized and when Williams, in his dream, asked who had been shot, he was told 'The Chancellor'. At that time Spencer Perceval was both the Prime Minister and Chancellor of the Exchequer.

Williams had the dream twice more in the course of the night.

During the next week he told several people of his experience—among them

MURDER IN THE LOBBY *Williams foresaw the assassination of Prime Minister Spencer Perceval almost exactly as it happened.*

his brother, his partner and two of the leading men in his home town of Falmouth, Cornwall.

On May 11, precisely as Williams had dreamt, Perceval was shot dead in the lobby of the House of Commons by John Bellingham. Every detail of his dream was verified by witnesses, right down to the appearance of the murderer and victim.

John Williams's experience was described in *The Times* five days after the murder took place.

JEANE DIXON PREDICTS

Death of 'a blue-eyed Democrat'

Clairvoyants—those people who claim knowledge denied to the rest of mankind—seem to predict bad news rather than good.

Mrs Jeane Dixon was the first person to warn friends of President Kennedy that he was in danger. And she repeated the warning frequently. In 1952, that is 11 years before his death, she predicted that 'a blue-eyed Democrat' would become President in 1960—and that he would be assassinated.

On the day in 1963 when Kennedy was shot, she told friends at lunch: 'Something dreadful is going to happen to the President today.'

Jeane also predicted the death of

President Roosevelt in 1945; of Mahatma Gandhi in 1948; and of Winston Churchill in 1965.

When she met Churchill, in Washington in 1945, she told him he would be out of office after the war, but would be back in power by 1952. Both predictions were correct—as were Jeane's forecasts of race riots in American cities in 1963–4 and of Russian pioneering in Space.

Jeane foresees a world holocaust for the 1980s, and the rise of a world leader from the Middle East. She also said that peace would come only in 1999. Similar predictions were made four centuries earlier by Nostradamus, who foresaw a great war, culminating in 1999.

VISIONS OF DEATH

The seer who sealed his own fate

Writer Jacques Cazotte was greeted with incredulity when he told guests at a Paris dinner party in 1788 what fates would befall them in the Revolution which would shortly overwhelm France. 'You don't have to be a prophet to foresee a revolution today,' someone scoffed. Most of the writers and courtiers present agreed.

There was a cry of protest when Cazotte went on to assert that the king would be executed—and so would several ladies at the party.

He was even more specific. Looking gravely at Nicolas Chamfort, a celebrated playwright who had risen from humble origins, he said: 'You will cut your veins with a razor 22 times—but you will not die until some months later.'

To the Marquis de Condorcet, a philosopher-mathematician married to one of France's most beautiful women, he announced: 'You will die on the floor of a prison cell, having taken poison to cheat the executioner.'

Perhaps the most surprising prediction was reserved for critic and playwright, Jean de la Harpe, a well-known atheist. Cazotte forecast that the Revolution would make him a devout Christian.

Chamfort worked for the Revolution in its early days, but later criticised its excesses. In 1793, faced with the threat of imprisonment, he tried—but failed—to kill himself by slashing his wrists. He died a few months later.

Condorcet was elected to the Revolutionary Assembly and for a while was its secretary. But when he opposed the Reign of Terror he was outlawed. Two days after being imprisoned, in 1794, he was found dead on the floor of his cell. He had cheated the executioner, just as Cazotte foretold. La Harpe, too, was thrown into prison. There he reconsidered his spiritual state and became an ardent Catholic.

As for Cazotte, his visionary powers brought him little happiness. For they enabled him to foresee the exact manner of his own death—arrest, release, re-arrest and finally the guillotine.

PROPHECY OF CAZOTTE *He became a legend by foretelling uncannily his guests' fate in the French Revolution.*

HOUSE OF BLOOD

'GOD will give him blood to drink!' With this curse on the man who secured his conviction for witchcraft, Matthew Maule went to the gallows 300 years ago in the Massachusetts seaport of Salem. Maule, a poor Puritan, owned a fine freshwater spring; Gilbert Pyncheon, a rich merchant, coveted the site, and engineered Maule's trial on a false charge. Then he acquired the land, and built himself a grand house. The building—the House of Seven Gables—was finished in 1668 and still stands.

But Pyncheon did not live long to enjoy the fruits of his scheming. On the very night of the housewarming Gilbert Pyncheon was found dead of a haemorrhage. Blood ran from his mouth and stained his fine white shirt. The people of Salem remembered Maule's curse—and shivered.

THE PROWLING FOXES

Death warnings of Europe's ancient families

The annals of European nobility abound in weird tales of super-natural portents, some of which have survived to this day. Among them is the sinister legend of The Foxes of Gormanston.

Whenever a Lord of Gormanston is about to die, Gormanston Castle in County Meath, Ireland, is surrounded by foxes. All the local people know the legend, whose origins stretch back into the remote past.

On the day of the 12th viscount's death in February 1860, a local hunt returned without having sighted a fox all day. A labourer told them: 'All the foxes have gone to see the ould lord die.'

In September 1876 Lady Gormanston saw a pack of foxes prowling by the castle gate. Her husband, the 13th viscount, died that night. And foxes followed the coffin to the graveside at the funeral a few days later.

When the 14th viscount died in 1907, a pack of foxes prowled all night outside the chapel where his body lay in state, despite attempts to drive them away.

The Arundells of Wardour, in Wilt-shire, also possessed private harbingers of doom. Immediately before the death of one of the family, two spectral owls would be seen perched on the battlements of Wardour Castle. Perhaps the owls will never appear again—the last Lord Arundell died in 1944 and the title became extinct.

A floating trunk

In 1586 the English antiquary William Camden recorded the omen of the Brere-tons of Cheshire. He said: 'I have heard it affirmed many times that for some days before the death of a Brereton heir, the trunk of a tree has been seen floating in the lake adjoining their mansion.' Curi-ously, this omen appeared only on the death of an heir—never when the master himself died.

Some ghostly portents are believed to be the spectres of long-dead members of the family. The famous White Lady of The Prussian Hohenzollerns, for instance, is thought to be the ghost of Countess Agnes of Orlamunde, who was walled up alive for infanticide.

Another tale says she is the Princess Bertha von Rosenburg. But whoever she may be, her appearance foretells the death of a Hohenzollern.

Frederick William IV of Prussia, who fashioned a great European nation out of his small German state, went mad in 1861 after a horrifying appearance.

Headless pall-bearers

A sentry on the castle gate saw the White Lady leading four headless pall-bearers carrying a coffin. They glided silently into the castle, and reappeared a few seconds later bearing a body in royal robes. The corpse was headless—but where the head should have been, there lay a crown.

The king never recovered, and died early the next year. The death of his father, Frederick William III, had been foretold by her appearance; and an ancestor, the Margrave of Bayreuth, had seen the White Lady just before his horse threw him to his death in 1678.

The royal family of Bavaria shared a death warning with the ducal family of Hesse. This was the Black Lady of Darm-stadt, who is generally thought to be the ghost of a long-dead Grand Duchess. In 1850 she was seen at Archaffenburg as the Grand Duke of Hesse-Darmstadt was taking tea with his parents. Within days, his mother died of cholera. In 1854, at Pillnitz Castle on the banks of the Elbe, the Queen of Saxony saw her dressed in black mourning clothes and hovering near a chair. The queen's anguished attendants were certain that their mis-tress's death was imminent; but they were wrong. Next day the news reached them that the King of Saxony had died in Dresden.

Haunted Borgias

The bloodthirsty Borgias were said to have been a haunted family—perhaps not without justice. The best-known incident occurred to Pope Alexander VI, the ruthless Rodrigo Borgia. A cardinal, on entering the papal apartments one night in 1503, found the pope lying on a spectral bier and lit by a ghostly light.

Terrified, he made the sign of the Cross and the vision faded. But before midnight, the pope had died.

THE TRIBE THAT DIED

When a prophecy was political

Superstition, a blind faith in witch-craft, total economic dependence on cattle, and a constant fear of the white man's encroachment were the elements that ruled the lives of South Africa's native peoples in the 19th century.

All four were tragically intertwined in the strange story of Nongqause, the 14-year-old Xhosa girl who saw a vision and all but destroyed her nation.

One of the largest Bantu tribes, the Xhosa were involved for decades in disputes over land, cattle and labour with the frontiersmen who pushed relentlessly inland to set up farms and townships.

An uneasy border between the Xhosa and the white man had been established in 1778 along the Fish River, bounding the Ciskei and Transkei territories in the east of Cape Province.

There followed a century of unrest, cattle-stealing and frontier disputes with the white farmers. Drought reduced the size of the Xhosa herds, and those cattle that remained were in poor condition—because, they thought, of spells cast by English witchdoctors.

Tribal elders and chiefs were as deeply under the influence of the witchdoctors as the people they ruled. In 1819, for example, Chief Ndlambe was persuaded to attack the whites at Grahamstown—because witchdoctor Makana assured him that his medicine would render the white man's bullets harmless. One thousand Xhosa died in the battle.

It was against this background of fear and superstition that, in May 1856, Nongqause, niece of the witchdoctor Umhlakaza, claimed to have had her vision. At this time she is thought to have been about 14 years old.

Ancestral messages

She went to the river near her village to fetch water, she said, and there she met five strong black men—messengers from the spirits of her ancestors. The spirits, they had said, grieved at the decline of the Xhosa nation and had resolved to appear among their people. They would be an invincible army that would drive out the white man and restore the Xhosa to their former glory.

But before this help was given, the ancestors required proof of the Xhosa's unquestioning obedience. They must kill all their cattle, destroy all their grain and abandon all cultivation of the land.

They were to build new barns for the fat, healthy cattle that would come from the ancestral abodes, and dig vast grain pits to take the overflowing crop that the spirits would bring with them.

Only when those instructions had been carried out would the ancestors return. They would be preceded by a frightful whirlwind that would sweep the unbelievers, and anyone who had not obeyed their orders, into the sea.

Chief persuaded

Nongqause's uncle persuaded Chief Kreli that the young prophetess's vision was a genuine message from the tribal ancestors. Kreli ordered the immediate destruction of crops and the slaughtering of cattle.

When a few doubters refused to obey, Nongqause received another message. While she was standing by the river, the ground rumbled beneath her feet—the mutterings of the discontented ancestors, her uncle explained. People from all over the tribal lands flocked to Nongqause's village to gaze into the swampy pool that was believed to be the gateway to the ancestral abode. They saw the horns of oxen and heard the bellowing of cattle impatient to rise.

Others reported that they had seen the dead Xhosa heroes rise from the Indian Ocean, some on horseback, some on foot, passing in front of them, then disappearing.

For ten months, there was no farming. The believers destroyed their crops and killed their cattle. Thousands of the Xhosa faithful died of starvation.

Despite the warnings of the British commissioner, Charles Browntree, that Nongqause's prophecies could never come true, the tribe refused to till the land, and carried on with the slaughter of cattle.

Then at last Nongqause named the date when the ancestors would return—February 18, 1857. The sun would rise blood red and stand still in the sky. Then it would move around and set again in the east. Whirlwinds and hurricanes would sweep the earth, scattering the whites and the non-believers among the Xhosa into the sea.

On the eve of the great day, the Xhosa decked themselves in beads and painted their bodies. Those who still had strength danced through the night. Others sat, hungry and patient.

The sun rose and made its slow passage through the hot February sky—only to set in the west. It left behind the bitterness and disappointment of a starving people.

The desperate tribe ate roots, berries, even the bark and gum of the mimosa tree. They gnawed the bones and hide of their long-slaughtered cattle and poured

into the mission stations and larger villages, looking for help.

Umhlakaza, the witchdoctor uncle, hid from his disillusioned people. His ambition to incite them to rise in a frenzy of hunger against the whites had failed, and he himself died of starvation.

Nongqause was arrested and sent to a farm in the Eastern Province, where she died in 1898—surely the most tragic single figure in the history of southern Africa.

And her people? More than 20,000 had died, and of the 43,000 remaining, some 30,000 were saved only by taking work on the white man's farms.

VEHICLE VISIONS

Cars and planes were just a matter of time

Andrew Jackson Davis, the son of a poor, drunken shoemaker, had virtually no education and was forced by poverty into a lifetime of menial work. Yet, from his mother, said to be a remarkable visionary, he inherited a clairvoyant talent which marks him out as one of the most outstanding soothsayers who ever lived.

He foretold the coming of both the aeroplane and the car.

Some time before 1842, his family settled in Poughkeepsie, N.Y., and it was there he met William Livingston, a jour-

neyman tailor and amateur mesmerist.

Livingston recognised Davis's rare clairvoyant abilities and gave up his job to promote him, initially, as a travelling faith healer.

Davis gave over 150 lectures, most of them in a state of trance, and wrote a number of books. In both his writings and lectures he made prophetic statements which achieved a startling degree of accuracy and detail.

Cars in the sky

He is said to have predicted prefabricated concrete buildings, and in his book, *The Penetralia*, published in 1856, he wrote of 'aerial cars . . . which will move through the sky from country to country'.

He predicted the internal combustion engine and the automobile in the same book: '. . . carriages and travelling saloons on country roads—sans horses, sans steam, sans any visible power, moving with greater speed and safety than at present. Carriages will be moved by a strange and beautiful and simple admixture of aqueous and atmospheric gases—so easily condensed, so simply ignited and so imparted by a machine somewhat resembling our engines as to be entirely concealed and manageable between the forward wheels. These vehicles will prevent any embarrassments now experienced by persons living in thinly populated territories. The first requisite for these land-locomotives will be good roads, upon which, with your engines, without your horses, you may travel with great rapidity.'

CLAIRVOYANT *Andrew Jackson Davis predicted aeroplanes and cars in a book that was published in 1856.*

521

The unconscious heritage shared by us all

Curious and bizarre beginnings

---•---

SPEAKING VOLUMES IN SILENCE

Sign language—from the aborigines to aviation

Before the development of even the most elementary vocal language, primitive man was forced to use a combination of basic noises and simple, evocative signs to communicate with his fellow-men. In much the same way that animals convey basic emotions such as anger, fear, aggression and contentment, early man used facial expressions and bodily gestures to supplement his limited repertoire of grunts, roars and growls.

But sign language, which began as an aid to communication, has survived the evolution of complex languages. It is still found around the world today among primitive peoples, like the aborigines of Australia, and in modern society, as an extra mode of conveying moods, feelings and commands. However, while many gestures are almost universal, others have totally different—and sometimes opposite —meanings in different countries.

PRIMITIVE TALK

Forefingers at the brow is a way of saying 'cattle'.

Rubbing the stomach is aboriginal for 'good'.

TWO WAYS TO SAY GOODBYE

In the East, beckoning says goodbye.

In other countries, the wave is standard.

AGREEING TO DIFFER

Head-shaking is 'yes' in Mediterranean lands.

Elsewhere, the nod is the sign of agreement.

The Arabs place their forefingers together like this when they want to agree or say 'yes'.

GIVING ODDS AT A GLANCE

Tic tac men use signs for numbers. This is the signal used for No. 1.

Touching the face this way means two, or odds of 2 : 1.

A hand beneath the chin is three, or odds of 3 : 1 are being offered.

Sideways wagging of the hand is four, or a change to 4 : 1 odds.

Touching the shoulder with the hand is five, or odds of 5 : 1.

Shoulder-to-head movement means six, or tougher odds of 6 : 1.

Right hand to left shoulder means the odds have changed to 7 : 4.

Fingertips on shoulders denote that the horse is on odds of 9 : 2.

Odds of 5 : 4 are signalled like this.

Up and down with the forefingers means evens.

AT THE GAMING TABLES

When a croupier crosses his fingers he wants to be relieved from his post.

Pointing to the thumb is a sign that a player be allowed to go on.

Anxious croupiers call for help like this.

Cheats are signalled by fingertips on the table.

BROADCASTING TALK

A producer or controller gives the signal to start a programme like this.

Circling the ear with a finger means the sound is too low.

Opening and closing the hands means a programme can run longer.

Crossing the forefingers: a sign that there is half a minute left.

This gesture says time is short.

Finger across the throat means 'cut'.

523

SEMAPHORE ON THE LANDING STRIP

On an airstrip this means a turn to the right.

The signal to stop is given by crossing hands.

Right arm circling means 'start engine'.

Arms swinging outwards says 'chocks away'.

LANGUAGE OF THE DEAF

To the deaf, an upturned thumb means 'good'.

Bad is signified by extending the little finger.

Pain is indicated by shaking the hand.

Hands crossed above the breast expresses love.

THE LANGUAGE DETECTIVES

How they found the tribe that gave us words

Tracing missing persons can take much patient detective work. But a special kind of 'private eye' can trace the missing ancestors of whole peoples by studying the clues buried in words.

These philologists, as the language detectives are called, have traced the word trail back from peoples in Europe, India, South Africa, the Americas and the Pacific Islands to a tiny, nameless and forgotten tribe, which roamed central Eurasia 5000 to 6000 years ago before the dawn of written history.

For a long time, scholars puzzled over the striking similarity of words in different languages. In Dutch, *vader*; in Latin, *pater*; in Irish, *athir*; in Persian, *pidar*; in the Sanskrit of distant India, *pitr*. These words all sounded alike and meant the same thing—*father*.

How did it happen that widely separated peoples used such closely related sound symbols? The problem baffled linguists for years, the more so because *father* was but one of a host of such coincidences. Towards the end of the 18th century it dawned on scholars that perhaps all these words stemmed from some common language.

The language law

At last a brilliant German, Jacob Grimm —joint collector with his brother Wilhelm of Grimms' Fairy Tales—and other scholars of his time worked out a 'law' of language changes. Their discoveries showed that the changes which take place as a language develops and spreads are regular and consistent enough to permit comparisons between languages, and to allow the earlier stages of languages to be reconstructed.

Once the pattern of change was clear, scholars could see that the many words for *father* all pointed back to an original, PATER. Also, *water* in English, *wasser* in German, *hydor* in Greek, *voda* in Russian (vodka is 'little water'), *udan* in Sanskrit, and even *watar* in the language of King David's captain, Uriah the Hittite—all could have come only from an original WODOR. Using the law, they could trace the origin of countless words.

Philologists evolved an entire ancient vocabulary. They labelled this early speech 'Indo-European', because it had both Indic and European branches. There is a Latin branch, from which stem Italian, Spanish, Portuguese, French and Romanian. There is a Germanic branch, which includes English, German, Danish, Dutch, Swedish and Norwegian. The Celtic branch includes Welsh, Irish and Breton. The Slavic includes Russian, Polish, Czech, Bulgar and Serb. In addition, Indo-European includes Lithuanian, Persian, Greek, Armenian and a score of dialects in India which have sprung from ancient Sanskrit.

What tribe first spoke that mother tongue which hatched out this brood of cousin languages? Today we know a good deal about these dawn people, even though archaeologists have uncovered not a single crumbling wall, nor any fragment of pottery which we can be sure was theirs.

How they lived

Our speech ancestors had domesticated the cow, GWOU, which gave them milk, MELG. From this strain they also bred oxen, UKSEN, which were joined together by a yoke, YUG. They also knew sheep (their OWA became English *ewe*) which must have been tame, for from their *fleece*, PLEUS, they got wool, WLANA, which they had learnt to *weave*, WEBH, into cloth and then *sew*, SIW, into garments.

We might think of these ancestors as only wandering nomads had we not found their word for plough, which was ARA. Because of Latin *arare* (to plough) we speak in English of land which is *arable*—capable of cultivation.

What did they plant? Their word GRANO gives English *grain*. One kind of GRANO may have been light in colour, for their word for *white*, KWEIT, coming down through Old Germanic *hweits*, gave us the English *wheat*.

These speech ancestors of ours ground their grain in a mill, MEL, added water, WODOR, and yeast, YES, to make a dough, DHEIGH, which they would bake, BHOG, in an oven, UQNO, to make bread, PA (Latin *panis*, hence English *pantry*, the place where bread is kept).

All this we know from those old root words, which have come down to us in a score of languages. So have their numerals, which were: 1, OINOS; 2, DUO; 3, TREIES; 4, QETWER; 5, PENQE; 6, SWEKS; 7, SEPTN; 8, OKTO; 9, NEWN; 10, DEKM.

Where they lived

Where did these ancestors live? Since all Indo-European languages lack a common word for lion, tiger, elephant or camel, the homeland could not have been far south. Their old word SNEIGHW (English *snow*, Russian *sneig*, Greek *nipha*, Welsh *nyf*, Latin *nix*, French *neige*) might even push this homeland far northwards.

Wild animals they knew were the snake, SERP, the beaver, BHEBHRU, the bear, the goose, the rabbit and the duck. They had a word for small streams, STREW, and another for little ponds, which came down into English as *marsh*, *mire* and *moor*, and into Latin as *mare*—hence English *mariner* and *maritime*. But of vast salt oceans they probably knew nothing. When, fanning out, migrating branches of the tribe met the thunder of ocean surf, each gave this new marvel a separate name.

Of trees, they knew the birch and the beech, and because, much later, the writings of North Europe were scratched on smooth boards of beech, BOK, we get the English word *book*.

All these animals and trees are natives of the temperate zone. Many other signs point to one possible location in Central Europe. But gradually, pushed by over-population or invaders, the 'Indo-Europeans' began to move. Their wanderings lasted thousands of years and led them far afield. One branch was to push Slavic up to the polar sea, another was to bring Latin down to the Mediterranean, while still others were to carry Celtic into what is today Britain and France, and Germanic down to the right bank of the Rhine and up into Scandinavia.

On their wanderings they must have pondered the origins of things, for the English word God has its roots in GHUTOM, meaning 'The Being that is worshipped'. To them, as to us, the syllable SAC meant *sac*red; and from PREK (praying) down through Latin *precari* (to pray) comes our word *prayer*. The ideas enshrined in these words are not the least of the inheritance from that long-forgotten tribe—an inheritance more ancient than the walls of Troy and more enduring than the Pyramids.

WORDS! WORDS! WORDS!

And the remarkable stories behind them

Assassin For 200 years a murderous sect of religious fanatics terrorised the Middle East, using the town of Alamut, in South Persia, as their base. They killed under the influence of drugs and became notorious through their Arabic name of Hashshishin—users of hashish. The sect was wiped out by the Mongols in the 13th century, but the Anglicised version of the name lives on.

Berserk Vikings and other Norse warriors of the 8th to 11th centuries sometimes used an extraordinary weapon: sheer rage. Gripped by an inexplicable fury they roared and howled, bit their shields, and charged forward, killing anyone in their path. People who fled from these wild, fur-cloaked hordes described the warriors as 'berserk'—Norse for 'clad in bearskin'. This rage, which may have been induced by drugs extracted from herbs, was thought to make the 'berserkers' invincible.

Blurb When the publishers of American comic author Gelett Burgess wanted to promote one of his books by giving away copies at a booksellers' dinner in 1906, they commissioned Burgess to produce a special cover. He wrote a brief and nonsensical text under a picture of a beautiful model whom he named as Miss Belinda Blurb. Burgess later wrote a dictionary of made-up words—for example, *agowilt* (fear); *looblum* (flattery); *pooje* (embarrass); and *yab* (fanatic). But blurb—meaning the fulsome praise on the cover

of a book—was the only one to survive for any length of time.

Book Early Europeans scratched their records on thin beechwood slices, bound into bundles, and it is from the old Teutonic word *bok*, meaning beech, that the modern word is derived.

Booze The Dutch had a word for drinking to excess—*buizen*. By the 16th century *buizing* had been adopted in English, and over the years the word became completely Anglicised as slang for alcoholic drink.

Boudoir Any well-bred young lady in the Middle Ages was sent to her room to get over the sulks. The word comes from the French *bouder* 'to pout'. So it is a pouting room.

Boycott During Ireland's agrarian troubles in the 19th century, Captain Charles Cunningham Boycott was agent for Lord Earne's estates in County Mayo. When, in 1879, landlords tried to impose harsh levies on their tenants, the Irish radical leader Charles Parnell urged tenants to isolate the greedy owners like lepers of old. Boycott was the campaign's first victim. Labourers refused to work for him, postmen would not deliver his mail, and traders imposed such a successful ban on dealings with the Boycott family that provisions had to be brought in by steamer. After a year the Boycotts were forced to flee to England. The captain died in Suffolk in 1897. But the year under siege had established his name firmly in the language.

BOYCOTT BOYCOTTED *Defeated by the Irish peasantry who refused to work for him, Captain Boycott is given military protection as he begins his journey to enforced retirement in England.*

Bunkum Felix Walker was determined to prove himself an active Congressman after the electors of Buncombe County in North Carolina sent him to Washington in 1820. On one occasion he made a rambling irrelevant speech just as Congress was about to vote on a slavery issue. When colleagues asked him later why he had delayed matters, he replied: 'I was not speaking to the House but to Buncombe.' From that moment 'Buncombe' became associated with absurd remarks. The spelling was changed when the English novelist Charles Kingsley first used it in a book in 1857.

Canard Belgian journalist Egide Cornelissen reported in the early 19th century on a macabre experiment he had carried out with 20 ducks. He said he had roasted one duck and fed it to the other 19, then fed one of the 19 to the other 18, and so on until he had only one left—a duck which had eaten 19 of its fellow creatures. The story was printed widely in Europe and America, and when Cornelissen admitted that he had made it all up, a rueful world adopted *canard*, the French word for duck, as the term for any preposterous hoax.

Candidate When a Roman politician went campaigning he wore an immaculate white toga to make a good impression on the voters. The Latin *candidatus*, meaning a person dressed in white, later became synonymous with someone seeking public office.

Carnival The Italians coined the word *carnivale* to describe the week of feasting that preceded Lent, when Christians were forbidden to eat meat. The word comes from the Latin *carnem levare*—to remove meat.

Chauffeur In the days of steamdriven cars, the men employed to drive them also had to keep the boiler alight. So, today, hired drivers are still called by the French word for 'stoker'.

Checkmate Like the game of chess, the word for the winning move comes from Persia. The Persian phrase *Shah mat* means 'The king is dead'.

Clue The hero Theseus used a ball of thread to find his way out of the labyrinth after he killed the Minotaur of Crete in the old Greek legend. And after the story was told in medieval England—where the word for a ball of thread was 'clew'—a guide to the solution of any problem became known as a 'clew' or 'clue'.

Coach Large horse-drawn carriages first appeared in the 15th century in the Kocs region of Hungary. They were known as *Kocsi szeker*—literally, a Kocs cart. By the 16th century similar carriages were being built in England, with the name Kocs amended to coach.

Codswallop English owes this word for nonsense to an American called Hiram Codd who, in the 1870s, invented a gastight bottle to keep the fizz in lemonade. Since 'wallop' is a slang term for beer, and beer was never kept in a Codd bottle, 'Cod's wallop' was a drink that was worthless, compared with beer.

Deliberate The word meant originally to 'weigh in the balance' from the Latin *libra*, meaning scales. So someone who makes a decision after careful thought is said to be acting 'deliberately'. From the same root comes the abbreviation for a pound weight, *lb*.

Derrick Of all the stories about the origin of this word the oddest is the one that dates it to the late 16th century, during England's wars with Spain. It seems that 24 soldiers from the English fleet were condemned to death for looting in a raid on Cadiz. Since no one was keen to carry out the sentence, one of the 24, a man called Derrick, was pardoned in return for hanging the other 23. Later he became hangman at London's Tyburn gaol, and gained accidental immortality from the dockyard crane that looks like one of his gallows.

HOORAY! HOORAY! *Dixie, the popular term for the Confederate States, was derived from this ten (dix) dollar bill issued in the 1850s.*

Dixieland America suffered such a flood of counterfeit money in the 1830s that nearly all banknotes were suspect. But notes from Louisiana bearing the name of the Citizens' Bank and Trust Company of New Orleans were trusted throughout the nation. They were printed in a mixture of English and French, and the popular $10 bill carried the French word

THE WORKING DOLLAR *This, the first $1 bill (1862), was named after a district in Bohemia.*

BRILLIANT 'DUNCE' *The followers of John Duns Scotus (1265–1308) were derisively labelled 'dunsers'.*

'Dix' on the back. Louisiana became famous as 'the land of Dixes' or 'Dixies', meaning solid currency.

Dollar Silver coins used in 16th-century Europe were minted in Joachimsthal, a region of Bohemia. They were known as *Joachimsthaler*, which was later abbreviated to *Thaler* or dollar. The dollar sign $ is thought to be derived from the symbol of Philip V of Spain—a ribbon winding between the two Pillars of Hercules, Gibraltar and Ceuta. Dollars became America's official currency in 1792.

Doughboy Originally, doughboys were small round dough cakes served to American sailors aboard ship. But from the late 1840s the term came to be applied to American soldiers, because the large brass buttons on their uniforms resembled the cakes.

Dunce By a curious twist of fate one of the most brilliant thinkers of the Middle Ages, John Duns Scotus, gave his name to fools. His teachings were dismissed after his death in 1308, and during the Renaissance, scholars at Oxford, Paris and Cologne who supported his ideas were contemptuously dubbed Dunsers.

Eavesdrop Before roof guttering was invented, houses in medieval England used to have very wide eaves so that rain cascading off their thatched roofs did not soak into the foundations. People who lurked near doors and windows to overhear conversations had to stand in this 'eavesdrop' space to be close enough to listen. They were therefore condemned as eavesdroppers.

Farce Originally, 'farcing' was the padding in clothing or the stuffing in a chicken. Then in the Middle Ages, when mystery plays—early dramas based on religious stories—were performed, it became the custom for English actors to liven up their lines by 'farcing' or padding them with topical asides and jokes. The ad-libbing became so popular that by the late 17th century comic padding had expanded into a dramatic form in its own right. The earlier meaning survives in forcemeat, so called because it is 'forced' or stuffed.

Fees These would be decidedly inconvenient if they were still paid with their literal meaning. The word comes from the old English *feoh*, meaning cattle, which were bartered for other goods before money was developed.

Fiasco Venetian glassmakers in the 15th century used only perfectly flawless material for their prized articles. If any glass showed a fault, it was set aside to be made into a small flask—*fiasco*.

Fireman The first firemen did not stop fires. They started them. It was the fireman's hazardous job in a coalmine to go first into the pit each morning. Wrapped in wet rags, he carried a candle on a long stick to ignite any 'firedamp'—an explosive mixture of methane and air—that had seeped out of the seam during the night. Because the fires he started in this way made the pit safe for his workmates, the name was eventually applied to anyone who saved people from blazes.

Foolscap Before the Commonwealth was set up in England after the 17th-century Civil War, the king licensed papermaking, and every sheet bore the royal cypher as a watermark. The republican leader, Oliver Cromwell, with characteristic contempt for the trappings of royalty,

528

abolished this and substituted a water-mark of his own showing a 'fool's cap'.

Gazette Countless newspapers bear this title, which is thought to derive from the Italian *gazetta*, a small coin that was the price of a government newspaper published in Venice around 1536. Alternatively, the word may come from *gazza*, Italian for tittle-tattle and gossip.

Gerrymander Elbridge Gerry, who became Democratic Vice-president of America in 1812, was accused during his governorship of Massachusetts of juggling the electoral boundaries to beat a Republican rival at the polls. One observer said of the twisting boundaries: 'They look like a salamander.' Another critic retorted: 'Gerrymander, rather,' and the word stuck for political manipulation.

GI In the Second World War, every piece of kit used by American soldiers was stamped GI for 'Government Issue'. It was only a matter of time before the men applied the initials to themselves.

Handicap Two men who wanted to barter possessions of unequal value in medieval England sometimes played a game known as 'hand in cap'. They found someone to act as umpire. Then all three put a token sum of money into a cap. The umpire was asked to decide which of the two possessions being bartered was less valuable and how much money should be added to it to make the exchange fair.

When the umpire announced his decision, the two men put their hands in their pockets. If both took out money it was a sign that they accepted the umpire's verdict, and the deal went through, with the umpire taking the forfeit money in the cap. If only one took out money, he took the forefeit money, but the possessions were not exchanged. And if neither did, the deal was abandoned and the umpire took the forfeit.

By the 17th century, the 'hand in cap' system was being used in racing to decide which horses should carry extra weight to make a race fair, and eventually the word came to mean anything which acts to someone's disadvantage.

Hitch-hike This term is said to have originated in America in the 19th century to describe how two men could travel with only one horse. One man rode ahead an allotted distance, then hitched the horse to a tree and continued on foot. When the second man reached the horse he rode it until he overtook his com-panion, and so the sequence went on.

Hoodlum This term for a criminal is said to have been coined around 1870 by a San Francisco newspaper reporter who was looking for a word to describe young ruffians. He took a local gang-leader's name and reversed it from Muldoon to Noodlum—but his writing was so bad that the typesetter thought it was Hood-lum, and this was the word that stuck.

Hooligan The Houlihans were a rowdy Irish family living in Southwark in South London in the 1890s. They became notorious for their wildness, and their name—mispronounced as stories about them spread—became part of the language.

Jargon Scientists who baffle laymen with the specialised language of their subject might feel less smug if they knew that the term comes from the old French *gargon*—meaning the twittering noise that birds make.

Jeep In 1937 the American cartoonist E. C. Segar introduced a creature called Eugene the Jeep into his popular Popeye cartoon strip. Jeeps, according to the strip, were tough little animals who lived on orchids and could become invisible. When, a few years later, the Willys company of Ohio won a US Army transport contract with a powerful open-topped 4-seater vehicle that was just 11 ft long and could go anywhere, soldiers gave the rugged little machine the same name.

Juggernaut Once a year a 45 ft high statue of a Hindu god is paraded through the streets of Puri in North-east India on

POPEYE'S PAL *Jeep*, part dog and wholly fantasy, gave his name to the tough little general-purpose vehicle of the Second World War. The car's achievements became as legendary as its namesake's.

RELENTLESS LORD *The 45 ft effigy crushed everything—including voluntary victims.*

a huge wagon pulled by hundreds of devotees. In the past, pilgrims threw themselves to their deaths beneath the wagon's massive wheels. When reports of the ancient custom reached Europe in the 14th century, the Westernised version of the local name for the god—*Jagannath*, which means Lord of the World—came to mean a relentless force that crushed everything in its path. More recently it has been applied to the giant trucks on modern roads.

Jumbo The word used for anything of great size comes from an African elephant of the same name which was a star attraction in Paris and then London Zoo in the mid-19th century. Jumbo, whose shoulders towered 10 ft 9 in. high, was eventually sold to the American showman P. T. Barnum, and died in 1885 after being struck by a train during a tour of Canada.

Love This word for a nil score in tennis comes from the French *l'oeuf*, meaning egg. In France *l'oeuf* became slang for zero because of its shape.

Namby-pamby The British poet Ambrose Philips wrote such insipid little verses for children in the 18th century that a skit on his Christian name has become the derogatory term for anything affectedly pretty and coy. The expression was coined in 1726 by dramatist Henry Carey, who scoffed at Philips's nursery poems with the words:

So the nurses get by heart,
Namby Pamby's little rhymes.

Nickname The 'nick' part of this word comes from the early English *eke* meaning 'also'. So an extra name was known as 'an eke-name', later slurred so that it became 'a nickname'.

Pagan To start with, this meant the same as 'peasant', from the French word *pays* meaning 'country'. But as towns grew up, their haughty inhabitants gave 'pagan' its present meaning of uncivilised or godless.

Pamphlet A Latin poem called *Pamphilus* proved so popular in the 12th century that numerous copies were produced. The title is Greek for 'Loved by All'. Thin paper-covered books were later dubbed pamphilets, shortened over the years to pamphlets.

Pedigree In old French, *pied de grue* meant 'foot of a crane', and the term came to be applied to family backgrounds because the arrow-shaped marks linking generations on a genealogical table look rather like the footprints of birds.

Perfume This was the name given at one time to a disinfectant, hence the link with the word 'fumigate'. The Romans combined the Latin *per* (through) with *fumus* (smoke) to describe a smell drifting through the air like smoke.

Quaker The religious sect called originally the Children of Light, and now known as the Society of Friends, is said to have acquired this nickname because members 'quaked' with religious fervour at its emotional prayer meetings.

Another version of the origin of 'Quaker' concerns the sect's founder, the 17th-century English preacher George Fox, who was regarded with open hostility by the authorities of his time. Once, in October 1650, Fox was hauled into court in Derby on a charge of preaching illegally. The defiant Fox thundered from the dock that it was not he, but the magistrate, who had the most to fear. 'Tremble at the word of the Lord,' he urged. Instead, the judge, Gervase Bennet, sneered that the only 'quaker' in court was Fox himself, and the nickname stuck.

Quarantine Sick people bored by a spell in an isolation ward may like to console themselves with the thought that originally quarantine meant being shut away for a full 40 days (from the Latin *quarantena*, meaning 40). By that time people who had been exposed to a disease were either dead, recovered, or presumed to be no longer contagious.

Quiz In about 1780, so the story goes, a Dublin theatre manager named Daly laid a bet that within 24 hours he could introduce a new word into the English language. He spent a whole night chalking the letters *QUIZ* on walls throughout the city, and next day the strange word was on everyone's lips—yet nobody knew what it meant. Thus it became a byword for a jokey puzzle. Later it came to mean a set of puzzling questions or, as a verb, to interrogate someone.

Robot The Czech dramatist Karel Capek invented this word in a play about mechanical men. The play was called *R.U.R.*, which stood for Rossum's Universal Robots, and the term entered the English language when it was translated in 1923. Capek made up the word by shortening the Czech term for a slave—*robotnik*.

School Children toiling at their lessons may be surprised to learn that this word comes from the Greek *schole*, meaning leisure. The Greeks saw learning as a purely leisure-time activity.

Serendipity The origin of this term, which means finding one thing while looking for another, can be traced to the day. In 1722 a fairy tale called *The Travels and Adventures of Three Princes of Serendip* was trans-

lated into English. In the story, the heroes from Serendip—the old name for Ceylon, now known as Sri Lanka—constantly made discoveries by accident. The English writer Horace Walpole was delighted with the tale. And in a letter to a friend about it, written on January 28, 1754, he coined the word to describe the princes' happy knack.

Silhouette When Étienne de Silhouette became France's finance minister in the mid-18th century, his cheese-paring economies over court salaries proved so unpopular that within a year he was replaced. Silhouette retired and practised his meanness at home by using cheap black paper cut-outs in place of conventional decorations. And he raised extra money by making portraits with the same technique. In 1759 the idea was taken up at an exhibition in Paris. Soon, black profile 'portraits' became a craze that spread to England—perpetuating the name of the tight-fisted M. de Silhouette.

Silly This word comes from the German

CUT-OUT *When deposed finance minister Étienne de Silhouette (1709–67) fell on hard times, he made a living by the portraiture style named after him.*

selig, meaning 'holy'. But over the years it came to mean innocent, rustic, plain, simple, simple-hearted, frail, weak and finally foolish.

Sirloin There is a persistent story that James I of England was so delighted with a certain cut of beef that he knighted it, giving rise to the term 'Sir Loin'. In fact, the word is just a misspelling of the old French *surloigne*, meaning 'top of the loin'.

Spinster Girls awaiting marriage would at one time spin threads to make household linen for their trousseau. It was said rather unkindly of the ones who never got husbands, that they kept spinning and waiting all their lives.

Teetotal The most attractive story to explain this word concerns a reformed 19th-century drunkard named Dicky Turner, who proclaimed in a stuttering voice at a temperance meeting in Preston, Lancashire: 'Nothing less than t-t-total abstinence will do.'

A more likely derivation is from a New York temperance society which demanded that members who signed the pledge against alcohol should write the letter T against their names to indicate Total abstinence. They were known as 'T-totals'.

Thug In the early days of British rule in India—and long, long before—thousands of travellers died at the hands of the Thags, members of a macabre religious cult. The victims were strangled in a ritual form of murder called *Thagi*, then their bones were broken to make burial easier in small graves. By the mid-19th century, a British campaign led by Sir William Sleeman had virtually wiped out the cult, but the Anglicised name lives on, as a description of a violent criminal.

Tip Customers at 18th-century English coffee houses were invited to drop coins into staff collecting-boxes bearing the words 'To Insure Promptness'. Later, only the three initials were used—and the name for a gratuity was born.

Tommy British soldiers have been known —to friends and foes—as 'Tommies' ever since they were issued with a Soldier's Account Book after the Battle of Waterloo in 1815. The book explained how they could collect their pay, and with each copy was a sample form filled out in the name of Thomas Atkins. The account book has long been superseded, but the imaginary soldier's name has stuck.

Treacle This term has its roots in the Greek for wild animal, *ther*. From that word came *theriake*, meaning the antidote to an animal's bite. This became 'treacle' in English to describe the balm put on a wound. It came to mean a sugary syrup because sugar was widely used in medicine.

Trivial In ancient Rome, serious business was carried out at the Forum, the main market place. But gossipers gathered at a crossroads—the *Tri-Via* (three streets)— and the name came to be used of the idle stories they exchanged there.

Tycoon One of Commodore Matthew Perry's souvenirs from the American expedition to Japan in 1854 was this term for a business magnate. It is an Anglicised spelling of the Japanese *taikun*, derived from the Chinese words *ta*, meaning 'great', and *kiun*, meaning 'prince'.

Walnut The name is probably derived from the Old English *wealh*, meaning foreign, to distinguish it from the native hazelnut. *Wealh* usually signified a Roman or Celtic foreigner, and the words Wales and Welsh come from the same root.

Wedding Cynics who suggest that marriage is a lottery can point to the fact that 'to wed' meant 'to wager'. In old English, 'weddian' meant to pledge money in a bet—or pledge yourself in marriage.

EASTERN VIEW *Commodore Perry, seen here through Japanese eyes, gave us the word 'tycoon'.*

WHAT'S IN A PHRASE?

The meanings and origins of popular sayings

Blue-blooded The expression is derived from the Spanish *sangre azul*, used by aristocratic families of Castile to describe themselves as being uncontaminated by Moorish or Jewish blood. It probably originated because the veins of people with fair complexions would appear blue.

By hook or by crook The metaphor has been credited with many different origins, but is most probably derived from the feudal custom of lords allowing their tenants to gather as much wood from their lord's land as they could rake up from the undergrowth with a hook or pull down from the trees with a shepherd's crook.

It is easier for a camel to go through the eye of a needle than for a rich man to enter into the kingdom of God This is a popular biblical quotation that, through a translation error, is inaccurate. The original Greek tells not of a camel, but a rope (*kamilos*). When it was translated into Latin, *kamilos* was confused with *kamelos* (camel). The error has been perpetuated in almost every language in which the Bible has been printed.

Catherine Wheel The firework was named after St Catherine, whose symbol was the wheel. According to legend, she was martyred by being tied to a spiked wheel and rolled down a hill. The spinning wheel then became the motif of institutions that were named after her, such as St Catherine's College, Cambridge.

Double Dutch An expression used by English-speaking people to describe something that to them is unintelligible. 'It's all Greek to me,' is another way of putting it. Other nations have similar forms. The French and Greeks say, 'It's Chinese to me', while Polish people say, 'I'm listening to a Turkish sermon'. The Finns speak of 'Pig German'. The Germans say *kauderwelsch*—meaning 'These are Bohemian villages to me'. Everyone, it seems is anti-someone!

Hip Hip Hooray! Crusaders in the Middle Ages used a version of this whoop of triumph. 'Hip' is thought to be a corruption of 'Hep'—from the initials of the Crusader battle-slogan *Hierosolyma est perdita*, meaning 'Jerusalem is fallen'. 'Hooray' could be from the Slavonic *Hu-raj!*, 'To Paradise!', the cry with

ST CATHERINE *A spiked wheel—the instrument on which she was martyred—became her symbol.*

which they pursued their non-Christian victims to their deaths.

Humble pie Medieval lords and ladies always feasted on the better parts of the animals that their hunters brought home. However, their servants had to make do with the 'umbles', or offal. Because it was a poor man's dish, 'umble pie' came to be misdescribed as 'humble pie'—the meal for those who are forced to make do with second or third best because they dare not claim the lion's share.

The gods The term was first used in London's Drury Lane Theatre where, around the early 19th century, the ceiling was decorated with paintings of classical gods and goddesses.

Kilroy was here The slogan that came to be chalked up on walls throughout the world in the Second World War was originally the 'signature' used by James J. Kilroy, a shipyard inspector at Quincy, Massachusetts, to indicate that he had passed a piece of equipment as satisfactory. It found its way to many American war zones, and the frequent appearance of Kilroy's signature everywhere tickled the soldiers' imagination so much that it was counterfeited almost everywhere there was something to write with and a surface to scribble on.

A similar character of obscure origin, known as Chad, appeared in Britain in the early post-war years, accompanied by phrases such as *Wot no butter, eggs, milk?*—as a lighthearted protest against food shortages and rationing.

Lumber room The Lombard family were more than just bankers in medieval England. Until Elizabethan times, they also had a monopoly in pawnbroking. So goods in pawn became known as Lombard goods. Eventually the term was widened to include all articles stored away, and boxrooms anywhere became known as 'Lombard' or 'Lumber' rooms.

Lynch law During the American Revolution, when the work of the courts was disrupted, a justice of the peace called Charles Lynch took charge of law and presided over an unofficial court in Bedford County, Virginia. Except in one case of conspiracy, for which he imposed the death penalty, the most severe sentences he handed out were fines and whippings. In 1782 the state government decided that Lynch had been perfectly justified in sentencing the conspirators during the war, because of their danger to the state. He was exonerated. Lynch died in 1796.

But a century later his reputation for mercy was forgotten, and all that was remembered was that he had meted out unofficial justice. So his name came to be used to describe the justices of vicious mob 'courts' that executed nearly 5000 people in the US.

Men of straw This expression, nowadays applied to someone of no substance, or of dubious trustworthiness, was originally used to describe professional perjurers. These were men who would hang around outside law courts in Paris and London in medieval times and could be hired to give false evidence. They identified themselves by a straw—the badge of their profession—sticking out of their shoes.

Not an iota of difference The expression stems from a religious controversy in the Byzantine Empire. There were two religious factions—the orthodox Catholics, who believed that God the Father incorporated God the Son, and the Arians, who believed that God the Father and God the Son were alike, but not the same being. In the original Greek, the idea of God the Father and the Son together is *Homo-ousion* and the idea of God the Father and God the Son as separate is *Homoi-ousion*. The only difference between the two phrases is the Greek letter *Iota*. In AD 325 the Arian doctrine was declared heretical.

P's and Q's Believed to stem from the days when alehouse-keepers used to chalk up customers' debts on the wall—the number of pints owed for under the letter P, the quarts in the Q column. There are, however, other explanations for the saying. One is that children, or printers' apprentices, were told to be careful in distinguishing between the back-to-front forms of 'p' and 'q'. Another suggests that dancing masters in the time of Louis XIV would tell pupils to mind their 'p's' (meaning *pieds*, feet) and 'q's' (*queues*, wigs) which might fall off when they bent low in a formal bow.

Queer Street The description began as Query Street, from the habit English shopkeepers had of putting a question mark in their books against the name of a customer whose credit was shaky. The customer was said to be in Query (later Queer) Street until he had paid his debts.

Robbing Peter to pay Paul A common fable about this phrase is that it refers to

LYNCH LAW *'Courts' that executed nearly 5000 people in the US between 1882 and 1951 took their name from Charles Lynch, a JP who took the law into his hands in the revolution of 1780.*

the fact that in 1550 many of the estates of St Peter's, Westminster, were appropriated to pay for the repairs of St Paul's Cathedral. But it seems the phrase was common long before this. In 1380 the preacher John Wyclif is reported to have said: 'How should God approve that you rob Peter, and give this robbery to Paul in the name of Christ?'

Show a leg Some sailors took their wives to sea in Nelson's day. When the bosun went around the crew's quarters in the morning he would tell any reluctant risers to 'show a leg'. If the limb was a woman's, she was allowed to sleep on.

Showing the white feather A gamecock with a white feather in its tail was taken by fanciers as a sign of inferior breeding and lack of courage. The symbol was later used to denote cowardice.

Not to be sneezed at During the 17th century, snuff-takers learnt to control their sneezing and reserve it as a sign of boredom or disapproval. Anything that merited their favour, therefore, was deemed 'not to be sneezed at'.

Selling down the river This dramatic way of expressing the idea of being badly let down came into use during slavery days in America. Colonists of northern states would be offered high prices for their domestic slaves by plantation owners in the south when slave ships from Africa were delayed and labour was scarce. A slave who was sold in this way, usually sailing down the Mississippi, could expect a much harsher way of life, much suffering and perhaps an early death at the hands of tougher taskmasters.

Tell it to the marines The diarist Samuel Pepys claimed that Charles II first used this phrase when a colonel of the marines told him he had seen a flying fish. It was a tall story, the king explained, but he would be prepared to believe it if the much-travelled marines believed it.

He'll never set the Thames on fire The origin of the phrase is believed to refer, not to the river, but to a piece of flour-mill equipment called a *temse*. When flour was sifted through this sieve by hand, it was sometimes said that a man worked so hard the friction made the wood smoulder. A slow worker, therefore, would never set the *temse* on fire.

The cold shoulder This term for a polite snub came into use in medieval France. A château guest who was served a cold shoulder of beef or mutton instead of hot meat was intended to take it as a gentle hint that he had overstayed his welcome.

To knuckle under There are two possible derivations of the phrase, which means to concede defeat. One is the medieval form of submission, bending the knee—then called a knuckle. The other is an old custom of rapping the underside of a table to admit defeat in a game.

To truckle under This expression, meaning to adopt an inferior or subordinate posture, comes from the truckle bed—a contraption rather like a wheelbarrow which noblemen had carted round with them in the days when travellers could not always count on comfortable night quarters. The master slept *on* the truckle bed, his servant under it.

Touch and go One of the many common expressions that come from the English seafaring tradition. Many a ship would touch bottom in shoal water and 'go' when the tide floated her off—a narrow escape from possible disaster.

White elephant Because albino elephants are so rare, custom at the court of the King of Siam used to decree that they be given nothing but the best by their owners. So whenever a courtier angered him badly, the king used to announce that he was planning, as a mark of his special regard, to present the man with one of his own royal white elephants. The courtier then had to choose between insulting the king by refusing the gift, or being ruined by the expense of keeping it. Mostly, the luckless courtiers decamped in a hurry—as the king had hoped. The phrase was brought into the English language by travellers. It now means any useless and burdensome gift.

THE NUMBERS GAME

How a king invented the yard by rule of thumb

In a world where nature creates nothing to a standard size, man since the earliest times has used his own body as the basis for measurement. Over the centuries he evolved rules of thumb—of arm and foot—to give himself units of length.

The cubit, the measure that Noah used in building his ark, was originally the length from elbow to middle fingertip, about 18 in. It was divided by the ancient Egyptians into fingers and palms. Four finger widths, or digits, made a palm, and six palms made a cubit. Later, about 4000 years ago, the Egyptians added a seventh palm, and the royal cubit, as it was then known, became standardised at approximately 21 in.

The inch first represented the width of a man's thumb, but it was standardised in classic Rome as one-twelfth of a foot. In 1305 Edward I defined the yard of three 12 in. feet, and decreed that the inch should be equal to three grains of dry barley laid end to end. The barleycorn unit is still used by shoemakers.

It is said that in the 16th century Henry VIII used his thumb to redefine the yard. According to tradition, Henry fixed the yard as the distance from the tip of his nose to the tip of his thumb at the end of his outstretched arm.

The foot, as its name suggests, was once the distance from the heel to the tip of the big toe. It, too, was standardised in ancient Egypt as two-thirds of a short (six-palm) cubit. It came to be used to measure an acre, thanks again to Edward I. Before Edward's time an acre was the amount of land a yoke of oxen could plough in a day. But since this could vary enormously, Edward pegged an acre at 40 rods by 4 rods—each rod being 16½ft long—a measurement that has survived unchanged.

The metric method

The first and only system based on logic, rather than physical accident, was worked out during the French Revolution, as part of a general reaction against the iron hand of tradition. The metric system of weights and measures was the creation of 12 scientists, appointed by the French National Assembly in 1791.

The scientists decided to find some fundamental length in the natural world —to be called a metre, after the Greek *metron*, meaning 'measure'—and to make it the basis of a system on multiples of ten.

The length they picked was the circumference of the earth measured on a line through the poles. The scientists measured a quarter of that circumference on a meridian through France and, to give themselves a convenient-sized unit, called it 10 million metres or 10,000 kilometres. So the metre, slightly longer than a yard, was fixed as 1/40,000,000th of the earth's circumference through the poles. Today it is defined in terms of wavelengths of light.

Marking time

In Britain and the American colonies, September 3, 1752, never happened. Nor did the ten days that should have followed it. For in that year Britain adopted the Gregorian calendar, and to get back in step meant 'losing' 11 days. The decision caused riots at the time because people thought that the government had stolen 11 days of their lives.

Most early calendars were based on the moon, which takes roughly 29½ days to circle the earth. The ancient Babylonian calendar, adopted by the Hebrews, was entirely lunar-based, with 12 months of alternately 29 and 30 days and thus a 354-day year.

Out of step

But this calendar rapidly got ahead of the seasons, so it was adjusted to keep it roughly in step with the solar year. The Babylonians observed that 235 lunar months coincided with a cycle of 19 solar years. So around 380 BC they decided that 7 of every 19 years should have 13 months instead of 12. The Jewish calendar still follows this lunar-solar arrangement, but the Muslim calendar remains lunar-based, with regressive months.

There were many attempts to devise a calendar that approximated the actual time it takes the earth to circle the sun— 365 days, 5 hours, 48 minutes, 46 seconds —without losing the all-important 12-month lunar year.

The ancient Egyptians had nearly succeeded, with a 365-day civil calendar. But it was apparently overlooked by the rest of the world until Julius Caesar adopted and modified it as the official calendar of Rome. His reformed calendar began on January 1, 46 BC.

Caesar's 'leap' forward

Caesar was also the first to introduce the idea of a four-year leap year (with a 30-day February), to make up for the extra fraction of a day over 365 that the earth takes to complete its cycle.

Caesar's Julian calendar lasted well. It was much more accurate than its predecessors. But it was still 0·0078 days too

EIGHT MINUTES SAVED THE DAY

RAILWAYS and a court case helped to sound the death-knell of local timekeeping in Britain. On November 24, 1858, at 10.06 a.m. by Dorset clocks, a Dorchester judge found against a man involved in a land battle because he was late for the 10 a.m. hearing. Two minutes later the man arrived and claimed he was on time —by the station clock in his home town of Carlisle in Cumberland.

The case had to be retried, and in 1880 Parliament ended the confusion by ordering the whole country to set its clocks by Greenwich Mean Time.

long. And 1500 years later the accumulated error had added up to ten full days.

At this time, Pope Gregory XIII established the calendar used in the West today. In 1582 he solved the problem of the ten extra days—by simply omitting them. He decreed that in that year only, October 4 was to be followed by October 15. The reason why England and her colonies had to lose 11 rather than ten days was that they did not adopt the Gregorian calendar until 170 years later, by which time it was another complete day ahead of the real year.

Gregory's calendar was a reformed version of the Julian one. Gregory rearranged the lengths of the months into their modern versions and, more important, devised a way of overcoming the slight inaccuracy in the Julian calendar. He decreed that in order to qualify as a leap year, a century year (100, 1500, and so on) had to be divisible not just by four but by 400. That is why the years 1700, 1800 and 1900 were not leap years, but 2000 will be.

The ten-day week

Weeks have always been an odd time out in mankind's measurement of the passing of the seasons. Days are related to the spin of the earth, months to the phases of the moon, and years to the earth's slow journey around the sun. But weeks have been as varied as the people who used them. The ancient Egyptians and Greeks split their month into three ten-day weeks, while some West African tribes used a four-day week, and the ancient Assyrians arranged their lives around a six-day cycle.

The seven-day week, which is now standard throughout the world, seems to have originated with the Babylonians about 4000 years ago; its days were named for the seven planets known at that time. Various countries have tried to change the habit, but always they have been defeated by the force of custom. In 1792 the French introduced a decimal ten-day week to go with their new metric system, but it was soon abolished by Napoleon. Russian efforts to start a five-day week in 1929 and a six-day week in 1932 failed because people ignored them.

Dividing a day into 24 hours is another man-made notion. The Sumerians divided their day into six watches (three day and three night), and the Babylonians divided it into 12 equal periods. It was probably the Egyptians who first picked a 24-hour day to mark their priestly ceremonies. They chose 24 because stargazers noticed that the night was marked off by the consecutive rising of 12 bright stars. Bent on nothing more than symmetry, they divided the day to match.

Then about 1400 BC the Egyptian Pharaoh Amenophis decided that he needed a better way to tell the time at night. He had his chief engineer build a water clock. Shadow clocks—primitive sundials—gave the approximate time during daylight. The water clock worked by allowing water to trickle slowly out of a carefully graded bowl. By dipping his fingers in and feeling how many of the bowl's ridged markings were above the water-line, Amenophis could then for the first time tell roughly how long it was until sunrise.

The idea was developed by Greeks and Romans, whose water clocks (called *clepsydras*) were able to measure fractions of hours.

Temperature scales

Of the three major temperature scales in use today, two got their figures by luck. Only Centigrade was deliberately arranged to divide the temperature between the freezing and boiling points of water into 100 equal parts.

The first thermoscope, having no scale, was invented by the Italian scientist Galileo. He had noticed that when alcohol was heated in a very narrow glass tube, it expanded and rose in the tube in proportion to the increase in temperature. A century or so later Gabriel D. Fahrenheit, a German physicist in Amsterdam, developed a temperature scale for a mercury thermometer.

He took as zero the lowest temperature he could produce—a mixture of ice and salt—and planned to fix the blood temperature of a healthy man at 12. But he found he needed a more finely graded scale, so he divided the interval into 96 parts instead of 12, with 96 for blood temperature.

Using this scale Fahrenheit found that pure water froze at 32, and boiled at 212. Later adjustments established 98.6 as normal blood temperature.

In 1730 the French physicist René de Reaumur tried to develop a Centigrade thermometer, using a solution of alcohol and water instead of mercury. He decided that logically zero ought to be the freezing point of water. So he marked that and scaled his thermometer so that one degree equalled 1/1000th part of the fluid's volume at the freezing level. Unfortunately, the solution boiled at the 80 mark, wrongly taken by others as the boiling point of water.

The scale was developed 12 years later by a Swede, Anders Celsius. It now has zero as the freezing point of water and 100 as boiling point. This scale has generally superseded the others.

Counting sheep

As soon as man the hunter became man the herdsman he began to need a way of keeping track of his flocks—hence numbers. Since fingers were the obvious thing to count on, most early men used ten as their basic number.

But there are primitive tribes who to this day use totally different systems. Some have no bigger numbers than six, so that any larger total has to be written as multiples of six plus whatever is the remainder. The Western figure 15, for instance, would in such a system be written as 23, meaning $(2 \times 6) + 3$.

Some of the earliest written numbers were chisel-shaped marks scratched on clay tablets by Mesopotamian scribes around 5000 years ago.

Some 3000 years later the Romans were still using the clumsy letter system of numbering (I, II, III, IV, V ... X ... L ... C ... D ... M), which expressed big numbers as a row of smaller numbers added together. For instance, DCCLXVI meant the numbers $500 + 100 + 100 + 50 + 10 + 5 + 1 = 766$.

Arabic numerals, similar to the ones used in the West today, were developed fully only in the 9th century AD. Fewer figures are needed because the positions of the figures themselves determine their values. In the number 234, for instance, the figures 2, 3 and 4 are not added together as in the Roman system to give the total value. Instead, each is multiplied by 100, 10 or 1 depending on its position in the sequence.

Without the zero, however, this simple positional way of writing numbers was impossible. And the Arabs owe that invention to an unknown Indo-Chinese mathematician who, in AD 683, hit on the idea of putting a dot for blank spaces when he was jotting down the numbers from his abacus. The dot was changed to a zero in Europe, becoming standard in modern mathematics.

Proof spirit

Spirits—vodka, whisky, gin, and so on—are composed of alcohol, water and flavouring substances. Before the 18th century, distillers had a simple method of determining a spirit's strength; equal quantities of spirit and gunpowder were mixed and a flame applied. If the mixture failed to burn, the spirit was too weak, and if it flashed, too strong. Only if the mixture burnt evenly with a clear blue flame was the spirit said to have been 'proved'. In 1803 an exciseman, Bartholomew Sikes, invented a hydrometer, which measured the specific gravities of alcohol and water mixtures. His device is still used by distillers and brewers to this day.

'Proof' is an arbitrary measure of the proportion of alcohol to water and varies from country to country. In Britain, 100 proof means 57·1 per cent alcohol to 42·9 per cent water. Spirits are usually less than 100 proof.

WHY 'ALL THE REST HAVE 31 ...'

'THIRTY DAYS hath September, April, June and November,' runs the children's mnemonic, 'all the rest have 31, except February, which has 28.' The reason months have different numbers is that when the Romans under Julius Caesar invented the Julian calendar they decided to give months with special religious significance 31 days and the ones of lesser importance 30 days. Thus January, named after the god Janus, March, after Mars, and July, in honour of Caesar himself, are among the months with 31 days. Caesar's successor, Augustus, named August after himself and, naturally, gave it 31 days. The Julian months of September (7th month) and October (8th month) became the 9th and 10th months when in 1582 Pope Gregory changed the New Year from the Julian date of March 25 to January 1.

A FEAST OF HISTORY

The origins of food and drink—from aperitif to dessert

Beer In one form or another beer has been brewed from various grains and plants for as long as historical records go back. And as early as 3400 BC a tax on barley wine, one of the most popular beers, was levied in the Ancient Egyptian city of Memphis, on the Nile. The Romans

BEER HARVEST *Made from fermented malt, beer is flavoured by hops (seen harvested here).*

picked up the knowledge of brewing from the Greeks, and Caesar's legions, whose main drink was beer, spread it throughout all the lands they conquered. It is made by fermenting malt, flavoured with hops or other bitters.

Chicken Marengo After a successful encounter with the Austrians at the Battle of Marengo in Piedmont, Italy, in 1800, a hungry Napoleon demanded a meal. The army's supply train had not caught up with the front-line troops, so a foraging party was sent out to find the emperor some food. Their 'bag'—a small hen, three eggs, four tomatoes and six crayfish—was cooked in a little garlic and oil and served with bread and a nip of brandy. So pleased was he with the result that Napoleon ordered the meal to be served after every battle. And today the original recipe is enjoyed, unchanged, in many parts of the world.

Coca-Cola This world-famous soft drink originated in the back kitchen of a chemist's shop in Atlanta, Georgia, in 1886. The chemist, John Pemberton—known as 'Dr Pemberton', because of his fondness for making up remedial concoctions—had been trying to find the recipe

for a pleasant soft drink, and at last he was satisfied. He sold the rights four years before his death. Within 40 years, Coca-Cola had become a name known the world over. The name comes from *coca* leaves from a South American shrub, and *cola*, an extract from the kola nut. The exact recipe is a closely guarded secret.

Cocktail Among the many stories of the origin of this name for a mixture of alcoholic drinks, the most attractive is that it was first drunk as a toast in the days of cock-fighting to the cock that had the most tail feathers left after a battle. Another theory is that it was called after a *coquetier*, a type of cup in which it was served during the early French influence in New Orleans. Yet another alternative says it stems from *cokale*, a fiery brew once used in England to keep fighting cocks on their mettle.

But the most likely origin is that the name derived from *coquetel*, a mixed drink from the wine-growing district of the Gironde, which is said to have been popular during the French Revolution.

Doughnuts The world-famous cakes that are simply a sugar-coated ring of fried dough with a hole in the centre were 'invented' by a New England schoolboy. Young Hanson Gregory, tired of having to eat his mother's cakes that always seemed too stodgy in the middle, persuaded her to remove the centre before frying the dough. His idea worked, quickly caught on in the neighbourhood and eventually spread to become a favourite coffee-break snack in many parts of the world.

Granny Smith The apple that has become internationally popular was named after Maria Ann Smith, who emigrated to Sydney from Sussex with her family in 1839. By budding and grafting on some seedlings which had sprung up in her garden, she developed a strain so superior to anything known in Australia that cases stamped 'Apples from Mrs Smith' became eagerly sought in the markets. Their fame spread rapidly, and soon professional fruit farmers were producing them as Granny Smiths.

Grog This was the name given to a mixture of rum and water, which was a daily issue in the British Navy for 200 years.

COCK-FIGHTING *Did the popular idea of mixing a cocktail derive from this savage old sport?*

It is derived from the nickname of Admiral Edward Vernon, known as 'Old Grog' because he used to wear a cloak of coarse cloth, or grogram. In 1740 he attempted to stamp out drunkenness in the navy by ordering that the sailors' daily issue of a half-pint of neat rum should be diluted and served in two instalments, with six hours between. The ration was abolished in 1970 as being out of keeping with the modern, highly technical—and sober—navy.

Ice-cream sundae It was forbidden to sell ice-cream with soda on the Sabbath in the puritanical town of Evanston, Illinois, in the late 19th century. But some confectioners got round the ban on soda by serving ice-cream with syrup instead. The confection became known as a Sunday. The final 'y' was changed to 'e' to overcome religious objections.

Peach Melba The French chef Auguste Escoffier was an ardent admirer of Dame Nellie Melba, the famous Australian soprano, but was too shy to send her flowers. When she dined alone at London's Savoy Hotel at the turn of the century, however, he concocted a special dessert for the singer. It consisted of a peach, poached in vanilla syrup, in a cup of vanilla ice-cream and covered with crushed raspberries. When she said how much she enjoyed it, and asked its name,

DAME NELLIE MELBA *It was after the famous soprano that the dessert Peach Melba was named.*

541

M. Escoffier said he would be honoured if he could call it Peach Melba. The idea became the rage of London and eventually a popular dessert all over the world.

Sandwiches The 4th Earl of Sandwich (1718-92) was such a compulsive gambler that he did not want to take time away from the card table to eat a cooked meal. Instead, he chose to have pieces of cooked meat served between two pieces of bread during his games. Although the snack now bears his name in recognition of the fashion he set, it is thought that the idea of eating meat in this way was introduced to Britain by Rome's conquering legions.

HEAVY GAMBLER, LIGHT SNACK *Portrait of the 4th Earl of Sandwich.*

Spam In Britain, Spam was first eaten as a wartime substitute for fresh meat. But it had been sold since 1936 in Minnesota, where a $100 prize was offered for the best name. The winning entry was the word derived from the main ingredient: SPiced hAM.

Tea Although popularly thought of as an 'English' beverage, tea was fashionable in Holland by 1640, about 12 years before it appeared in Britain. The Dutch established plantations in Java in 1606, and by 1610 began to import tea to Europe. Forty years later they took it to America. The first tea to reach England was a small amount found on a captured Dutch ship in 1652. It was another eight years before it was first publicly sold in London, despite outraged protests by preachers and writers that it was 'inimical to health, morals and public order'. It was at first considered an aphrodisiac and people not only brewed it, but ate the leaves on bread and butter.

The people of Eire are the world's greatest tea-drinkers today: 7·76 lb (about

'IMMORAL' TEA *Tea, grown and dried in the Far East, outraged many English preachers.*

WINE: MAN'S ANCIENT COMFORT

WINE MAKING can be traced back to the ancient civilisations of the Near East—those of Babylonia, Assyria, Phoenicia, Palestine, Syria and Egypt. One of the earliest references occurs in the Old Testament book of Genesis, which says that Noah 'planted a vineyard: And he drank the wine and was drunken'.

This fresco from a tomb shows how wine was made in ancient Egypt.

542

1200 cups) per head was the average consumption in 1973.

The practice of tea-drinking is world-wide, but the way in which it is drunk varies. In Tibet, for example, the traditional method is to mix the tea with a rancid yak milk and churn it in a wooden cylinder until it is like a thick soup. The Tibetans, moreover, do not use tea leaves. They buy their tea in bricks from China. The leaves are compressed with rice flour, and pieces were flaked off when needed.

Toasts The custom of drinking to a person's honour is so-called because in Elizabethan times pieces of toast were put in celebration drinks.

Tomato The word began in Mexico as *tamatl*, entered Spanish as *tomate* and Italian as *pomo d'ore*—golden apple. The French mistakenly translated this as *pomme d'amour*—love-apple—from which the Portuguese hopefully presumed that the plant was an aphrodisiac. This apart, it was grown only as a decoration until the 1830s.

Whisky The earliest written record of whisky—a spirit liquor distilled from malted barley—is in Scotland, dated 1494. But the process of distillation was known in Britain from at least the 10th century, and may have been brought to the British Isles by Arab traders seeking tin. There is evidence that the ancient Egyptians knew how to distil spirits from grain. The name 'alcohol' is derived from the Arabic *al-koh'l*, meaning 'powdered antimony'. It came into use in English to mean any fine powder or extract, including that used in spirits.

But the word 'whisky' is from the Gaelic *uisge beatha*, meaning 'water of life', a name used by many other nations to describe various alcoholic drinks—*eau de vie* in French, *akvavit* in Swedish and *aqua vitae* in Latin.

Worcestershire sauce This internationally famous food dressing was concocted almost by accident. When Lord Sandys returned to England about 1835, after a period of colonial service in Bengal, he brought with him a recipe for an Indian sauce. He asked the chemists John W. Lea and William Perrins, of Broad Street, Worcester, to make it up for him. The two men also made a quantity for themselves, but found it so unpalatable that they stored the jars away and forgot about them for a time. Later, they found the sauce in their cellars and tasted it again. It had matured and was delicious. Lea and Perrins got permission to market it and called it Worcestershire sauce.

The sauce that was almost lost is still made from the same recipe today. The ingredients are stored in wooden hogshead barrels to mature for several months —up to 1000 barrels, each containing 54 gallons at any one time. Once a week they are rolled over to blend the ingredients and the liquid is refined and bottled.

An ancient Persian legend of how wine was discovered is perhaps the most attractive. Prince Jemshed ordered a number of goatskin bags to be labelled 'poison' after the grapejuice in them, which was fermenting, had given him stomach ache.

His favourite wife, having lost his attention, decided to kill herself by drinking from the bags. But by that time the wine had matured, and she became gay and vivacious again—and won back the favour of her wandering husband.

Wine was introduced into Northern Europe about 600 BC, but was always 'still' after maturing because it was brewed in open vessels. Originally, bottles were stopped with wool dipped in oil and wax, and it was only in the late 17th century that corks were introduced by a Benedictine monk, Dom Perignon. It was that development, the introduction of a leak-proof stopper, that allowed the secondary fermentation of champagne-type wine and blissfully put the bubbles into 'bubbly'.

WHAT'S IN A NAME?

How kindergarten, Kodak and Christmas trees happened

Ampersand The symbol '&' is one of the few signs surviving from the world's earliest-known shorthand system, invented by Marcus Tiro in Rome in 63 BC. It is used today to represent the word 'and' in several hundred languages.

Blotting paper Sand was used to mop up damp ink until early in the 19th century, when blotting paper was discovered by accident by a papermill worker in Berkshire, England. He forgot to size some writing paper (by treating it with a glutinous wash to give it a finished surface), and it was thought that the batch was spoilt. The mill owner thought he might as well use up the paper as scrap, and tried writing on a sheet. The ink from his pen was simply absorbed—giving him the idea for blotting paper.

Christmas trees The 16th-century Protestant reformer Martin Luther is one of the first persons recorded as having had a candle-lit tree in his home at Christmas.

Tree worship, however, has its roots much deeper in German history. In pagan times, trees were regarded as fertility symbols because their leaves sprout after winter. This probably led directly to the tree becoming a symbol of the feast of Christ's birth.

The familiar conifer that we still use was probably chosen because it is green at the right time and its shape resembles a church steeple.

Cigar bands In Cuba, in the days of the Spanish Empire, it was fashionable for rich and titled women to smoke cigars. They started the custom of wrapping narrow paper bands round the cigars to protect their fingers from nicotine stains.

Cigarettes A group of Turkish soldiers are said to have invented cigarettes while defending the city of Acre from Napoleon in 1799. When their hookah (a water-cooled communal smoking pipe) was destroyed by cannon fire, they rolled tobacco in touch papers used for firing their guns.

Kindergarten Memories of an unhappy childhood inspired Frederick Froebel to establish a 'small child occupation institute' (*Kleinkindbeschäftigungsinstitut*) at Blankenburg, in Germany, in 1837. Later he decided that 'kindergarten' (child's garden) was a happier-sounding name for his schools, where children of four and five could enjoy themselves playing in the sun or listening to poetry and stories. After 14 years the authorities closed the schools because of the 'dangerous freedom' of Froebel's ideas. But the schools caught on rapidly in America.

Kodak Cameras were big and cumbersome until George Eastman, an American inventor, marketed the first handy Kodak camera in 1888. He chose the name Kodak because it was 'short, vigorous, could not be misspelt and, to satisfy trademark laws, meant nothing'.

Madame Tussaud's When the Bastille was stormed in 1789, young Marie Grosholtz, already famous in Paris for her wax portraits, was summoned to mould the likenesses of the prisoners whom the revolutionaries had released. As she descended to the dungeons, the story goes, her foot slipped, and she was saved from falling by a young man, Maxmilien Robespierre. Only a few years later, she was to hold his severed head in her lap while she created his death mask, for inclusion in her wax museum in the Boulevard du Temple, in Paris.

In the same way, she modelled the heads of hundreds who perished on the guillotine.

Marie Grosholtz became rich and, in 1795, she married an engineer named Tussaud. But the marriage was not a success, and in 1802 she sailed for England, taking most of her wax collection with her. She toured Britain successfully for 30 years with her portraits of royalty and famous personalities, until she opened a museum in London's Baker Street in 1834. She died in 1850 at the age of 90.

Manneke Pis fountain A prominent citizen of Brussels, distraught because his son was lost, promised to present the city with a bronze statue of the little boy if he could be found. The father kept his word, and the statue and its fountain have been a landmark in Brussels since 1648. Tourists who may be slightly shocked by the statue should know the father made a condition to his promise: he stipulated that the statue must represent the 'manneke' (little man) exactly as he should be seen when found. And when found, the child just happened to be relieving himself.

CANDID KODAK *The first box camera and celluloid roll film were both invented by George Eastman in 1888 and 1889. The entire camera had to be returned to the manufacturers for reloading.*

Matches John Walker, a chemist of Stockton-on-Tees, County Durham, hit on the idea of matches when he discovered that friction ignited a mixture of potassium chloride and antimony sulphide. He sold his first box in 1827, but never bothered to take out a patent. A small piece of sandpaper to strike the matches on was given free with each box.

Paper money The world's first banknotes were used in China in 1170 because copper was scarce and not enough coins could be minted. The first paper money in Europe was issued by the Bank of

MANNEKE PIS *The famous statue depicting exactly how searchers once found a little boy lost.*

Sweden in 1661, though this was also a temporary measure. In 1694 the Bank of England was founded and began to issue promissory notes, originally handwritten but later printed. These quickly became a universally acceptable form of exchange and were the first true bank notes.

Queen Mary The liner *Queen Mary*, launched in 1934, got her name through a misunderstanding. The Cunard Line had decided to call her *Queen Victoria*. The company chairman went to see George V and told him they wanted to name their new ship after one of England's most noble queens. Before he could finish, the king interrupted: 'Oh, Her Majesty will be so pleased.' So *Queen Mary* it had to be.

Red Square The famous square in Moscow got its name not from the 1917 revolution but from a Russian word, *krasnya*, which means red and beautiful. It has been Red Square since the Middle Ages.

Rubber boots Centuries ago, Indians of the Amazon basin used rubber in a way that oddly anticipated the Wellington boot. They would dip moulds of their feet and legs in latex, the raw liquid from the rubber plant. The result, when dry, was a tight-fitting 'boot' which protected the skin against thorns and insect bites.

The original Wellington boots were made from leather. They were named after the Duke of Wellington who, along

FROM SMALL BEGINNINGS . . .

An ornamental box decorated with tropical shells of the kind imported into Britain by shopkeeper Marcus Samuel. He also imported oil—and his interests eventually merged into the Shell combine.

SHELL, the giant oil combine, was named by one of its founders, Marcus Samuel. He ran a business in Houndsditch, London, known as The Shell Shop, because of its brisk trade in boxes fancifully decorated with seaside shells. Another side of his business was transporting oil. It was the merging of this firm with other companies in 1897 that created the mighty Shell concern. Its familiar symbol of a scallop shell on the petrol pumps was retained as a reminder of the company's beginnings.

with some other officers, wore them at the Battle of Waterloo. The first reference to the boots came in a play written by the English dramatist William Moncrieff, in 1817. The first rubber Wellingtons appeared in shops in 1851, a year before the duke died.

Safety glass Thousands of road-crash survivors owe their lives to a trivial accident in a Paris laboratory in 1904. For the idea of safety glass came to a French scientist named Benedictus when he knocked an empty bottle off a shelf. The bottle smashed, but to his surprise kept its shape. Benedictus noted that it had contained a collodion solution. The solvent had evaporated, leaving on the inside of the bottle a cellulose skin which had held the glass splinters together.

Saluting Roman soldiers may well have invented the military salute to show that they did not conceal a weapon in the right hand. The Roman salute—a raised arm, hand slightly to the left and palm opened away from the face—may be seen on the statues of Emperor Trajan and Emperor Marcus Aurelius in Rome.

Historians believe that the modern form of salute may have originated with soldiers in armour raising their visors to show their faces to a friend or superior. A British tradition, sometimes discounted, holds that saluting began at a naval tournament attended by Elizabeth I to celebrate the defeat of the Spanish Armada in 1588. The officer in charge ordered that 'on account of the dazzling loveliness of Her Majesty, all seamen, upon receiving their prizes, should shield their eyes with their right hand'.

HAIL CAESAR! *This statue of Emperor Marcus Aurelius in Rome demonstrates what was probably the ancestor of all military salutes.*

Scotch tape Paint-sprayers were responsible for the development of Scotch tape in America in 1925 as the answer to the problem of masking separate colour areas. It was called 'Scotch' because the makers were accused of being over-economical in the use of adhesive, for the tape would not stick properly.

Scotland Yard The medieval kings of Scotland stayed in a residence on a site at Whitehall when they visited London. The area was divided into portions, or yards, and the residence came to be known as Great Scotland Yard. The first Metropolitan Police headquarters, established in 1842, backed on to the site and was soon nicknamed 'Scotland Yard'. When the Metropolitan Police moved to the Thames Embankment in 1890, the new building—originally designed as the National Opera House—was named New Scotland Yard, but gradually came to be called just 'Scotland Yard'. The next move was in 1967, to a tower block a quarter of a mile away in Victoria Street. It, too, has been named New Scotland Yard. The Embankment building, however, survives—but only as a departmental offshoot.

Shorthand Several forms of shorthand were tried out by the ancient Greeks and Romans. The first known inventor of a system was Marcus Tiro in Rome in 63 BC. It eventually had about 13,000 symbols, and was in use for about 1000 years. The system was rediscovered by German scholars in the 15th century and provoked a new interest in the subject. It is thought that the shorthand was used to record the speeches of Martin Luther.

In Britain nearly 500 methods of shorthand have been published since the 17th century. Samuel Pepys, in writing his famous diary, used a method he had invented himself. In the mid-18th century, Thomas Gurney became the first official shorthand writer at the Old Bailey Courts of Justice in London. His Gurney system was in use well into the present century, gradually being superseded by a method that had been invented in 1837 by Englishman Isaac Pitman.

The Pitman method employs 26 strokes and their derivations to represent consonants, and a range of dots and dashes representing vowels and diphthongs.

The fastest-ever Pitman speed—350 words a minute—was achieved by Nathan Behrin in New York in December 1922.

547

THE FIRST WILLOWS *An 18th-century drawing of Alexander Pope's house flanked by weeping willows, including the one grown from a Turkish basket. It is the ancestor of all weeping willows in Britain and the United States.*

The fastest user of Pitman's rival—the Gregg system—was Englishman Leslie Bear, who was an editor of the official Parliamentary report, *Hansard*, until 1972.

The two systems have millions of users throughout the world.

In the US, 99 per cent of secretaries use Gregg; in the UK, 80 per cent use Pitman.

Silk China has been producing silk for well over 2000 years. The discovery of how to rear the worms on mulberry trees, reel the thread and weave the cloth is credited to an emperor's wife, Lady Hsi-ling-shi, who was worshipped as the Goddess of Silk. The fabric was first brought to Europe from Persia. Elizabeth I was the first woman in history to wear knitted silk stockings.

Starlings A serious environmental problem in America owes its origin to a quotation from Shakespeare's *Henry IV*, which runs: 'I'll have a starling that shall be taught to speak nothing but "Mortimer".' A wealthy New Yorker named Eugene Schieffelin, whose two consuming passions were Shakespeare and birds, decided in 1890 to introduce into America every bird mentioned in the Bard's plays. Most of them died, but not 40 pairs of starlings. They bred so prolifically that they became a pest, and remain so in most cities today.

Table knives Diners ate with pointed daggers until the 17th century, when the French Cardinal Richelieu was so upset by courtiers using them as toothpicks that he ordered the ends to be rounded.

Vaseline 'Petroleum jelly', as Vaseline was first called, was developed by a London-born chemist, Robert Chesebrough, while working in the Pennsylvania oilfields in 1859. He noticed that workers soothed cuts and burns with a colourless residue which collected on the pump rods of drilling rigs. He took supplies of this 'rod wax' with him to New York and refined it into the ointment we know today. Chesebrough, who lived to the age of 96, claimed that he swallowed a spoonful of Vaseline every day.

Weeping willows All the weeping willows in Britain and the United States are descended from a Turkish basket sent to Lady Suffolk in England early in the 18th century. The poet Alexander Pope was present when the basket, containing figs, arrived. He had one of the withies from the basket planted in his Thameside garden at Twickenham, where it grew into a fine weeping-willow tree. Years later a British officer took a twig from the tree before leaving for the American colonies. It was planted in Abingdon, Virginia, and became the ancestor of thousands, perhaps even millions, of trees.

FRANKENSTEIN'S MAKER

The monster born in a dream

Outside the gloomy Swiss chateau the night was wild, split by storms. Inside, by a flickering fire, an 18-year-old girl listened to her husband talking about the evolutionary theories of Erasmus Darwin. Later the same night she was woken by a nightmare so vivid that she dared not sleep again.

At dawn she began to write it down. 'By the glimmer of the half-extinguished light, I saw the dull yellow eye of the creature open; it breathed hard, and a convulsive motion agitated its limbs.'

It was the birth of Frankenstein's monster. The year was 1816, the girl Mary Shelley, wife of the English poet, and the place, the Swiss home of Lord Byron.

The three friends had agreed before retiring that each should write a ghost story. Only Mary had the inspiration.

Two years later, her dream was published as *Frankenstein*, a horrifying novel about a medical student who builds a living body from parts of corpses.

Mary's creation, however, was not the first example of an artificial man. According to historical legend, the medieval German theologian Albertus Magnus built a robot that answered questions. And in 1580, Rabbi Löw of Prague made a giant human figure from river mud and brought it to life by magic—the Golem of Jewish mythology. The 16th-century Swiss alchemist Paracelsus was also rumoured to have devised a formula for creating life.

Mary Shelley used these themes. But her character, Baron Frankenstein, used a more modern technique to bring his spare-parts creature to life: the newly discovered science of electricity.

ROBINSON CRUSOE, SCOTTISH PIRATE

DANIEL DEFOE's *Robinson Crusoe* might never have been written without an argument Alexander Selkirk had aboard a Scottish privateer one night in 1704.

Selkirk was the ship's first mate on an expedition to the South Seas, and in the heat of the dispute with the captain, he demanded to be put ashore. He was—on the uninhabited island of Juan Fernandez,

off the coast of Chile. Nobody knows now what the row was about. But it led to Selkirk living on the island for nearly 4½ years, until he was rescued in 1709 and taken back to England.

As a journalist, Defoe heard about Selkirk, and used the pirate's story as the basis of his own tale—about a pious man marooned for 24 years.

The castaway pirate Alexander Selkirk dances with a goat in this romantic 18th-century picture. His story made front-page news in British papers when he was rescued in 1709.

BULLSEYE *William Tell takes aim at the apple on his son's head. Beyond them stands the tyrant Gessler. But it seems that they existed only in the imagination of a 16th-century writer.*

WILLIAM TELL

Real-life hero or a writer's creation?

The order was clear and humiliating. Every Swiss citizen had to bow before the Austrian tyrant's hat, stuck on a post in the village square. One man only was brave enough to refuse: the marksman William Tell.

The tyrant, Hermann Gessler, made Tell the victim of a savage jest. He could have his freedom if he shot an apple from the head of his son, Walter. If he missed or refused, he would be executed.

Outside the village of Altdorf, Tell faced his son. One deadly bolt lay on his crossbow. Another jutted from his belt. He fired—and the apple split in two. Why, asked Gessler, had he taken the second bolt from his quiver?

'It was for your heart if the first had harmed so much as a hair of my son's head,' replied Tell. Gessler yelled to his soldiers: 'Take him to the castle.' Tell was bundled into a boat with Gessler, and his guards took him across Lake Uri to Gessler's grim fortress.

On the way a storm blew up. The guards freed Tell so that he could guide them to shore. He did—then leapt out and pushed the boat back into the lake.

Gessler's men were swept to their deaths, but the tyrant himself struggled back to shore. Tell was waiting with his second bolt. He fired—and Switzerland was free of the Austrian yoke.

William Tell's story was first told in the Swiss chronicles of Aegidius Tschudi, a 16th-century writer, 200 years after Tell was supposed to have lived. But there is no contemporary evidence at all that Tell or Gessler ever existed.

It seems that Tschudi's account is a Swiss embellishment of an 11th-century legend, for stories of expert archers occur all over Northern Europe. In an early Scottish legend, a bowman called Gilpatrick has to shoot an egg from his son's head. In a 12th-century Saxon story a Tell-like figure appears as Toki, opponent of Harold Bluetooth, and in Norse legends as Toko.

Tschudi seems only to have added details—and made Tell the Swiss folklore hero he is today.

THE REAL-LIFE TRAVIATA
Verdi's opera was inspired by a courtesan

Operas are often based on classical legends. But Verdi's *La Traviata* owes its existence to a real-life Parisian street-waif and the talent of Alexandre Dumas, son of the man who wrote *The Three Musketeers*.

The girl was Rose Alphonsine Plessis, who was born in 1824 at the village of Nonant, near Bayeux in Normandy. At the age of 13, Rose ran away from home. She arrived penniless in Paris and, faced with starvation, turned to prostitution.

By the time she was 18, Rose, who had climbed high on the social ladder, had changed her name to Marie Duplessis so that she could not be traced by her family. A famous courtesan, she lived in an apartment on the fashionable Boulevard de la Madeleine, and was visited by many wealthy men such as Count de Stackelberg, former Russian ambassador to Vienna.

Dumas first saw Marie stepping out of a carriage in the Place de la Bourse. He was captivated by her beauty, and when he saw her again, in a box at the Théâtre des Variétés, he managed to arrange an introduction.

The meeting started a strange romance which survived her marriage to another man and lasted until her death. Marie, who was racked by chronic tuberculosis, told Dumas: 'You will have a sorry mistress, a woman who is nervous, ill, sad and gay with a gaiety sadder than grief, a woman who spits blood and spends 100,000 francs a year. All the young lovers I have had have very soon left me.' But the young writer, utterly in love, ignored her warnings.

As her illness grew worse, Dumas bankrupted himself to pay for doctors. Even when she married an old flame, Vicompte de Perregaux, he remained faithful. None of it made any difference. On February 3, 1846, she died. She was 23 years old. Covered with camellias, her favourite flowers, her coffin was lowered into the earth of the cemetery in Montmartre.

Dumas began *La Dame aux Camélias* soon after Marie's death. He rewrote the novel later as a play, which in 1853 supplied the inspiration for Verdi's opera, giving Marie a musical immortality she would have considered no more than her due.

CRUSHED EXPECTATIONS
Dickens and the jilted Australian bride

A jilted bride 11,000 miles away may have given Charles Dickens the idea for one of his famous characters—Miss Havisham, the aged recluse of *Great Expectations*.

In 1856 Miss Eliza Emily Donnithorne, of Cambridge Hall, Newton, in Sydney, Australia, was left standing at the altar on her wedding day. She was so heartbroken by the experience that she became a hermit in her own home. From that day until her death, 30 years later, she never went out again.

The door of the room in which the wedding celebrations were to have been held was locked. The decorations and the wedding breakfast inside rotted untouched on the tables.

In Dickens's novel, Miss Havisham lives and dies in an almost identical way. This is how Pip, the young hero of *Great Expectations*, describes his first meeting with the formidable old lady:

'I saw that the bride within the bridal dress had withered like the dress, and like the flowers, and had no brightness left but the brightness of her sunken eyes. I saw that the dress had been put upon the rounded figure of a young woman, and that the figure upon which it now hung loose, had shrunk to skin and bone.'

There is no conclusive evidence that Dickens based Miss Havisham on Miss Donnithorne. But through his contacts with travellers and journalists he would have been among the first in England to hear of the recluse on the other side of the world.

The novel was completed in 1861, just five years after Miss Donnithorne's fiancé disappeared. It enshrined her loneliness and misery for ever.

DEACON BRODIE'S SECRET LIFE
The man who was Jekyll and Hyde

William Brodie was a well-respected man in Edinburgh in the mid-18th century. In a strait-laced city, he shone as a model of civic sobriety. The son of a prosperous cabinet-maker, he was a deacon, or leader, of the masons' guild, and a city councillor.

But the deacon was also the model for one of English literature's most horrifying characters, Robert Louis Stevenson's schizophrenic scientist, Dr Jekyll.

For Brodie, like the gentle doctor, had a secret life behind his mask of virtue. By day, he was a businessman. By night, he was a gambler and a vicious thief.

No one knew his secrets, not even the two mistresses he kept and who had his five children. They did not know even about each other.

Brodie was 27 when he turned to crime. In August 1768 he made copies of the keys to a city bank and robbed it of £800. But though he went on to burgle scores of buildings over the following 18 years, no hint of suspicion ever fell on him.

Getaway and capture

The beginning of the end came in 1786, when he joined forces with three petty thieves. Together, they planned Brodie's most daring raid—on the headquarters of the Scottish Customs and Excise. The gang were surprised by an employee, and though Brodie got away, one of the thieves, John Brown, turned king's evidence to escape transportation for other crimes he had committed in England. Brodie fled to Amsterdam, hoping to escape to America.

But on the eve of his departure, police caught up with him. Brodie was extradited and put on trial in Edinburgh in the same courtroom where, only a few months before, he had sat as a juryman.

The evidence was damning; police found the proof of his double identity: false keys, pistols and a burglar's black suit. Brodie was condemned to death. But the man who had laughed at the law for two decades was not yet finished. On the night before his execution, he wired his clothes from neck to ankle to lessen the jerk of the rope, and lodged a silver tube in his throat to cheat the noose.

Neither trick worked. On October 1, 1788, he died on the Edinburgh gallows.

Nearly a century later, Robert Louis Stevenson and William Henley wrote a play based on Brodie's exploits. *Deacon Brodie, or The Double Life* was first produced at the Prince's Theatre, London, in 1884. In it, the burglar explains the freedom he finds in his nocturnal life of crime.

Two years later, Stevenson turned the theme into *The Strange Case of Dr Jekyll and Mr Hyde*, his glittering short story about the darker side of man.

In the story Dr Jekyll discovers, through experiments with a drug, that 'man is not truly one, but truly two', and describes how 'I learned to recognise the thorough and primitive duality of man'.

He explains his fascination with the experiment: 'If each, I told myself, could but be housed in separate identities, life would be relieved of all that was unbearable; the unjust might go his way, delivered from the aspirations and remorse of his more upright twin; and the just could walk steadfastly and securely on his upward path, doing the good things in which he found his pleasure, and no longer exposed to disgrace and penitence by the hands of this extraneous evil.'

In this way Stevenson rationalised the way in which the evil inherent in man took its hold on the good Deacon Brodie.

DOUBLE TROUBLE *Deacon Brodie with the dice and cards that led to his downfall.*

AMERICA'S UNCLE SAM

The legend on a barrel of meat

Samuel and Ebenezer Wilson boasted that their meat-packing company was the best in New York State. It could butcher and pack 150 head of cattle a day, they used to claim.

So when America and Britain went to war with each other in 1812, the confident brothers went after—and won—a contract to supply the troops with barrels of beef and pork.

Samuel Wilson was delighted. He was a jovial, popular man who stood out in any crowd with his mane of grey hair and his high top hat, and he was known to everyone as Uncle Sam. He was always happy to let visitors wander round his factory in Troy to see what he was doing for the boys at the front.

Then, one day, one of the visitors noticed that each barrel was stamped with the initials E.A.-U.S. (standing for the government contractor Elbert Anderson and United States), and asked a worker what the letters meant. 'I don't know,' said the man, 'unless it means Elbert Anderson and Uncle Sam.'

It was one of those jokes that stuck. The visitors spread it near their homes, and employees of the firm who joined the army took it there too. Cartoonists picked up the idea in the 1830s and, though Sam himself died in 1854, Congress eventually gave him a permanent niche in the nation's heart. In 1961 they passed a resolution formally recognising Samuel Wilson as the symbol of the USA.

WHIP-ROUND *A raffish Uncle Sam guards the nation's wealth in an English cartoon of 1886. In real life Samuel Wilson was clean-shaven.*

Unlike his American counterpart, Britain's plump and cheery mascot, John Bull, had no real-life model. He made his first appearance in a somewhat heavy-handed political satire by John Arbuthnot, which was published in 1712 under the title *Law Is A Bottomless Pit*.

In the book, which became known later as *The History Of John Bull*, he is an Englishman, Lewis Baboon is a Frenchman, and Nicholas Frog a Dutchman. But only John Bull won the hearts of the historians, commentators and cartoonists who have immortalised him.

HOW LITTLE JACK HORNER BECAME A BIG OWNER

ACCORDING to legend, the original Horner was steward to Richard Whiting, the last of the abbots of Glastonbury. In the 1530s, the time of the Dissolution of the Monasteries, it is said that the abbot, hoping to placate Henry VIII, sent His Majesty an enormous Christmas pie containing the deeds of 12 manors. The task of carrying the pie to London was entrusted to Horner who, on the journey, managed to open the pie and extract the deeds of the Manor of Mells in Somerset—presumably the 'plum' referred to in the rhyme.

Certainly, one Thomas Horner did assume ownership of Mells, but both his descendants and the present owner of the house, the Earl of Oxford and Asquith, claim that the rhyme is a slander. Horner, they say, bought the manor from the king; his name was 'Tom' and not 'Jack'; and there is evidence that children recited the rhyme long before the time of the Tudors.

THE INCREDIBLE DOCTOR BELL

The man who was Sherlock Holmes

One evening, about the turn of the century, after a weekend shoot in Scotland, a dozen guests sat around a dinner-table discussing famous unsolved crimes. One of the guests, Dr Joseph Bell, had the others wide eyed with his deductive acrobatics. Dr Bell was an eminent surgeon whose classroom wizardry influenced five decades of Edinburgh University students, including Conan Doyle, Robert Louis Stevenson and James M. Barrie.

'Most people see, but do not observe,' he said. 'Glance at a man and you find his nationality written on his face, his means of livelihood on his hands, and the rest of his story in his gait, mannerisms, watch-chain ornaments, and the lint adhering to his clothes.

'A patient walked into the room where I was instructing some medical students. "Gentlemen," I said, "this man has been a soldier in a Highland regiment, and probably a bandsman." I pointed out the swagger in his walk, suggestive of the Highland piper; his shortness told me that if he had been a soldier it was probably as a bandsman. But the man insisted that he was a shoemaker and, furthermore, that he had never been in the army.

'I asked him to remove his shirt, whereupon I could see a little blue D branded on his skin. That was how they used to mark army deserters during the Crimean War. He finally confessed having played in the band of a Highland regiment. It was really elementary, gentlemen.'

At that one listener remarked: 'Dr Bell might almost be Sherlock Holmes.' To which Dr Bell snapped, 'My dear sir, I am Sherlock Holmes.'

Dr Bell was, indeed—as Arthur Conan Doyle admitted in his autobiography—the inspiration for the immortal detective of fiction.

Important trifles

Sherlock Holmes's rules for deduction and analysis merely echoed the real-life gospel of Dr Bell. 'I always impressed upon my students the vast importance of little distinctions, the endless significance of trifles,' Dr Bell once told a reporter.

'Nearly every handicraft, for example, writes its sign manual. The scars of the miner differ from those of the quarryman. The carpenter's callosities are not those of the mason. The soldier and sailor differ in gait. And with a woman, especially, the observant doctor can often tell exactly what part of her body she is going to talk about.'

SUPER SLEUTHS *On the right, Conan Doyle's creation, Sherlock Holmes. Behind, Dr Joseph Bell, the university lecturer used by Conan Doyle as the model for his famous detective. The author once told an interviewer that Bell's powers of observation were so acute that he could diagnose a patient's illness and give details of his past life before the man had even opened his mouth. He taught his students the 'vast importance of little distinctions, the endless significance of trifles'.*

Dr Bell believed that the development of observation was a necessity to doctors and detectives, but every man, he argued, can transform his world from one of monotony into one of excitement and adventure by developing the faculty.

One afternoon, Dr Bell was at his desk in Edinburgh's Royal Infirmary when someone knocked. 'Come in,' he called. A man entered. Dr Bell stared at him.

'Why are you worried?'

'How do you know I am worried?'

'The four knocks. Unworried people content themselves with two, or at the most, three.'

The man was worried.

Conan Doyle himself told of one example of Dr Bell's skill. In silence Dr Bell studied an outpatient, then spoke.

'Well, you've served in the army, in a Highland regiment, and you're not long discharged.'

'Aye, sir.'

'You were a noncom officer, stationed at Barbados?'

'Aye, sir.'

Dr Bell turned to his students. 'You see, gentlemen, he was a respectful man, but did not remove his hat. They do not in the army, but he would have learned civilian ways had he been long discharged. He has an air of authority and he is obviously Scottish. As to Barbados, his complaint is elephantiasis, which indicates the West Indies.' Years later, Conan Doyle was still sufficiently impressed by this incident to reproduce it closely in his Holmes story, *The Greek Interpreter*.

Doyle graduated from Edinburgh University in 1881. He put up his oculist's plate and waited for patients. Six years later he was still waiting. Desperate for any kind of income, he turned to writing. After one false start, and under the influence of Gaboriau and Poe, he decided in 1887 to try a detective story. And for it he wanted a new kind of detective.

'I thought of my old teacher, Joe Bell,' Doyle recalled in his autobiography. 'If he were a detective he would surely reduce this fascinating but unorganised business to something nearer an exact science. It is all very well to say that a man is clever, but the reader wants to see examples of it —such as Bell gave us every day. The idea amused me. What should I call the fellow?'

He called him Sherlock Holmes, after a cricketing acquaintance and the American jurist Oliver Wendell Holmes.

COUNT DRACULA

Was the fanged demon based on a human tyrant?

Count Dracula, the Transylvanian vampire, has haunted the imagination of the world for less than 100 years. But the blood-sucking creatures of which he has become the horrible chief have lurked in the legends of Europe since the 9th century.

The fanged noble came out of the shadows in 1897—in the pages of the Irish author Bram Stoker's novel, *Dracula*. And it seems that Stoker partly based his diabolical character on a real and fiendish Romanian tyrant, Vlad V. For Vlad, nicknamed The Impaler, was also known as *Draculaea*, the Romanian word for Son of the Devil.

Vlad ruled Wallachia, now part of Romania, from 1456 to 1462. In those six years he is said to have executed 40,000 people—by impaling them on long stakes. No one was immune from his brutal whim: captives in his wars with Turkish invaders, noble hangers-on in his own court, even priests and holy men who were usually revered.

He was well known, too, for his directness in diplomacy. On one occasion he nailed the slipper of the Turkish Ambassador to his skull and sent him back to Constantinople in a litter. This he did to express his contempt for all Turks.

Stake through the heart

Stoker, who never visited Transylvania but researched his novels in the British Museum, knew the vampire legends and knew that to kill an 'undead' body, a stake had to be driven through its heart. It seems that Vlad's habit, which Stoker heard about from a Hungarian historian, pierced the author's imagination and vibrated a chord which has quivered the nerves of readers ever since.

Stoker may have been further inspired by another bloody noble—the Hungarian countess Elizabeth Bathory. She was the

BLOOD AND THUNDER *Actor Christopher Lee is the latest in a long line of film Count Draculas. Author Bram Stoker (inset), who created Dracula, was once manager to the actor Henry Irving.*

wife of General Ferencz Nadasdy, and lived at Csejthe Castle in the dark Carpathian mountains.

While her husband was away on his numerous military campaigns, the beautiful countess gathered around her a sinister band of witches, sorcerers and alchemists who indulged her in her belief that drinking and bathing in the blood of young girls would preserve her beauty.

At dead of night, the countess and her henchmen would criss-cross the countryside in a black coach hunting for girls. Any they found were kidnapped and driven back to the castle.

There, the girls were tortured and hung on chains while their blood was drained to fill the countess's bath.

News of her reign of terror finally reached the ears of Hungarian king Matthias II. When his men searched the castle, they found scores of bodies still hanging from chains in the dungeons.

Entombed alive

At her trial, the countess was convicted of murdering some 60 girls. Her accomplices were beheaded or burnt at the stake. But Countess Elizabeth Bathory herself escaped execution because of her noble birth. Instead she was condemned to a living death—walled up in a tiny room in the castle of doom, and kept alive only by scraps of food pushed through a small slit. She died four years later, still in her tomb.

There is a spine-tingling echo of the countess's fate in Stoker's short story called *Dracula's Guest*. In the story, a man journeying to Castle Dracula and seeking shelter from a storm in a cemetery finds the tomb of a noblewoman—with an iron stake driven into her coffin.

The 'vampire' children

Like many stories that have been absorbed into folklore, the vampire legend has some medically factual backing. During the late Middle Ages, interbreeding among Eastern European nobles led to various genetic disorders, including a rare disease known as *Erythropoietic Protoporphyria*. The disease itself was not diagnosed until the 19th century, but from records of the time doctors are now convinced that many so-called vampires were in fact victims of this disease. Since sufferers rarely lived long, most would have been children.

The disorder makes the body produce too much porphyrin—a substance that is the basis of red blood cells. This results in redness of the skin, eyes and teeth, a receding of the upper lip, and cracks in the skin which bleed when exposed to light.

Doctors of the time could treat the condition only by locking the patients away during the day, and by encouraging them to drink blood to replace what they lost by bleeding. But rumours of these nocturnal blood-drinkers could have led to a spate of vampire stories in the region —and encouraged Stoker to set Castle Dracula in the strange Eastern European land of Transylvania.

MANTLE MAKETH MAN

The chequered pedigree of fashion

Bathing costumes owe their existence to George Stephenson, the pioneer of the Railway Age.

Annual seaside holidays were made possible only by the coming of the railways, when coastal towns such as Brighton and Margate, and their continental equivalents Ostend and Blankenberge, were quick to point out the therapeutic advantages of salt-water bathing, hitherto regarded as the province of eccentrics.

There were no swimming costumes at that time. Men and women disported themselves in the surf naked—though on separate beaches. Victorian rectitude began a long, hard struggle to restore the proprieties.

Between 1855 and 1865 *The Times* devoted hundreds of column inches to the seasonal controversy about the scandal of naked bathing. Then, a Dr J. Henry Bennett returned from a holiday in Biarritz aglow with enthusiasm for a French innovation.

'Both ladies and gentlemen wear what is called a Bathing Costume,' he wrote to *The Lancet*. 'With the ladies, it consists of woollen drawers, and a black blouse descending below the knees and fastened by a leather girdle. The gentlemen wear a kind of striped sailor's costume.'

The answer had been found, and swimming was to remain relatively respectable until the advent of the bikini—so devastating in its effect on the fashion scene that it was named after an atomic explosion on Bikini Atoll in the Pacific.

While the controversial bikini is a fairly recent means of attracting attention, a woman's hair has always been regarded as one of her most exciting features. Until very recently women were required to wear hats in church, in obedience to a medieval ecclesiastical ruling forbidding them to expose their hair lest the thoughts of men be distracted from Higher Things.

The terrifying topper

Male headgear, too, has had its brushes with authority. In 1797, when James Hetherington gave the top hat its first public airing in London, an immense crowd collected around its embarrassed inventor. So intense was the crush that several women fainted. Dogs barked,

BEACH BELLES *By the 1860s, girls wore bathing costumes of modern serge. Earlier belles wore nothing, or were dunked in vast canvas smocks.*

children screamed and the son of a cordwainer had his arm broken.

Hetherington was arrested and charged with a breach of the peace, having 'appeared on the public highway wearing upon his head a tall structure of shining lustre and calculated to disturb timid people'. The innovating Hetherington was bound over to keep the peace in his own recognisance of £50.

That other badge of Victorian gentility, the bowler hat, arrived about 50 years later. Apparently the public had regained its composure by this time, for there was no comparable flutter when Mr William Coke, a Londoner, produced his notion of a more practical headgear for riding.

Coke envisaged a low-crowned hat of hard felt, firmly reinforced, and submitted some sketches to the hatting firm of Lock's of St James's. They in turn submitted the problem to a manufacturing house whose principal was a man called Beaulieu— from whose name (pronounced in French 'Bowl-yer') the name of the hat is derived.

Lock's, however, piqued at the idea of publicising a mere sub-contractor, refer to the bowler to this day as a 'coke' or 'hard felt'. In America it is called a 'Derby', because Lord Derby was the first

557

to popularise the hat in the United States.

Mr Coke's innovation in male head-gear is only one of the many fashions whose origins may be traced back to man's long association with the horse.

For example, the most formal evening wear, the tails suit, was the hacking jacket of some 175 years ago. The front was cut away so that the knees of the wearer should not become entangled while his feet were in the stirrups. The stripes down the sides of the trousers are all that remain of a fly down the legs, which allowed them to be closely buttoned in the manner of breeches. The tails are divided to fall comfortably on each side of the horse—or, while the wearer was in the saddle, they might be attached to the two buttons still present in the small of the back of the tail coat.

Man and horse

Though the horse has been eclipsed as a means of transport, its influence lingers still. Cross pockets—pockets placed at the front of the trousers—were admirably suited to the horseman, but were abandoned in favour of side pockets as man took to the motor car. Then, as trousers became tighter, the cross pocket made a triumphant return. Convenience, in this case, had yielded to fashion.

Many aspects of male attire are left-overs from early fashions. The buttons on the cuff, which once closed the wristband against inclement weather, are useless nowadays, yet few tailors would omit them. A really first-class suit is still identified by the fact that it not only has buttons on the cuff, but also has real buttonholes into which they are fastened. Curiously, buttons were worn for about 3000 years simply as decorations and had no functional use until well into the late Middle Ages.

A man's jacket always buttons left over right so that the flap of loose material will

TAILS FOR ALL SEASONS *In the back of the modern tailcoat are two buttons—reminders of the days when the tails were buttoned back to facilitate a gentleman's ascent to the saddle.*

IRON CHANCELLOR *Prince von Bismarck in a tunic from which lapels derived.*

INFORMAL HUSSAR *Tunic undone, Marshal von Mackensen shows his lapels.*

not impede the swift drawing of a long-vanished sword. It is said that the woman's jacket fastens right over left in order to facilitate breast-feeding, while the child is supported by the stronger right arm. Lapels almost certainly evolved from the wrap-over stand-up collar style of Prussian military uniforms. When the wearer was off duty, he would unbutton the confining tunic across the chest and at the throat. The fronts would then fold back in two triangles of material cut in almost exactly the same way as the present-day collar and lapels.

One of the buttons, incidentally, is still retained in some jackets at the top of the lapel, together with a small flap of cloth. In more elegant days, this used to house the *boutonnière*—a small posy of flowers.

Many dress innovations evolve from practical adaptations of an earlier age. Trouser turn-ups, for example, evolved initially out of the habit of turning up one's trousers to avoid contact with the mud of Victorian and Edwardian streets.

But because a gentleman was never at particular pains to look after his clothes —he had servants to do it for him—the habit was considered rather vulgar. *The People* of September 23, 1894, quotes an American observer: 'I have never seen men of fashion in London turn up their trousers under any circumstances. In wet weather they take cabs, but to appear on Rotten Row in the season with his trousers turned up would be justly considered a serious breach of decorum.'

Only after the First World War, when the Prince of Wales was seen with trouser bottoms turned up, were gentlemen finally persuaded to follow suit.

His Royal Highness was probably responsible for more innovations in dress than any other personage in the last 50 years. He is credited, among other things, with popularising suède shoes, Fair Isle sweaters, midnight-blue dinner jackets, wide shirt collars and, of course, the

COLOURFUL PRINCE *Among the many fashions popularised by the Prince of Wales (later Duke of Windsor) was the Fair Isle sweater.*

revolutionary Windsor knot in the tie. But even these notable achievements pale beside those of his grandfather, Edward VII, whose improvisations include pressing the trousers down the front and back of the leg instead of down the sides; the wearing of white waistcoats and stiff dickey shirts in the evening; and the introduction of the Homburg hat to Britain. (The hat was named after the German spa often visited by the king.)

He is also held responsible for the curious habit of leaving the bottom waist-coat button undone. Apparently His Majesty's stomach advanced too rapidly for his tailor to keep up with it.

But despite his fondness for his own inventions, he frowned on any member of his circle who attempted experiments of his own. When Lord Harris had the temerity to appear in the Royal Enclosure at Ascot wearing a somewhat cheerful tweed suit, the king looked him over with a baleful eye. 'Mornin', Harris,' observed His Majesty coldly. 'Goin' rattin'?'

A good deal of fashion comes from following the examples of famous people. The long coat, it is said, was first worn by Louis XIV to conceal his bandy legs—whereupon even straight-legged courtiers made haste to their tailors.

Sartorial immortality

On the other hand, some men have achieved immortality by having garments named after them. The Raglan sleeve, for instance, is named after Lord Raglan, the Crimean War Field Marshal. The sleeve, which slants up the shoulder to the neck, was the result of his thoughtfulness in clothing his soldiers in sacks as an extra layer of clothing against the savage Russian winter. A hole for the head and a slightly caped effect gave the lead for the sartorial innovation still with us today.

The cardigan came from another Crimean warrior, the 7th Earl of Cardigan, who led the charge of the Light Brigade.

The blazer, surprisingly enough, is not so called because it is a blaze of riotous colour, but because the captain of HMS *Blazer* decked his crew out in a brass-buttoned blue livery in the 1840s before there was an official naval uniform.

Many fashions, of course, are the result of slow evolution through the centuries. Originally, the tie was simply a draw-string at the neck of the shirt, while the shirt itself was underwear and not sup-

MERRY MONARCH *Edward VII (1847–1910) is seen here wearing a Homburg hat and double-breasted coat—both his own innovations.*

posed to be seen at all. But garments tend to work outwards, as in the case of the suntop, which is, after all, no more than a visible brassière.

The loose cloth once worn about the neck evolved into a collar, and was later elaborated into the cravat—named after the Croatian Guards at the court of Louis XIV who popularised the style. In the 18th and early 19th centuries, the cloth was wound several times round the neck and tied in a flouncing bow. In the bowtie it has been simplified to a pair of short, hanging folds.

Hats also reflect this evolutionary process. Hatters continue to tuck a tiny, brightly coloured feather into the hatband of soft felt trilbies—a reminder of the days when hats were decorated with plumes.

The band itself is all that remains of a ribbon which allowed the hat to be adjusted to the head size of the wearer.

Travellers and empire builders have made several contributions to our ward-

ROYAL GRACE *In this portrait of 1682, the Duke of Bourgogne, son of the Dauphin, is wearing a cravat, named after the Croatian Guards.*

to imprison criminals for minor offences.

Despite the efforts of the immortal Jeeves, the effect of servants upon fashion has been mainly a negative one. Living in close proximity with the gentry, they either adapted their styles by taking over the hand-me-downs of their employers or had the fashions forced upon them. This is especially true of formal dress; and so great is the gentleman's terror of being mistaken for a butler or footman that the moment servants are attired in something approaching his own dress, then that particular fashion is dead.

Tails doomed

The rise and fall of the evening dress tailcoat is an excellent example of this process. Though it is still worn on occasions hallowed by tradition—the opera, City dinners and the like—it was doomed as general evening wear as soon as it was seen on the backs of waiters.

It was this factor more than any other which helped to popularise the dinner jacket—a garment of truly international ancestry. It began in mid-19th-century Europe as the smoking jacket, which gentlemen wore on informal bachelor evenings. Then, on October 10, 1886, a Mr Griswold Lorillard electrified American society by appearing at the Autumn Ball of the Tuxedo Park Club in New York in a short jacket with satin lapels.

Le smoking

And so the tuxedo was born, though France still knows it as *le smoking* and Britain as the dinner jacket.

Despite its adoption by orchestras in the 1920s and 1930s it managed to survive. The bandsmen wore white or coloured jackets; only the customers wore black.

It was the inclusion of breeches and stockings in servants' livery that eventually excluded them from the gentleman's wardrobe, though they were a long time dying. In the 1820s, the great Duke of Wellington was refused admission to his club, Almack's, because he arrived wearing trousers instead of breeches.

During the same period, students at Oxford and Cambridge Universities were marked 'absent' if they appeared in Hall with their lower limbs clothed in trousers.

As the 20th century progresses, so the number of dress taboos decreases. The dictators of fashion are no longer royalty, but pop stars and actors.

robes. Pyjamas were adapted from the normal day wear of northern India, though the name is derived from that of the baggy trousers worn by ladies in Persian harems. The so-called safari-style jacket is an adaptation of the bush shirt, long favoured by old Africa hands, which was in itself a lighter version of the belted tweed Norfolk jacket introduced to the veldt by Victorian explorers.

HM's socks

That prince of adventurers, Sir Walter Raleigh, is on record as having introduced socks to the English court. In 1600, when he was Governor of Jersey, he sent Queen Elizabeth a pair of 'Jersey Stockes', which so delighted her that she granted Jersey a licence to trade freely in knitted articles.

Apart from the obvious connection of Jersey with knitted sweaters, it is interesting to note that the Elizabethans used the word 'stockes' when referring both to stockings and the wooden leg-halters used

SONG AND DANCE

The men who wrote the world's favourites

Rock of Ages The Rev. Augustus Montague Toplady was taking a stroll at Burrington Combe, in Somerset, when a violent storm forced him to take shelter in the cleft of a large rock. The date is not known—it was some time between 1762 and 1775.

Sheltering from that storm Mr Toplady, then the curate of Blagdon, Somerset, composed the words and music of one of the best known of all hymns, 'Rock of Ages, Cleft for Me'. Anxious to get the words on paper, he is said to have written the verse on the only piece of paper on his person—a playing card.

Home Sweet Home The words of this most sentimental of all Victorian ballads were written by an American, John Howard Payne, who had no home.

He wrote 'Home Sweet Home' in the 1820s to the music of an Englishman, Henry Rowley Bishop. As late as 1851, Payne wrote to a friend: 'It is strange that it should have been my lot to cause so many to boast of the delights of home when I never had a home of my own and never expect to.' However, he did later find a roof over his head when he became American consul in Tunis.

Bishop was a well-known London conductor and the first musician ever to be knighted. When 'Home Sweet Home' was first heard, he was accused of stealing the tune from Sicilian sources. But eventually it was acknowledged that he had composed the tune himself as a national anthem for Sicily in his opera *Clari, the Maid of Milan*.

DULCE DOMUM *Victorians decorated their walls with the title of Payne's sentimental song.*

Colonel Bogey The stirring marching tune owes its origin to an army officer who was playing golf on the West of England course in 1913.

Major F. J. Ricketts, who was bandmaster of the Argyll and Sutherland Highlanders, happened to be on the fairway when a colonel wanted to drive off from the tee. Instead of shouting 'Fore!', the colonel whistled two warning notes at the major. They stuck in Ricketts's head and later he wrote them down as the first two notes of a new march.

He called it 'Colonel Bogey' in memory of the whistler. In British golfing terms 'bogey' refers to a hole that is scored in par—the rating given to a hole that any 'scratch' player is supposed to score.

Major Ricketts, who composed 17 other marches, wrote under the name of Kenneth Alford. No words were officially put to his tune, but in both world wars anonymous British barrack-room poets wrote bawdy lyrics which were sung with gusto.

Major Ricketts became Director of Music of the Royal Marines in 1926. He died in 1944, knowing that his march had inspired two generations of soldiers.

Paul Jones It is generally agreed that the Paul Jones, the 'change-your-partners' dance, is named after John Paul Jones, the American naval commander. But there are several theories about why this brilliant, dashing sailor should be linked with the ballroom.

John Paul Jones, who was born in Scotland in 1747, saw service with both the American and the Russian navies. He became known as 'the sailor England feared'.

Some say that the men in the dance change partners in the way that Jones abandoned his own ship to go to seize another which lay grappled alongside. Others believe that the dance got its name because Jones was a notoriously fickle lover.

The Tarantella A strange sickness kept striking the southern Italian port of Taranto. It was said to be caused by the bite of the tarantula spider, and the only cure was to dance madly and sweat out the spider's poison.

Fortunately Taranto had a special, wild dance to work the cure. Called the tarantella, it caught the imagination of many composers by its frenzied death-cheating, rhythm.

But doctors, who investigated the disease of tarantism and its cure, found little proof that people suffered from spider bites, or that the dance was much of an antidote if they did. They came to the conclusion that tarantism was a myth.

Historians now believe that, in the pre-Christian era, Taranto was a cult centre for the rites of the Greek god Dionysus—the Roman Bacchus. These rites always included drunken, licentious festivities and frenzied dancing.

Naturally, the Christian Church expressly forbade the cult of Dionysus and its feasts. But in Taranto the dancing was so popular that it was maintained, though ostensibly for another and more respectable purpose—as a medical treatment. It has survived as a folk dance.

DANSE MACABRE *People of Taranto, Italy, believed that the tarantella cured them from the bite of the tarantula (inset). Probably the dance was a survival from Bacchanalian rites.*

563

The Marseillaise Ironically, the stirring French national anthem has twice been banned because of its revolutionary connections—and the man who commissioned it, himself an aristocrat, ended on the guillotine.

It was written in Strasbourg, the French city on the Rhine, in the desperate year of 1792. Three years after the storming of the Bastille, France was still in the throes of revolution and Austria had declared war on her. The mayor of Strasbourg called for a rousing marching song to fire the revolutionary troops with enthusiasm.

In the city's garrison was a captain of engineers, Claude Joseph Rouget de Lisle, who answered the appeal by composing in one night what he called 'War Song for the Army of the Rhine'. On the way to Paris, volunteers from Marseilles sang the anthem with such gusto that the Parisians attributed it to them and it became known as 'La Marseillaise'.

A decree of July 14, 1795, confirmed Rouget de Lisle's song as the French national anthem, but it was outlawed because of its rabble-rousing nature when Napoleon came to power, and remained banned until the July revolution of 1830. Banned again by Napoleon III, it was not restored as the country's national anthem until 1879.

P. F. Dietrich, meanwhile, the wealthy mayor of Strasbourg who commissioned the song, had, like so many other aristocrats, gone to the guillotine.

The Star-Spangled Banner The melody of the American national anthem was written by an Englishman—and was not officially adopted by the United States for 117 years after the words had been composed.

In 1814 America was at war with Britain—the only war the two countries fought since the American Revolution. As the British were shelling Fort McHenry, near Baltimore, a young American, Francis Scott Key, went to ask them to release a friend who had been taken prisoner some time before. A naval commander agreed to his friend's release, but kept both men in protective custody until the attack was over.

Throughout the bombardment, the Stars and Stripes flag fluttered over the fort, and in the end the British had to admit failure.

Scott Key, his heart aglow with patriotic fervour as he gazed upon the scene, set about writing a poem on the back of an envelope:

> *Oh, say can you see by the dawn's early light*
> *What so proudly we hail'd at the twilight's last gleaming,*
> *Whose broad stripes and bright stars through the perilous fight*
> *O'er the ramparts we watch'd were so gallantly streaming?*

While writing his lyrics, Scott Key had had the tune in mind—a melody used at hymn meetings. Ironically, it had been written in England by John Stafford Smith (1750–1836) as an anthem for a London social club.

It was not until 1931 that an act of Congress adopted Key's song as the official American national anthem.

There's a Long, Long Trail a-Winding For the American and British troops slogging through the mud and dust in the First World War, the long, long trail they sang about was right before their eyes. And the land of their dreams that it led to was across the seas in Britain and the United States. But when Alonzo Elliott, a student at Yale University, wrote the song he was thinking not about the trenches of Flanders, but about Napoleon's retreat from Moscow.

Elliott wrote the words and music in 1913, and tried to sell it in America but could arouse no interest among music publishers. When he went to England in 1914 to complete his studies at Cambridge, the song was snapped up. It sold 4 million copies and was even more popular in the United States than in Britain.

With the many thousands of pounds the song brought him, Elliott studied how to write operas. After 19 years he completed his first, *What Price Glory?*—just as another generation of soldiers was about to march down the 'long, long trail' to Alamein and the Ardennes.

Tipperary The song, which all over the world is associated with the British Tommy marching off to the First World War, was written for a bet in a pub at Stalybridge, Cheshire, in 1912.

Jack Judge, who wrote the words, and his musical friend Harry J. Williams were challenged by a group of actors to write a song and perform it in the same day.

They did. Within 24 hours 'It's a Long, Long Way to Tipperary' was complete, and Judge had sung it himself at the Stalybridge Grand Theatre.

part
5

Contents

Triumph of man . . . or Armageddon?

The world of tomorrow

———————— ◆ ————————

SLOWING DOWN THE AGEING PROCESS

Can science help man to grow old more slowly?

Ageing begins at the very moment we are born. The long process of running down and wearing out gradually reduces the body's capacity to cope with illness, shock and damage, so that at the last, even the most athletic of us must yield to the weight and toll of our years.

Some parts of the body, such as the brain and the muscles, develop and, barring accidents, gradually wear out. Others, such as skin cells and blood corpuscles, are renewed regularly every day, even up to the end of life, in a constant programme of replacement.

But something seems to go wrong with the copying mechanism with age. The skin loses its elasticity, nerve cells lose their sensitivity, and the body as a whole becomes less resistant to disease and less able to adjust to strain or injury. Some cells may even become such poor copies of their active predecessors that the body may reject them.

Delaying this process is a matter of deep concern to most of us, and some researchers believe that by ensuring that older people maintain the same hormone levels as younger people through injections, cell replacement can carry on almost indefinitely.

Others have submitted the notion that the replacement system breaks down because of chemical reactions. In an attempt to reverse this process, rats and mice have been fed with massive doses of chemicals which reduce the oxygen con-

tent of the blood, while others have been given doses of DDT to stimulate the liver. In some cases it appeared that ageing processes were slowed down, although the precise reasons for this are not yet clear.

But the most promising method of retarding age is through diet. Laboratory animals given a carefully balanced diet containing all the essential ingredients, but with the calorie intake reduced to only three-fifths the normal level, have shown a lifespan two-fifths longer than normal.

All the normal deteriorations in vigour and age-related complaints also occurred some 40 per cent later than usual. The effect is to stretch the whole ageing process.

In theory, then, the lives of humans might be made nearly half as long again. All that is needed, it seems, is the perseverance to stick to the recommended diet for long enough. The main problem so far has been that the doctor could see whether the diet worked only when a patient eventually died after a lifetime following it—by which time the physician might well be dead, too.

But new ways are being found for measuring ageing rates more quickly. By such methods as checking skin elasticity and the sharpness of a patient's hearing, it should soon be possible to check the diet against results in a matter of only a few years. Before long, therefore, the choice may be up to the individual—unrestricted eating or a longer, more active life.

THE ADVENT OF SUPERSOUND

Bringing 'ear-sight' to the blind

Blind people usually possess one advantage over other people who *can* see: their sense of hearing is far more acute. Sounds which most others would miss can carry a great deal of information to a sightless person. For instance, teams of blind children can enjoy fast-moving games of soccer with a bell inside the ball and a new hand-held ultrasonic device to guide them. And that sound-location system could help to build up an even more complete sound picture of a blind person's surroundings.

Bats, whose sight is poor, use a sound-location system to help them avoid obstacles in the dark. They send out pulses of sound waves, pitched at 50,000 cycles per second, far above the limits of the human ear, which can hear sounds up to frequencies of about 20,000 cycles per second. As the echoes bounce back off obstacles such as trees and walls, the bats are able to take appropriate action.

The first steps to help blind people to see with sound are based on exactly the same principle. The sound is emitted by an ultrasonic torch, shaped like a double-barrelled version of a normal electric torch. It works in a similar way to a sonar unit on a warship or submarine.

The unit's transmitter sends out pulses of ultrasonic waves at the same frequency as the bat, and the receiver picks up the returning echoes. Because these are still above the frequency at which the human ear can pick them up, the echoes are filtered through circuits which turn them into clearly audible 'bleeps' before passing them into headphones.

This means that a person holding the torch can point it ahead of him and 'scan' the area for obstacles over a range of about 25 ft. If there are no return echoes coming through the headphones, then there is nothing in the way.

If echoes *do* come back, then the closer the obstruction the faster the succession of bleeps and the deeper the pitch of each bleep. With practice the torch could help a blind person to lead a more normal life —without needing a constant companion to guide him. Experienced operators of the torch system claim they can distinguish grass from bushes, trees, posts and kerbstones.

Hearing with spectacles

But before blind people can be helped to feel really independent, the system needs to be more streamlined.

At present, the experimental ultrasonic torch requires a shoulder bag to carry the batteries, cables for the power supplies and earphones, in addition to the torch itself. But miniaturisation of electronic equipment is making such rapid progress

'SEEING' WITH SONAR *Prototype demonstration of the ultrasonic transmitter which by means of sound waves may enable the blind to locate the exact position of obstacles up to 25 ft away.*

that it should not be long before the whole set-up can be reproduced in a form small enough to fit into a pair of spectacles.

The transmitter and power supplies, with all the circuitry, would be packed into the bridgepiece above the nose. The sending and receiving sensors would be in the 'lenses'. And the filtered bleeps

would be passed on to the wearer through the earpieces, as with present-day hearing-aid spectacles.

This would mean that scanning one's surroundings would become instinctive. The wearer would face in the direction he wanted to check, and lift or lower his head just as a sighted person would.

THE CHANGING FACE OF MAN

How man may become an egg-headed cyborg in a million years

In science fiction, the man of the future is often depicted as a weird and, to present-day eyes, repulsive monster. He may be a bald, egg-headed creature of superior intellect. He may be tall, with firm muscles, but covered in scales and with webbed hands and feet. He could be part-human, part-machine with replaceable, artificial limbs and organs, and immense strength—a combination known as a cyborg.

Oddly enough, these characteristics may be a description of what could happen to man in the next million years.

The already-established medical practice of transplanting living organs and tissue to replace damaged parts is a pointer to future development. Although still in its infancy, the technique of spare-part surgery could save millions of lives in tomorrow's world.

Today, man has the necessary surgical skills to carry out operations to replace almost every organ and limb in the body. All that surgeons now need to overcome is the rejection of 'foreign' tissue by the body of the recipient.

Rejection is basically caused by the body's own defences. White blood cells attack and digest invading organisms. So far, surgeons have tried to overcome this by using drugs that suppress these defence mechanisms. But this method can lower the body's resistance to infection, which in turn can lead to death.

Just as somebody needing a blood transfusion can accept it only from a donor whose blood group is compatible with his own, so there are compatible and incompatible tissue groups. Researchers are trying to improve the methods of matching types of tissue to prevent rejection without impairing a patient's resistance to infection. In America, attempts are being made to perfect a synthetic blood

that would not react to 'alien' matter. Already the University of Cincinnatti medical centre has used a synthetic blood,

NEW PARTS FOR OLD *Future man will prolong life and activity by replacing defunct organs with transplants or synthetic spare parts. Here are some of the possibilities envisaged:*

1 Liver
2 Heart
3 Lungs
4 Kidney
5 Pancreas
6 Metal or bone skull plate
7 Wig to cover surgery scars
8 Silicone skull plug
9 Artificial acrylic cornea
10 Silicone, acrylic or glass eye
11 Contact lenses
12 Spectacles
13 False teeth
14 Silicone ear
15 Silicone chin
16 Plastic or silver windpipe
17 Hearing aid
18 Tube to drain water from brain
19 Rubber larynx
20 Battery-powered pacemaker
21 Metal upper arm
22 Plastic, fibre or metal heart valves
23 Silicone breast implant
24 Arteries of concertina-pleated Dacron
25 Woven artificial vein
26 Metal elbow joint
27 Cap and hinge for elbow
28 Fibre patch for abdomen wall
29 Metal hip joint
30 Articulated artificial limbs
31 Silicone or acrylic testicles
32 Metal thigh support
33 Metal finger joints
34 Metal knee joint
35 Metal knee plate
36 Metal shinbone

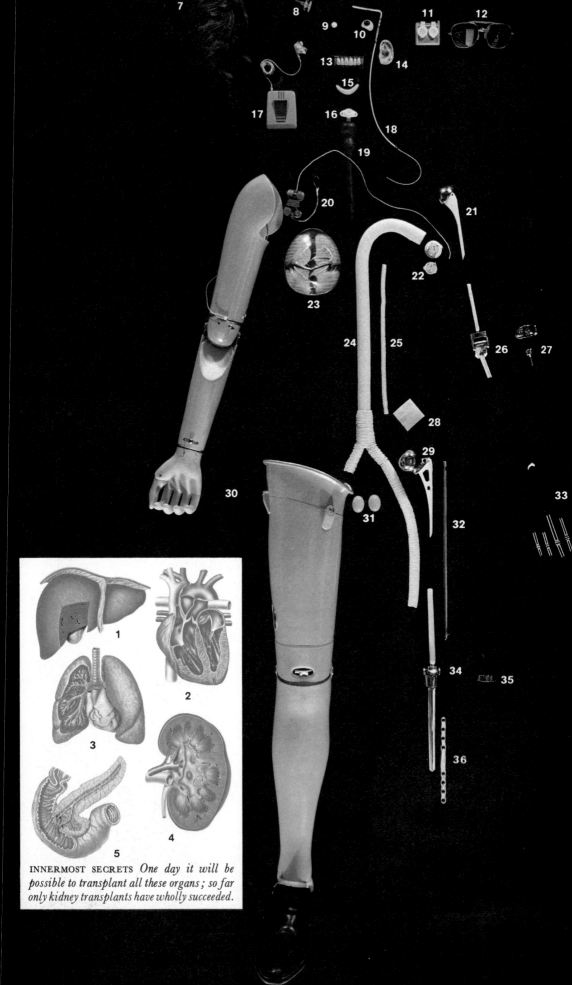

7
8
9
10
11
12
13
14
15
16
17
18
19
20
21
22
23
24
25
26
27
28
29
30
31
32
33
34
35
36

INNERMOST SECRETS *One day it will be possible to transplant all these organs; so far only kidney transplants have wholly succeeded.*

1
2
3
4
5

made of inert, inorganic oxygen solvents, to keep rats alive.

Side by side with the transplant of living tissue the development of man-made spare parts is progressing. But in this field, too, there are many complicated problems to be overcome.

Miniature power-packs to drive artificial limbs, for example, are often too short-lived, or too heavy. Materials that are acceptable to the human body, and at the same time totally reliable, are difficult to come by. And, often, motors cannot respond as sensitively as the signals given out by muscles.

But all these problems are regarded by researchers as temporary. They could be solved virtually overnight as break-throughs occur in materials technology.

Already, experts in cybernetics—the science of systems involved in artificial-limb development—are working out ways of improving the sensitivity of man-made extensions to the human body.

While it is at present considered unlikely that such sensations as touch, temperature, pressure and pain could ever be fed directly into the nervous system from an artificial sensor, there are other ways of passing on to the brain 'information' about the outside world. Vibrations, sound tones, lights, or mild electric currents, for example, could be used as codes to inform the wearer of an artificial limb about the temperature and texture of objects around him.

But what about the long-term future of man? By studying man's adaptation to his changing environment over the last few million years, scientists can form some idea of possible future changes in his appearance and capabilities.

From the squat, but upright, *Australopithecus* creature of around 5 million years ago, to *Homo erectus* of 500,000 years ago, man has evolved through variants of *Homo sapiens*, like Neanderthal Man of 70,000 years ago, to his modern form, *Homo sapiens sapiens*.

An American anthropologist, H. L. Shapiro, has studied these physical trends and believes that futureman, or *Homo futurus*, will be taller, have a dome-shaped, almost hairless, head, an improved slightly larger brain, and possibly lose his little toe. This new-look man, already envisaged in science fiction, should be around in about 500,000 years, according to Shapiro.

On the other hand, a Russian scientist, A. P. Bystrov, believes that man's evolution stopped long ago. He does not believe that *Homo futurus* will be any different from *Homo sapiens sapiens*. Bystrov's belief is supported by experts in the anthropology department of the Natural History Musem in London. They say there is little sign that *Homo sapiens sapiens* has shown much biological change since the last Ice Age.

Other scientists, concerned about overpopulation, envisage an offshoot of futureman called *Homo aquaticus*, or water man. As earth's resources on land become depleted, it is thought that man could adapt to a marine environment, farming and mining the ocean floors.

The adaptability of man is pointed to by Francisco Figueroa of the University of Manila who, in 1965, claimed he had found a 12-year-old 'sea boy', who spent more time in the sea than on the Pacific Island where he lived. He was an astonishing swimmer, weighed 12 st., but had only limited powers of speech. Without the benefit of a racing-dive start or flip-over turn in a swimming pool, the boy was said to be able to do 100 metres in only a few seconds more than the 51-second world record.

But before man could seriously contemplate living in the sea, there would have to be an artificially stimulated mutation of his breathing capabilities. Dr Johannes Kylstra has been experimenting with an artificial liquid breathing system which he hopes will enable man to live and breathe underwater.

He believes that a lung filled with water instead of air would be able to withstand the higher pressure of the outside water because liquids are virtually incompressible. Water would take the place of nitrogen or any of the other gases used in deep-diving mixtures as a carrier for oxygen.

Dr Kylstra experimented with mice immersed in containers filled with salt water through which he bubbled high-pressure oxygen. The animals managed to live in the containers for 18 hours without putting their heads above water. Dr Kylstra claimed that the essential breathing mechanism of the mice's lungs had not been impaired by the experiment, and that they took oxygen from the water as easily as from air.

An American scientist, Dr Walter Robb, has developed another technique designed to facilitate underwater life for man. He constructed a bubble made of fine, silicone rubber membrane, 1/1000th in. thick, that would provide an air supply direct from sea-water. The membrane can allow gas, but not water, to pass through it. Such a membrane, with sea-water flowing past it, would extract oxygen if the pressure on the inside were lower than on the outside. Dr Robb claims that animals have lived inside such a membrane for extended periods.

Over thousands of years living underwater, man's body might eventually adjust to a new environment, so that he would ultimately need no artificial equipment to survive at all.

But, despite his adaptability, it is unlikely that man—without artificial aids —will ever develop into a superman.

While it may appear that men are growing stronger and more resilient, as new athletic records are broken from year to year, there are limits to the capabilities of the human frame. The main one is man's inability to renew the high-energy chemicals used in exercise.

It is unlikely, therefore, that any one will run a mile in less than 3 min. 45 sec. The barrier of the four-minute mile seems to have been largely a psychological one, though credit for breaking it must also be given to modern methods of diet and training.

All the same, Superman will remain in the realms of science fiction. But super-cyborg—man raised to incredible strength and endurance through artificial limbs and organs—could very well be the form of futureman.

OUTLOOK SUNNY

How man may overcome the energy crisis

Archimedes built a giant solar reflector, generally known as his 'burning mirror', to concentrate the sun's rays on Roman warships and set them on fire. Primitive tribes channelled ocean water into shallow pans so that it would evaporate in the sun, leaving its salt behind. We use oil to generate heat and electricity, and are in effect burning concentrated eons of sunlight, for oil is nothing more than the product of centuries of plant and animal life, impacted under the earth. The sun, in fact, is the source of almost all the earth's energy.

But the notion of trapping and storing the heat of the sun for conversion into heat, steam or electricity is relatively new. And for people in industrialised countries who are accustomed to creating energy from coal or oil, solar energy—cheap, non-polluting, and ever-renewable— seems like a fairytale solution to the energy crisis. Nevertheless, solar enthusiasts believe that we are already well on the way to a functioning solar technology; and with concentrated, well-endowed research, within a decade the United States, for example, could have a solar industry that would supply a good proportion of the country's power needs. Already the first solar-heated council house is going up in Britain at Milton Keynes, near Cambridge.

The world's first solar-heated school, St George's in Wallasey, Cheshire, has been operating since the early 1960s. The school is built like a great insulator, absorbing heat directly from the sun. Shutters outside the walls, which are made of thick masonry and concrete, can be adjusted to deflect some of the sunshine in summer and avoid over-heating, or to attract it in winter.

Another indication of the shape of things to come is the increasing number of boat owners who are using solar cell units that absorb sunlight to generate electricity to power navigation lights at night. Even in a British winter there is enough sunlight to keep the batteries charged.

Solar power

The term 'solar power' covers a number of different and seemingly unrelated methods of creating energy. Wind energy, solar heating and cooling, bioconversion (transforming plant life into fuel), ocean-thermal technology, the transmutation of light into electricity are all energy systems that are powered by the sun. With the exception of solar heating and cooling, they are in the beginning stages of development—which means that even when theory proves out in practice, the costs are still too high for large-scale use.

Tomorrow, or next year, the story may be very different.

Spotted here and there throughout the United States are houses that seem completely conventional, except that their roofs are covered on the sunny side with large, flat panels. Called solar collectors, these panels are usually made of piping mounted on a flat, dark-painted surface and enclosed between two sheets of glass or plastic. Water or some other liquid is run through the pipes. Heated by the sun, the liquid can reach temperatures of 54°C (130°F) or more. The hot water is piped to an insulated storage unit, and its heat is circulated via fans. The heat can also be used for cooling, by powering refrigerators and air-conditioners.

Of course, man has known for centuries that the sun is a source of energy. In 1868, for instance, Sir Henry Bessemer, the Victorian steel pioneer, built the first solar furnace. It would not work on sunless days, however; the storing of the sun's energy for later use is a new technology.

France enjoys a fortunate heritage from the days when it controlled much of North Africa. Before the colonial empire broke up, a solar furnace near Algiers was generating 40 kilowatts. Now, as a development from that, a huge concave mirror near Odeillo in the Pyrenees concentrates 1000 kilowatts of energy at its focal point. It can generate temperatures of up to 4000°C in a crucible containing 3 tons of raw materials.

The kind of heat produced is also an advantage. The sun is a completely clean source of energy—there is, for instance, no smoke, soot or ash to contend with—and it is used at Odeillo to manufacture rare alloys and crystals that must be produced under sterile conditions. It has even proved possible to cover the crucible with transparent paper, to protect the contents from impurities in the atmosphere, without the thermal beam destroying the paper.

Wind, another creation of the sun's rays, offers still another energy-producing possibility. Wind generators, already in use today, can create enough electricity to power a house. Technologists foresee armies of huge windmills in windswept areas like the Great Plains or anchored off the northeastern US coast, and producing perhaps one-quarter of the nation's total electricity.

A large proportion of the sun's heat is absorbed and stored in the surface layers of tropical oceans, while their deeper layers remain cold. It is possible to exploit the temperature difference to make electricity, using a turbine powered by a fluid—tammonia, for instance—which expands and becomes a gas when warmed by the surface water and condenses back to a fluid when it meets the colder water pumped up from the ocean depths.

WASTE-NOT-WANT-NOT *The future house's self-contained system (below) provides everything from gas for cooking to water.*

Solar panel heats water
Rainwater
Water-storage tank
Hot-water tank
Purifier
Rainwater purified for drinking
Waste water from sinks and bath collected and purified
Purifier
Water for lavatory only
Sink-disposal unit
Solid organic waste
Solid organic w.
All househ. waste is fe. into a dige. containing algae whic. acts on the waste, separating methane g
Garden waste is collected to make methane gas
Methane gas for cooking
Sludge goes to make garden compost

Researchers in the field of ocean-thermal technology believe that the first ocean-based power plant could be operational in the Gulf Stream near Florida within eight years. By the turn of the century fleets of these plants could be producing about 4 per cent of America's total energy requirements.

But this is only the beginning. The United States is spending $50 millions a year on solar energy projects. Professor A. B. Meinel, of Arizona University, calculates that if the sunlight on 14 per cent of the western deserts were collected efficiently, it could supply the additional power needed by the whole country until 1990.

His idea is to collect heat during daylight and store it at 38°C (100°F) in molten salts. A heat exchanger would

POWER FROM THE SUN *The solar house of the future would be virtually self-sufficient. An outside wind-generator would provide all the household power needed, stored in batteries in the basement. The sun would contribute energy for heating and growing greenhouse vegetables.*

Solar generator
to power fuel cells
in the roof

Freshwater
storage tank

Insulation

Fish pond

Double-glazed
windows over
greenhouse area

transform the stored energy into steam and later electricity. The proposal is for a plant in Arizona with the containers—insulated pipes containing chemicals that are poor conductors—covering just over a square mile.

Solar cells

All these techniques use sun power as a catalyst to create energy. It is also possible to convert sunlight directly into electricity. The solar cells used as energy generators in space satellites function as 'photo-chemical reactors'. When light strikes them, an electric current is created that can be used immediately or stored in batteries.

The material used in the newest solar cells is silicon, which will last almost forever. But constructing a silicon cell is so expensive that mass production is virtually ruled out at present. (It would cost some £145,000 to power a house with the kind of silicon cells used in spacecraft.) However, a new technique for producing the cells in the form of a hair-fine ribbon promises to lower costs enough so that, if today's research is successful, electric plants using solar cells could be operating by 1985.

Another remote possibility for solar-cell energy is the building of 6 mile long solar panels in orbit around the earth, and beaming the power they generate back to land on micro-waves. But the technology and tools for space construction are still relatively primitive. The giant solar panel will have to wait until space science is considerably more advanced.

Solar energy is being used for heating in hot countries such as Israel, India and Australia. Japan, for instance, invested $3 million on solar energy in 1974.

Research work is pursuing many different lines. In addition to the sun transmitting thermal energy, it is a source of photons, the particles from which light is composed, and these can be converted directly into electrical power. Photo-electric devices, such as the solar cell, convert the photons into electrons. These have been used to power satellites in the American space programme. Research is aimed at improving efficiency and reducing costs.

Alternatively, instead of converting light directly into electricity, it can be converted into a chemical fuel which can be stored. For instance, sunlight can be used to separate the hydrogen from water so that it can be burnt later.

Another interesting idea for harnessing the sun to solve the energy crisis goes back to nature again. Research is being carried out on cultivating vast areas of quick-growing plants to use as hydro-carbon fuel. It has been calculated that harvesting and burning 5 per cent of the yearly growth of new plants throughout the world would supply as much energy as man consumed in 1970.

By the year 2000, greenhouses covering 700 million acres could harness the sun to provide all the food and fuel needed by 7000 million people.

In colder parts of the world, where the use of solar energy will be limited, a possible alternative for heating houses and other buildings would be the simplest and most obvious source of warmth—the hot interior of the earth. Early uses of this geo-thermal energy were not confined to volcanic areas. The hot springs at Bath, which were enjoyed by the Romans, are 1000 miles from the nearest volcano.

Natural 'hot spot'

Where easily accessible, the heat, steam and hot water trapped in the earth, often under tremendous pressures, are already utilised for heating and energy production. The world's largest geothermal power plant, The Geysers, 90 miles north of San Francisco, uses the steam created naturally by a 'hot spot' in the earth's crust. Tapping the steam, however, requires drilling, often to depths of 2 miles or more. The process is often dangerous.

The Geysers is one of the few 'dry-steam' facilities in the world. More common are plants that use wet steam—a mixture of steam and hot water. (Old Faithful, at Yellowstone National Park, is a wet-steam geyser.) Power production from wet steam is more complicated because the water, often heavy with dissolved minerals, must be removed before the steam can be used. But steam fields are tapped today for heating homes in Iceland, Siberia, and in the United States.

The US Geological Survey has identified a geothermal belt that runs through almost 2 million acres in the western states and Alaska—where molten rock from the earth's interior has forced its way into the crust, forming the hot spots that create the heat and steam. These are potential future sites for more power plants—when man's technology is finally capable of taming the earth's immense interior pressures.

And when the power is produced finally in the form of electricity, a recent development can be used to convert it cheaply to heat—by conducting it through the paint on the walls of houses.

The principle employed is simple. When an electric current is passed through a resistor—say an element, or the wires of an electric fire—heat is generated.

Conductive paints, invented by the British Paint Research Association, pro-vide resistance to a low-voltage current—less than 40 volts—and become warm. They can be made to generate temperatures as high as 300°C. (572°F.), but for domestic walls 40°C. (104°F.) is ample.

Patents have been taken out in 25 countries and ten companies have been licensed to manufacture the paints.

Electricity, whether it comes from nuclear reactors, wind or water, will remain the primary source of energy. So not only is the future for domestic heating bright, but also you will be able to pick your own shade of brightness.

SALVATION FROM THE SEA

The oceans may become earth's larder

One of the greatest challenges facing mankind is feeding the world's ever-growing population. Vast new food sources must be found, for by the year 2000 there will probably be 8000 million people in the world, compared with 3247 million in 1970.

The sea is likely to provide much of the extra food. Oceans occupy 70 per cent of the earth's surface area, yet so far their food potential has been exploited only in a haphazard way. Many nations are now looking on the sea as a farm with almost limitless resources.

British marine zoologist Sir Alistair Hardy forecasts that new techniques will allow divers to weed out unwanted fish that compete with edible breeds for food, paving the way for undersea 'cowboys' to stage gigantic fish round-ups in submarine 'tractors'.

In Britain, popular fish such as plaice, sole and turbot are already being bred on experimental fish farms at the Suffolk port of Lowestoft. Trout and carp are being produced in huge numbers from fresh-water hatcheries at other centres.

The oyster—only a century ago considered a vulgar food for the lower classes —is being turned rapidly into a thriving product of intensive farming. It is bred in brackish, shallow estuaries close to Britain's shores after starfish, fungi, bacteria and other natural enemies have been eliminated from the area. In Japan, oysters are cultivated in hanging farms consisting of cast and spun concrete floats which preserve them from predators lurking on the ocean bed.

In the Far East, hopes for vastly increased fish harvests are pinned on the Asian milk fish. Similar to a mackerel, its larvae are collected from sandy beaches in Taiwan, Indonesia and the Philippines, then cultivated in man-made ponds.

But perhaps the most ambitious fish-farming project is envisaged by the Mexican Government, which hopes to convert the country's huge coastal lagoons into the world's biggest fish farms, with a yearly output measured in millions of tons.

Ocean fish farming will have its own inverted form of irrigation. Nuclear-powered blowers on the icy depths of the sea-bed will force up nutrition into the

FOOD FOR MILLIONS *The fastest-growing known plant, the giant kelp, grows to a height of 200 ft, at a rate of 1½ ft a day.*

poorer surface layers. Chemical nutrients will also be introduced to the fish ranch, while giant mirrors on the surface will trap the sun's rays to encourage the growth of algae. The ranch hands will have miniature submarines and underwater televisions to supervise operations.

Nova Scotia development

By the end of the century it is likely that every possible fish product will be utilised. The Canadian Government has helped to set up a plant in Nova Scotia which converts waste from fish-processing factories into a near-tasteless, but nutritious, powder containing 95 per cent high-grade protein. The process is so cheap that it costs little more than £1 to provide a year's protein supply for an adult. And the powder can be processed further to look and taste like fish again.

Plant farming in the sea also offers the prospect of rich new food supplies. In most ocean areas light does not penetrate below about 160 ft, and plants cannot grow in darkness. But the black depths contain enough fertilising materials from decayed animal and vegetable matter to support plant life on land for centuries.

Biologists hope to find a way of lifting these fertilisers to within about 20 ft of the surface, and so convert ocean 'deserts' into flourishing areas of life. The number of fish would then increase dramatically.

Seaweed—a traditional food in Wales —is now used to a limited extent elsewhere as a processed-food additive. In Japan it is harvested and put into mincemeat. But the most promising crop is the fastest-growing plant on earth—the giant kelp, which thrives in polluted water.

Off California it grows 200 ft tall, with fronds extending at the rate of $1\frac{1}{2}$ ft a day. This towering underwater tree stores nutrients such as iodine and potassium. So far it has been used only in cattle food, but in the future it could become an important food source for man.

FARMING FISH *In this fish-farm, biotrons in fish hives (bottom left) contain spawn which is carried by divers to hatcheries (left background), where the eggs are fertilised and then piped into corrals and reared under mesh at a depth of no more than 100 ft. A feeding device (centre foreground) sends synthetic food on currents into the corrals. The fully grown fish are transported in tube-shaped containers by crane to waiting ships. Fish can also be raised in pens made of residue gases bubbling up from perforated pipes on the sea-bed (centre right).*

BLACK GOLD FROM THE SEA

Present-day oil rigs, although considered a marvel of modern technology, are actually inefficient and dangerous. In the future oil may be drilled and refined on the sea-bed. Storms, the chief hazard of surface rigs, will be avoided, while the crews, working four or five-hour shifts, will live in undersea houses, breathing gases at the same pressure as the water outside. Slow de-pressurisation to prevent 'the bends'—killer of many divers in the past—will therefore be necessary only when they eventually surface at the end of a tour of duty.

ALTHOUGH OCEANOGRAPHY, as a science, came into being over 100 years ago, men have obtained most of their knowledge of the sea through instruments carried on board ships. Few pioneer investigators have ventured down to the bottom of the ocean to explore its vast mineral resources.

The new era of ocean studies dawning may see men working and living on the ocean bed, with the aid of aqualung, bathyscaphe and undersea houses.

Oil, already discovered in vast quantities off the Scottish and Irish coasts, may be drilled on the ocean bed rather than from the surface. Balloon-shaped balls (above) hold the drills in place while the crude oil is stored in containers (left) and pumped into a refinery, (cross section foreground) and then sent to the surface by pumps on the sea-bed (background left), or carried by giant underwater plastic tanks (centre background), towed by submarines.

IRRIGATION FROM ICEBERGS

Turning mountains of polar ice into a fresh-water supply

By the end of this century, giant tugs may be plying the South Atlantic, towing icebergs 7 miles long to water the green fields of the Sahara.

More than three-quarters of the world's fresh water is locked in the ice-caps of the Arctic and Antarctica. These caps are created from snow that has fallen for the past 50,000 years. Thus they contain no trapped particles of salt, as sea-ice does.

If only a fraction of this pure water could be transported, the parched areas of the world might be transformed into crop-bearing prairies.

Moreover, the water is ready-packaged in an easily transportable form. Along the edges of the ice-caps, icebergs are constantly breaking off, pushed by the pressure behind them. In the North Atlantic, about 16,000 icebergs, some many miles in extent, are 'calved' each year, mostly from the enormous glaciers along the shores of Greenland.

They slowly float away, their drift dictated by ocean currents, gradually melting in the sea. The closer they approach to the warm waters of the Gulf Stream, the faster they disappear.

Many icebergs are too small to be towed very far without disintegrating. But some Antarctic monsters are as big as the Isle of Man; and one sighted in 1956 was more than 200 miles long and 60 miles broad. It covered an area of 12,000 square miles—bigger than Belgium.

It would be impossible, using any known technique, to tow a berg of anything like this size. But engineers think it feasible to cope with one up to 7 miles long by 1½ miles wide. A tug as big as a supertanker could tow such an iceberg at a rate of about 20 miles a day.

An iceberg of this manageable size would contain more than 250,000 million cubic feet of water—as much as flows over the Niagara Falls in two months.

Such quantities would be sufficient to turn parts of the world's most forbidding deserts into rich farmland.

The Sahara, the Yuma desert of California, the Atacama of Chile, the dry wastes of Arabia and Western Australia all have the advantage of lying close to the sea. They are therefore open to irrigation without the prohibitive cost of long-distance pipelines.

Some of the ice would obviously melt during the voyage, particularly if it had to be made through tropical seas. But the melting would not be so great as might be deduced from observation of small icebergs, which last only a short time.

The bigger the berg, the smaller its outer surface in proportion to each ton of ice it contains. So, weight for weight, less heat gets into the ice of the big berg through its exposed surfaces from the sun, the atmosphere and the sea.

The same principle can be seen in children's snowmen left in the garden after a thaw. The little snowman disappears in a few hours; the really big one sometimes takes weeks to melt.

Even with the giant tug envisaged, a 7-mile long iceberg would perhaps require a voyage of six to 12 months from polar region to desert. But it should not be beyond the bounds of technology in the coming decades to improve this performance. And in many regions ocean currents could be used in the same way that airliner pilots utilise the 100–200 mph jet streams 10 miles above the earth to increase speed and cut down on fuel.

Irrigation system

Once the big iceberg reached its destination, there would be no need for expensive docking installations. The berg would simply be left near the shore to melt into the sea. Because fresh water is less dense than sea-water, the melted ice would lie uncontaminated on the surface, while the displaced salt water would sink.

The fresh surface water could easily be pumped ashore and into the irrigation pipeline system.

Greenland's icy mountain would have come at last to India's coral strand.

MAKING THE DESERT BLOSSOM

Can the Sahara again become the fertile plain it once was?

The arid moonscape of the Sahara covers millions of square miles of lifeless sand and rock, upon which the sun glares without respite. Except at oases, not a blade of grass or a drop of water relieves the monotony.

A man stranded there without shelter would die of heat stroke and dehydration within 48 hours. The superheated bone-dry atmosphere extracts the moisture from the body like blotting-paper. Here and there, on the fringes of the wilderness, a handful of nomads manage to scratch a precarious living, depending for their survival on animals which crop the few pathetic strands of vegetation, thus widening the desert's borders year by year.

Yet fossils and cave paintings on the Tassili plateau indicate that thousands of years ago the Sahara was covered with luxuriant vegetation. And, etched into this now dry and barren world, are the traces of huge river systems and plentiful oases, which once supported flourishing communities.

An American research team has put forward a theory as to why the land became a desert. They believe that goats, herded for centuries by every community of desert dwellers, devastated all the

MAN'S BATTLE AGAINST THE DESERT *Despite erosion and lack of moisture, experiments with plants and patterning prove that desert cultivation may be possible.*

region's foliage, leaving the land exposed to soil erosion.

The source of the Sahara's problems is the soil itself. The lack of trees means there is no shade to prevent the sun burning off the surface water. The earth dries up and the scant plant life dies.

As the ground itself grows hotter and hotter, the few rain showers which do fall sink uselessly into it, washing away the salts and trace elements which could make it fertile, until only rocks and sand are left. In time, the sand becomes so hot that many of the showers which leave the clouds never even reach the ground, but evaporate on the way down.

So poor is the sand at retaining heat that the desert grows bitterly cold at night. The droppings of the nomadic herdsmen's animals become prized as fuel, and even that meagre nourishment is prevented from being returned to the land.

Yet the same sun that causes the Sahara's problems is the world's most powerful source of energy. But day after day it is squandered in heating up more than 3 million square miles of desert to

temperatures of more than 54°C (130°F).

Focusing and concentrating this awesome power to create still hotter temperatures may seem the last way to improve conditions, yet this could be the first small step in making the desert bloom again.

Free electricity

Scientists in Spain and the Sahara have already used the sun's rays to generate virtually free electricity in huge quantities. This power can then be used to drive pumps and drilling machines to tap the vast reserves of water which have filtered down through the sands of the desert. Over the centuries these have formed enormous natural reservoirs thousands of feet under the arid surface.

Some deep wells have already been established for supplying the oil-prospecting teams at work in the desert. One drill, more than a mile down, produced a fountain of pure ice-cold water at the rate of 80 gallons a second in the parched heart of the Sahara.

Energy from the solar furnace can also be used to help with the 'fixing' of nitrogen

579

from the air to produce nitrogen-based fertilisers on an immense scale—food which could begin to put nourishment back into the sand.

Harnessed rays

In the short term, even more use can be made of the sun by harnessing its ultra-violet rays. For example, they can be used to refine heavy oil into high-grade fuels, and at an almost nominal cost they can speed up the chemical reactions required to produce insecticides to clear the scourge of malaria from existing oases and village wells.

But the greatest use of the sun's radiation is its ability to stimulate the growth of algae, the simple microscopic plants which thrive in the most hostile conditions. By exposing a mixture of raw chemicals to the sun's rays man can obtain a burgeoning crop of algae, an adequate source of food for humans

and animals alike in the parched desert.

In the long term—given chemical fertilisers, water and power—men could begin to re-create the old fertile world which vanished thousands of years ago.

First they could lay a carpet of tarmac of any size and cover it with a layer of moisture-absorbing material. On top would go a thick layer of artificial soil, built up from dry desert sand, mixed according to a precise formula with all the minerals and elements present in normally fertile soil.

The results of experiments on these lines are astonishing. The combination of ample water, bright sunshine and the right proportion of chemicals produces a rich harvest. Experimental farms on the fringe of the Sahara and Negev deserts are already producing acres of corn and wheat, beans and peas, maize, onions and barley.

The base layers of tarmac and moss capture the water and hold it at a depth where the plants' roots can easily reach it to drink their fill. Even the occasional showers which still fall right in the stony heart of the desert are put to good use instead of being left to evaporate or sink into the sand.

But this type of farming, however encouraging, is only a temporary victory. The new face for the desert will be assured only when trees can be grown successfully. There are two major obstacles: trees require more complex conditions than crops in which to flourish, and they take longer to grow. While no trees have yet been grown to maturity in the desert, except at oases, researchers are hopeful that this will be possible.

HOPE FOR THE FUTURE *While no trees have yet been grown to maturity in desert conditions, researchers hope they can be made to thrive.*

PUTTING DOWN ROOTS *Trees will be vital in the cultivation of desert. Their shade would cool the earth and let rainfall moisten the soil.*

Shade for the desert

Groves of fruit trees established on a large scale will then provide the shade that the desert so desperately needs. Gradually the ground temperature will begin to drop, and rain will reach the earth and do its job properly. More trees will thrive, and the desert will grow progressively cooler and more fertile. There is no reason why the process should not work on a small scale at first. Then, as the fertile areas extend, their effect on the rest of the desert will multiply, until eventually the whole Sahara may be transformed. And all, ironically, thanks to the sun which contributed to its becoming a barren waste to begin with.

TRAIN WITHOUT WHEELS *An experimental monorail system built at Châteauneuf-sur-Loire, near Orléans in France.*

WILL THE WHEEL SOON BE OBSOLETE?

Man's first great invention is reaching the end of the road

One of the most crucial steps on early man's long road to civilisation was the invention of the wheel. Yet it looks as if the day of the wheel is over. Already the wheel is running into problems as a means of transporting people and goods.

It was the aeroplane that signalled the beginning of the end for the wheel. Once it takes off, an aircraft's wheels are useless and have to be folded away into the wings or fuselage so that they do not cause wasteful drag.

Now it is possible to take off without wheels. The development of directional jet nozzles, like those on the Hawker Siddeley Harrier, is giving birth to a whole new generation of aircraft that can hover and land and take off vertically, like helicopters.

Many helicopters have landing pods in place of wheels. Unlike wheeled aircraft, they can touch down safely on almost any surface—sand, snow, ice, swamp, water and rough or uneven ground. Even on paved runways the comfort is greater and the wear and tear much less. Tomorrow's vertical take-off airliners and private planes are likely to adopt the same techniques.

The wheel is becoming a prisoner of its own disadvantages, even for transport which stays on the ground. Designers of high-speed train projects for inter-city travel are anticipating problems with vibration, lubrication and complicated suspension systems, all because the wheels have to be kept in contact with the rails.

The most likely future development seems to be hovercraft suspension combined with power supplied by a linear motor—roughly like a normal electric motor slit down one side and then stretched out flat, parallel to the rails. This would eliminate wheels altogether, and with them would go all the present complex difficulties of wear and tear, vibration and metal fatigue.

Punishing tests

Hoverpower provides its own cushioning effect. When engineers tested a hover-suspension system, they hammered it with punishing vibration equivalent to those caused by 2 in. bumps to a train travelling at 300 mph. Yet the only movement that would have been transmitted to passengers in the carriage was less than $\frac{1}{4}$ in. Conventional wheels turning these speeds would create vortices, or whirling pockets of air, under the train, causing drag and absorbing power.

There are other advantages of hover-suspension. Steel wheels on steels rails weaken and break up through metal stress at very high speeds. Wheel bearings can break and there is always the possibility of derailment at full speed. Stopping a high-speed train from maximum speed by normal braking multiplies the stresses several times over, and an emergency stop to avoid an accident might easily cause a far worse calamity should the suspension give way under the strain.

Letting air carry the weight instead of wheels—with no axle boxes to overheat or springs to break—avoids all these problems. Stopping ceases to be a strain—a linear motor can be put into full reverse power at the touch of a switch. This gives a powerful braking force with no dangers of slip, wheel-locking or vibration, since it acts on the main structure of the train and not through its wheels.

German engineers are designing an electro-magnetic suspension system to drive the train, as well as carry it. British Rail also has plans for a linear motor-driven high-speed passenger service.

The Council of Europe decided several years ago that, in its view, the future would be wheel-less. After studying rival systems, the council opted for a 4000-mile hovertrain network covering the Continent, linking Brussels, Luxembourg and Geneva with Paris, Hamburg, Milan and France's Channel ports.

The council decided that city-centre routes for hover-train tracks would cause far less pollution and disruption than urban motorways of similar capacity.

The 500 mph shuttle

America's gravity-vacuum shuttle project is even more futuristic. This proposes an underground, 500 mph inter-city train, closely tailored to fit into a tunnel, and driven by suction from powerful pumps with a steep downward gradient out of each station. The same force in reverse would bring it smoothly to a halt.

At such speeds, wheels would be useless. The carriage, cushioned upon and surrounded by a layer of air, would be between the walls of the tunnel—rather like the old-fashioned department store vacuum system for transporting bills.

Space travel demands far higher speeds and space vehicles are almost totally without wheels. The powerful rocket motors that make space-flight possible are relatively simple, without the compressors and turbines of the jet engine. Long-distance spacecraft for exploring the further reaches of the solar system will have no landing and take-off problems anyway, since they will be assembled in orbit outside the atmosphere of the earth. This would save having to cater for the enormous stresses of taking off and landing under earth's gravity.

Relatively cheap space-shuttles, combinations of rocket and glider, that can land on retractable legs or skids would ply between the spacecraft in orbit and the planet to be explored.

Last stronghold

Even the transporting of freight may eventually dispense with wheels. Hovercraft engineers are experimenting with bases supported on air cushions. With all the weight carried by the suspension, one man could push heavy objects around on such floating trolleys, even over bumpy surfaces, and place them exactly where they were required. A similar type of vehicle, already in existence, is the hover lawn mower.

For carrying small objects in bulk over long distances, like parcels through the post, for example—there is no good reason why pipes could not carry these goods suspended in liquid. One such pipeline could carry a succession of different consignments, and branch pipelines and crossfeed pipes could allow door-to-door service, all without a wheel having to turn.

But one of the main developments in tomorrow's transport may hark back to the past—to the giant airships that vanished from the skies after the Hindenburg exploded and burnt in 1937. The trip from Britain to Australia would take less than a week. And the ships could be fuelled with cheap natural gas.

The last stronghold of the wheel may well be cars and lorries on which industry depends so heavily. Yet in more than half the world, road transport is still a relative rarity, because of the difficulty and expense of building highway networks. The hovercar or hoverlorry, able to drive at will over sand, swamp or grassland, is far more practical.

Even private transport must change eventually. As hoverpower grows cheaper and more efficient, wheel-less private cars will be able to leave roads and take to the countryside or water—provided man has devised adequate hover traffic controls.

The American army has experimented with personal, strap-on jet packs and one-man helicopters for lifting soldiers into battle. Civilian equivalents would give man a mobility never dreamt of.

The wheel may be reaching the end of its long road at last.

MOVING PAVEMENTS *In cities of the future pavements may well be replaced by 10 mph integrators swiftly carrying people to work and shops without the misery of the rush-hour jams.*

A STEP AHEAD

Conveyor-belt pavements to beat the rush-hour

Pedestrians in the cities of the future could speed through the streets at up to 10 mph—just by standing still. For a network of moving pavements could slash travelling time in city centres, and, by cutting out the necessity for buses and cars, end rush-hour jams for ever.

Moving walkways have been known for years, of course—underground escalators and airport ramps. But city authorities have fought shy of them because they are too slow for long-distance travel.

Now, however, Switzerland's Battelle Institute, working with the Dunlop tyre firm, have invented an accelerating device which makes high-speed moving pavements a practical proposition. Their invention means that pedestrians will be able to step on and off a high-speed network as easily as they now step on to an ordinary escalator.

The device, called an integrator, looks like a flat escalator. But at one end it moves at only $1\frac{1}{2}$ mph—a comfortable speed for a pedestrian to step on to. At the other it can be travelling at up to 10 mph—a little slower than the track record for the mile. At the fast end, pedestrians could step across to a main pavement going at the same speed alongside. This main pavement—which could be covered to keep out bad weather—would link up with other pavements to give access to any destination on the future city network. And, unlike queuing for buses and tube trains, there would be no waiting.

As a pedestrian was approaching his destination, he would step on to a reversed version of the integrator—and be carried comfortably and slowly back to firm ground.

Freight container
on pallet

Passenger
vehicle on
through track

Maintenance walkway
and emergency escape

Through track
for all vehicles

Handling and
storage building

Vehicle
and contain
transfer wa

Acceleration track
for passenger vehicles

Traffic entry
point from
local roads

Incoming car at
pick-up point

Ground-floor exit
for passengers

Vehicle storage floor

Container
in elevator

Freight containers
being transferred
laterally

Freight containers
in storage

DREAMWAY *This PAT system, designed for Puerto Rico, envisages an overhead motorway. In most metropolitan areas, however, it would be more convenient to have the garage space underground.*

ON THE RIGHT TRACK

Robot trucks could end road chaos

In a few decades the strain and tedium of motorway driving could be a thing of the past—thanks to an American system of high-speed robot trucks called PAT. The system has been designed to combine the advantages of cars and trains; drivers using it will be able to sit back and relax, while the trucks whisk them towards their destination at a smooth 120 mph—whatever the weather or the traffic.

PAT, standing for Palletised Automatic Transportation, was born at the Massachusetts Institute of Technology in 1968. So far it is little more than a collection of theoretical studies and a few small-scale models. But it may be the key to faster, and safer, inter-city travel.

The system could work like this. Drivers would take their cars or trucks, in the normal way, to the nearest motorway interchange. There they would find an underground storage building or garage with a subway entrance from street level. To join the PAT system, the driver merely loads his vehicle on to a pallet which is waiting underground. A lift will then transfer both the driver and his vehicle to ground level. There, the driver and his friends will board one of the PAT passenger vehicles while his car travels separately on a nearby pallet. Mounted on the passenger trucks will be a dial, and by using this he will be able to dial the nearest junction to his destination. Each vehicle will move at a precise 2 miles a minute until its dialled exit is reached when, together with its pallet, it will be smoothly shunted off.

Then the motorist will disembark and, taking the elevator to the underground storage park, he will rejoin his car for the last stage of his journey.

AT THE SPEED OF THOUGHT

Pilots might soon be able io fly simply by thinking

The split-second decisions that a modern jet pilot has to make may soon involve linking up the pilot's brain with the mechanics of his aircraft— via a computer. By hooking up his brain directly into a computer system connected to an aircraft's controls, vital seconds could be saved when they matter most. The pilot would have only to think of an action—and the plane would obey immediately.

The idea is an offshoot of work being done at the Advanced Research Projects Agency of the US Department of Defence. Electrodes implanted in a pilot's helmet would pick up and relay impulses to the computer that would instantly feed back information, such as altitude, airspeed or engine temperature, on a screen in front of the pilot. The pilot would have to learn a code system, possibly of colours, to trigger off the correct impulses that would signal to the computer what information was required.

In this way a pilot would save the time-wasting and risk of errors caused by having to search through a cockpit of crowded dials, and more of his attention could be kept on the essential duty of controlling his aircraft.

For military purposes, the electrode implants could be linked to a computer connected to the firing circuits of a fighter-plane's armaments. At a simple thought, missiles could be launched, or bombs dropped with split-second accuracy.

Once missiles were on their way, the computer could take over any last-second adjustments to ensure they were on target, again guided by the pilot's 'thought-instructions'.

On low-level missions, where a fighter-pilot's full attention is concentrated on manoeuvring his aircraft, the brain-linked firing mechanism is seen as a great advantage. The first computer designed for this purpose has already been installed in a Phantom fighter on an experimental basis.

ENIGMA OF THE UFO

Are they alien visitors, hallucinations or natural phenomena?

Unidentified flying objects exist. Of that there is absolutely no doubt. They have been seen, photographed and filmed by astronauts, airline pilots, policemen, astronomers, housewives, meteorologists and farmers.

The big mystery, that has remained unsolved since the popular term 'flying saucers' was first coined in 1947, is: What are they and where do they come from?

All kinds of explanations have been put forward to account for the worldwide sightings of discs, egg shapes, spheres and other oddly shaped aerial objects.

They have been explained away as unusual cloud formations, fireballs, meteorites, weather balloons, optical illusions, hallucinations or simply fabrications engineered by publicity-seeking cranks.

But not every reported case can be dismissed in this way. The most logical attitude towards UFOs is that man is faced with a series of inexplicable, but none the less real, phenomena.

The attitude of ufologists—students of

UFOs—goes a step further. They usually claim that the earth is under surveillance by alien intelligences.

Tomorrow, perhaps, the truth will emerge. Meanwhile, mankind is left with a puzzling mass of evidence that ranges from impartial, level-headed accounts to the totally implausible.

The first saucers

The flying saucer story began on June 24, 1947, when a private pilot, Kenneth Arnold, who was taking part in a search for a missing transport aircraft, saw nine disc-shaped objects flying over Mount Rainier, Washington.

He described the objects as 'flying like a saucer would if you skimmed it across the water'. Arnold's veracity and professional reputation were beyond question, and his account of the incident was accepted by the authorities. Newspapers picked up the story and labelled the objects 'flying saucers'.

Since then, there have been waves of

reports throughout the fifties, sixties and into the seventies. Even the US House of Representatives' Committee on Science and Astronautics has held special hearings to take evidence from witnesses.

One of the most spectacular recent reports came from a United States Gemini 4 astronaut, James McDivitt, in June 1965. In orbit, about 90 miles above the earth, McDivitt saw a cylindrical object, apparently with arms sticking out of it, which he took to be another spacecraft with antennae.

It appeared to be in free flight over the Pacific, somewhat higher than the Gemini capsule. McDivitt took one still photograph and some film.

He observed that the object was moving in a parallel path to his own spacecraft, but closing in fast. McDivitt and his fellow-astronaut, Edward White, were hastily preparing to take evasive action when the UFO disappeared from view.

After splashdown, the film was taken away and McDivitt did not see it again for several days. When he did inspect the film, the object was 'hazily' outlined against the sky. But he remained convinced it was a positive identification.

Originally, McDivitt thought he had seen some unmanned satellite. The official view was that he had spotted the unmanned US photographic satellite Pegasus. But that was 1200 miles away at the time of his sighting.

UFOs in orbit

However extraordinary their content, such reports must be given serious consideration. As highly trained observers, astronauts are unlikely to give way to speculation or imagination.

LANDING BY SAUCER *An engineer photographed an alleged UFO in July 1951 in Italy's Bernina Alps. The saucer-shaped object landed, a figure emerged, re-entered, then took off again (below).*

Captain Ed Mitchell, the sixth man to walk on the moon, told a press conference in 1974: 'I am completely convinced that *some* UFO sightings are real. The question isn't where the UFOs are from. The question is what they are.'

About 26 astronauts have reported seeing UFOs. The first sighting was in 1962, and later reports include those made by men on Skylabs I, II and III. NASA (the National Aeronautics and Space Administration) takes them seriously and has allocated a codeword— 'bogey'—to these UFOs.

During their stint of duty in Skylab II, astronauts Jack Lousma, Owen Garriott and Alan Bean watched and photographed a red UFO for ten minutes. They were then 270 miles above the earth.

They said the object rotated every ten seconds, and was 30 to 50 miles away in an orbit very close to their own.

In a prepared statement, put before the Committee on Science and Astronautics of the US House of Representatives in 1968, Professor James E. McDonald, a physicist from the University of Arizona, said: 'My own present opinion, based on two years of careful study, is that UFOs are probably extra-terrestrial devices engaged in something that might tentatively be termed "surveillance".'

An 'occupant sighting' was reported on April 24, 1964, in Socorro, New Mexico. Police patrolman Lonnie Zamora gave up chasing a speeding motorist to chase a UFO instead, when he saw one apparently coming in to land about a mile away.

Zamora reported that he found it outside the town, a bright, metallic oval, the size of an upturned car. Standing beside it, he said, were two humanoid figures, about the size of ten-year-old children.

As he called HQ to report, the figures retreated inside and the object took off.

On July 1 the following year, a French lavender grower in the Provence village of Valensole saw what he thought were youths trying to steal his valuable plants. There were two diminutive figures, standing by an object 'about the size of a Renault'.

He got within 5 yds of them before one of the 'boys' pointed an instrument at him and he claimed to have become paralysed. The two figures then boarded their craft and it sped away.

UFO SIGHTING *This object was seen near the hamlet of Areal, Central Brazil.*

Symptoms of shock

It was regarded as just another sighting— until an interviewer showed the lavender grower a photograph. The man became terrified, showing all the symptoms of severe shock.

It was a picture of a model, constructed from the detailed description given by Zamora, 15 months earlier in New Mexico.

On October 11, 1973, two shipyard workers out fishing in Pascagoula, Mississippi, claimed to have been taken aboard an egg-shaped UFO and examined by three silvery-skinned creatures with no eyes. Charles Hickson, then 42, and Calvin Parker, 19, said the creatures kept them for about 20 minutes, 'photographed' them and took them back to a pier.

Parker said he fainted when he first saw the humanoid creatures. Each had a slit

587

for a mouth and three pointed protrusions instead of noses and ears. Their vehicle had descended from the sky to hover a few feet over the Pascagoula River.

After their ordeal, the two men were interviewed by Dr J. Allen Hynek, an astronomer who investigated UFOs for the US Air Force. Later, the men were questioned under hypnosis by Dr James Harder, of the University of California.

Traumatic experience

Dr Hynek said: 'They had undergone such a shocking thing that they couldn't put it exactly into words. Whatever happened to them definitely affected their rationality.'

In Holsworthy, north Devon, England, two police constables on motor patrol got involved in a high-speed chase with an object resembling a shiny cross for about 50 minutes in the cold dawn of October 24, 1967. PCs Roger Willey and Clifford Wycott later held a press conference.

Willey said: 'It looked like a star-spangled cross, radiating points of light from all angles. At times we drove at 90 mph to keep up with it.

'It seemed to be watching us and would not let us catch up. It had terrific acceleration and knew we were chasing it.'

The Ministry of Defence later said that the mysterious object was a giant jet tanker of the USAF on a refuelling mission. However, it was soon established that none of the tankers was airborne at the time.

UFOs appear to be attracted to England's West Country. The Wiltshire town of Warminster is the UFO sightings capital of the world. Since the mid-sixties there have been thousands of reports.

Thunderous explosion

The best-substantiated incident was more a hearing than a sighting—by a whole company of Welsh Guards on Christmas morning 1964. Thirty of the men were awakened by 'the sound of a thunderous explosion'. The noise was repeated so many times that the men were alerted for duty. But outside there was nothing to be seen.

Later that morning, at 6.15, a woman on her way to church was knocked down and pinned to the ground by some sort of sonic blast wave. The noise, described as a low drone with a beating rhythm,

passed over several houses in the town, shaking foundations and lifting roof tiles.

Some months later, there were reports that animals were suddenly and inexplicably collapsing 'as if they had been hit by some sort of ray'.

Sightings and strange phenomena became so prevalent in and around Warminster, that local people began to refer to anything unusual as The Warminster Thing.

It has been said that the sights and sounds are caused by experiments with new weapons at the School of Infantry, near Warminster.

Twilight zone

The objects are generally seen in rural areas, but occasionally sightings are reported over cities. Most reports are in the two twilight periods, early morning and early evening, at a time when the glare of a city would make it difficult to observe a UFO in flight.

While most UFO sightings are reported by people on the ground, there are also many sightings by airline pilots and private flyers. But it is more than likely that the number of such sightings greatly exceeds the number of actual reports. Pilots, particularly those with major airlines, are understandably reluctant to be thought of as cranks.

Most pilots' reports relate to some strange object which often goes through aerial manoeuvres that no man-made aircraft could execute—such as halting suddenly and hovering, after travelling at amazing speeds—then disappears.

But in one or two cases, UFOs appear to have been inexplicably linked with disasters.

In 1953 the pilot of a DC-6, flying from Wake Island in the Pacific to Los Angeles, reported seeing some objects in the sky. Then communications ceased. Next morning, searchers found fragments of the plane and 20 bodies.

Disappeared without trace

In the same year, two USAF personnel in an F89 jet chased a UFO over Lake Superior, on the US–Canadian border. Tracked on radar, both the jet and the UFO appeared to merge on the radar screen. Then the jet disappeared and the UFO passed out of range.

Rescue aircraft and ships were sent out, but no trace of the jet or its occupants was found, despite the rigorous searches.

There are cases in which motorists claim their cars have been immobilised by UFOs. Other people say they were burnt, put into trances or knocked unconscious when approaching strange craft on the ground. There is even a police chief who claimed he chased a 6 ft creature in a metallic suit in October 1973, at Falkville, Alabama. But, police chief Jeff Greenshaw said, the humanoid ran faster than his car could go.

But still no one has put forward a satisfactory explanation for all the strange happenings logged up on UFO files, whether by amateurs or experts. Is earth being watched by beings from another planet? If so, what is the purpose of these aliens?

Man, it seems, will simply have to wait until the extra-terrestrials make themselves properly known to learn the answers to these and other questions. Either that or find another explanation for the strange objects seen over and on the earth.

LOOKING INTO THE FUTURE

A conversation with science writer Isaac Asimov

Prophets have been forecasting the end of the world for centuries. What sort of natural end do you envisage for this planet?

One natural end that is unavoidable, even if nothing else goes wrong, is of course the death of the sun. It will gradually use up its hydrogen fuel and, in about 8000 million years from now, it will destroy the earth. When the hydrogen has been used up, the helium that is left will burn into carbon. In response to that, the sun will expand and become only red hot. But it will have a much larger surface, so the total amount of heat will be much greater than now, and the earth will fry.

What hope then is there? What can mankind do about it? Could we get off and live somewhere else?

It is almost certain that before the death of the sun we will have spread through our own galaxy, and perhaps others. The most practical way, barring new kinds of

THE GREAT TREK *Before earth's resources are exhausted, man will capture wandering asteroids and convert them into huge spaceships in which he will set off to find inhabitable planets.*

NEW YORK, 8000 MILLION AD *About this time, the sun will burn itself out, becoming enormously enlarged in the process and turning the earth into a barren, airless, waterless desert.*

technical advances that it is hard to foresee, is to build large ships which are self-contained ecologies—small self-contained worlds—and just send them off, not even with any special destination in mind. Every once in a while, one of them will come across a world that can be colonised.

The most logical way to do it seems to be to convert small asteroids—hollow them out and supply them with whatever they are short of. Certainly in 8000 million years we have plenty of time to fill space with these ships and, before the end of this planet, we shall have colonised probably millions of worlds all over the universe. We shall almost certainly meet other intelligences doing the same thing.
Could we set up colonies on other planets in our solar system?
None of them is habitable without heavy engineering. Some of them could be en-

gineered—the moon, certainly, and Mars. But they will suffer the same eventual fate as the earth when the sun dies. So they do not represent any long-term solution.
How long a journey will it be? How far will we have to travel in these mobile worlds?
Eventually these space travellers will come across another solar system with an asteroid belt. They will perhaps be able to discard their original asteroid, which by then will be in pretty bad shape, and take on a new one.

At the moment we can't say how far they will have to travel altogether to find a habitable new earth.

If we consider our galaxy alone, it has 135,000 million stars—and almost all of them are likely to have their own planetary systems. There could, in our galaxy, be as many as 640 million earth-like planets—in other words, the chances of our finding such planets are about 1 in 200. The odds in favour of finding such planets in the whole of the universe are even greater.

Besides, perhaps there may be more bodies than we expect between the stars. We know nothing about possible dark bodies except for those very close to our own sun. They may not be at all uncommon—let us say in the space of a thousand years, we may come across something suitable.

How feasible is all of this? What about the speed of travel? Light is the fastest thing known in the universe, travelling at more than 669 million miles an hour. Just as there is a sound barrier, there seems to be a light barrier. How long will these journey's take?

As long as the speed-of-light limit lasts, we cannot expect to communicate between the stars in any way that we know about now. If we sent some ship to the stars by any present system, it would take years to reach even the nearest star (Proxima Centauri), thousands of years to reach moderately distant stars, tens of thousands of years to span a galaxy, millions of years to reach even the nearer galaxies.

The only hope of doing anything about this is if there is some way of going faster than the speed of light—without breaking the theory of relativity, which seems to correspond to the universe as it is.

For instance, scientists now theorise that there are some kinds of particles called tachyons that always go faster than the speed of light. They have not actually been detected. If they do exist, they will be extremely difficult to detect.

However, we can speculate on the possibility of changing all the particles in a spaceship simultaneously into the corresponding tachyonic particles, taking off at many times the speed of light in an appropriate direction for an appropriate

591

distance and then suddenly turning everything back into ordinary particles. And there you are—no time lapse, practically, and you are at the end of the galaxy, 120 thousand million miles away.

Of course the engineering problems involved in changing all the particles in the ship, including those of the human beings, into tachyons—and of changing all of them back with such simultaneity that you do not come back missing half your heart, or just enough atoms to spoil things for you, are staggeringly enormous. *You say the earth will probably last another 8000 million years. Will mankind also survive that time or will we blow ourselves up?*

That could happen at any time—except that the longer it does not happen, the more I believe it will not. We have had opportunities for nuclear wars and we have avoided them.

Could the earth be destroyed in a collision with another planet or huge meteor?

It is highly unlikely. Space is largely empty, and the chance of our being the target for any sizeable body is very small. For example, the average distance between the stars in our own corner of the galaxy is nine light years—about 50 million million miles.

In fact, the stars in our galaxy are in the same proportion as would be a few grains of sand in the whole of New York's Central Park.

What about a possible invasion and annihilation by people from elsewhere in the universe?

That is a very well-known science-fiction situation, but it seems to me unlikely. The nearest intelligence to us is likely to be as much as 50 light years away, and that is not an easy distance to cross. If a people could cross it, they would be extremely advanced, and I think that a race far in advance of ourselves would probably also have advanced in humanity and would be unlikely to act like barbarians.

What then are the dangers that you see facing mankind? I think it extremely unlikely that mankind could ever be wiped out completely, but unless we take firm action now, immediately, I believe that we could destroy civilisation as we know it within 30 to 50 years. We are heading rapidly in that direction.

That seems an alarming idea and an alarmingly short space of time.

Well, that is how desperate the situation is. At the present moment, the population of the world is higher by far than it has

ever been—it is now nearly 4000 million, compared with 2000 million only 50 years ago. It has doubled in the last 50 years, and is going to double again, barring some new control, in the next 35 years. So we are having trouble feeding people. A substantial proportion of mankind is in constant danger of starvation.

By the year 2009, we are going to have somewhere between 7000 and 8000 million people on earth and we are not going to double our food supply by then. This means that within 30 or 50 years famines may have become an all-too-common occurrence.

In addition, with a great many people ill-nourished, there would be an increase in disease. There would be more general unrest in the world, for even those nations which we do not usually associate with famine conditions would by then be in a bad way. They are not likely to become economically self-sufficient.

But would that necessarily spell the end of civilisation?

I think that it is questionable whether our highly complicated, therefore rather rickety, technological civilisation could withstand that kind of crisis.

The history of mankind has been one of advancing technology. At those times when technology declines for a period, you have what we call a dark age. In the past, there have been dark ages in human history a number of times, but they have always been local.

We think of the dark age in Western Europe between the 5th and 11th centuries as being enormous, but it was very local really. The only reason that we pay any attention to it whatsoever is that culturally we are West European.

Actually, the Byzantine empire was flourishing, the Arab world was at its cultural height and there was a brilliant civilisation flourishing in Spain—as near as that—through the dark ages.

It was just in the Frankish Empire that there was a dark age. In fact, when Europe started climbing out of its dark age, it was because it got rays of civilisation from the rim. But if our technology is going, then we are going to have a dark age that for the first time will be worldwide. There will be no untouched portion to act as the saviour of the rest.

Furthermore, it would be a dark age which would have come after we had burnt up the oil, used up the easiest supplies of coal to get out, scattered the best pockets of minerals thinly over the face of the earth, perhaps rendered part of the environment radioactive, and destroyed a great deal of the earth's soil by over-farming in a desperate attempt to feed the population.

But what of new sources of power and new sources of food?

Well, of course it is possible that we shall learn to derive much more food from the oceans, that we shall turn existing plants and trees into protein foods. This is already being done, and undoubtedly we shall develop that kind of technology.

It is true, too, that solar energy will become our principle source of power. But remarkable progress has to be made very soon if we are to avoid the eventual crisis.

Is there no hope that any other part of the universe would be able to help us?

I think the crisis is coming much too soon —in the lifetime of people who are not children even today. I would say that a person who is now 20 is going to see the crisis while he is still in the vigour of his life.

Rescue by some superior intelligence is of course possible but; frankly, if we are rescued by something like that, life will not be worth living. We would be just a form of domestic animal.

I suppose I would not object to being saved if the alternative was destruction, but I would no longer be a member of the lords of creation. I would be a member of man, a rather intelligent domestic animal—and I would not like it!

How then can we help ourselves?

It is not enough to provide extra sources of energy or food. Supposing that, say, by AD 2000 we have worked out some scheme whereby we can feed 7000 million people. If we do so and everyone continues having children, then in 35 more years there will be 14,000 million. And then what? Somewhere, sometime, the growth must stop.

But there are only two ways in which growth can stop. Either the death rate goes up to match the birth rate, or the birth rate comes down to match the death rate.

Have we then any right to feel optimistic in this situation?

Yes, for it is amazing how fast human beings can change, given pressure. Only 20 years ago, birth control was banned in vast areas where it is now helping to keep the size of the population under control. Perhaps as the death rate starts to go up, it will dawn on people that the birth rate must come rapidly down.

But surely this would take worldwide agreement of a kind that has never been managed before?

Yes indeed, but the fact that we are facing global problems—declining resources, rising population, pollution and so on—has made it very clear that no nation is an independent unit. It has made it very clear that war is impossible, not only nuclear war but ordinary war.

We in the West are now in a position of détente with Russia and China, and it was the same people in America who had been anti-Communist, and the same people in Russia and China who had been anti-American who brought about that détente. It was forced on us by events, and as the crisis approaches each year, the whole of mankind will be forced to make more drastic efforts and do things that we now consider impossible.

Remember, too, that mankind has found ways to overcome catastrophes in the past. During the Black Death, for example, in the 14th century, perhaps one-third of all human beings were killed. That was a catastrophe, but the amazing thing is that with a disease so contagious and so fatal, and with a human race that was ignorant of the most elementary methods of hygiene, two-thirds did survive.

And if we do find a way to overcome the crisis that you outline, what then?

If we can solve the population problem, however narrowly, and we can spend the 21st century recovering and rebuilding a civilisation on a philosophy of growth in quality, growth in sophistication, growth in new forms of technology—if we can do that, it seems to me that the future has the capacity to be enormously, enormously wonderful.

Mankind is the first creature on earth to be potentially immortal. Since we can now control evolution, control our environment—and in the future to an extent and in ways undreamed of now—we become invulnerable.

Then we could live here for a long time and, when scientists foresee the dangers from the sun, we could just move off?

Long before that. If we don't recklessly and needlessly commit suicide, we will almost certainly reach a point where nothing else can hurt us except the overall end of the entire universe.

INDEX

Roman figures indicate a text-only entry on the subject. Figures in *italics* indicate there is an illustration, text or caption entry

D

H

I

QR

S

UV

W

XYZ

STRANGE STORIES
AMAZING FACTS

Alphabetical list of titles

605

ACKNOWLEDGMENTS

The publishers express their thanks and indebtedness to the following people and organisations who have helped in the preparation of this book

Paul Alexander; Australian Information Bureau, London; Bramah Security Equipment Ltd, London; Brewers' Society; British Airways; The British Computer Society; British Interplanetary Society; British Museum; British Museum (Natural History); British Petroleum Co. Ltd; British Typewriter Museum; British UFO Research Association; Calculator Services; H. H. B. Capes; Ceylon Tea Centre; N. H. Chapman; Civil Aviation Authority; Clinical Research Centre; College of Arms; L. F. E. Coombs; Courtaulds Ltd, London; Culham Research Laboratory; Daily Telegraph Information Service; The Decca Navigator Company Ltd, London; Department of the Environment for Wales; Electricité de France, Paris; EMI Ltd, London; Enfield (Automotive) Motor Engineers; R. G. Feltham; Flat Earth Society; GPO Telecommunications Headquarters; Geological Society of London; Charles H. Gibbs-Smith; P. W. Hammond; Honeywell Information Systems Ltd, London; Hover-infants International Ltd, Southampton; Professor D. E. Hughes; M. J. Humphries; Tim Hunkin; Imperial Chemical Industries Ltd, London; Imperial War Museum; Institute of Geological Sciences; Monsieur F. Jauberti; Jesuit Information Office; Christopher Jordan; Kodak Ltd, London; Professor Hubert Lamb; D. F. Lee; Joseph Lucas Industries Ltd, Birmingham; Medical Research Council; Meteorological Office; Metrication Board; NASA Centre, Houston, Texas; National Army Museum; National Institute of Medical Research; National Institute of Oceanography; National Maritime Museum; Novel Protein Unit, Ministry of Agriculture; Alex Parker; Philips Electronics and Associated Industries Ltd, London; P. Powell; *Psychic News*; Richard III Society; Royal Anthropological Society; Royal Geographical Society; Royal Institute of British Architects; Royal Military School of Music; Royal Observatory; Sankey Ltd, Telford; Science Museum; Scotland Yard; Scott Polar Research Institute; Dr P. A. H. Seymour; Smiths Industries Ltd (Aviation Division), London; Society for Psychical Research; Statens Sjöhistoriska Museum, Stockholm; Strangeways Laboratory; Thames Water Authority; Theosophical Society in England; Dr D. A. Tyrell; US Information Service; Robert Vincent; Waterman Pens (UK Ltd); B. Waters; Wellcome Foundation Ltd; D. Williams

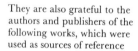

They are also grateful to the authors and publishers of the following works, which were used as sources of reference

Abu Simbel and the Glories of Ancient Egypt W. Macquitty (Macdonald & Janes Publishers; G. P. Putnam's Sons); *Admirals in Collision* R. A. Hough (Hamish Hamilton Ltd; The Viking Press, Inc., Collins (Toronto)); *Aircraft Detective* by S. Barlay (Hamish Hamilton Ltd); *All about King Arthur* by Geoffrey Ashe (W. H. Allen & Co. Ltd); *The Amazing World of Nature* (The Reader's Digest Association Ltd); *America* by Alastair Cooke (*The Listener*; Alfred A. Knopf, Inc.); *Ancient America* J. N. Leonard & the Editors of Time-Life Books (Time, Inc.); *Ancient Egypt* by L. Casson & the Editors of *Life* (Time, Inc.); *Ancient Explorers* by M. Cary and E. H. Warmington (Methuen & Co. Ltd; Dodd, Mead & Company); *Ancient Rome at Work* P. Louis (Routledge & Kegan Paul Ltd; Alfred A. Knopf, Inc.); *Animals My Adventure* L. Heck (Methuen & Co. Ltd); *The Art Stealers* by M. Esterow (George Weidenfeld & Nicolson Ltd); *Australian Folklore* by W. Fearn-Vannan (Landsdowne Press, Pty, Ltd; Fernhill House, Ltd); *The Autobiography of Sir Henry Morton Stanley* G.C.B. D. Stanley (Sampson Low, Marston & Co. Ltd); *Before Civilisation* C. Renfrew (Jonathan Cape Ltd; Alfred A. Knopf, Inc.); *Beyond Belief* by B. Branston (George Weidenfeld & Nicolson Ltd; Walker & Co.); *Beyond the Pillars of Hercules* by R. Carpenter (Delacorte Press); *Biofeedback: Turning on the Power of Your Mind* M. Karlins & L. M. Andrews

(Warner Books); *The Biological Time-Bomb* G. R. Taylor (Thames & Hudson Ltd; World Publishing Co.); *The Biology of the Algae* F. E. Round (Edward Arnold (Publishers) Ltd; St Martin's Press, Inc.); *The Birds* R. T. Peterson & the Editors of *Life* (Time, Inc.); *Black Holes: the End of the Universe?* J. Taylor (Souvenir Press Ltd; Random House, Inc.); *The Body* A. E. Nowse & the Editors of *Life* (Time, Inc.); *The Body* A. Smith (Penguin Books Ltd; Walker & Co.); *Body Time* G. G. Luce (Panther Books Ltd; Pantheon Books); *Book of British Birds* (Drive Publications Ltd); *A Brief History of Flying* by C. H. Gibbs-Smith (HM Stationery Office); *Call This an Opera House?* Yes J. Pringle (*Observer*); *Camelot and the Vision of Albion* by Geoffrey Ashe (William Heinemann Ltd; St Martin's Press, Inc.); *A Casebook of Murder* C. Wilson (Leslie Frewin Publishers Ltd; Cowles Book Company, Inc.); *The Challenge of Chance* A. Koestler, A. Hardy & R. Harvie (Hutchinson & Co. (Publishers) Ltd); *Christmas* W. Sansom (George Weidenfeld & Nicolson Ltd); *Christmas and its Customs* C. Hole (G. Bell & Sons Ltd; Barrows Co., Inc.); *Cleopatra's Needles* A. Noakes (H. F. & G. Witherby Ltd); *Collins Guide to Mushrooms & Toadstools* (William Collins, Sons & Co. Ltd); *The Colosseum* P. Quennel & the Editors of *Newsweek* (Newsweek Book Division, published by The Reader's Digest Association Ltd in association with *Newsweek*); *The Common Cold* C. Andrewes (George Weidenfeld & Nicolson Ltd; W. W. Norton & Co. Inc.); *The Computer Revolution* N. Hawkes (Thames & Hudson Ltd; E. P. Dutton & Co. Inc.); *The Computerised Society* J. Martin & A. Norman (Penguin Books Ltd; Prentice-Hall Inc.); *A Concise History of Costume* J. Laver (Thames & Hudson Ltd; Harry N. Abrams Inc.); *The Conquistadors* H. Innes (William Collins Sons & Co. Ltd; Alfred A. Knopf, Inc.); *Cosmic Clocks* by M. Gauquelin (Peter Owen Ltd; Henry Regnery Co.); *Counterfeits* by S. Cole (John Murray (Publishers) Ltd); *Curious Customs of Sex and Marriage* G. R. Scott (Torchstream Books); *Curiosities of Medicine* B. Rouché (Victor Gollancz Ltd; Little, Brown & Co.); *Curious Myths of the Middle Ages* by S. Baring-Gould (Longmans, Green & Co.); *Dada* by K. Coutts-Smith (Studio Vista Publishers); *Dada* H. Richter (Thames & Hudson Ltd; Museum of Art, Rhode Island); *The Deserts* A. S. Leopold & the Editors of Time-Life Books (Time, Inc.); *The Development of Two Standards* J. R. Smith (Survey Review); *A Dictionary of Fabulous Beasts* by R. Barber & A. Riches (Macmillan Publishers; Walker & Co.); *Easter and Its Customs* C. Hole (G. Bell & Sons Ltd; Barrows Co., Inc.); *An Egg at Easter* V. Newall (Routledge & Kegan Paul, Ltd; Indiana University Press); *Eggs, Milk and Cheese* N. Lyon and P. Benton (Faber & Faber Ltd); *Encyclopaedia of Superstitions* E. & M. A. Radford (ed. and rev. by C. Hole) (Hutchinson & Co. (Publishers) Ltd); *Encyclopedia of the Unexplained* ed. by Richard Cavendish (Routledge & Kegan Paul Ltd; McGraw-Hill Book Co.); *Energy* M. Wilson & the Editors of *Life* (Time, Inc.); *The Engineer* by C. C. Furnas & T. McCarthy & the Editors of *Life* (Time, Inc.); *Enigmas of History* H. R. Williamson (Michael Joseph Ltd); *Everyday Life of the Pagan Celts* A. Ross (B. T. Batsford Ltd; G. P. Putnam's Sons); *Explorers of the World* by W. R. Clark (Aldus Books Ltd; Doubleday & Co. Inc.); *Exploring the Planets* I. Nicolson (The Hamlyn Publishing Group, Ltd; Grosset & Dunlap, Inc.); *Fabulous Frauds* L. Jeppson (Arlington Books; Weybright & Talley, Inc.); *Fact, Fake or Fable* by R. Furneaux (Cassell & Co. Ltd); *The Fascinating Secrets of Oceans & Islands* (The Reader's Digest Association Ltd); *The First Book of Firsts* (A Golden Hands Book published by Marshall Cavendish); *The Fishes* F. D. Ommanney & the Editors of *Life* (Time, Inc.); *Flight* J. J. Haggerty & the Editors of *Life* (Time, Inc.); *Geography of Strabo* H. L. Jones (William Heinemann Ltd); *Grand Deception* A. Klein (Faber & Faber Ltd; J. B. Lippincott Co.; Longmans (Toronto)); *Great Dramatic Stories of the 20th Century* by Rupert Furneaux (Odhams Books Ltd); *The Great Orm of Loch Ness* F. W. Holiday (Faber & Faber Ltd; W. W. Norton & Co. Inc.); *Great Swindlers* by A. F. L. Deeson (W. Foulsham & Co. Ltd; Drake Publishers Inc.); *The Great Swindlers* Judge G. Sparrow (John Long Ltd); *The Great Travellers* M. Rugoff (Simon & Schuster, Inc.); *Greek Calendar Customs* G. Megas (Prime Minister's Office, Greece); *A Handbook of Medical Hypnosis* by G. Ambrose & G. Newbold (Ballière, Tindall Publishers; Williams & Wilkins Co.); *Harvest of the Sea* by J. Bardach (George Allen & Unwin Ltd; Harper & Row, Publishers); *Haunted England* C. Hole (B. T. Batsford Ltd; Clarke, Irwin & Co. Ltd (Canada)); *Historic Oddities & Strange Events* by S. Baring-Gould (Methuen & Co. Ltd); *Historic Tinned Foods* (International Tin Research and Development Council); *Historical Whodunits* H. R. Williamson (J. M. Dent & Sons Ltd); *A History of Chess* H. J. R. Murray (Clarendon Press); *A History of Flight* by C. Canby (Clarke, Irwin & Co. Ltd); *A History of Playing Cards* R. Tilley (Studio Vista Publishers; Clarkson N. Potter Inc.); *Hoaxes* C. D. Macdougall (Dover Publications; Dover Publications Inc.); *Hoaxes and Swindles* by R. Garrett (Pan Books Ltd); *Hypnosis: Fact and Fiction* F. L. Marcuse (Penguin Books Ltd; Penguin Books Inc.); *The Identity of Jack the Ripper* D. McCormick (Arrow Books Ltd); *The Importance of Can Openers* W. R. Lewis (Tin Research Institute); *In Search of Lake Monsters* by P. Costello (The Garnstone Press Ltd; Coward, McCann & Geoghegan Inc.); *Innovations: Scientific, Technological and Social* by D. Gabor (Oxford University Press); *Invasion 1940* by Peter Fleming (Hart-Davis, MacGibbon Ltd); *It's a Small, Medium and Outsize World* J. Taylor (Hugh Evelyn Ltd; World Publishing Co.); *Jack the Ripper* by Daniel Farson (Michael Joseph Ltd); *Jack the Ripper in Fact and Fiction* R. Odell (George G. Harrap & Co. Ltd; Clarke, Irwin & Co. Ltd (Canada)); *King Henry VIII's Mary Rose* A. McKee (Souvenir Press Ltd; Stein & Day Publishers); *Lady Hester Stanhope* J. Haslip (Cobden-Sanderson; Oxford (Toronto)); *Larousse Gastronomique* P. Montague (The Hamlyn Publishing Group, Ltd; Crown Publishers, Inc.); *Legend and Reality* by R. Furneaux (Allan Wingate (Publishers) Ltd; Smithers and Bounellie, Ltd (Toronto)); *Leonardo da Vinci* (Leisure Arts Ltd); *The Living House* G. Ordish (Hart-Davis, MacGibbon Ltd; J. B. Lippincott Co.); *The Living World of Animals* (The Reader's Digest Association Ltd); *Loch Ness Monster* by Tim Dinsdale (Routledge & Kegan Paul, Ltd; Chilton Book Co.); *The Longest Day* C. Ryan (Victor Gollancz Ltd; Simon & Schuster, Inc.); *Lost Discoveries* C. Ronan (Macdonald & Janes Publishers; McGraw-Hill Book Co.); *Lotus and the Robot* A. Koestler (Hutchinson & Co. (Publishers) Ltd; Macmillan Publishing Co. Inc.); *Machines* R. O'Brien & the Editors of *Life* (Time-Life International); *Magic and Superstition* D. Hill (The Hamlyn Publishing Group Ltd); *Making Fire* (Science Museum); *The Mammals* by R. Carrington & the Editors of *Life* (Time-Life International); *Man's Presumptuous Brain* A. T. W. Simeons (Longman Group Ltd; E. P. Dutton & Co. Inc.); *Mary Celeste* J. G. Lockhart (Hart-Davis, MacGibbon Ltd; Fernhill House Ltd); *Masada: Herod's Fortress and the Zealot's Last Stand* Y. Yadin (Sphere Books Ltd; Random House Inc.); *Mermaids and Mastodons* by R. Carrington (Chatto & Windus Ltd; Holt, Rinehart & Winston, Inc.; Clarke, Irwin & Co. Ltd, Canada); *The Millionth Chance* J. Leasor (Hamish Hamilton Ltd; Reynal & Co.); *The Mind* J. R. Wilson & the Editors of *Life* (Time, Inc.); *The Money Pit Mystery* by R. Furneaux (Tom Stacey Ltd; Dodd, Mead & Co.); *Mysteries of the Solar System* R. A. Lyttelton (Oxford University Press); *The Mystery of Jack the Ripper* L. Matters (Arrow Books Ltd); *A Night to Remember* W. Lord (Longman Group Ltd; Holt, Rinehart & Winston, Inc.); *On the Track of Unknown Animals* B. Heuvelmans (Hart-Davis, MacGibbon Ltd; Hill & Wang, Inc.); *Pagan Celtic Britain* A. Ross (Routledge & Kegan Paul Ltd; Columbia University Press); *The Parable of the Beast* by J. W. Bleibtreu (Victor Gollancz Ltd; Macmillan Publishing Co. Inc.); *The Person in the Womb* by N. J. Berrill (Angus & Robertson (UK) Ltd; Dodd, Mead & Co.); *A Pictorial History of Inventions* by U. Eco and G. B. Zorzoli (George Weidenfeld & Nicolson Ltd); *Pictorial History of Magic and the Supernatural* M. Bessy (The Hamlyn Publishing Group Ltd); *Popular Fallacies* A. S. E. Ackermann (Old Westminster Press); *Portugal in Quest of Prester John* E. Sanceau (Hutchinson & Co. (Publishers) Ltd); *Premonitions: A Leap Into the Future* H. B. Greenhouse (Turnstone Books; Bernard Geis Associates Inc.); *The Promise of Space* by A. C. Clarke (Hodder & Stoughton Ltd; Harper & Row Publishers); *The Prophecies of the Brahan Seer* A. Mackenzie (Æneas Mackay); *Purnell's Encyclopaedia of Animal Life* (BPC Publishing Ltd); *The Pyramids of Egypt* by I. E. S. Edwards (Penguin Books Ltd; The Viking Press, Inc.); *The Pyramids and Sphinx* D. Stewart & the Editors of the Newsweek Book Division (The Reader's Digest Association Ltd in association with *Newsweek*); *The Quest for Power* M. & H. P. Vowles (Chapman & Hall Ltd); *The Reader's Digest Pocket Guide to Nature Records* (The Reader's Digest Association Ltd and Guinness Superlatives Ltd); *The Real Book of Robots and Thinking Machines* J. May (Dennis Dobson (Dobson Books Ltd; Doubleday & Co. Inc.); *Regent's Park: A Study of the Development of the Area from 1086 to the Present Day* A. Saunders (David & Charles (Holdings) Ltd; *Restless Earth* by Nigel Calder (BBC Publications Ltd; The Viking Press, Inc.); *The Road to Xanadu* J. L. Lowes (Houghton & Co. Ltd; Houghton Mifflin Co.); *The Sea* by L. Engel and the Editors of *Life* (Time-Life International); *Sea Enchantress* by G. Benwell and A. Waugh (Hutchinson & Co. (Publishers) Ltd); *The Sears Tower (Chicago): World's Tallest Building* L'Acier (Centre Belgo-Luxembourgeois d'Information de l'Acier, Brussels); *The Secret Life of Plants* P. Tomkins and C. Bird (Harper & Row Publishers); *The Secret of Mary Celeste* by G. Bradford (W. Foulsham & Co. Ltd); *Secrets of the Great Pyramids* P. Tomkins (Allen Lane, Penguin Books Ltd; Harper & Row Publishers); *Secrets of the Seas* (The Reader's Digest Association Ltd); *Sieges of the Middle Ages* P. Warner (G. Bell & Sons Ltd; Clarke, Irwin & Co. Ltd (Canada)); *Space* Patrick Moore (Lutterworth Press; Doubleday & Co. Inc.); *The Spirit of St Louis* C. Lindbergh (John Murray (Publishers) Ltd; Charles Scribner's Sons; S. J. R. Saunders (Canada)); *The Square Pegs* I. Wallace (Hutchinson & Co. (Publishers) Ltd; Alfred A. Knopf, Inc.; McClelland & Stewart, Ltd (Canada)); *Stonehenge* A., A. S., & A. S. Thom (*Journal for the History of Astronomy* ed. by M. A. Hoskins—Science History Publications); *Stonehenge Decoded* G. S. Hawkins (William Collins Sons & Co. Ltd; Doubleday

& Company Inc.); *Stories of Famous Ships* by R. Garrett (Arthur Barker Ltd); *The Story of Astronomy* Patrick Moore (Macdonald & Janes Publishers; Grosset & Dunlap Inc.); *Suez: De Lesseps' Canal* J. Pudney (J. M. Dent & Sons, Ltd); *Sunken Cities* F. J. North (University of Wales Press); *Supernature* L. Watson (Hodder & Stoughton Ltd; Doubleday & Co. Inc.); *Superstition and the Superstitious* E. Maple (W. H. Allen & Co. Ltd; A. S. Barnes & Co. Inc.); *The Swedish Warship Vasa* L. A. Kvarning & B. Ohrelius (Macmillan Publishers Ltd); *There could be light soon at the end of the long bore* T. Whiteside (*Observer*); *Time* S. A. Goudsmit, R. Claiborne and the Editors of *Life* (Time, Inc.); *Tomorrow's World* by Raymond Baxter and James Burke (BBC Publications Ltd); *Travel and Travellers in the Middle Ages* Sir E. D. Ross (Routledge & Kegan Paul Ltd); *Treasure Seekers* H. Roden (George G. Harrap & Co. Ltd; Walker & Co.); *The Tuatara, Lizards and Frogs of New Zealand* R. Shareel (William Collins, Sons & Co. Ltd; Triocean Books c/o Western Book Service Co.); *Unbidden Guests* W. O. Stevens (George Allen & Unwin Ltd; Dodd, Mead & Co.); *Unfinished Symphonies* by R. Brown (Souvenir Press, William Morrow & Co. Inc.); *The Universe* by D. Bergamini and the Editors of *Life* (Time-Life International); *Upper Pleistocene Radiocarbon-dated Artefacts from the Northern Yukon* W. N. Irving & C. R. Harington (*Science*); *Victorian Inventions* L. De Vries (John Murray (Publishers) Ltd; McGraw-Hill Book Co.); *The Water Closet* R. Palmer (David & Charles (Holdings) Ltd; Dufour Editions Inc.); *Welsh Folk Customs* T. M. Owen (Welsh Folk Museum); *Where is the Mona Lisa?* H. Pulitzer (Pulitzer Press); *Who was Ann Ockenden?* by D. Bloxham (Neville Spearman Ltd); *Wild Mushrooms* L. Zeitlmayr (Frederick Muller Ltd); *The Wilder Shores of Love* by Lesley Blanch (John Murray (Publishers) Ltd; Simon & Schuster, Inc.); *The World's Great Religions* Editors of *Life* (William Collins Sons & Co. Ltd; Time, Inc.); *With Intent to Deceive: Frauds Famous and Infamous* R. A. Haldane (William Blackwood & Sons Ltd); *The World's Most Intriguing Mysteries* by R. Furneaux (Odhams Books Ltd; Arco Publishing Co. Inc.); *World's Tallest Building: Asian Building and Construction* (Far East Trade Press Ltd, Hong Kong); *The Wreck Detectives* K. Macdonald (George G. Harrap & Co. Ltd; A. S. Barnes & Co. Inc.); *1974 Yearbook of Astronomy* Patrick Moore (Sidgwick & Jackson, Ltd; W. W. Norton & Co. Inc.)

The following articles were based upon material already published

THE ACADEMIC HOAXER—*The Theoretical Joker* by Norman Moss (by permission of A. D. Peters and Co.); ANIMAL SENSES—*The Magic of the Senses* by Vitus B. Droscher. (Translated by Evelyn Haggard © 1964 E. P. Dutton and W. H. Allen & Co. Ltd. Reprinted by permission of the publishers, E. P. Dutton & Co. Inc.; W. H. Allen & Co. Ltd; Paul List Verlag); ANNA'S ICE PALACE—*A Forgotten Empress: Anna Ivanovna and Her Era, 1730–1740* by Mina Curtiss (Frederick Ungar Publishing Co. New York); BREAD AND CIRCUSES— *Arena: The Story of the Colosseum* by J. Pearson (Thames & Hudson Ltd; McGraw-Hill Book Co.; CHARGE OF THE HEAVY BRIGADE—*The Railway Navvies* by Terry Coleman (Hutchinson & Co. (Publishers) Ltd); THE COMMERCIAL TRAVELLER, THE MAN WHO SOLD THE EIFFEL TOWER—*The Deceivers* by Egon Larsen (John Baker Publishers Ltd); THE DINOSAUR LIVES?—*The Flying Dinosaurs* by Brian Silcock (*Sunday Times*); DOUGHBOYS, G.I., QUIZ, HIP HIP HOORAY!—*Brewer's Dictionary of Phrase and Fable* (Cassell & Co. Ltd; Harper & Row, Publishers); EARLY PLANS TO TUNNEL UNDER THE CHANNEL—*Is this the Gateway to Europe?* by A. Motson (*Daily Telegraph*); THE FLOATING SCOTSMAN —*Alexander Mackenzie: first across Canada* by B. Hutchinson (*Kiwanis Magazine*); GIANT WITH A JINX—*Atlantic Bridgehead* by H. Clayton (The Garnstone Press, Ltd); THE GREAT PALACE—*Versailles* by Ian Dunlop © 1956, 1970 Ian Dunlop (Hamish Hamilton Ltd; Taplinger Publishing Co., New York; Clarke, Irwin & Co. Ltd, Canada); THE GREAT PALACE—*The Sun King* by Nancy Mitford (reprinted by permission of A. D. Peters and Company; Harper and Row Publishers); HEART OF THE VATICAN—*Saint Peter's: the Story of St Peter's in Rome* by James Lees-Milne (Hamish Hamilton

Ltd; Little Brown & Co.; Collins, (Canada)); THE HUMAN FLY (and other articles)—*Mad and Magnificent Yankees*—Ed. by C. M. Silitch (Yankee Inc.); HUNTING THE YETI—*Yeti-like Monster gives Staid Town in Illinois a Fright* by A. H. Malcolm © 1973 by the New York Times Co. Reprinted by permission); INNER FIRES— © 1967 by Emile C. Schurmacher. Adapted from *Strange Unsolved Mysteries* by Emile C. Schurmacher (Warner Paperback Library); IS THIS HOW WE LEARNED TO WALK?—*How we started* (Time); KING HAROLD WAS SHOT IN THE EYE BY A NORMAN ARROW—*The Bayeux Tapestry and the Norman Invasion* by L. Thorpe (The Folio Society); LINCOLN'S DREAM—*Parapsychology: An Insider's View of ESP* by C. Robbins (Copyright by J. Gaither Pratt. Used by permission of Doubleday & Co. Inc.); DR LIVINGSTONE'S DARK CONTINENT— adapted from *The Very Great Dr Livingstone* by Janet Graham (*Reader's Digest* May 1973); THE LONG AND THE SHORT AND THE TALL (and other articles)—*The Guinness Book of Records* by N. McWhirter and R. McWhirter (Guinness Superlatives Ltd). *The Guinness Book of World Records* by N. McWhirter and R. McWhirter (Sterling Publishing Co. Inc.); *The Guinness Book of Animal Facts and Feats* by N. McWhirter and R. McWhirter (Guinness Superlatives Ltd; Doubleday & Co. Inc.); LOST CONTINENTS, TOP HAT, WHITE FACE . . . AND SKULL, THE PRICK OF A NEEDLE (and other articles)—*Man, Myth and Magic* (BPC Publishing); THE MAGIC OF MAKE-BELIEVE—*The Oxford Book of Nursery Rhymes* by I. and P. Opie (by permission of the Clarendon Press, Oxford; Oxford University Press (Toronto)); 'MAJOR WILLIAM MARTIN, R.M.'—*The Man Who Never Was* by Ewen Montagu (Evans Brothers Ltd; J. B. Lippincott Co.); MALADIES OF FATE— *MEDICAL BIOGRAPHIES: The Ailments of Thirty-three Famous Persons* by Philip Marshall Dale, MD. (Copyright 1952 by the University of Oklahoma Press); MIGHTIEST CRUSADER FORTRESS—*Crusader Castles* by R. Fedden and J. Thomson (John Murray (Publishers) Ltd; F. A. Brockhaus); MIGHTIEST CRUSADER FORTRESS —*Castles of Europe* by G. Hindley (reproduced by permission of the Hamlyn Group Ltd); THE MOST VALUABLE FIND EVER—*Diving for Sunken Treasure* by Jacques-Yves Cousteau and Philip Diole (Cassell & Co. Ltd; Doubleday & Co. Inc.); THE MOST VALUABLE FIND EVER, PIECES OF EIGHT!—*The Treasure Diver's Guide* by John S. Potter, Jr. (Copyright © by John S. Potter, Jr. Used by permission of Doubleday & Co. Inc.); MOUNTAIN OF FIRE, BUSHMAN'S PARADISE, GUARDIAN OF THE TREASURE—*The Coast of Treasure* by Lawrence Green (Howard Timmins; G. P. Putnam's Sons); NATURE'S UNDERTAKER—*Nature's Undertaker* by Alan Devol (The American Mercury Inc. 1960); NEW LIMBS FOR OLD—*Drinkers of Infinity* by Arthur Koestler (Hutchinson & Co. (Publishers) Ltd; Macmillan Publishing Co. Inc.); ON THE RIGHT LINES, GIANT WITH A JINX—*Brunel and His World* by J. Pudney (Thames & Hudson Ltd); ON THE RIGHT LINES, GIANT WITH A JINX—*Isambard Kingdom Brunel* by L. T. C. Rolt (Longman Group Ltd; Penguin Books Ltd); MR PAXTON'S WONDROUS PALACE *The Crystal Palace 1851– 1936*—by Patrick Beaver (Hugh Evelyn Ltd); PRIESTESS OF THE NILE—*Dorothy, the Nile Priestess* by Irene Beeson (*Observer Colour Supplement*); PRIESTESS OF THE NILE—*The Cathars and Reincarnation* by Arthur Guirdham (Neville Spearman Ltd); RISE OF MARVIN HEWITT —*The Eight Lives of Marvin Hewitt* by Herbert Brean (*Life* © Time Inc., 1954); THE ROARING U.P. TRAIL— *Union Pacific* by Garry Hogg (Hutchinson & Co. (Publishers) Ltd; Walker & Co.); SHIP OF PREY— *Sea Eagle* by E. P. Hoyt (Allan Wingate (Publishers) Ltd); SHIPWAY TO THE PACIFIC—*The Impossible Dream: Building of the Panama Canal* by Ian Cameron (Hodder & Stoughton Ltd; William Morrow & Co. Inc.); SLOW TRAIN TO IZMIR—*The Dorak Treasure Mystery— Was it a Robber's Plot or a Scholars' Vendetta?* by K. Pearson and P. Conner (*Sunday Times*); SPEAKING VOLUMES IN SILENCE—*The International Dictionary of Sign Language* by Theodore Brun (Wolfe Publishing Ltd); SUPER SCULPTURE—*Gutzon Borglum* by Willadene Price (EPM Publications Inc.); SUPER SCULPTURE— *Statue of Liberty* by Oscar Handlin and the Editors of Newsweek Books; THE SUPER SENSES OF ANIMALS—*The Infrared Receptors of Snakes* by R. I. Gamow and J. F. Harris (*Scientific American*, May 1973); THE SURVIVOR—*The Fish named L. C. Smith* by J. Dugan (Crowell Collier Publishing Co.); THEY FEEL NO PAIN—*Book of Life* (Marshall Cavendish); THE TREASURED METAL—*Through the Crust of the Earth* by Lord Energlyn (Macdonald and Janes Publishers; McGraw-Hill Book Co.); TURNING BACK NATURE'S CLOCK—*Vanishing Animals* by Philip Street (Reprinted by permission of Harold Ober Associates Inc. Copyright © 1961 Philip Street, Faber & Faber Ltd); TURNING BACK NATURE'S CLOCK—*A History of Domesticated Animals* by F. E. Zeuner (Hutchinson & Co. Ltd; Harper & Row, Publishers); WHEN CONTINENTS COLLIDE—*Floating about on Colliding Plates* by J. Maddox (*Daily Telegraph Magazine*); WHEN CONTINENTS COLLIDE—*The Break up of Pangaea* by R. S. Dietz and J. C. Holder (*Scientific American* Oct., 1967); WINE: MAN'S ANCIENT COMFORT; TEA—*Folklore and Odysseys of Food and Medicinal Plants* by F. & J. Lehner (Tudor Publishing Co.; Farrar, Strauss & Giroux Inc.); WORDS! WORDS! WORDS! *Word Origins and their Romantic Stories* by W. Funk © 1950 Wilfred Funk, Inc. (Funk and Wagnall's Publishing Co. Inc.)

The publishers also acknowledge these sources of illustrations. Credits are arranged in the following sequence for each page: top left/bottom left/top right/bottom right

12 California Institute of Technology and Carnegie Institution of Washington; Mt Wilson Observatory 14 Photri 15 Cambridge University Press 17 NASA; Henry Groskinsky, LIFE © Time, Inc. 19 NASA 22 California Institute of Technology and Carnegie Institution of Washington 24 California Institute of Technology and Carnegie Institution of Washington; California Institute of Technology and Carnegie Institution of Washington; Patrick Moore 26 Photo Science Museum London; Michael Holford Library 27 Dick Kent Photography 29 Photo Science Museum London 31 Photo Science Museum London; Middle East Archive 32 Ronan Picture Library 33 Aerofilms 34 Photo Science Museum London 37 Royal Astronomical Society 45 C. M. Dixon 47 Mary Evans Picture Library 57 Pictor Limited 58–59 Mats Wibe Lund; Mats Wibe Lund; G. R. Roberts; Editorial Photocolor Archives; Pictor Limited 60 Picturepoint Limited 61 Editorial Photocolor Archives 64–65 Pictor Limited; Pictor Limited; Photri; Popperfoto 66–67 Camera Press 68 Steve McCutcheon 70 Dr B. J. Mason, CB, FRS 72 Camera Press 73 John Freeman and Company 75 Photri; Photri 76 Camera Press 77 Camera Press; Dr John Christian Jensen 79 Pictor Limited 81 Mitchell Library, Sydney 82 De Beers Consolidated Mines Limited 84 Shell International Petroleum Company Limited 86 US Forest Service 88 Redwood Empire Association; K. R. Gaardern 89 Heather Angel; Heather Angel 90 Stephen Dalton/NHPA; Stephen Dalton/NHPA; Clive Wyborn; Clive Wyborn 93 Edward S. Ross 95 Nina Leen © Time Inc., 1974 97 David Houston/Bruce Coleman Limited; Jane Burton/ Bruce Coleman; J. M. Bassou/Jacana; Peter M. David/ Seaphot 98 Peter M. David/Seaphot; Oxford Scientific Films/Bruce Coleman Limited 99 Anthony Bannister/ NHPA; David Hughes/Bruce Coleman Limited; David Hughes/Bruce Coleman Limited 100 Jane Burton/Bruce Coleman Limited 101 Scientific American Inc. (February 1966) 102 A. G. Wells/NHPA; Dr H. C. Bennet Clark 103 Jane Burton/Bruce Coleman Limited 104 French Government Tourist Office; Jane Burton/Bruce Coleman Limited; Toni Angermayer 105 Scientific American Inc. (December 1955) 106 A. van den Nieuwenhuizen 108 Mansell Collection 111 Dr Masao Kawai 112 Roger Perry/NHPA; Peter M. David/Seaphot; Karl W. Kenyon 113 Axel Poignant 116 Trustees of the British Museum (Natural History) 118 Scientific American Inc. (August 1961) 120 George Ordish 125 NASA; NASA 127 R. Saunders Mount Vernon Hospital 128 GE Research and Development Center, USA 129 Middlesex Hospital, London; Harold E. Edgerton, MIT 130 Palestine Archaeological Museum of Jerusalem/Kodak 132 Keystone 133 Stan Wayman, LIFE © Time Inc. 1974 134 Courtaulds Limited 137 Camera Press 138 Bell Telephone Laboratories 139 Microfilm Reprographics 140 Fritz Goro, LIFE © Time, Inc. 1974; Fritz Goro, LIFE © Time, Inc. 1974 141 *Daily Telegraph* 142 J. R. Eyerman, LIFE © Time, Inc. 1974 143 Henry Groskinsky, LIFE © Time, Inc. 1974 144 Photographie Giraudon 146 Cliché Musées Nationaux 150 Associated Press 151 Michael Holford Library; Emil Muench/Ostman Agency 152 Mondadoripress, Milan 154 Mansell Collection 155 J. Powell, Rome 156 Aerofilms 158 Trustees of the British Museum; Roubier—Rapho 160–1 Mary Evans Picture Library; Victoria and Albert Museum; Mander and Mitchenson Collection; Mander and Mitchenson Collection; Mansell Collection 162 Mansell Collection 165 Mansell Collection; Mary Evans Picture Library; Mansell Collection 167 Mansell Collection; Mary Evans Picture Library 168 Photo Science Museum London 169 Imperial War Museum; Imperial War Museum 171 Mansell Collection 172 Mansell Collection 174 Mansell Collection 175 Picturepoint Limited 176 Mansell Collection; Picturepoint Limited 177 Mansell Collection; Sears, Roebuck and Company 178 Mary Evans Picture Library 180 Radio Times Hulton Picture Library 181 Trustees of the Pierpont Morgan Library; *New York Times* 182 John Freeman; Crown copyright 183 John Freeman; Photo Science Museum, London; John Freeman 184 Thames and Hudson Limited; Thames and Hudson Limited 185 Imperial War Museum 186 John Murray Limited 187 Photo Science Museum, London; Photo Science Museum, London; Photo Science Museum, London; London Council Print Collection; Ardea 188 Photo Science Museum, London; Photo Science Museum London 189 John Murray Limited; Photo Science Museum, London; Photographie Giraudon 191 Imperial War Museum 193 Radio Times Hulton Picture Library 194 Radio Times Hulton Picture Library 196 Mary Evans Picture Library; John Murray Limited 197

Typesetting by Tradespools Limited, Frome.
Separations by Commercial Process Company Limited, London, and Mullis-Morgan Limited, London.
Printing by Garrod and Lofthouse International Limited, Crawley, and Jolly and Barber Limited, Rugby.
Paper and bookbinding material by Gerald Judd Limited, London; Bowaters Paper Sales Limited, London; Winterbottom Products Limited, Salford.
Endpapers © 1973 Gallery Five Limited. Adapted from a design by Jan Pienkowski.
Bookbinding by Hazell, Watson and Viney Limited, Aylesbury.
Published by The Reader's Digest Association Limited, 25 Berkeley Square, London W1X 6AB